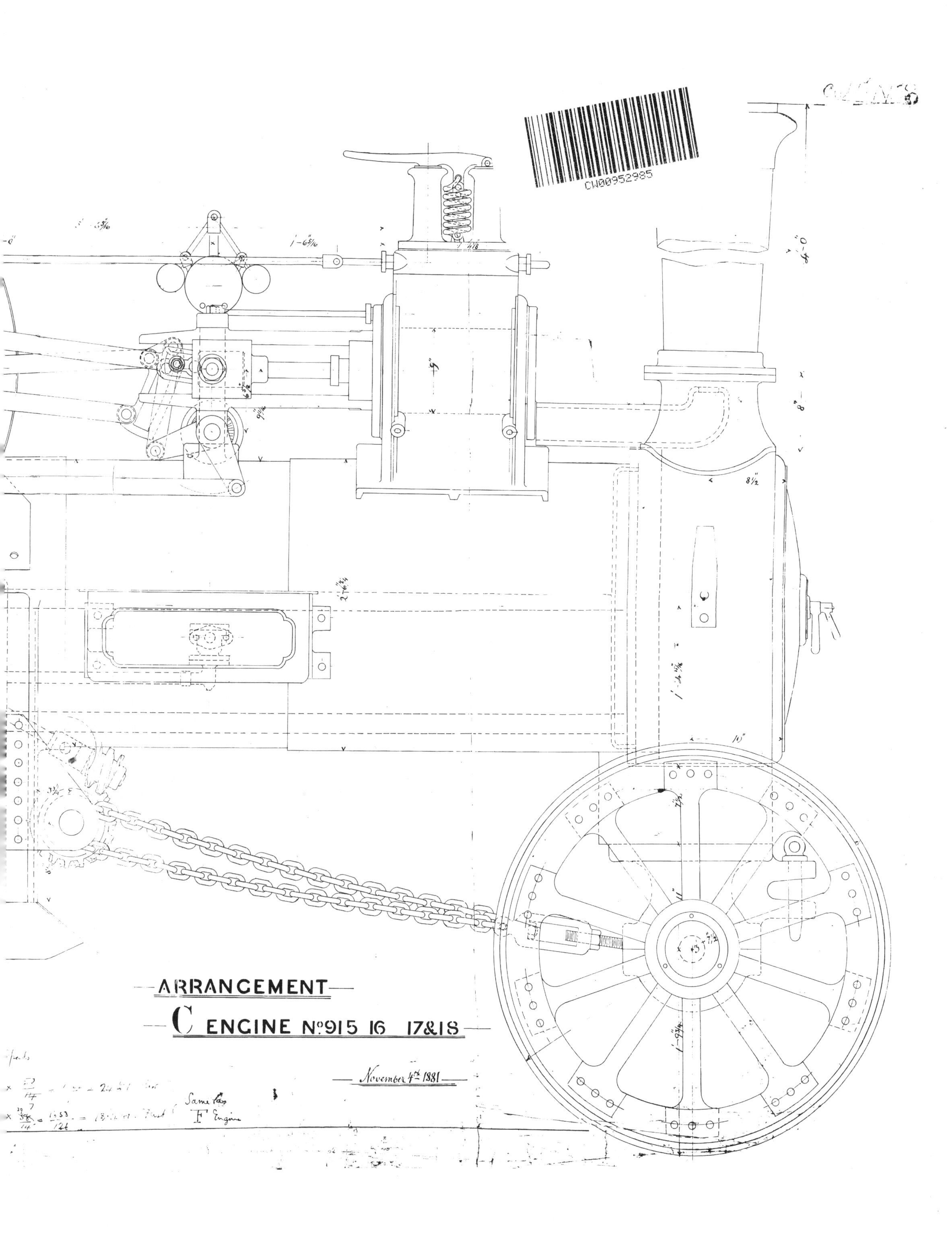

ARRANGEMENT
C ENGINE No. 915 16 17&18
November 4th 1881
Same Pas
F Engine
CW00952985
1'-6 5/16
8 1/2"
10"

THE STORY OF THE

ST NICHOLAS WORKS

A History of Charles Burrell & Sons Ltd

Michael R. Lane

UNICORN PRESS
STOWMARKET

First published 1994 by Unicorn Press
College Farm
Forward Green
Stowmarket IP14 5EH

ISBN 0 906 290 07 4

Produced by Hugh Tempest-Radford *Book Producers*
Typeset by Goodfellow & Egan Ltd, Cambridge
Printed in Great Britain by St Edmundsbury Press

Contents

Foreword

As a native of Norfolk I am always eager to learn more about the history and achievements of Norfolk people.

The story which Michael Lane tells here is indeed a distinguished one. For over 150 years Charles Burrell and Sons Co. Ltd of Thetford and their predecessors were responsible for the design and manufacture of an interesting variety of diverse engineering products. As the company grew from its origins as a small country millwright's shop to a manufacturer of international repute its success mirrored that of England. Its products went from the little market town of Thetford to every corner of the Empire on which the sun never set.

Burrells played a part too in every area of national life. As their threshing machines delivered the rich harvests of Norfolk their engines powered the trams of Birmingham and Bradford. Burrell's skills ranged from the majestic old fairground roundabouts to the bacon slicer in the village shop. Their craftsmanship can still be seen locally – in the iron castings on Thetford's Town Bridge and the staunches across the River Little Ouse. But it is above all as traction engine manufacturers that Burrells will be best remembered.

And Michael Lane is *the* historian of the traction engine. This book, together with his histories of John Fowler and Co., Leeds and of Marshalls of Gainsborough form a trilogy covering this fascinating aspect of our industrial heritage.

I thoroughly recommend this book to all who love engines and to all who love Norfolk and want to learn more about this most interesting aspect of our history.

Gillian Shephard

THE RT. HON. GILLIAN SHEPHARD, M.P.
MEMBER FOR SOUTH WEST NORFOLK
MINISTER OF AGRICULTURE

Introduction

Whenever steam traction engine men are gathered together, inevitably, the conversation will turn sooner or later to the subject of Burrells. Some will passionately proclaim that Thetford built engines are the finest ever made; others will champion engines originating in their own locality. Arguments will range far and wide on such subjects as the merits or otherwise of 3-shaft or 4-shaft engines; the overhang of the gearing on the end of the crankshaft; and the difficulty of starting a single crank compound when the piston stops on top dead centre. Often preferences and prejudices are passed from father to son and indeed there are today many instances of the third generation following in the family footsteps.

The inescapable fact is that there are more Burrell engines surviving in preservation today than any other make of engine built. Near the heyday of steam in the 1890s, Henry Marshall, the first Managing Director of the great firm Marshalls of Gainsborough, compiled a listing of engines and threshing machines built by the thirty leading British manufacturers. This included both traction engines and portables. Clayton & Shuttleworth of Lincoln headed the list with the greatest number of engines built, the majority being portables, and dominated the market until the 1880s. Marshalls were second, Rustons were third and Garretts fourth. Burrells came twelfth in the listing. It is true of course that some like J & H McLaren of Leeds and William Foster of Lincoln were late comers in the traction engine market, but they never succeeded in catching-up.

Having previously written the history of John Fowler of Leeds and Marshalls of Gainsborough, your author claims to be catholic in his opinions, although it must be said, the only engines he has actually owned have been Burrells. Hopefully, the opinions expressed in this book remain objective.

We do not know exactly how many engines Burrells built because the company's records and engine registers are incomplete. Very little is known about production prior to 1867, although it is certain that most engines built before that date were portables. The numerical index at the end of this book lists all known engines between No. 395 of 1867 and No. 4094 of 1930. From this we may deduce that about 1,000 portables and 2880 traction engines and their derivatives were built at Thetford between 1848 and 1928.

A few very early portable engines sold by Charles Burrell I in the period 1846–1848 were probably manufactured by his father-in-law, Robert Cowen, in Nottingham; for we know Burrell acted as his East Anglian agent. Other engines listed were stationary and marine engines; other numbers were never used and a few numbers remain unidentified. The final thirteen engines carrying the Burrell name under the aegis of Agricultural & General Engineers Ltd were completed by their associate company, Garretts of Leiston.

Folklore in Thetford insists that many early records and drawings were burnt in a huge bonfire in the Works Yard when Burrells finally closed in 1928. One is tempted to refer to the culprits as vandals but how often have many of us destroyed things in the past which are now regarded as precious and valuable. Nevertheless, they would be amazed to learn today that some of the engines which were held in so little regard sixty years ago, are now changing hands at thirty-five times their value when new.

By no stretch of the imagination could Burrell ever have been described as a large concern. They never employed more than 300 people, but they were truly international in their operations. When the British Empire was in its prime and during the period when the great cereal growing regions of Eastern Europe were being developed, they supplied engines to more than a score of countries overseas. New Zealand and Germany were their best overseas markets and in the space of thirty years 155 G.P. traction engines were shipped to the Antipodes through the Reid & Gray agency.

It has for long been claimed that the company was established in 1770. It is true that Benjamin Burrell became established as a whitesmith and blacksmith in the town sometime between 1750 and 1758, but his son Joseph, who is usually credited with founding the agricultural machinery business, was only eleven years old in 1770. He is listed in the records of the Williamson Charity established in the town as being his own master in 1790. What we do know for certain is that Joseph, together with his sons Joseph Jnr., James and William, established a foundry in St Nicholas Street, Thetford, in 1803, and that this in due course became known as St Nicholas Works. Could it be that in later years, Joseph's grandson, Charles I, confused his own father James' birthday in 1770 with the date of founding the firm? Or was Benjamin Burrell (1725–1807) the real founder of the business which at some date after 1770 was taken over by his son Joseph who started manufacturing agricultural implements? I am deeply indebted to David Osborne and Mary Feakes, local historians, for making the results of their research into the Burrell family freely available to me.

The first history of this remarkable firm was written by my good friend Ronald H. Clark over 40 years ago. A great deal of additional information has come to light in the intervening years and Ronald's book has long been out of print. It is time for another history of Burrells, but it should not be forgotten that it was he who originally aroused the great interest in the chronicles of this country works. I am very grateful for his constant help and encouragement.

I am greatly indebted to many other friends who over that past decade have helped put together this fascinating story. The Hon. Sir William McAlpine, at my suggestion, purchased the Burrell drawings and records and made them freely available to me. I spent three years copying, analysing and cataloguing these documents which are now safely in the possession of the Road Locomotive Society.

I had wonderful assistance from the late Alan Duke, custodian of the splendid records compiled by the Road Locomotive Society. His knowledge of engine ownership was unique. Librarians at the Public Records Offices, the Patent Office Library, the Science Museum Library and the Museum of English Rural Life, Reading have all been tremendously helpful. I have corresponded with dozens of engine enthusiasts and many have generously provided information and illustrations. Sadly it is not possible to list them all, but I am very grateful to them.

I must make special reference to Mrs Florence Evelyn Owen, Charles Burrell's grand-daughter. She made a great deal of family history and photographs available to me. Sadly, she died in 1989 and I deeply regret she did not live to see this work finished.

Mrs Sue Ponton of Llanberis typed the original draft while I was working on the Snowdon Mountain Railway. Later, Mrs Siobhan Kemp of Lawshall expertly put the whole thing on a word processor, producing the 'floppy' discs so necessary for modern type-setting. I owe also my book producer Hugh Tempest-Radford a great debt for his constant support and professionalism in all stages of the production of this book, he has been a joy to work with. Finally, to my wife Margaret a big thank you for allowing Burrell into our lives during the long period this book has been on the stocks. I think she has often secretly felt 'two is company, but three is a crowd!'

Michael R. Lane

Street House
Boxted
Bury St Edmunds

Michael R. Lane

Charles Burrell I (1817–1906) chairman Charles Burrell & Sons Ltd 1884 to 1904.

CHAPTER ONE

Prologue 1770–1851

George III, upon his accession in 1760, declared his intention to "Ride forth to kill dragons, the monsters of corruption and immorality", but few thought that this 22-year-old radical king would preside over a sufficient break in English history to be called the beginning of an epoch. The beginnings of both the agricultural and industrial revolution can be traced from this date and the British, so often labelled a conservative nation, blazed a trail for the whole world to follow. Because they were the first to tread the new ground they gained tremendous rewards, but equally they made some terrible mistakes, the social consequences of which are still discernible in the midst of the present day technological revolution.

The steep rise in the population is perhaps one of the most striking features of the reign of George III. In 1760 England and Wales had a population of 6.75 million, 60 years later it exceeded 12 million. Upon the accession there were only two cities in England with a population exceeding 50,000; London had 75,000 inhabitants and Bristol some 60,000. Both were quite different in size and character from the multitude of small market towns and ports which made up the remainder of the borough franchise in Parliament and which handled the greater part of the commerce of the country. The old colonial system was basically mercantile rather than imperial and the merchants were concerned primarily with the export of agricultural produce and textiles and the exploitation of Clive's India, Spanish America and the West Indies.

The total value of exports in 1760 was officially estimated at £16 million. Imports into England amounted to approximately £11 million. The great strategic objective of the day was the defeat of the Dutch and the French in a trade war. The importance of the colonies in the promotion of trade was understood and the gentlemen of the inland shires were always ready to support the expenditure of money for increasing our maritime strength rather than improving the lot of the agricultural worker.

The majority of the King's subjects were still employed in agriculture but Old Rural England was on the eve of change typified by the wholesale enclosures of the land. Begun in the reign of Charles II, the process of increasing the great estates by extinguishing the small, largely culminated in the reign of George III. Though less fatal to the landowners than the present system of taxation, the 17th and 18th century land taxes were a sore burden to many small estates. Trade wars and the resultant taxation certainly hastened change, but at bottom, the creation of great estates at the expense of smaller ones was a natural economic process, analogous to the absorption of small businesses by larger ones in the industrial world of today. Once agriculture came to be regarded as a means of maintaining a given state in society, change became inevitable. The exploitation of capital in the hands of the large landowners and their devotion to business and profit were necessary conditions of the 18th century agricultural revolution, resulting in the greatly increased productivity of the English soil and the general application of new agricultural methods.

In the experimental stage begun immediately after the Restoration in 1688, agricultural writers were advocating and a few enlightened farmers were practising the improvements which became generally acceptable in the following century. These included the scientific rotation of crops; the correct feeding of stock in the winter months; roots and clovers; the field cultivation of potatoes, turnips and oil cake; the proper drainage of the land and the storage of water. Initially, the adoption of these improved methods was retarded primarily by the open-field, communal system of agriculture then in operation and by the want of capital and education amongst the small squires and yeoman freeholders.

It was 18th century men like Jethro Tull, Lord "Turnip" Townshend and later Thomas William Coke, the first Earl of Leicester of Holkham in Norfolk, who successfully exploited the new found knowledge. Between 1770 and 1815 Coke so improved his land as to raise the rental of his estates from £2,200 to £20,000 per annum. His tenants prospered in spite of these greatly increased rents and he granted them the security of long leases on strict terms as to the methods of cultivation. He pioneered the famous Holkham Sheep Shearings and Agricultural Shows which were soon imitated throughout the land. He introduced a new entrepreneurial and competitive spirit in both agriculture and the manufacture of agricultural implements and did much to spread the knowledge of improved farming.

Townshend, a retired statesman, brother-in-law of Robert Walpole, and friend of George II, whose name is so firmly linked with turnips and the rotation of crops, was equally active in demonstrating that poor land could be brought into cultivation and made productive by the correct use of the right manures. Jethro Tull stands out as a pioneer of horse-hoeing husbandry in order to produce a fine tilth and destroy weeds, and of sowing in drills as opposed to the broadcast method.

The "Spirited Improvers of the Age" put East Anglia at the very head of English agriculture. The improvement of the land was carried to such a point that wheat was grown where previously only rye, oats and barley had been possible. Englishmen of all classes soon became so sophisticated as to insist upon refined wheat bread, until that time the exclusive prerogative of the wealthy. The ports of Lynn, Blakeney and Yarmouth handled half the corn exported by the United Kingdom, and with its textile industries still flourishing, East Anglia was at the height of its prosperity in 1770. Between 1750 and 1770 the United Kingdom had become for the first time net exporters of cereals.

The counties most advantageously affected by the Enclosure Acts and the advent of new methods of farming were to be found east of a line from the North Riding of Yorkshire to the Dorset coast, embracing all of East Anglia and the Midland Shires. The majority of the agricultural machinery and implement manufacturing concerns established in the next 100 years were located within this area. The northern and western counties were little affected by the Enclosure Acts because a high proportion of their acreage consisted of moorland and was economically unsuitable for enclosure.

British manufacturing industry in the 1760s was prosperous too, but not yet Revolutionary. It determined the way of life of thousands of people in the North East, in Shropshire, Staffordshire and in parts of Lancashire and Yorkshire, but it was not yet generally drawing unto itself the rural population. It had not begun to sap the institutions nor affect the political attitudes of Englishmen. Few leading social or political figures were yet attracted by the new sources of wealth. Coal, iron and glass tended to be regarded as an additional crop in otherwise predominantly agricultural districts.

Abraham Darby, the famous Quaker ironmaster purchased his little Tudor smithy at Coalbrookdale in Shropshire in 1709. The story of his and his successors' achievements is so well known that it is often forgotten that the advance they made, although highly significant for the future, was itself a limited one. Darby was able to use coke in the furnace to produce pig-iron that was well adapted for making cast iron goods but it was unsuitable for turning into bar at the forge, and for a further fifty years the industry was dependant upon charcoal and Swedish imports for manufacturing pots and pans and later cast iron cylinders for steam engines. By 1760 the annual home consumption of iron was said to be only 18,000 tons, four fifths of which was imported from Sweden. Richard Reynolds, who took over the Coalbrookdale concern in 1763, did not produce cheap iron by puddling until 1766 and cast iron rails until 1767.

It was only at the end of the 18th century that the opportunities for large scale industrial investment developed with the growth of the new techniques and the industrial capitalist became an important element in society. Formerly, it was the merchant, able to provide credit and secure markets who held the dominant position. Entrepreneurs such as Matthew Boulton (1728–1809), who sold his Birmingham-made brass buttons all over the world, used his considerable financial resources to ride the difficulties of credit and risk involved in such trade. The resultant profits enabled him to reinvest in new factories and ultimately to form his highly successful partnership with James Watt.

Generally, 18th century farmers' tools were manufactured from wood and wrought iron and were basically crude and inefficient. The style and size of the implements varied enormously from area to area and local designs often persisted late into the 19th century. Indeed, a remarkable feature of the period was the slow pace at which new tools and machinery were brought into general use. There are known instances of wooden ploughs being seen at work during the period of the Great Exhibition in 1851, and at the same date corn was still frequently threshed by hand. The cheapness of agricultural labour and its stability in the face of steadily rising prices was an important factor in the rate of change.

It was in just such an environment that Joseph Burrell (1759–1831) established his business in Thetford. His Father, Benjamin Burrell (1725–1793) had established his whitesmith and blacksmith business sometime between 1750 and 1758. We know that in 1740 he had been apprenticed for seven years to one Stephen Rowning, a locksmith, whitesmith and blacksmith of Thetford under the terms of the Sir Joseph Williamson charity. Rowning died in 1748, and his widow Sarah carried on the business for sometime, but by 1758 Benjamin is on record as being a master employing his own apprentice. It seems quite probable that he had acquired Rowning's business from his widow.

In 1757, Benjamin married Mary Bull of Bury St. Edmunds and they resided in Thetford Market Place in St. Cuthbert's parish. They had three sons, Joseph born 1759, William 1766 and James 1770. In 1773, Joseph was apprenticed to his father, the premium being paid by the Williamson charity. By 1790, Joseph is recorded in the charity's entry book as being a master in his own right and following his father's death in 1793 he is known to have expanded his activities to include the manufacture and development of agricultural implements.

This research, undertaken by local historian David Osborne and published in the Journal of the Norfolk Industrial Archaeology Society in 1990, places in doubt the widely held belief that Joseph established his business in 1770. His nephew, Charles Burrell (1817–1906) and subsequent members of the family have traditionally referred to the origins of the firm as 1770, but at that date Joseph would have been only eleven years of age and he did not commence his apprenticeship until three years later. In 1874, the "Agricultural Gazette" printed an article describing Burrell's works adding the firm were "amongst the oldest implement manufacturers in the kingdom having been established in 1770", but that now appears to be incorrect.

Joseph Burrell's great-great-great grandfather John was resident in the area in the 16th century. Furthermore, it seems probable that John was related to one, Andrewes Burrell who in 1628 filed a patent describing, "Engines for draining marsh and fen grounds". The Duke of Bedford had invested no less than £100,000 of his personal fortune draining 300,000 acres of Fenland in the region of the Isle of Ely and Andrewes Burrell was placed in charge of this work. Later, in 1646 the same Andrewes Burrell anticipated Samuel Pepys by presenting to Parliament a memorandum for "The reformation of the English Navie". A second cousin of Joseph Burrell's was George Bird Burrell (1756–1823) a well know local antiquary.

Parish records 1803 tell us that Joseph occupied a

dwelling house, two shops and a foundry on the eastern corner of Tanner Street and King Street, Thetford and that he had been joined in the business by his brothers William and James. On 5th December 1803 the three brothers attended a ceremony in St. Cuthbert's church to mark the double wedding of Joseph to Mary Pooley of Bury St. Edmunds and James to Elizabeth Pryke of Barnham. Shortly after this event the business was removed to new premises sandwiched between St. Nicholas Lane and Minstergate Street and became known as St. Nicholas Foundry, where it remained for the next 125 years.

Seen in retrospect, Thetford was undoubtedly a good place in which to establish an agricultural machinery manufactory. Situated at the confluence of the rivers Little Ouse and Thet, on the borders of Norfolk and Suffolk, communications were good, labour was plentiful and it was situated near the geographical centre of a fast growing market for agricultural machinery. The Little Ouse was navigable as far as Thetford and until the coming of the railway in 1845 was frequently used for the shipment of machinery to distant parts of the United Kingdom.

The growth of the business was slow by present day standards but by the turn of the century Joseph had clearly built up a reputation for quality and reliability and had progressed from repair and jobbing work to the manufacture of a range of simple agricultural machines. His first real triumph came in 1803 when at the 25th Holkham Sheep Shearing and Agricultural Meeting he was awarded a Silver Cup for the excellence of his seed drill, "For sowing oil cake manure with wheat, turnips, etc." This trophy still survives as a treasured heirloom of the Burrell family. Following their success at Holkham the firm advertised that they were "Manufacturers of Chaff engines, Dressing machines, Drill rolls and Drill machines, Kitchen ranges, Stoves, Grates, Iron fencing and Iron work of every description and dealers in Gutta Percha".

One of the most significant and far reaching developments in agricultural machinery at this time was the introduction of the threshing machine. The credit for the first really practical horse driven machine rests with two north-countrymen, John Rastrick and Andrew Meikle. Meikle's invention resulted from improvements to a model sent to him by Sir Francis Kinloch of Gilmerton, who had himself improved a model built by a Mr Smart of Morpeth in Northumberland in 1772. Both Kinloch's and Smart's models were defective in working since they caused a rubbing instead of a beating action. In 1785, Meikle succeeded in producing a machine with beaters. Further improvements were made and in 1788 he applied for and obtained a patent. It was then claimed that Smart's machine was based on Rastrick's earlier invention, but the evidence is only presumptive. An engraving of Rastrick's machine survives, but the similarity between that drawing and that submitted with Meikle's patent is too close to be accidental. The first application of steam power for driving a threshing machine took place on a Yorkshire farm in 1799, but upon that occasion the motive power was derived from a fixed stationary engine installed in a barn. Other machines had been demonstrated driven by water wheels.

The first threshing machine exhibited in East Anglia, the invention of a Devonshire mechanic name Balls, was demonstrated working at the 1805 Holkham Show, but Joseph Burrell was not far behind. In 1804 he filed patent No. 2757, which described an improved machine capable of threshing corn in three stages in a single process, producing clean, straw-free grain. Almost simultaneously at the 1805 Holkham Show he demonstrated a greatly improved mowing machine which aroused considerable interest amongst the local farming fraternity.

In the midst of all this innovative activity, when the firm was obviously growing and prospering, Joseph Burrell already a constable of Thetford was gazetted a Lieutenant in the Local Volunteers then being raised throughout the country to meet the threatened French invasion. Joseph and his two brothers also began to take a greater interest in local affairs, a tradition which subsequent members of the family maintained until the works' closure in 1928.

In 1827, shortly before Joseph's death in 1831, he, his brother James and his nephew, James Jnr., had the distinction of simultaneously holding the office of Aldermen. No doubt it was their interest in local Government affairs which precipitated their involvement with the engineering works undertaken to improve the navigation on the Little Ouse in the years 1827–1835.

Isabel, the first Duchess of Grafton granted the Little Ouse navigation rights to Thetford Council in 1696 making them responsible for maintaining the six staunches then existing between Thetford and Brandon as well as piling where the banks were weak, cutting back the inside of bends and cutting weeds in season. Unfortunately, conditions in the river were allowed to deteriorate and in 1742 the Council were compelled to erect a seventh staunch below Thetford. No further major works were carried out for 85 years when the complete rebuilding of all seven staunches became a matter of some urgency. The Brandon staunch was rebuilt by a Mr Beeton in 1827 and the staunches at Thetford Middle, Croxton, Sheepwash and Santon were rebuilt by Burrell & Sons. The remaining two at Turfpool and Thetford were rebuilt by J & W Gathergood in 1834 and 1835 after James' death.

Whilst the Council were preparing its plans for the work to be carried out at Thetford Middle staunch in 1827, James Burrell reported to the Council on the bad state of St Christopher's Bridge, the main bridge in the town. Apparently only Burrell & Sons tendered for this work and ultimately their tender was accepted. This attractive cast iron structure still stands today and it is generally presumed that the castings were produced in St Nicholas Foundry.

Joseph died in 1831 and his brother James in 1837. Control of the business passed to James' 20 year old son Charles, whom we shall in future refer to as Charles I to distinguish him from his as yet unborn son. The Council immediately elected Charles I to succeed his father on the Navigation Committee, although one suspects that other concerns were of greater interest. His brother, James, elected not to stay with St Nicholas Works and took over his uncle's ironmongers shop and foundry which produced both brass and iron castings, but both were closed down by 1845. Relationships between the brothers appear to have been not good. At this time Charles I was also very interested in the development of plant for producing coal gas for lighting purposes. His father had seen the potential of Samuel Clegg's work when in 1813 he had been

GENEALOGY OF THE BURRELLS OF THETFORD

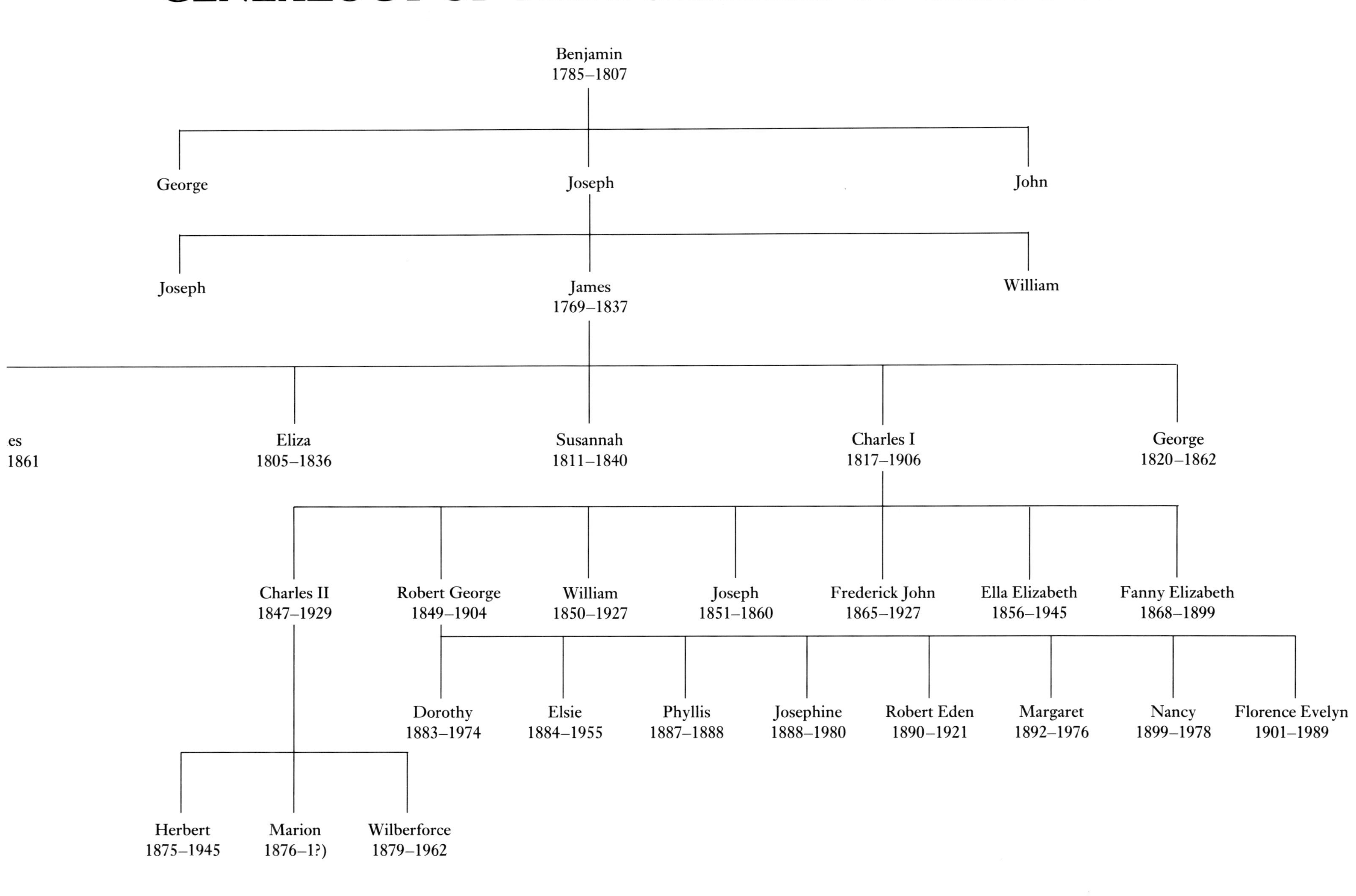

appointed engineer to the recently established Gas Light and Coke Company in London. He illuminated his private residence in Thetford with gas many years before it came into general use in the country. Charles I was anxious to carry on his father's work and became the prime mover in establishing a gas works in Thetford.

Papers dealing with James' estate have survived and give us the first clear indication of his lifestyle and the precise nature of his business. He lived in a substantial 4-bedroomed house in the centre of Thetford and left an estate valued at £2537-11s-7d gross. The house and its contents, including a small gasometer were left to his widow, Elizabeth. The ownership of the St Nicholas Foundry passed to his younger son, Charles I and the residue of his estate amounting to £211-0s-10d was divided equally between his sons James Jnr and Charles I.

The works were described in the valuation as comprising a workshop, forge, iron foundry, brass foundry and iron warehouse together with a yard. All manner of smiths, moulders, wheelwrights and carpenters hand tools were listed, but the only machine tool to be mentioned was a drilling machine, there being no reference to a lathe or a shaping machine or any other metal working machinery.

Little is known about events at the St Nicholas Foundry during Charles I's first ten years control. He changed the name to Charles Burrell, Engineers and Agricultural Machinists and he participated in the ever increasing number of agricultural shows held in East Anglia. All the indications are that he prospered. In October 1846 he married Elizabeth Cowen who remained his faithful consort for nearly 50 years, bearing him five sons and two daughters.

The most important of our annual agricultural shows, the Smithfield Club Show and that of the Royal Agricultural Society of England have been major influences upon the growth of the British farming industry. It is a tradition that the idea of forming a Club arose out of the crowds who gathered annually on the Friday before the Christmas Market to witness the arrival at Smithfield in London of the extraordinary fat beasts purchased by Mr Giblet, a leading local butcher. Originally called the Smithfield Club and Sheep Society, the inaugural meeting was held in Giblet's drawing room on 17th December, 1798. Francis, Duke of Bedford took the Chair and Arthur Young, the leading agricultural writer of the day, was appointed Secretary.

The Club held its first show at Wootton's Livery Stables in Dolphin Yard, Smithfield in 1799, which was followed by an enormous dinner at the nearby Crown and Anchor Tavern. Both were a great success and in the following year the Society was constituted as a permanent club. George III gave the Club his Royal Patronage by exhibiting two oxen and later Queen Victoria and the Prince Consort became regular visitors to the show.

Farm implements were exhibited from 1820 and all types of steam engines were included from 1854. In the middle of the 19th century it became urgently necessary to obtain larger premises and in 1862 the show moved to the newly completed Agricultural Hall at Islington in North London. This annual gathering, now held at Earls Court, remains a mecca for farmers, livestock breeders and machinery manufacturers. For many years the list of subscribers included such names as Nathaniel Clayton and Joseph Shuttleworth of Lincoln; Frederick and James Howard of Bedford; John Fowler and his successors of Leeds; Richard Garrett of Leiston in Suffolk; Richard Hornsby of Grantham; and Alan Ransome and William Jefferys of Ipswich. In the period 1916–1918 and again in 1923–25 Charles Burrell II served as a member of the Council.

It has been said that the Royal Agricultural Society of England, "was formed during one of those recurring fits of associative activity to which Englishmen are periodically prone". Established in 1838, it had as its prototype the then defunct Board of Agriculture which was formed by the Government during a period of acute labour unrest and recurring food crises to provide landowners with a forum for discussing new ideas and technical problems. The idea of forming a new National Institution was proposed by the Duke of Richmond at the Annual Dinner of the Smithfield Club. At a subsequent crowded meeting held at the Freemasons Tavern under the Chairmanship of Earl Spencer, it was resolved that "A society for the improvement of agriculture in England and Wales should be formed and that the society should concern itself purely with agricultural matters and that no political interests should be permitted". Further, it was agreed that the Society's annual meetings should be held in different parts of the country each year, with both farmers and manufacturers participating. The first show was held at Oxford in July 1839 and several leading implement manufacturers took part, including Ransomes of Ipswich and Richard Garrett of Leiston. The latter exhibited a new high rate of delivery threshing machine which aroused considerable interest amongst the farming fraternity.

The origins of the use of steam power in agriculture are far from being precisely defined. There is no doubt that the attitudes of James Watt towards high pressure steam and the strength of his condensing beam engine patents greatly retarded developments. It was only when the protection provided by the latter expired at the end of the 18th century that a number of interesting experiments were carried out by the early pioneers. Richard Trevithick, the "Father of high pressure steam engines", Matthew Murray and the Rev. Edward Cartwright were early patentees of engines suitable for agricultural applications. Trevithick's semi-portable engine, built in 1812 for the Cornish landowner, Sir Christopher Hawkins, survives today in the London Science Museum. It was used for many years for threshing corn in a Cornish barn.

The 40 years, 1800–1840, were essentially years of mechanical experimentation in both agriculture and upon the common road but progress was markedly slower than upon the railways. A writer in the Journal of the Royal Agricultural Society (RASE) commented, "It has been remarked to the disparagement of the farmer, that while in the course of the last half century, every other industrial class in the country have found the means to lessen the expense of producing their articles of commerce, the farmer stands alone a notable exception, his working expenses not having been sensibly diminished." At the 1821 Holkham Sheep Shearings the judges reported that, "No new implement exhibited possessed the merit sufficient to entitle it to a premium".

Undoubtedly, the main reason for this apparent inertia was that during the greater part of the period the country

Fig 2 Ransomes of Ipswich self-moving threshing machine – 1841.

Fig 3 Alexander Dean's portable engine – 1841.

Fig 4 Tuxford's of Boston portable steam threshing machine – 1842.

Fig 5 Charles Burrell's original 1846 Portable Engine lying derelict in the works' yard in the 1920s.

was plunged into an economic depression which lasted until 1844. Industry came almost to a standstill, unemployment reached hitherto unknown proportions and with high food prices, coupled with inadequate relief, the manufacturing population faced hunger and destitution.

The first really practical portable steam engine was not produced until 1839. It was built by William Howden, a small implement maker of Boston, Lincolnshire and was exhibited at the first RASE show held at Oxford. Two years later, Alexander Dean, a Birmingham engineer produced another interesting engine having a vertical boiler and two vertical cylinders mounted on a four wheel carriage drawn by two horses. It was not until 1845 that Clayton and Shuttleworth, who soon became the largest manufacturers of this class of engine, produced their first model. William Waller, the firm's chief engineer, addressing the Institution of Mechanical Engineers in 1856 claimed that in the previous 10 years the company had sold no less than 2,200 portable engines. The Journal of the RASE reported that there was only one portable engine at work in the County of Norfolk in 1843, which confirms the rapid growth of the industry in the years 1840–1855.

In 1842, at the RASE Bristol Show, Ransomes of Ipswich exhibited a portable engine made self moving by the addition of a pitch chain drive from the crankshaft to the hind axle. The frame on which the Davies Patent disc type engine and boiler were mounted also carried a small portable threshing machine. On test it was said to consume half a hundredweight of coke and 36 gallons of water per hour and failed to achieve even passing popularity.

William Tuxford of the Skirbeck Ironworks near Boston in Lincolnshire was rather more successful, although his engine was not self-moving. In 1839 he was persuaded by a Mr Morton, Earl Dulcies farm manager and a Mr Wingate of Hareby, near Horncastle, to produce a steam driven portable threshing machine. The project was not completed until after the 1842 RASE show, but it subsequently received wide publicity in the farming press. The single oscillating cylinder was mounted on top of the boiler adjacent to the chimney, the layout suggesting a return flue type boiler. The drive to the threshing machine was taken through a bevel gear working off the rim of the flywheel. It is said that a total of 19 sets were produced.

We do not know the precise sequence of events which led young Charles Burrell to produce his first portable steam engine, but we can be reasonably certain that his future father-in-law, Robert Cowen, the founder of the Beck Foundry, Brook Street, Nottingham had a considerable influence upon him at the time. It is known that G R Cowen & Co. produced steam engines and boilers although no precise details appear to have survived; and that after his marriage in 1846 Charles Burrell acted as their agent in East Anglia. His sister's son, Robert Burrell Bond was apprenticed to the firm in this period. Shortly afterwards Charles I produced his own portable engine at St. Nicholas Foundry.

Fortunately, this engine lay derelict in the works' yard

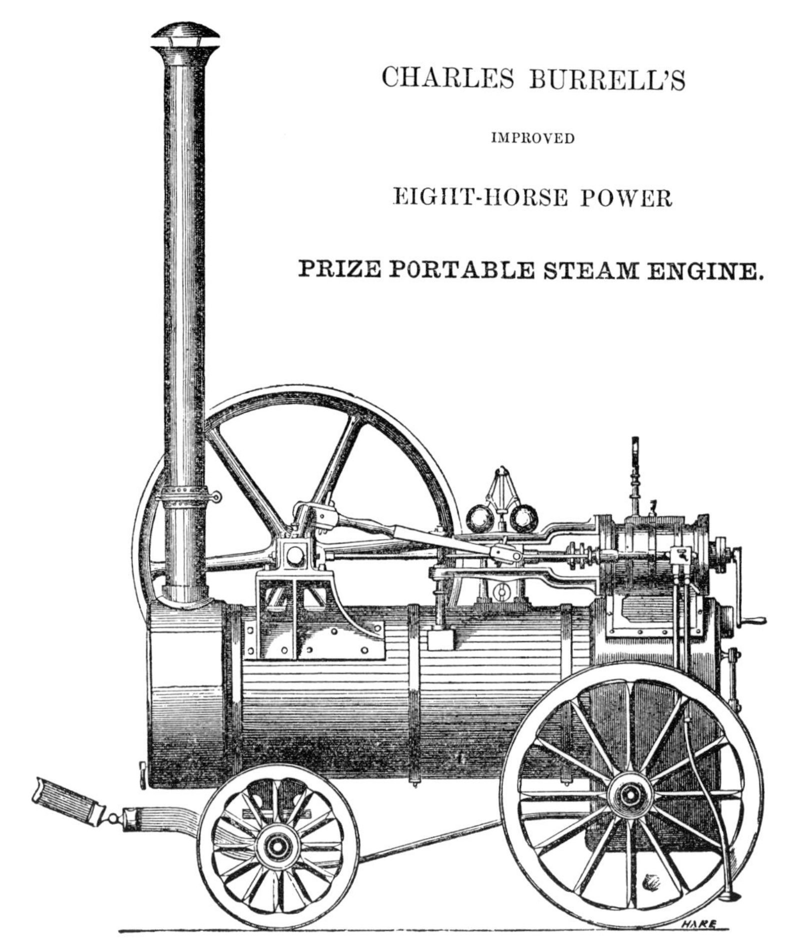

Fig 6 The second generation Burrell portable steam engine as exhibited at the Great Exhibition 1851.

for many years before being cut up for scrap, leaving us with a clear picture of its design and construction. The locomotive type boiler was of single row lap joint riveted wrought iron construction with a haystack type firebox reminiscent of the early Bury railway locomotives used on the London and Birmingham Railway. One can imagine that apart from Cowen's influence, Charles I travelled to Boston to make enquiries of Tuxford and Howden before finalising his designs and during this visit he was introduced to Edward Bury, who had recently taken control of the Great Northern Railway's workshops in the town. Bury remained head of Bury, Curtis & Kennedy, the Liverpool based locomotive builders, until its forced closure in 1850 and was known to have undertaken consultancy work of this nature. It is entirely consistent with Charles I's character that he should seek professional advice before embarking upon the manufacture of a fundamentally new product such as a pressure vessel.

The firebox domed top carried a single Slater type spring safety valve and the regulator valve was mounted on the off-side of the firebox. The single cylinder measuring 8 inches diameter × 12 inches stroke was mounted on top of the boiler adjacent to the firebox. The forged crankshaft was carried in large cast iron brackets riveted to the boiler shell adjacent to the hinged chimney and a large Watt type governor was mounted on the motion bracket and belt driven from the crankshaft. Wrought iron spoked wheels were fitted fore and aft and the engine was arranged for horse haulage in shafts.

It seems probable that only two or three engines of this design were produced although one was successfully exhibited at the 1848 RASE show held in York. Development was rapid and by 1851 designs had settled into a pattern which basically remained unaltered for the rest of the steam era.

Gone was the haystack firebox to be replaced by a conventional round top firebox and the cylinder was placed on top of the firebox. The regulator valve and the cross head driven boiler feed water pump were mounted externally on the cylinder block. Four sizes of engine, 5, 6, 7 and 8 Nominal Horse Power (NHP) were advertised at prices ranging from £170 to £225. Charles I produced a rather splendid comprehensive catalogue of his full range of products to support his participation in the 1851 Great Exhibition held in Hyde Park. The introduction is worth special note.

> "Charles Burrell in introducing his improved portable steam engine to the notice of the public begs to state from the experience he has gained from being situated in a part of the country where the application of steam power to agricultural machinery has made great progress, having himself supplied upwards of 20 engines to agriculturalists in the County of Norfolk alone within the past 18 months . . . and having made

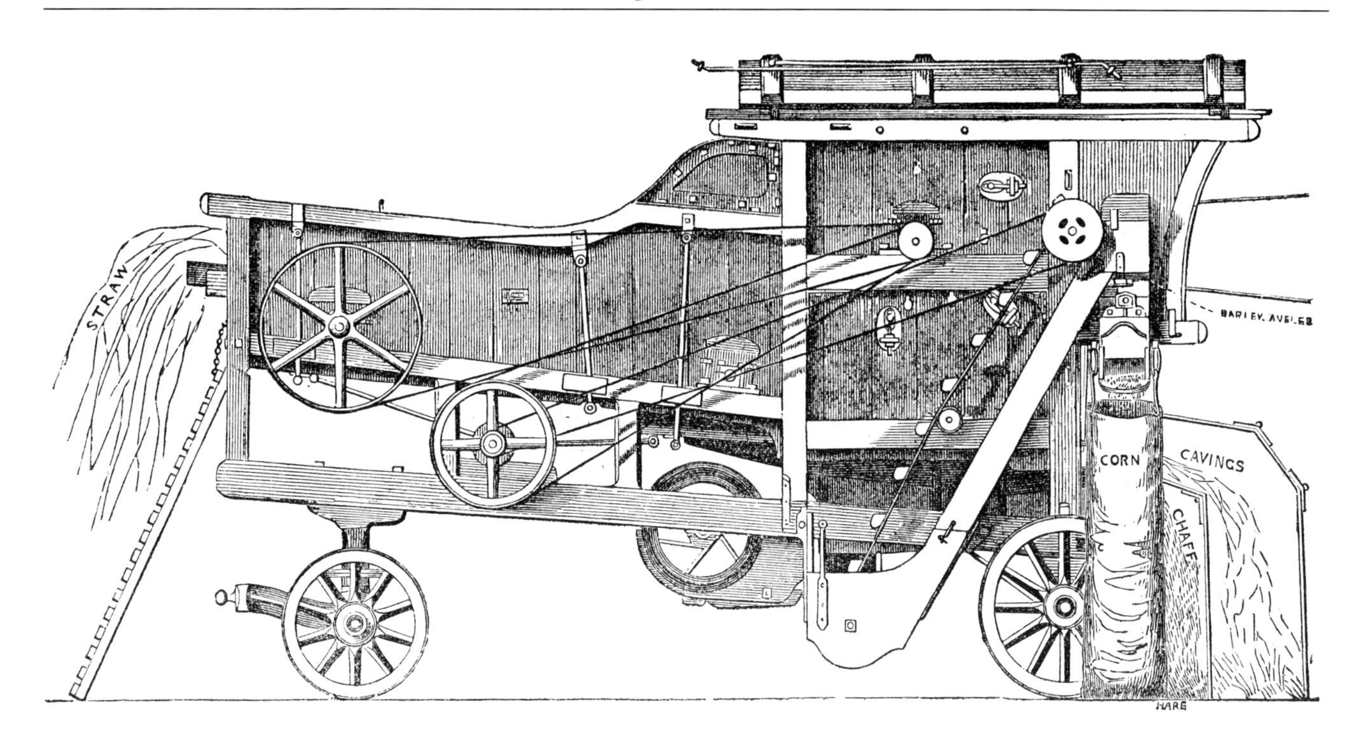

Fig 7 An early Burrell threshing and dressing machine similar to that awarded a silver medal at the RASE York Show in 1848.

extensive additions to his works, as well as a considerable outlay in the most modern and improved machinery, with workmen of the first class, he is enabled to offer such workmanship as cannot be excelled and at such prices as will meet the depression in the value of farm produce."

The reference to extensive additions to the works is of great interest, confirming that at this time the firm acquired its first real machine shop facilities. These would be essential for machining engine cylinder blocks and for turning such items as crankshafts and motion parts. It is recorded that at this time the works employed a total of 50 men and boys. The introduction to the catalogue referred also to the governors fitted to the early portable engines. These were arranged to work at 3 different speeds without the necessity of shutting off the steam, which was important when threshing very dry corn, enabling the speed of the threshing drum to be reduced thereby preventing injury to the corn and straw.

The 1851 catalogue also listed 6 and 8 NHP Table Engines and 10 and 15 NHP Barn Engines which may have been produced at Beck Foundry. These were intended for use in permanent installations on larger farms such that threshing, riddling, winnowing and the dressing of corn, as well as the conveying of straw from the threshing machine to wagons could be carried out under cover. Other operations likely to be performed in the barn by steam driven plant were grinding and dressing flour, sawing timber, chaff cutting, cake breaking, crushing and pulping and turnip cutting.

At the 1848 RASE Show held in York Charles had been awarded a Silver Medal for his improved threshing and dressing machine and this also featured prominently at the 1851 Great Exhibition. It was capable of threshing 5 or 6 quarters of corn per hour without injuring either the corn or the straw and of delivering corn, chaff, straw and siftings or short straw through separate outlets, thereby showing a great saving in labour costs.

Other machinery and implements exhibited in Hyde Park were simple threshing machines and straw shakers; 4-horse portable gins which had received the judges' commendation at the 1849 RASE Norwich Show; and a circular saw bench with attachments for making hurdles and gates. This latter machine was awarded a Silver Medal at the 1849 RASE Show after demonstrating that a hurdle could be cut out and manufactured by one man in the space of 12 minutes.

The Great Exhibition was a symbol of the ideals and achievements of the Victorians and was in every way an enormous success, far exceeding the hopes of its promoters lead by the Prince Consort. Designed by Joseph Paxton, formerly the Duke of Devonshire's head gardener, the huge glass and iron structure was aptly christened by 'Punch', the Crystal Palace. It was visited by over 6 million people and the 100,000 exhibits covered every imaginable aspect of mid-Victorian life. Bizarre as were some of the exhibits, the Machinery Hall left no doubt as to the reality of the 19th century technical achievement. It set the seal upon Great Britain becoming the "Workshop of the World" for the next five decades. Enterprising firms like Charles Burrell became internationally known overnight and from that moment the products of this little Thetford family concern began to flow to the four corners of the world.

CHAPTER TWO

The Endless Railway Era

During the 1840s many learned and respected men, including the pioneers George Stephenson and I. K. Brunel, spoke out against the use of steam on the common road. Giving evidence before a Royal Commission, George Stephenson expressed doubts about the adhesion of a road engine and its ability to pull a worthwhile payload. The resistance of smooth, rigid wheels in pounds per ton on newly laid gravel was calculated as 200 pounds; on soft grassland, 300 pounds; whereas the resistance on a well laid railway with moderate gradients was stated as being 8 to 10 pounds. The railway companies pressed for, and indeed almost obtained, an exclusive right to carry both goods and passengers at this time. The hostile trustees of our main roads imposed tolls, which were often more per diem than the total cost of operating a road locomotive. The idea of using the existing highways for the mechanical transportation of goods and people was virtually abandoned until men like William Bray, James Boydell and Charles Burrell re-opened the subject in the mid 19th century. For a time their work to progress the development of the steam powered road locomotive hung by the most fragile of threads.

It seems probable that the first British built self-moving traction engine, designed solely for the haulage of goods on the common road, was constructed by R & W Hawthorn, Newcastle-Upon-Tyne engineers. Sir Daniel Gooch described an encounter with the engine on the Great North Road near Morpeth in 1829 in his diaries which were published in 1892. Supplied to a Mr Robson of Alnwick he used the engine for hauling a threshing drum on his farm and for haulage duties at his North Sunderland Lime Works. Unfortunately no other details appear to have survived, but Sir Daniel commented, "It made a strong impression upon me."

The next notable development was the 'Farmer's Engine', designed in 1849 by Robert Willis, the chief draughtsman at E B Wilson's Railway Foundry, Leeds, and built by them for Ransomes & May. Designed for hauling a train of wagons and farm implements it was reported to have done good work in the Ipswich and Norwich areas, at times attaining speeds of 12 mph, but eventually the rough roads of the day shook the engine to pieces. The judges at the RASE Norwich Show apparently showed little enthusiasm for the engine, although they commended the workmanship.

In spite of the lukewarm reception given to these two pioneering examples of steam haulage, man, since time immemorial, has welcomed each new means of defeating gravity, time and space. It is, therefore, not surprising that in the early stages of the Industrial Revolution we find inventive men working on the idea of a portable railway or artificial road, capable of moving along with any vehicle to which it was attached. Good roads were virtually non-existent at the time, having improved little since the Romans departed. With the advent of the unpopular system of turnpike roads, the first of which received the Royal Assent in 1663, some isolated improvements were made, but they continued to place severe restrictions upon the movement of heavy loads and prohibitive charges were levied on the hauliers. Complaints about the shocking state of the roads were frequent, especially during the winter months when many became an impassable sea of mud.

In 1770 Richard Lovell Edgeworth patented a portable railway to move along with any carriage to which it was applied: "Several pieces of wood were connected to the carriage which it moved in regular succession in such a manner that a sufficient length of railway was constantly at rest for the wheels to roll upon and that when the wheels had nearly approached the extremity of this part of the railway their motion laid down a fresh length of rail in front, the weight of which in its descent assisted in raising such part of the rail as the wheels had already passed over, thus the pieces of wood which were taken up in the rear were in succession laid in front, so as to furnish constantly a railway for the wheels to roll upon."Edgeworth was ahead of his time, for there is little doubt he had in mind that his invention should be applied to a mechanically propelled carriage. It seems probable he was aware of the pioneering work of Nicholas Cugnot in Paris, who built a steam powered tractor for gun haulage in 1769 and his correspondence with fellow members of the famous Birmingham based Lunar Society is most revealing. This famous club was founded to enable literary and scientific men to come together for group intercourse and included amongst its members James Watt, Matthew Boulton, Josiah Wedgwood, Joseph Priestley and Erasmus Darwin. All were undoubtedly conscious of the potentialities of high pressure steam, but the combination of James Watt's inertia, the lack of suitable machine tools, especially those necessary for boring cylinders, and the opposition from the turnpikes and those with vested interests in horses retarded development.

In the following half century many patents proposing alternative forms of Endless Railway were filed, but success eluded their inventors. The first commercially exploited patent was filed by James Boydell in August 1846. Allocated No 11357 it was entitled "Applying apparatus to carriages to facilitate the draft" and although the principle was not applied to a steam engine until 1854, it was used on haulage and farm wagons and was also successfully applied to military gun carriages. James Boydell was originally a 'Black Country' ironmaster and by 1840 was a managing partner in the Oak Farm Iron Company of Kingswinford, near Dudley. In 1843 he published an illustrated brochure describing the company's products which made reference to his several earlier patents. No 6815 of 1835 described apparatus for towing boats and other vessels. Another, filed in 1837, described an extraordinary device for giving forward motion to railway locomotives in the event of the driving wheels slipping. Termed "Boydell's Patent Locomotive Propeller", the device was reminiscent of David Gordon's abandoned 1824 steam carriage. This was fitted with six feet or propellers driven by a six-throw crankshaft which successively forced the feet against the ground in a backward direction and drew them up again, to repeat the operation upon the next revolution of the crankshaft.

Although the 'bread-and-butter' products of Boydell's firm were wrought iron fencing, gates and keel plates for ships, he appears to have exerted considerable pressure upon his partners to move the company into more technically advanced fields and this may have been the prime reason for him leaving the firm in 1848. He put up his plate as a Land, Mine and Machinery Valuer, with offices at 54 Threadneedle Street in the City and founded a new manufacturing company styled Boydell & Glasier, with premises in Hawley Crescent,Camden Town, having an extensive wharf on the Grand Union Canal. The factory was adjacent to the Camden Brewery which was owned by the Garretts of Leiston and this may well account for a Garrett engine being used for the second application of Boydell's patent Endless Railway to a self-moving traction engine. He established also close links with the Camden Town and Anchor Iron Works of Smethwick, near Birmingham. Initially he took up residence at No 17 Regent's Park Terrace, a few minutes walk from the Camden factory, but later, in 1854, he removed to a more commodious residence in fashionable Gloucester Crescent, Regent's Park.

Boydell took two stands at the Great Exhibition in Hyde Park. One exhibited a wide variety of iron goods, including several novelties for the construction and shipbuilding industries; the other was devoted to carts and wagons fitted with his Endless Railway. He also published a lengthy treatise in which he referred to his 1846 patent in the following terms:

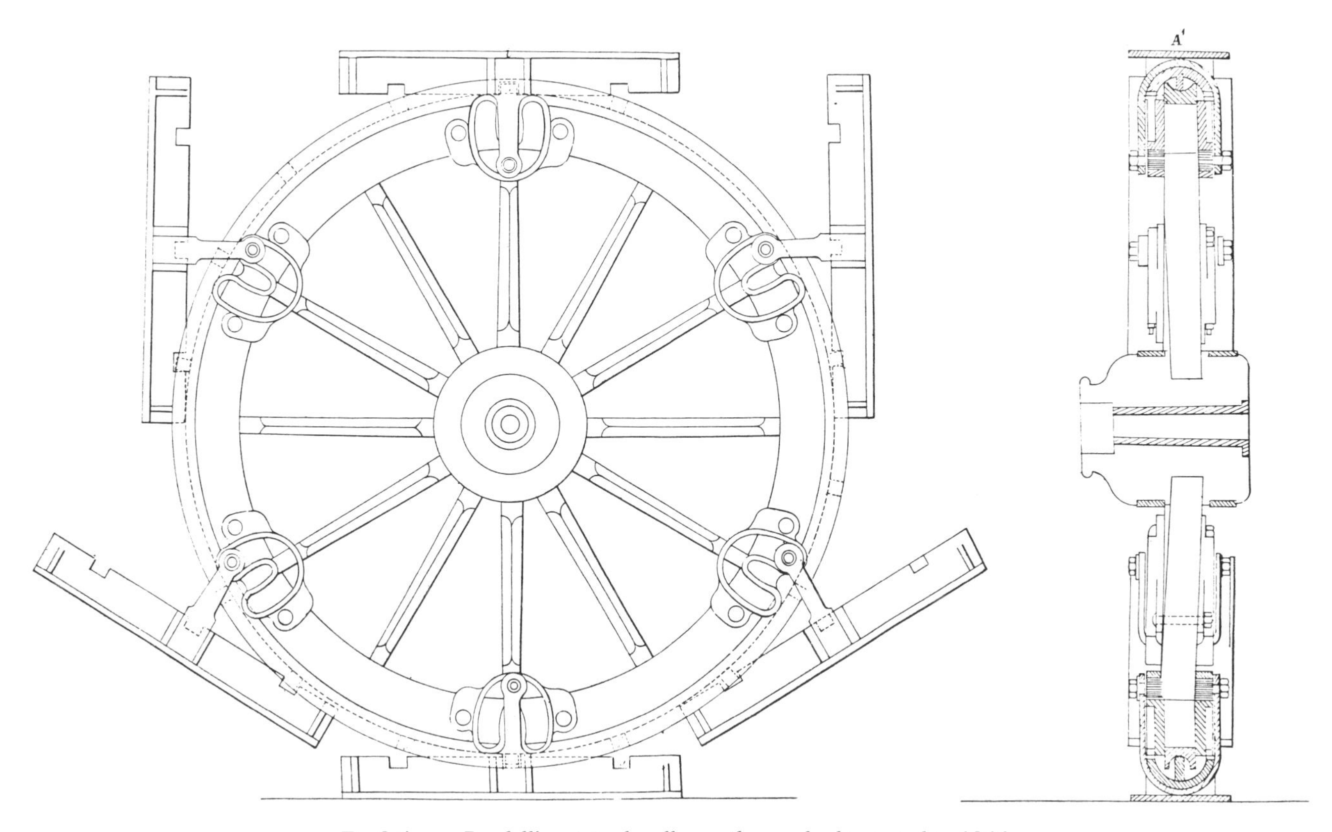

Fig 8 James Boydell's original endless railway wheel patented in 1846.

> "The author has taken out a patent for an invention by which he can effect a great saving in the draught of horses and prevent the land being cut up by the passage of heavy carts, which is accomplished simply by making every wheel lay down its own rail. He has satisfactorily proved that on heavy land at least one half of the draught may be saved. Steps will be immediately taken to bring the invention before the public and it is hoped and believed that it will be found of great value to agriculturists. It will effectively do away with the difficulty of working locomotive engines for ploughing or drawing and although it is admitted that steam could only be employed in this way on very large farms or kept

and hired to many farmers living in the neighbourhood, yet to those who do farm extensively and can afford the necessary capital in making the engine complete it would produce a very great saving, as well all the work of a farm might be done with it and it might even be made to carry the coals for its own consumption."

It is interesting to note in the same publication that Boydell was also thinking along the same lines as John Fowler with regard to mole draining, for he stated his belief in the "possibility of laying drain pipes without being under the necessity of taking out any soil." He declared his intention of manufacturing such a machine, but there is no evidence of this ambition being fulfilled, no doubt due to the strength of Fowler's 1852 patent.

In 1854 Boydell made arrangements with Richard Bach, a prominent Birmingham engineer, for the conversion of a portable type steam engine to a self-moving engine. Boydell's Endless Railway wheels were fitted on the hind driving axle. Earlier Bach had been credited with designing the first conventional portable engine with the cylinder bolted to the top of the firebox casing and the crankshaft plummer blocks and guide bars mounted on the boiler shell. Bach's firm was later absorbed by the world renowned Bellis & Morcom concern. The design of the Bach-Boydell engine was subject to patent No 431, dated February 1854, which described improvements to the 1846 patent by the addition of side pieces to each portion of the moveable rails, so as to obtain a more extended bearing for the rails whilst the wheel was passing over it. The construction of the parts was also modified, enabling wood and wrought iron to be combined to give greater strength without increasing the weight.

The Bach-Boydell engine was rated 8 NHP and the single cylinder was mounted on the smokebox end of the boiler shell; the drive to the hind axle being through a pinion carried on the end of the crankshaft engaging with a large spur wheel bolted to the offside hind wheel spokes. The pinion, free to slide on the crankshaft, could be engaged or disengaged by the driver at will. The engine was exhibited at the RASE Carlisle Show in 1855 and aroused much interest gaining the admiration of the crowd. However, the judges' report published in the Society's journal contained the following comment which may or may not have been aimed at this engine:

"The conditions of competition laid down by the Society for steam engines have unfortunately led to the production of engines only intended for winning the Society's prizes and known as 'Racing Engines', requiring the nicest care, instead of those simple and effective engines which may be safely entrusted to the

Fig 9 The Garrett-Boydell engine under construction in Boydell & Glasier's yard at Hawley Crescent, Camden Town in 1856.

management of intelligent farm servants . . . It is absolutely necessary in future for the Society not only to make such conditions in reference to the construction and trial of engines as may prevent a recurrence of this evil, but to secure the Society and the public from disappointment in their practical value by submitting the prize engines to subsequent trials for a lengthened period under the ordinary management of a farm establishment."

This report laid the foundations for a series of steam engine trials held under the aegis of the Society which became a regular feature of the RASE shows for the next 50 years. It also highlighted another important contemporary question which was to be the subject of much debate and many practical tests in the following decade, namely the application of steam power to the cultivation of the land.

"No satisfactory attempt appeared at Carlisle (1855) to carry out the much sought for application of steam power to the cultivation of the soil. It is evident, however, that the minds of mechanicians have been extensively turned to the subject. The time is probably not far distant when mechanical invention may yet produce a machine satisfying the Society's conditions – viz, that it shall in the most efficient manner turn the soil and be an economic substitute for the plough and the spade."

Fig 10 First generation Burrell-Boydell engine built at St Nicholas Works 1856.

We now know that this statement was made on the very eve of major developments which revolutionised agriculture and within the space of two years the debate shifted as to whether steam cultivation should be by means of stationary engines and ropes or by direct traction.

Undoubtedly it was during the RASE Carlisle Show that Charles Burrell I made the acquaintance of James Boydell and his colleagues. Subsequent events confirm that shortly after the show a licence agreement was concluded whereby St Nicholas Works undertook the design and construction of a road locomotive fitted with Endless Railway wheels. Charles Burrell appears to have insisted that he would require two years to produce a proven prototype.

In July the following year, 1856, Boydell exhibited an engine built by Richard Garrett of Leiston in Suffolk at the RASE Chelmsford Show. This was Garrett's first self-moving engine and as with the Bach engine was adapted from their standard portable engine production, the Endless Railway wheels being fitted to both the front and hind axles. It was rated 12 NHP, had duplex cylinders measuring 6½ ins diameter × 10 ins stroke and the boiler working pressure was given as 60 PSI.

The Editor of the *Artisan* enthusiastically commented, "Road locomotion without injury to the roads is here, most perfectly and efficiently attained," but a writer in the RASE journal was rather more sceptical: "Mr Boydell again exhibited his engine (at Chelmsford) drawing with ease any implements attached to it, but it still remains to be proved if it will ever be found serviceable in agriculture." Due to the keen public interest shown in the traction engines entered for the land cultivation contest, the RASE judges decided to hold the trials away from the showground on land owned by W Fisher Hobbs at Boxted Lodge, near Colchester. The John Fowler team put up a formidable performance with fixed engines and ropes and demonstrated that a 600 acre farm could be ploughed at 7s 2½d per acre with their tackle, including all labour, fuel and repair charges and including 15 per cent depreciation on a capital cost of £550. Boydell failed to impress the judges with the cultivating ability of his tackle.

Shortly after the RASE Chelmsford Show in 1856 a series of trials were conducted with the Garrett engine on Francis Hamilton's farm at Willesdon and upon a Mr Middleton's farm at Hounslow in Middlesex, each trial being conducted over a two day period. Hamilton, of Friar's Place, Acton, was in partnership with Boydell and Glasier and was a co-patentee with Boydell and Charles Burrell in patent No 231, filed in January 1857 and entitled, "Improvements in combining plough with locomotive engines," confirming that co-operation between Boydell and Burrell had been established for some time. The Editor of *The Engineer* observed that, "Several traction engines of a superior construction to the Garrett engine are now manufacturing and nearly ready to enter the field," an obvious reference to the Burrell engines being built.

Later in the year, the Garrett engine took part in the Lord Mayor's Show, giving the people of London their first glimpse of a self-moving traction engine. The following month the engine was shipped to Australia. The same engine was depicted on the cover of a share prospectus issued by Boydell in the following December. The driver stood on a platform built as an extension to the rear of the firebox and the Garrett type regulator and safety valve of the period are clearly visible. The off-side hind wheel was driven through a pinion attached to the crankshaft and a spur wheel attached to the wheel spokes. The duplex cylinders were mounted on the boiler shell adjacent to the smokebox, but there is no evidence in the illustration of a reversing gear being fitted. The water tank was suspended under the boiler and the forward steering platform was arranged very much as in subsequent Burrell built engines, with a ship's type steering wheel and a direction indicator mounted forward.

Fig 11 An early Burrell-Boydell under construction in St. Nicholas Works yard – circa 1857.

We do not know why Garrett did not build further engines fitted with Boydell's Endless Railway but a clue probably lies in subsequent editorial comment in the RASE journal which stated that the Garrett engine was designed primarily for agricultural purposes and lacked the robustness of the subsequent Burrell-Boydell engines which where specially designed for continuous road haulage. Even as late as 1858 Garrett exhibited a self-moving engine at the RASE Chester Show, adding in his supporting sales literature, "The self-propelling gear is intended to act as an auxiliary, rather than to supercede the use of horses altogether for the purpose of transport." Such was the power and prejudice of the horse breeding fraternity in the 1850s.

It is clear from comment in several contemporary technical journals that the military authorities were interested in Boydell's invention from an early date. A number of horse drawn wagons, carts and gun carriages had been successfully employed in the Crimea and a letter of recommendation, signed by Sir William Codrington, the General commanding the troops at Sebastopol, survives. We learn also that although Boydell and Glasier manufactured the patented porte rail components employed on the Garrett engine, the Royal Arsenal, Woolwich, produced the wheels. The *Mark Lane Express*, 30th June 1856, featured a detailed report of tests carried out by a Select Committee of the Board of Ordnance shortly before the RASE Show, in which the Garrett engine was put through its paces on Plumstead Common.

The first Burrell-Boydell engine was completed in late

Fig 12 A second generation Burrell-Boydell engine illustrating the 1857 patented arrangement for drawing a gang of ploughs.

1857.

PLOUGHING BY STEAM,

By the TRACTION ENGINE and ENDLESS RAILWAY,

(BOYDELL'S PATENT.)

On THURSDAY, MAY 7th, & FRIDAY, MAY 8th, from 11, a. m., to 4, p. m.

To enable every person to see the operations of the day, and to prevent accidents, it is earnestly requested that they will strictly adhere to the following regulations.

All Visitors to the Ploughing Field are requested to keep on the headlands and sides thereof, and not to trample on the newly ploughed land.

A Blue Staff will be handed to a limited number of persons each time of the Engine going up and down the Field, entitling them to follow the Engine, and on their return to the same place, they are requested to hand them to other Gentlemen who are desirous to do the same.

The Whistle of the Engine will be sounded previous to its being put in motion, and while moving, all persons following it, to keep at a distance of two yards from the same.

The Operations will take place as follows:

Drawing Heavy Weights on Common Roads will be shown immediately on the arrival of the train leaving London at 8. 0., a. m., and will be repeated at 4. 0., p. m., on the Road near to the point of arrival by Railway.

Ploughing with Six Ploughs, made by Mr. BURRELL of Thetford, will commence at 12. 0. noon, and will continue for one hour.

Subsoil and Draining Ploughs, Mr. Cotgreave's Patent will then be used for one hour.

At 2. 0. p. m., the Ploughing operations will be repeated until 4. 0. p. m.

A Traction Engine as applied to all Stationary Purposes, and a Portable Engine as now in use, having the Endless Railway attached, under Mr. C. BURRELL'S PATENT, and drawing a Thrashing Machine will be shown at intervals during the day.

Mr. BOYDELL, the Inventor of the Traction Engine will attend and explain the same.

The Two Traction Engines and the Portable Engine as altered, are manufactured by Mr. C. BURRELL, THETFORD.

For further information apply to FREDERICK H. HEMMING, *Secretary*, to "THE TRACTION ENGINE AND ENDLESS RAILWAY APPARATUS COMPANY, Limited," No. 47, MARK LANE, LONDON, E.C.

Refreshments will be provided by Mr. EDWARDS, at the BELL INN, THETFORD, as also Conveyances to and from the Ploughing Field:—Fares either way, 1s. each.

R, Carley, Printer, King Street, Thetford.

Fig 13 Facsimile of poster advertising the Croxton trials of the Burrell-Boydell engines in May 1857.

1856 and preceded its main competitor, the Bray traction engine, designed by the well known railway engineer, Daniel Kinnear Clark, by a few months. Little is known of the commercial arrangements concluded with Boydell in 1855 but in Burrell's 1857 catalogue he describes himself as "The Licensed Manufacturer", adding that, "It is considered by all the most practical and scientific men to be one of the most important inventions of the present day." The scant technical data to survive describes the following mechanical details. The engine had duplex cylinders measuring 7½ ins bore × 12 ins stroke. The boiler working pressure was 100 PSI having a total heating surface of 275 sq ft. There were 71 smoke tubes 1¾ ins dia and the grate area was given as 5.5 sq ft. Two speed gearing was provided and the total weight in working order was given as 11 tons 10 cwt. The boiler was carried in a wooden frame or chassis, the steersman standing in front of the smokebox and having a horizontal ship's type steering wheel. Endless Railway porte rails were fitted to both the front and the hind driving wheels. The water tanks were carried either side of the main frame underneath the boiler.

Between 1856 and 1862 Charles Burrell manufactured not less than a score of engines fitted with Endless Railway wheels and these appear to have been of seven different designs, although few precise details of the earlier types appear to have survived. It is said the original drawings were burnt in the works yard in 1928. The first public appearance of a Burrell-Boydell engine was at a ploughing demonstration held at Croxton, two miles north of Thetford, on May 7th and 8th 1857. The engine was put through its paces drawing six ploughs and then later

Fig 14 A third generation Burrell-Boydell engine based upon the ordinary portable engine made self moving and steered by a horse in shafts.

demonstrating a Cotgreave subsoil and draining plough. A second engine having Endless Railway wheels gave a series of demonstrations on the public roads near Thetford railway station. This engine, which we will refer to as a second generation type, had slightly smaller cylinders than its predecessor, measuring 7 ins × 12 ins and the boiler working pressure was reduced to 70 PSI, giving a nominal rating of 10 NHP and a calculated 37 HP. The driving wheels were 6 ft dia and the front wheels 4 ft 6 ins dia. The single drive to the hind axle was through a pinion mounted on the off-side of the crankshaft engaging with a 5 ft dia cast spur ring bolted to four enlarged wrought iron spokes in the driving wheel. The pinion had 10 teeth, engaging with 96 teeth in the spur ring. The hind wheels ran in cast iron brackets, bolted to the sides of the firebox, and all four wheels were unsprung. The front wheels ran on a fixed axle and steered the engine by means of a 9 ft long coach pole and wheel operated by chains, exactly as on a ship, the pole representing the tiller. Unlike the first generation engine, the steering wheel was vertical, the steersman being provided with a seat.

The poster advertising the Croxton event is reproduced in Fig 13, and the reader will note reference to a portable type engine fitted with Endless Railway wheels which we will refer to as a third generation engine. In April 1857 Burrell obtained a provisional patent, No 960, describing the conversion of an ordinary portable type engine to a self-moving engine by means of a pitch chain drive from the crankshaft to the hind wheels. Although the application was never sealed due to the establishment of a prior claim by John Allin Williams, an associate of John Fowler, the patent abstract is of interest.

> "The improvements have reference to applying apparatus to such descriptions of steam engines in order that the power they are capable of exerting may be used in propelling their carriages from place to place. The improvements consist of applying chain wheels to the shafts driven by such steam engines and by means of endless chains or bands, suitable to work in gear with chain wheels, to give motion to the running wheels of such carriages . . . These improvements are peculiarly applicable when using what is known as a Boydell patent apparatus, but they are also applicable when such apparatus is not employed and when the running wheels run directly on roads or on the land."

The single cylinder engine demonstrated at Croxton had Endless Railway wheels on the hind axle only and steering was achieved by means of a horse in shafts. It was claimed that this arrangement "removed in a great measure the liability to accidents incurred by horses passing a puffing engine and its black smoking funnel on the high road." Subsequently, in an article in the *Engineer*, Charles I's fifth son, Frederick, described the attitude of horses to this new employment in the following terms:

> "It was very amusing to see the effects it had upon a strange horse in shafts. The horse would probably refuse to start at the right moment, with the result that it would gradually be pushed forward until it assumed a sitting position like a dog and then would be slid along until he realised that such a position was not a comfortable means of progression, when he would get up and commence to push as hard as possible and, of course, having no effect upon the engine behind him.

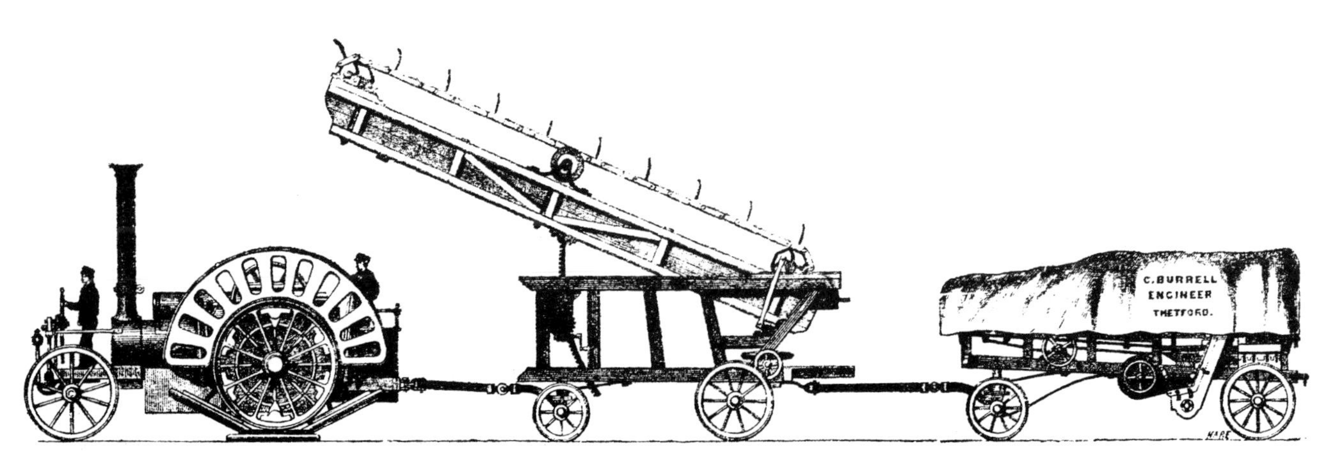

Fig 15 A second generation Burrell-Boydell engine as demonstrated at Thetford in May 1857.

This would last until it gradually dawned upon the animal that dragging was unnecessary when all would go well."

The climax of the Thetford trials was the departure for London of the first generation Burrell-Boydell engine on Thursday May 14th with a net load of 17 tons. The journey was graphically described in the June edition of the *Engineer* by W McAdam, the General Surveyor of Turnpike Roads and later a principal witness before the Committee of the House of Commons on Steam Locomotion of Common Roads, convened in 1859. In his evidence he remarked:

"Up to the year 1857 I was perfectly convinced that locomotives would never travel upon turnpike roads, but then I was induced to see how they were constructed with what is called the Endless Railway. My curiosity then led me to look at it and when I saw it I was so satisfied with the mechanical construction of it that I saw the Company and requested that they would give me an opportunity of travelling with an engine, so that I might see the effect of it, both as to draught and as to its effect upon the road.

"They allowed me to do so and I went to Thetford and accompanied the engine which with its load exceeded 30 tons and brought it into London. It was then in its infancy. I promised the Company that I would keep a log of the proceedings of the engine."

Subsequent comment by McAdam before the Committee makes interesting reading and is reminiscent of the arguments that raged at the beginning of the 19th century as to whether railway locomotives could satisfactorily obtain adequate adhesion upon smooth rails.

"I had previously gone much into the subject with several gentlemen who had suggested engines years before. I had talked a great deal with Mr Brunel and the conclusion which I always came to, and which Mr Brunel said was a correct one, was that the resistance of the road to the engines which were then suggested was so great that there would be no balance of power left to draw the carriages so as to pay."

McAdam's log of the historic journey from Thetford to London is reproduced in Ronald Clark's *Chronicles of a Country Works*. Although undoubtedly a milestone in the history of locomotion on the common road, in terms of speed and cost of haulage the experiment must be regarded as a failure.

Six months before the Thetford demonstration Boydell and his partners floated a new public company with the object of raising additional working capital in order to further develop their invention. Known as The Traction Engine and Endless Railway Company Limited, the new company had an authorised capital of £120,000 divided into 12,000 shares of £10 each. The directors were Boydell, Glasier and Fancis Hamilton. Frederick Hemming, later well known as Fiskins's London agent, was appointed Secretary and the Registered Office was established at 47 Mark Lane in the City.

The prospectus, illustrating the original Garrett engine on the cover, a copy of which survives in the British Library stated:

"The parties interested in the invention have already received applications for licences from many of the most eminent engine builders in England. They feel that in such hands they may safely entrust the construction of the engine portion of the apparatus and that, eventually, advantageous arrangements may be made with these parties for the supply of the required number of engines; and, consequently, that it will not be necessary or expedient for the company to incur the large additional outlay of capital which would be necessary to enable them to become their own engine builders. They, therefore, intend to limit their manufacturing operations to the wheels and the distinctive apparatus which constitutes the special feature of the Endless Railway."

Boydell's activities created something of an Endless Railway mania and a number of gentlemen filed patents describing variations of Boydell's invention but their attempts to commercialise upon their ideas proved abortive. The list of would-be competitors included such prominent names as Sir James Anderson, James Braby, Isaac and Robert Blackburn, William Cambridge, Thomas Elty and Hamilton Fulton, Henry W Ford and David Gordon.

The next major recorded public appearance of the Burrell-Boydell engines was at the RASE Salisbury Show in July 1857. Two engines were presented at the showground, a second generation engine, almost certainly the one used for the Thetford demonstrations two months earlier, and a self-moving portable engine fitted with Endless Railway wheels. The judges were enthusiastic in their praise of the former engine. The zig-zag, steeply inclined route from the showground to the trial field, which caused the other competitors so much trouble, enabled the Burrell-Boydell engine to demonstrate its docility and power and ability to make acute turns. Unfortunately the engine was less successful in the ploughing contest, probably due to the inexperience of the ploughman, who had difficulty getting the ploughs to work at sufficient depth. Later the engine drew a huge Coleman scarifier with complete success, but once again the most impressive performance of the day was achieved by John Fowler, although that too failed to satisfy the exacting requirements of the judges and the coveted £500 prize offered by the Society was withheld.

Immediately after the show two of the self-moving portable engines were sold to William Goldsmith of Ixworth in Suffolk, who used them successfully for many years hauling and driving his threshing machine and working for hire in the area. In 1859 he claimed that the engines had worked satisfactorily for two years, often travelling 20 miles a day, and that repairs to the Endless Railway had cost only £5 and other repairs to the engines £9. At least one of the pair of engines survived at West Row, near Mildenhall, until the 20th century.

In August 1857 the *Illustrated London News* published a fine full page engraving illustrating a ploughing match organised by the Louth Agricultural Association in the preceding month. The engine depicted is a fourth generation Burrell-Boydell engine, similar to the second generation, but of heavier construction, with a wrought iron frame replacing the earlier wooden frame. The long

Fig 16 Ploughing trials at Louth in Lincolnshire, July 1857, with Burrell-Boydell engine showing patent whippletree arrangement for hauling the ploughs.

steering pole and direction indicator and the whippletree arrangement for towing the three pairs of ploughs are clearly visible in the engraving. A detailed report of the event appeared in the *Illustrated London News*.

The success of this trial was repeated in August 1857 when an unspecifed Burrell-Boydell engine was awarded first prize at the Yorkshire Agricultural Society's Show at York. A commentator at the time remarked, "Only let the item of wear and tear be improved upon and the Endless Railway will become invaluable for enabling the farmer's engine to draw his tackle home, lead out manure and market his produce and especially for bearing the ponderous burden of a massive engine over arable land with little detriment to the tillage condition of moist and clayey soil."

During 1857 three other manufacturers exhibited engines fitted with Boydell's Endless Railway. Lee of Walsall in Staffordshire demonstrated a gear-driven engine at the RASE Salisbury meeting, and Collinson Hall and Thomas Charlton produced their patented high pressure steam engine with Boydell wheels, but both appear to have had limited success. Tuxford & Son of Skirbeck Iron Works, Boston, built several three wheel road locomotives with the boiler and inverted cylinders mounted vertically in a massive plate frame, all of which appear to have been shipped to Cuba for working in the sugar plantations. There is also evidence that in the early stages of their development this old established Lincolnshire firm manufactured complete Endless Railway wheels for Boydell and Glasier, but few precise details of their activities have survived. In April 1858 the *Engineer* gave a brief description of a Clayton & Shuttleworth engine fitted with Endless Railway wheels which was supplied to the Russian Government for heavy artillery haulage in the Crimea in the post-war period.

In February 1858 the House of Commons, acting upon behalf of the East India Company, instructed Sir Proby Cautley and Colonel F Abbott to report upon the suitability of the Burrell-Boydell engine for use on the Indian sub-continent. A second generation engine was put through its paces at the Royal Arsenal hauling a gross load of 43 tons and, although the power was found adequate, including negotiating a 1 in 13 incline, its ability to turn corners with its load was found unsatisfactory. Clearly this was due to the gear drive from the crankshaft pinion operating on the off-side wheel only. The Inspecting Officers reported:

> "The experiment, in so far as regards this individual engine for general purposes of draught, must be pronounced a failure. But the powers and capabilites as exhibited inspires us with the greatest confidence in its final success, when the machinery shall be perfected to work both wheels together or either wheel singly. An engine so constructed and equipped with a train of carts would be able to traverse any country where an ordinary bullock cart could travel and being able to move continuously at the rate of 3.5 to 4 MPH would perform journeys of little less than 100 miles in 24 hours. The establishment of such engines and carts would enable Government to dispense with half the ordinary military force in India. Seeing that troops would then be concentrated in one-fifth of the time required by even forced marches, such self acting railways, though immeasurably inferior in speed to fixed railways, will be more generally useful for military purposes as they will travel in any direction and will be safe from the designs of enemies."

C F T Young, a leading writer on transport matters and a great enthusiast of the Endless Railway, expressed the opinion that Boydell had made a great mistake by introducing his engine primarily for agricultural purposes, "So exclusively as almost to prevent its adoption for any other purpose." It seems probable that this error of judgement, if such it was, resulted from the selection of Charles Burrell as his working partner, for clearly the little Thetford firm was at the time orientated entirely to the needs of the agriculturalist. However, Boydell responded quickly to the criticisms of the Government Inspectors and within three weeks of the trials filed patent application No 356 entitled "Improvements in Locomotive Carriages" which described his claim in the following terms:

> "This invention is more particularly applicable to locomotive carriages which run on common roads and which have to turn in a short space. Locomotive carriages of this description have sometimes been so arranged that the driving wheel on one side or the other side of the carriage may be thrown out of gear when going round a sharp curve, but this arrangement is open to serious inconvenience.
>
> "Now this invention consists of lifting one of the driving wheels off the ground (or easing its pressure on the ground) when the carriage is turning. For this purpose a strong arm is mounted on each side of the carriage, turning at its upper end on a centre fixed to the frame; on the lower ends of these arms small wheels or rollers are mounted, and when it is desired to turn the carriage, one or other of these arms is forced down by a screw or other mechanical means, so as to lift one of the driving wheels sufficiently to allow it to slip freely on the ground while going round the curve."

The engine tested on behalf of the East India Company made a further public appearance at Francis Hamilton's farm in East Acton in March 1858. Such was the interest in the Endless Railway that the event was given advance notice in *The Times*. C F T Young attended this demonstration and provided us with further techncial details of the engine. All four wheels were fitted with the Endless Railway attachments, the hind wheels being 6 ft dia, running on short axles mounted in cast iron brackets attached to the sides of the outer firebox. The 5 ft dia final drive or plate wheel was bolted to four enlarged wrought iron spokes in the off-side hind wheel and driven by an independently mounted pinion, driven by another carried on the end of the crankshaft. This is the first reference to an independent motion shaft being employed in the final drive arrangements of a traction engine. The two cylinders, 7 ins bore × 12 ins stroke, were mounted on the smokebox either side of the chimney, thus permitting the use of comparatively long connecting rods, the piston speed being 120 ft/minute. Stephenson's link reversing gear was employed. The boiler working pressure was 70 PSI and the water tank was suspended under the locomotive type boiler and fitted with an exhaust steam water heater.

Even at this early stage in the development of the road locomotive very stringent laws were imposed requiring an

Fig 17 The general arrangement of the fifth generation Burrell-Boydell engine built in accordance with Burrell's patent 2701 with boiler raising and lowering gear operated by the steersman.

engine to consume its own smoke. The engine was designed such that a small valve on the footplate allowed a jet of steam to pass through a hollow tube stay into the firebox above the burning coals. This had the effect of drawing into the firebox additional secondary air which forcibly mixed with the unburnt gases, converted the lurid red blaze into an intensely hot white flame, totally destroying every vestige of smoke and it worked equally satisfactorily whether the engine was standing or running.

Young tells us that during these trials the engine drew its train consisting of six two-wheel carts each loaded with 1.5 tons of mangold-wurzel by a chain attached to a shackle in a strong wooden beam bolted to the rear end of the footplate in a direct line with the driving wheel – "A very ugly, cumbersome affair, but it works admirably," wrote Young. The engine and its train, weighing in excess of 20 tons, then left the farm yard and moved onto the common road, vividly demonstrating its power and manoeuvrability, starting and stopping on a steep hill adjacent to the Horse and Groom Inn. Then there followed a ploughing demonstration using six ploughs, working at a rate equivalent to 8 acres a day and an exhibition of the engine belt driving a threshing machine from its flywheel. Young's final judgement was, "The engine worked as nearly perfect as may be and the carts followed in line beautifully, without the least injury done to the road."

The Royal Agricultural Society's 1858 show, held on the banks of the River Dee at Chester, contained the largest number of implements and steam engines ever presented to the public. The judges tested no less than eighty-nine threshing machines and in the words of a contemporary writer, "There was an avenue of steam engines neatly arranged at equal distances, their flywheels in perpetual motion, presenting a very animated scene; but what would have been the effect produced upon a visitor's nerves had he known that three of these steam engines were liable to burst their boilers at any moment? Fortunately the stewards were at hand and ordered the fires to be drawn and disqualified the offenders from any further competition."

The cultivating trials were the centre of attraction at the 1858 show and it was upon this occasion that John Fowler demonstrated the indisputable superiority of his cable hauled tackle, winning the Society's £500 prize. Charles Burrell entered a third generation Burrell-Boydell engine based upon his self-moving portable engine but unfortunately some mechanical problems developed at the last moment and the engine was withdrawn from the contest. Later it demonstrated its prowess hauling a Coleman's cultivator and a Williams frame of ploughs. The show catalogue listed the ex-works price of the engine as £750.

A second fourth-generation engine, similar to that demonstrated at Louth, was sold to the Enniskillen Railway Company in Northern Ireland in August 1858. It was successfully demonstrated at the Londonderry Agricultural Show, greatly impressing the spectators by its ability to haul and manoeuvre a 170 ft long road train.

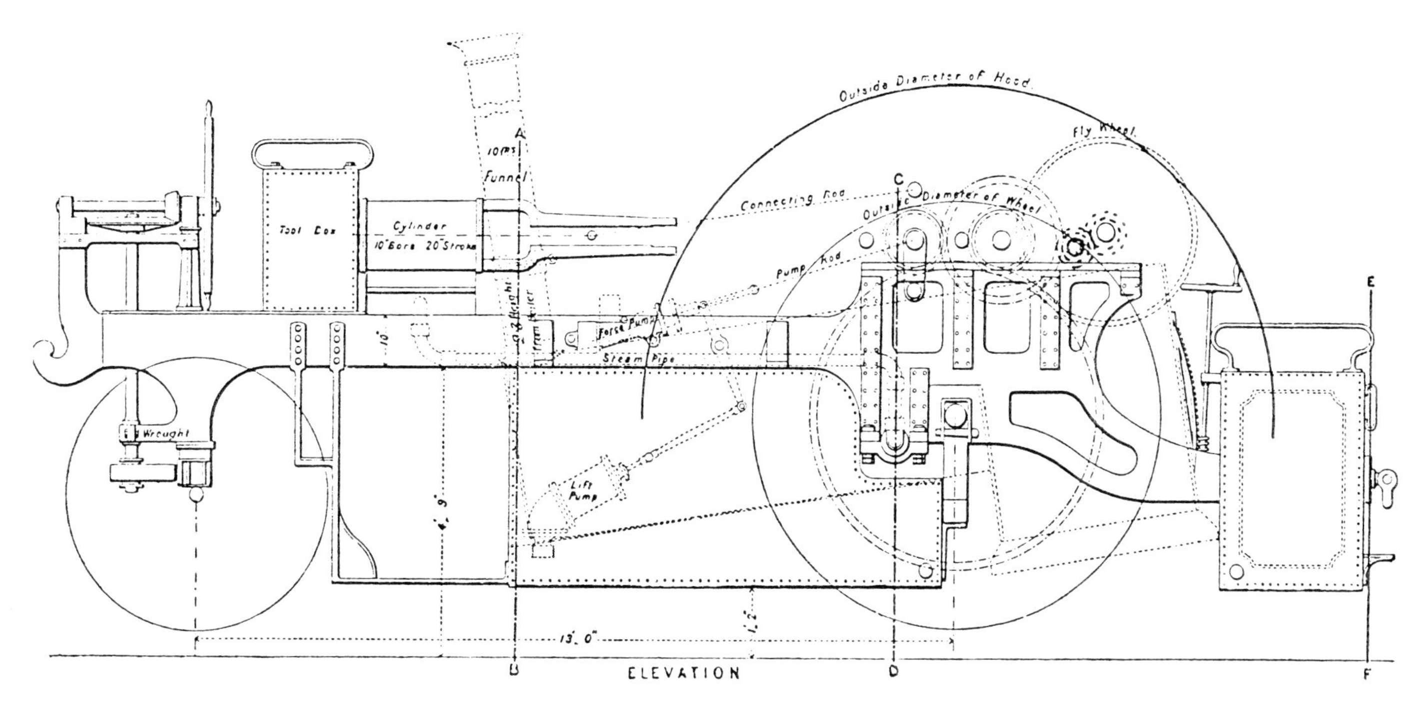

Fig 18 Constructional details of the sixth generation Burrell-Boydell engine showing the pivotted boiler mounting.

Subsequently, the engine worked for many years in the ownership of an Ulster farmer named McCormick.

Clearly the wide publicity given to the Burrell-Boydell engines caused John Fowler some concern. In September 1857 he filed patent No 1684, which described an alternative form of Endless Railway incorporating a differential or compensating gear similar to that patented by Richard Roberts in 1833. Fowler proposed that instead of having five or six sections or feet, known as porte rails, passing over the wheel in succession as in the Boydell system, two sections only should be used for the wheel to traverse. These were operated by a system of cranks driven by the axle and arranged each side of the wheel, such that the Porte Rails were placed on the ground and traversed alternately. Although this patent effectively prevented Boydell from using the differential gear to overcome the problems of negotiating corners, which in any event was probably Fowler's prime objective, the mechanical complexity of his porte rails inhibited further development of this proposal. The following year, in August 1858, Fowler filed patent No 1948 describing yet another form of Endless Railway. This proposal was undoubtedly the precursor of the caterpillar track, but the idea was ahead of its time and was not fully exploited for a further fifty years.

In the latter part of 1858 Boydell was taken seriously ill and was unable to take any further part in the development and commercial exploitation of his inventions. Clearly Charles Burrell tried to salvage the situation and took steps to safeguard his own interests. In November 1858 he filed patent No 2701 which described substantial improvements to Boydell's 1854 design. Burrell's wheel comprised two rows of wrought iron spokes attached to the nave, the outer ends being attached to a two part wheel rim, the inner rim being combined with a large spur ring driven by fixed pinions on each end of the crankshaft. The space between the two rows of spokes was utilised to support 'A-formed bars' or handers to which the Porte Rails were attached, forming a connection between the wheel and the rails on which the engine travelled. A lead screw and lever system was provided on both sides of the footplate, enabling the driver to lift either wheel at will, thus disengaging the pinions from the spur wheels to facilitate turning corners. Additionally the steersman was provided with means of raising or lowering the boiler longitudinally so that the water level over the crown of the firebox could be maintained when ascending or descending hills.

We will call this design the fifth generation, but there is no confirmation that more than one engine was actually sold to this specification, although undoubtedly a prototype was built and thoroughly tested. Following the publication of this patent specification a number of indignant letters appeared in the technical press accusing Burrell of pirating Boydell's ideas and it appears that the relationship between the two concerns cooled. In April 1859 Boydell's partners filed provisional patent No 983 with the object of trying to give added protection to his earlier patents and proposed further improvements to the porte rail guide plates and 'A-formed bars' which were described as cycloidal so as to be capable of "moving somewhat to and fro," but by this date the initiative was completely in Burrell's hands.

The first of the improved sixth generation engines was completed at St Nicholas Works in the early part of 1859. It was designed as a heavy duty engine for continuous operation on the common road, incorporating completely redesigned gearing giving two road speeds. The fast pinions were arranged to slide on the ends of the crankshaft; the slow speed pinions were mounted on the ends of the second intermediate countershaft; all four pinions were operated from the footplate, giving the driver the facility of disengagement for turning corners. A third motion shaft was employed in the drive to the hind wheels and carried a 3 ft dia flywheel on the near side of the engine. Water was carried in tanks mounted fore and aft of the hind wheels.

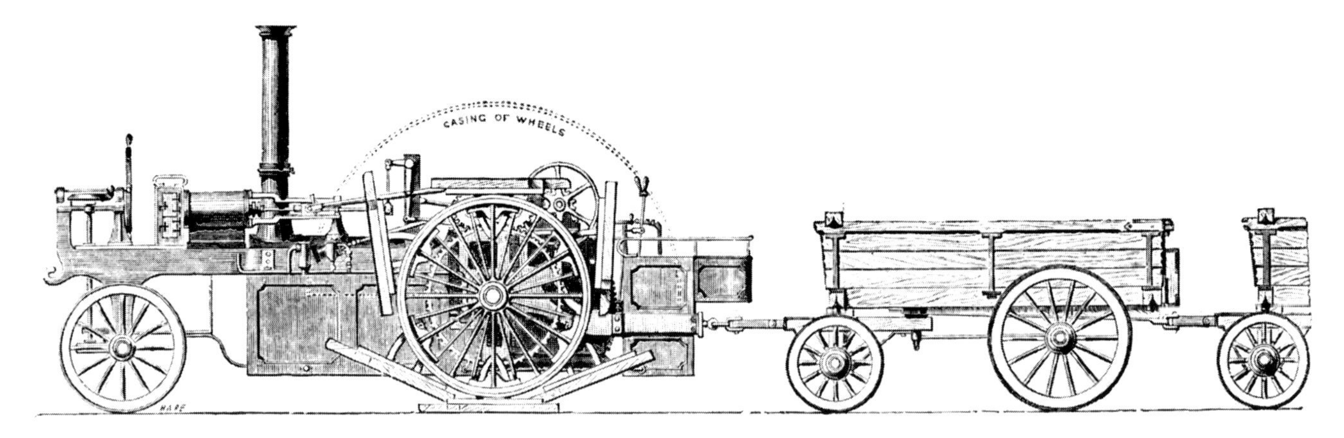

Fig 19 Sixth generation Burrell-Boydell engine for heavy haulage, supplied to Willet & Las Casas in Venezuela in 1859.

Two sixth-generation engines were supplied to Willet and Las Casas who had recently secured an exclusive 10 year contract for heavy road haulage in Venezuela. The engines rated 12 NHP had 7 ins dia × 20 ins stroke duplex cylinders and 6 ft dia hind wheels. The total weight of the engines in working order was given as 11 tons. Before shipment at least one of these engines was employed by J Gibson & Company at Little Halton Colliery at Worsley, near Manchester, for hauling coals into the city. The train consisted of five wagons each having a gross weight of 6 tons giving a gross train weight of over 40 tons and an overall length in excess of 100 ft. It was said that the engine handled these loads with the greatest ease despite the undulating nature of the 8 mile route and the numerous sharp corners to be negotiated. The secret of the "following" qualities of the train was that all ten axles of the wagons were arranged exactly equidistant. Subsequently the writer of an article in the *Scientific American* referred to these engines in the following terms:

> "The engines were assembled on the coast at La Guaira and their route was to Caracas, seven miles in a straight line or twenty-seven miles by the wild crooked roads, which rose 1 in 7 to a height of 7,000 ft. The engines each drew 10 wagons loaded with coal with perfect ease and safety. This is the greatest feat of mountain travelling that has ever been performed by a steam engine."

Penal legislation at home continued to restrict sales in the United Kingdom, but further orders were received for sixth generation engines from Egypt, India and Brazil. In the post-Crimea era the British Government was actively trying to develop trade with the Turks, especially with Mohammed Said, the mechanically minded Viceroy of Egypt. Many leading British engineers, including Robert Stephenson, visited Egypt and the Viceroy became an almost fanatical steam engine enthusiast. An especially interesting railway locomotive was built at Stephenson's Forth Street Works for his pleasure in 1858. It was extravagantly decorated to the design of Sir Digby Wyatt, Professor at the Slade School of Fine Art, probably the first occasion on which an independent designer has been employed by the mechanical engineer to style his products. Two Burrell-Boydell engines were presented to the Viceroy and shipped out to Cairo in September 1859, the Royal Carriage Department at Woolwich Arsenal acting as agents and inspecting engineers.

In August 1859 *The Times* reported fully on the trials of two sixth generation engines held in London's Hyde Park. These had been built for the Indian Government for use in the Bombay area. They had 7 ft dia hind wheels and convincingly demonstrated their ability to draw 60 ton loads across level parts of the park at 6 MPH. Five specially built wagons of 3 tons tare weight were supplied by A & E Crosskill of Beverley, designed in such a manner that they followed each other exactly, without drift, whether going straight or turning corners. The forecarriage pins were attached to the body of the wagon at a mid-point in its length, the distance between each wagon being exactly alike, and each wagon was drawn by the engine and not by the wagon in front, thus reducing the wear and tear on the forecarriage. A chain passed from the buffer plank at the rear of the engine to each wagon forecarriage, the chains incorporated a screw coupling, such that the strain of the draught of each wagon was taken entirely by the engine.

Similar public demonstrations of these engines were given at Acton in West London in September 1859. The road selected for the trials was a bridle lane leading from East Acton to Friars Place and not withstanding the adverse state of the ground following heavy rain, we are told, "The most sanguine expectations of the inventors were fully realised." Abrupt turns were demonstrated and the 102 ft long road train was turned in a space of 39 ft. The engine also showed its paces on a 1 in 6 incline. The price of the engine was stated as being £680 ex-works and £60 each for the wagons.

Lord Stanley, speaking in Parliament on the Locomotive Bill, announced that the Government was so satisfied with the principle of Boydell's Endless Railway that a further two engines had been ordered for use in the Calcutta district. Later, in 1872, Lieut R E Crompton, the pioneer operator of the Thomson Road Steamer, reported seeing one of these engines at work as a stationary pumping engine in the service of the Punjab Railway Company. It is to be regretted that nothing is known of the performance of these engines on the excellent Indian military roads but one suspects that the short life of the porte rails resulted in their early demise.

Boydell died in December 1859 and in the following

Fig 20 The final form of the Burrell-Boydell engine designed by Richard Roberts and built in 1862.

August a sixth generation engine was publicly demonstrated in Hyde Park prior to shipment to a coffee plantation in Brazil. Rated 20 NHP, it weighed 15 tons compared with the Indian engines 11 tons, the duplex cylinders measured 10 ins dia × 20 ins stroke and the motion shafts and 2-speed gearing were carried in bearings mounted on the engine frame, independent of the boiler and firebox. The working pressure was 125 PSI. The facility for raising and lowering the boiler in the engine frame was retained in order that the water level could be maintained over the crown of the firebox on a 1 in 7 gradient.

A similar engine was supplied to the order of Jones & Palmer of Sydney, Australia, in the early part of 1860. On June 20th it left Sydney, hauling two heavy wagons loaded with salt and a water cart for Goulburn, 120 miles south west of Sydney. The gross road train weight was 50 tons and the overall length some 80 ft. A vivid description of this pioneering journey is to be found in the Goulburn Herald, 29th December 1860. Although the actual travelling time was only 111 hours, the total journey time was a little over 6 months due mainly to the unprecedentedly wet weather. Flooding made travelling impossible for weeks on end and the crew had the greatest difficulty in finding dry wood for the engine's fire. Another prime cause for the stoppages and delay was the repeated failure of the cast iron spur wheels bolted to the hind wheel spokes. They proved quite unfit for the rugged tracks which constituted the roads in the colony at the time. The bulk of the load was lost in the flooded River Berrima en route but the road train, nevertheless, made its final triumphal entry into Emanuel's yard in the centre of Goulburn on Boxing Day 1860, bedecked with flags and carrying forty enthusiastic passengers.

Writing in the *Engineer* in 1896, Frederick Burrell referred to other Burrell-Boydell engines which were supplied to the Russian and Peruvian Governments in the same period but few details have survived. During the period 1857 to 1862 various technical journals referred also to Burrell-Boydell engines in the ownership of Sturgeons of Stanton in Suffolk, which were almost certainly third generation engines, a Mr Cooper and a quarry owner at Royston in Hertfordshire. The earliest surviving Burrell engine register, dated 1866, refers to a 25 HP Russian engine having 7 ft dia hind wheels and 4 ft 6 ins dia front wheels, which would seem to indicate a sixth generation engine and was probably the same engine mentioned by Frederick Burrell. Reference to this engine in the 1866 register arose from an order for the supply of a new set of porte rails.

A latecomer to the use of Boydell's Endless Railway was Edward Bellhouse of Eagle Foundry in Manchester. Formerly employed by Sir William Fairburn and the Grand Junction Railway he established his own Company in 1842 and quickly prospered. So far as is known he built only one traction engine and this was shipped to Brazil in 1860 for use on the extension of the Petropolis Railway, which rose some 3,000 ft in a distance of 8 miles.

The final form of Burrell-Boydell engine appeared in 1862 and was exhibited at the Great International Exhibition held in Battersea that summer. Rated 10 NHP it had 6½ ins dia × 12 ins stroke duplex cylinders and weighed only 7 tons without coal and water. It was single-geared having a 1 to 8 ratio and was clearly designed with the agricultural users' needs in mind. Its draught was stated as 20 tons on the level and 10 tons on a 1 in 20 incline. The arrangement for raising and lowering the boiler was dispensed with and the makers drew attention to the greatly reduced number of working parts and the simplicity of construction. The exhibition catalogue, which listed the ex-works price as £750, illustrated the engine hauling a combined threshing and dressing machine and a straw elevator.

The makers also put forward a nicely reasoned argument claiming that the Endless Railway did a great deal less damage to the land than did a horse. No doubt, they were influenced by similar arguments expounded by John Fowler in support of his methods of cable cultivation. The agricultural fraternity remained unconvinced and no further Endless Railway engines were built at St Nicholas Works.

So far we have been able to consider only brief snatches of information regarding the daily usage and performance of engines fitted with Boydell's Endless Railway, for most recorded details refer to public demonstrations organised by makers and other interested parties. However, in November 1863 Mr E Edwards Hewett, a Locomotive Superintendent on the Midland Railway, wrote to the *Sheffield Telegraph* describing in detail a journey by two Burrell-Boydell engines in the Sheffield area. The load comprised a huge steam anvil destined for Butcher's Engineering Works mounted on a specially constructed dray and having a gross weight of 54 tons. The load was hauled initially by a fifth generation Burrell-Boydell engine, which had been supplied to Messrs Harris, Ironfounders of Rotherham, in 1859. It is not clear whether this was the original fifth generation prototype or a further engine of this type, but we are told the whole operation was under the supervision of Mr Bastrick, Burrell's Superintending Engineer. The commentary continues:

"The journey to Sheffield was commenced on Monday, November 2nd, the engine proving itself quite equal to its task whilst on level and good roads, dragging its monster load to the bottom of Eccleshill, where, the road being steep and bad, the engine was overcome and the dray sank.

"In this dilemma Messrs Burrell were telegraphed for further assistance, who immediately sent off a second engine which was unloaded at Victoria railway station on Friday afternoon, arriving at the scene of the disaster the same evening. In the meantime the dray had been lifted by powerful hydraulic lifts, bulks of timber and iron plates being placed under the wheels. The two engines and four horses having been coupled to the dray a new start was made and the procession moved off at a good pace until it arrived at the canal bridge over which planks had been previously laid. The dray had only just been drawn over when the right leading wheel of the first engine left the track which had been laid down by the South Yorkshire Railway Company. This incident delayed matters until Monday morning, November 9th, when another start was made. Such satisfactory progress was then established that the horses were dispensed with. In Corporation Street in the centre of Sheffield, the second engine (clearly the 10 NHP 1862 Exhibition engine) was discarded and the original engine unaided continued its journey to Butcher's Yard in Gibraltar Street, arriving at 5 o'clock on the Tuesday evening. The following morning the two engines were employed to manoeuvre the anvil casting to within a few feet of the hammer."

By modern standards this is perhaps not a very impressive performance, taking 10 days to move a load of 54 tons no more than 10 miles, but this mid-Victorian newspaper article does provide us with an interesting insight into the problems associated with the transportation of large, indivisible loads at that time, and emphasises the enormous progress made in this area during the past hundred years.

In 1873 John Head, a partner in Ransomes of Ipswich, presented a masterly paper before the Institution of Civil Engineers entitled *Steam Locomotion on Common Roads*. His verdict upon Boydell's Endless Railway a decade after production ceased: "An extraordinary combination of inharmonious mechanism."

CHAPTER THREE

Chain Drive Traction Engines

In the 1860s Charles Burrell I successfully managed his enterprise almost single-handed, for his sons were not yet of an age to be employed in the works. Undoubtedly, like so many of his contemporaries, he relied wholly upon his native skill and experience for survival, adopting perhaps almost subconsciously, attitudes of benevolent paternalism in his relations with his men, such that both the receiver and the giver knew exactly what was expected of them and both sides abided unquestioningly by the rules. James Boydell was dead, the Endless Railway Company was in liquidation and the much vaunted Boydell wheel was out of favour. One suspects that St Nicholas Works were busy enough manufacturing portable steam engines and a variety of agricultural implements, but Charles Burrell undoubtedly appreciated the need for a self-moving traction engine in his range if he was to maintain the reputation and markets established in previous years.

The 1861 census indicated that 5 per cent of the United Kingdom population of twenty million were engaged in agriculture; 1205 male persons were listed as being wholly employed as agricultural steam engine drivers; and a further 236 persons were listed as being agricultural implement contractors. One of the major obstacles to the introduction of steam power on smaller farms had been the high capital cost of the machinery, which was quite disproportionate to the means of the average yeoman farmer and to the quantity of work to be done on the farm. Largely as a result of the introduction of John Fowler's cable-hauled cultivating machinery in the 1850s, the problem was overcome by the advent of the village capitalist who made a comfortable living by purchasing one or two machines and hiring them out to his neighbours. Following the introduction of the self-moving traction engine, the large landowner, farmers, and the agricultural contractor became the main source of Charles Burrell's business for the next fifty years.

Morton's *Handbook on Farm Labour*, published at the time claimed that in the preceding four years farmers had purchased some 6,000 steam engines, representing 40,000 HP, the great majority being portable type steam engines. Only a very small proportion were self-moving traction engines. Many large farms continued to employ stationary barn engines for threshing and similar duties and there is some evidence that Charles Burrell maintained a small foothold in this market until the late 1860s. It is recorded that prior to 1851 only 500 portable type steam engines were produced in the United Kingdom, which indicates the very rapid growth of this market in the years following the Great Exhibition. Clayton and Shuttleworth of Lincoln, as already noted, quickly became the largest manufacturers of this class of engine. They established their Stamp End Works in 1845 and by 1860 were employing over 1,000 hands, a factor which no doubt influenced Charles Burrell's decision to concentrate upon a new generation of self-moving traction engines.

The decision was supported by J Evelyn Denison, MP, who commented in a report to the President of the Board of Trade:

> "No farmer who has ever employed a steam engine on his farm will ever again be without one; no farmer who has threshed his corn with steam power could bear again to see his horses toiling in the wearisome circle, now jerking forwards when the whip sounds, now brought almost to a standstill when the machine is clogged by a careless feeder. The regular stroke of the untiring steam engine gives excellence to the work, keeps everybody in his place and introduces among men, even the most careless, something of its own excellence and precision."

With the introduction of improved methods of threshing and cutting chaff, the agricultural fraternity increasingly demanded more powerful engines. In 1851 the average nominal rating of a portable engine was 5 NHP; by 1855 this had increased to 7 NHP. This arbitrary method of power classification was based solely on piston area and took no account of the boiler working pressure, which was also steadily increasing, or the piston stroke, or engine revolutions, all of which are a direct function of an engine's power output.

Mere fragments of information in surviving Burrell papers clearly indicate the diversity of the works activities in this period, perhaps marking the final transition from a country agricultural implement workshop to an internationally known engineering concern. In 1863 we learn Burrell completed a travelling steam grab, a steam winch, a timber-framed gun carriage, a pillar crane and a ship's gun carriage; new wheels were supplied to replace the Endless Railway wheels on Mr Cooper's Burrell-Boydell engine and the final design of Burrell-Boydell engine built for the 1862 Great Exhibition was rebuilt as a conventional chain-driven traction engine. The first reference to St Nicholas Works building Fowler Ploughing Engines under licence appeared in 1862.

In 1864 we learn that third generation Burrell-Boydell engines with horse steerage supplied to Mr Sturgeon of Stanton and to Cammell & Baker of Hopton were rebuilt as double chain drive traction engines. Gun limbers and

Fig 21 A Burrell threshing and dressing machine circa 1865 built with either 4 ft 6 ins or 5 ft 0 ins drums. The corn was delivered into sacks after passing the barley awner.

Fig 22 The improved Clover and Trefoil seed drawing and dressing machine with Burrell's patent screen for separating extraneous seeds, grass and stones – circa 1865.

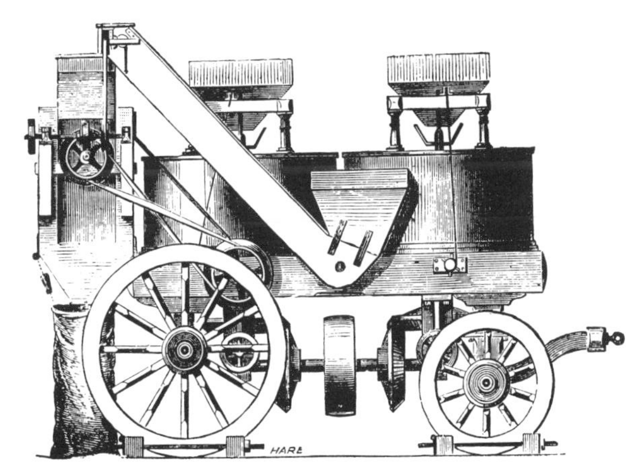

Fig 23 Burrell's portable corn mill with two pairs of stones and apparatus for dressing 400 lbs. flour per hour. Designed specially for use in thinly populated areas.

Fig 24 A smart looking DL series 8 NHP single chain driven traction engine. Probably the prize winning engine at the Hamburg International Exhibition 1863.

gun carriages for 12 lb and 18 lb breech loading guns were built for the military authorities. A Coprolite Mill with 4 ft 4 ins dia stones, a bone mill with double cutters and a large portable corn mill were completed, as well as a number of improved threshing and finishing machines. A number of 7, 8, 9 and 10 NHP portable engines were built and Mr Hubbard's portable engine was converted to a self-moving traction engine.

In 1865 reference is made to a 40 ft high steam pile-driving frame and a number of steam winches. Further orders were received from the military authorities for gun lorries with 9 ft dia and 5 ft 6 ins dia wheels. A steam crane was supplied to Messrs Appleby and the first 8 NHP duplex cylinder traction engine was completed. By this date all reference to manufacturing cast iron grates and stoves and iron fencing had been removed from the company's sales literature.

Richard Roberts, the celebrated railway locomotive builder and inventor of the self-acting spinning mule, had been consulted during the design stages of the 1862 Burrell-Boydell engine and it seems highly probable that he was also associated with the design of the 1863 type DL chain drive traction engine. Born at Llanymynech in Wales he found employment originally with John Wilkinson, the first ironmaster capable of accurately boring James Watt's engine cylinders, and later, in London, with Henry Maudsley. In 1816 he established his own works in Manchester where he played a major role in the development of early machine tools and his original planing machine today rests in the London Science Museum. In 1828 he was taken into partnership by Thomas, Robert and John Sharp and in 1833 the company became Sharp, Roberts & Co. They built many famous railway locomotives which were quickly distinguished by their superior workmanship and finish, stronger framing and larger bearing surfaces than was customary at the time. In 1845 the works were removed to Glasgow and Roberts retired from the partnership, putting up his plate as a Consulting Engineer until his death in 1864. It appears that Charles Burrell originally made contact with Roberts when John Fowler filed his patent in 1857 describing an alternative form of Endless Railway incorporating Roberts's differential gear. Without doubt Roberts's great experience as a locomotive designer was of immense value to Charles Burrell as he struggled to transform St Nicholas Works from implement builders to engine builders.

Unfortunately few details of the first generation of traction engines built at St Nicholas Works have survived, but all were chain-driven by a pitch chain drive from the crankshaft to the hind axle. We do not know exactly how many were built in the years preceding 1868 because the surviving works records start with engine No 395, completed in November 1867. We do know, however, that an 8 NHP engine, allocated works No 317 and classified as type DL, was built in 1863. We know also that a 12 NHP engine No 328 was built in 1863. By simple extrapolation it

Fig 25 General arrangement of the 8 NHP single cylinder double chain engine as illustrated in John Head's paper before the Institution of Civil Engineers in 1872.

would seem unlikely that more than twenty chain engines were built in the five years to the beginning of 1868.

In total we can positively identify fifty-three 8 NHP traction engines, twelve 10 NHP single cylinder engines, one 10 NHP duplex cylinder engine, and three 12 NHP duplex cylinder engines built between 1863 and 1880. Additionally two unique chain-driven road locomotives were built. The 8 NHP engines appear to fall into four distinct classes, although during the early evolutionary period it is very doubtful if any two engines were exactly alike. The one common factor seems to be that the majority went new to customers in East Anglia, although several were exhibited overseas and in 1863 one of the original design engines fitted with an elegant fluted chimney won a silver medal at the International Exhibition held in Hamburg.

The identifiable class DL engines carried the following works numbers and building dates.

8 NHP SINGLE CYLINDER SINGLE CHAIN TRACTION ENGINES

No	Built		No	Built	
No 317	Built	1863	No 427	Built	1868
408	"	1868	444	"	1869
417	"	1868	455	"	1870

The cylinder was mounted on top of the firebox and the crankshaft and intermediate drive shaft with the single chain pinion at its outer end were carried in brackets bolted to the boiler shell. The handsome fluted and flared top chimney was abandoned for a simple stove pipe chimney. Forward steering was retained, the steersman being provided with a clutch for operating the sliding gear pinion on the outer end of the crankshaft. Originally the forecarriage was made of wood, but by 1868 a metal structure was employed. The wheels had cast iron rims with wrought iron spokes and the off side hind wheel was provided with pins for disengaging the chain drive to the hind axle, which unlike previous self-moving engines ran the full width of the engine in front of the firebox. The driver stood on a manstand which carried some coal and the water was carried in a 160 gallon tank slung under the boiler ahead of the firebox. The boiler back plate mountings included the regulator, a water gauge, test cocks, two Salter type and adjustable spring safety valves and a pressure gauge. The feed water was delivered by a large brass bodied feed pump driven by an eccentric on the crankshaft and the Watt governors were belt-driven from the crankshaft.

An improved version was introduced in September 1869 and engines in this series carried the following works Nos:

8 NHP SINGLE CYLINDER DOUBLE CHAIN DRIVE TRACTION ENGINES

No	Built		No	Built	
No 452	Built	1869	No 495	Built	1871
463	"	1870	496	"	1871
464	"	1870	497	"	1871
471	"	1870	522	"	1871
472	"	1870	523	"	1872
473	"	1870	524	"	1872
484	"	1870	544	"	1872
485	"	1870	568	"	1873
486	"	1870	569	"	1873

Fig 26 An early single chain type DL chain engine at work in the 1880s.

Many entirely new patterns and forgings were produced, the main improvements being the introduction of the 'J' class boiler with a Lowmoor iron inner firebox and two driving chains to the hind axle, one on each side of the boiler, replacing the original single speed, single drive arrangement. The single cylinder, similar to that employed on the majority of the first generation engines, measured 9 ins dia × 12 ins stroke. The curved spoke flywheels were 4 ft 6 ins dia × 6 ins wide. No brakes were fitted to the engine and the weight in working order was given as 9.5 tons. The hind wheels were generally 5 ft 6 ins dia × 14 ins wide and the rims were drilled for attaching iron paddles or 'spuds' used for traversing soft ground. The front wheels were generally 3 ft 7 ins dia × 9 ins wide.

The leading dimensions of the new 'J' type boiler were:

Working pressure	100 PSI
Diameter	2'7½"
Fire box – Length	1'10½"
– Width	2'0"
– Depth	2'9"
Smoke tubes – length × dia.	2'6" × 2¼"
No. tubes	33
Smokebox – length × dia.	1'2⅝" × 2'7½"
Grate area	3.71 sq ft
Heating surface – firebox	24 sq ft
– tubes	119 sq ft
– total	143 sq ft

It should be noted that all leading dimensions quoted in this text were from time to time subject to variation in order to meet individual customers' specific requirements. For example, although the majority of 8 NHP chain engines had 14 ins wide hind wheels, others varied between 12 ins and 18 ins. Similarly the 'J' type boilers normally had 6 ft 6 ins long smoke tubes, but engine Nos 544, 568 and 569 were built with lengthened boilers and 7 ft 7 ins long smoke tubes. It may be assumed that until the 20th century no two engines were precisely the same. It is of course impossible to give exact details of all such variations in a work of this kind.

Design ratios are sometimes useful to the student of engine design for comparative purposes and listed below are those applicable to the 'J' boiler expressed per nominal horse power:

Grate area	0.45
Firebox heating surface	3.0
Tubes heating surface	15.0
Total heating surface	18.0
Ratio heating surface to grate area	38.5

Given the benefit of present day knowledge one suspects that the steaming quality of these boilers could have been improved if the smoke tubes had been a smaller diameter and longer and the grate area was increased in size. In this connection it is interesting to note that a forced air fan driven off the hind axle was fitted to first generation engine No 427 in an endeavour to improve the engine's steaming qualities.

Each end of the crankshaft carried sliding pinions of differing sizes, which drove the chain sprocket wheels carried on the intermediate shafts, giving a two speed drive to the hind axle. The sliding pinions were operated by the steersman as in the earlier design, the fast speed drive being on the off side and the slow speed on the near side of the engine. The dimensions of the chain wheels and gear wheels were as follows:

ROAD GEAR		PITCH	WIDTH	TEETH
Pinion wheel	– Fast	2"	2⅜"	12
	– Slow	2"	2⅜"	9
Spur wheel	– Fast	2"	2⅜"	29
	– Slow	2"	2⅜"	32
Chain wheels	– Pinion	6"	1⅜"	5
	– Spur	6"	1¼"	26

In the 1870s the company's sales literature defended the use of the chain drive, claiming that engines driven by two chains had been found in practice to be a great improvement over engines fitted with cast iron gears. This claim may well have contained an element of truth in the days before steel was available for gear wheels and before the differential or compensating gear was universally adopted. Undoubtedly the introduction of spring gear on the hind axle raised a whole new set of problems for the engine designer, but in spite of these, Charles Burrell, as other leading manufacturers, completely abandoned the chain in favour of gears by 1880.

The Royal Agricultural Society tested engine No 495 at the famous engine trials held at Wolverhampton in July

Fig 27 The type DL 8 NHP single cylinder double chain driven traction engine as illustrated in Burrell's catalogue.

1871 and the judges commented favourably upon the engine's performance and economy of working. The boiler working pressure was increased to 120 PSI for the purposes of the trial and on the dynamometer brake the engine developed 16 BHP at 150 RPM. The fuel consumption was recorded at 4.19 lbs per gross IHP per hour, the water evaporated was 7.36 lbs per pound of coal and the lubricating oil used amounted to 4 ozs per hour.

Engine No 463 was exhibited at the 1870 Smithfield Show and No 569 at the 1873 Smithfield Show. It was customary for show engines to be given special treatment in the works and the paintwork and brass fittings were prepared to an exceptionally high standard before despatch. Most of the engines in the series went to East Anglian farmers, although No 544, it is believed, was the first Burrell engine to be sold to an Irish customer.

The malpractice of screwing down spring safety valves in order to increase the boiler working pressure had recently been the subject of much comment in the technical press. Informed opinion was also pressing for the introduction of mandatory hydraulic tests to be carried out annually and the result of the outcry was the formation of the influential "Manchester Association for the Prevention of Steam Boiler Explosions." The first chief engineer was R B Longridge, George Stephenson's old friend and colleague, and henceforth engine builders paid a great deal more attention to the integrity of boiler design and to the adequacy and reliability of the safety valves employed.

Allen Ransome of Ipswich referred to the subject in a paper given before the Royal Agricultural Society in the following terms:

> "It has always been a source of great concern to me that there should be such great ignorance of the effects of confining a large body of steam in a small space. As soon as the water begins to boil the safety valve should be opened by hand and examined to make sure that it is not obstructed in any way. The spring balance may then be screwed down to a pressure of about 10 PSI and when the steam blows off at that point, it may gradually be screwed down to 45-50 PSI as the steam rises. The spring balance should on no account always be left screwed down to full pressure when the engine is not at work. It is to be feared that the spring balance is too often left screwed down when the men are at dinner!"

Fig 28 illustrates engine No 524 hauling a threshing drum and elevator. This engine was supplied new to Richard Parrott of Brandon, Suffolk in 1872 and a grandson today owns the oldest surviving Burrell engine, No 748, now appropriately named 'Century'. The reader will note the proverbial man with the red flag leading the road train. The Locomotive Acts of 1861 and 1865 limited the speed of mechanically propelled vehicles on the common road to 2 mph and required that the vehicle be accompanied by a man with a red flag walking not less than 60 yards ahead to warn oncoming traffic. These Acts caused great inconvenience and hardship to farmers and hauliers alike, but forty years elapsed before any relief was granted.

The third generation of chain-driven traction engines introduced during 1873 incorporated two major improvements. The judges at the RASE Wolverhampton Show held in 1871 strongly recommended the steam jacketing of cylinders in order to reduce condensation and thus considerably improve the engine's efficiency, and from the introduction of this series most engines manufactured at St Nicholas Works incorporated this feature. Undoubtedly in the early days of the chain engine stretching chains had caused problems. Thomas Aveling, the founder of the famous firm Aveling & Porter of

Fig 28 No. 524 8 NHP chain driven traction engine in the ownership of Mr. Richard Parrott of Brandon in Suffolk – May 1872.

Rochester, Kent, solved the problem by the addition of a jockey wheel or chain tightening pulley mounted on the side of the boiler, enabling the chain to be tensioned as wear and stretching occurred and Burrell quickly adopted this feature. The third generation engines carried the following works Nos and building dates:

THIRD GENERATION 8 NHP CHAIN DRIVE TRACTION ENGINES

No 570	Built	1873	No 595	Built	1874
571	"	1873	596	"	1874
572	"	1873	597	"	1874
573	"	1873			

Three other features were incorporated in this series which later became standard practice. Firstly the engines were fitted with a hand brake, although unfortunately its application and method of operation remains obscure. Secondly cast iron replaced brass for boiler mountings such as clack valves and feed pump bodies. Brass had shown a tendency to de-zincify, especially in hard water areas. Thirdly the original chain steerage was replaced by an improved worm drive which was still operated from the front manstand. A drawing is extant showing a bevel wheel drive from the crankshaft to the forecarriage enabling the boiler front end to be raised and lowered when ascending or descending hills in order to ensure that the crown of the firebox was at all times covered with water, but there is no confirmation that this feature was ever incorporated.

Engine No 572 was exhibited at the RASE Show held at Hull in 1873 and once again the judges were full of praise for the neatness of design and operation, the efficiency of working and workmanship and finish of the Burrell products. By this date it had become customary for the company's latest products to be exhibited each year at both the Smithfield Show and at the RASE Show and undoubtedly Charles Burrell derived much benefit from what must have been, even in those days, a costly exercise. The company also increasingly participated in overseas exhibitions. In 1874 they were awarded the gold medal at the Mariestad Exhibition in Sweden, having previously won silver medals at the International Exhibition at Bremen in Germany, at the Gottenburg Agricultural Show and at the Great Exposition Universelle in Paris. Two years later they were awarded another silver medal at the Swedish Agricultural Exhibition held at Norrköping. These awards were gained at the time continental manufacturers were establishing local, often state subsidised industries of their own.

The final form of 8 NHP chain engine emerged in 1875 and the series carried the following works Nos and building dates.

FOURTH GENERATION 8 NHP CHAIN DRIVE TRACTION ENGINES

No	Built	No	Built	No	Built	No	Built
No 672	Built 1875	No 738	Built 1876	No 787	Built 1878	No 834	Built 1879
673	" 1875	739	" 1876	788	" 1878	857	" 1879
692	" 1875	740	" 1876	816	" 1878	858	" 1880
693	" 1876	747	" 1877	817	" 1879	859	" 1880
721	" 1876	748	" 1877	832	" 1879		
722	" 1876	749	" 1878	833	" 1879		

These were sturdier engines than the previous models and although the 'J' class boiler was retained the firebox was lengthened by 10½ ins giving a substantially improved steam raising performance. Cast iron wheel rims were replaced by wrought iron and the diameter of the hind wheels was increased to 5 ft 8 ins and the front wheels to 3 ft 10 ins. The hind axles were sprung with helical springs inclined backwards at 45 degrees, so that when the axle was deflected the chain tension remained constant. The last two engines in the series had winding drums carrying a wire rope on the hind axle, precursors of standard practice employed on all traction engines in future years. Exhaust steam feed water heaters were also fitted, a feature most leading engine builders were experimenting with at the time. The chain drive with Aveling chain tightening pulleys remained substantially as before, but the two speed ratios were improved to give 12.56 to 1 fast speed and 18.5 to 1 slow speed ratios. No 833 and subsequent engines were fitted with straight spoke flywheels and engine Nos 787, 816 and 857 were subsequently converted to tender steerage.

The larger and more powerful 10 NHP traction engines built in the period 1867 to 1877 carried the following works Nos and building dates:

10 NHP SINGLE & DUPLEX CYLINDER CHAIN DRIVE TRACTION ENGINES

No	Built	No	Built
No 405	Built 1867	No 498	Built 1871
414	" 1868	531	" 1871
430	" 1868	543	" 1873
443	" 1869	734	" 1876
478	" 1870	737	" 1876
487	" 1870	769	" 1877
488	" 1870		

The first four engines were simply a bigger version of the 8 NHP engine, having 10 ins dia × 12 ins stroke cylinders and double chain drive to the hind axle. One suspects that they were poor steam producers, for we find a contemporary writer plaintively commenting, "If only engine builders would lay down as an invariable rule 5 sq ft of heating surface to evaporate one cubic foot of water, engine men would never complain for want of steam." Engines Nos 478 to 543 inclusive were of an entirely new design fitted with the new 'K' class boiler, although with the exception of No 498, they retained the old 10 ins dia × 12 ins stroke single cylinder. The drive to the hind axle was by means of twin pitch chains arranged to give two road speeds. The dimensions of the boiler were as follows:

Working pressure	100 PSI
Diameter	2′7½″
Inside firebox – length	2′1¼″
– width	2′0″
– depth	2′10″
Smoke tubes – length × dia.	7′6″ × 2¼″
No. tubes	37
Smokebox – length × dia.	1′2⅝″ × 2′7½″
Grate area	4.25 sq ft
Heating surface – firebox	26 sq ft
– tubes	154 sq ft
– total	180 sq ft

The design ratios were very much as the 'J' class boiler fitted to the 8 NHP engines, with the exception of the heating surface to grate area ratio, which showed a significant increase.

All except No 498 were supplied to East Anglian buyers. Nos 734, 737 and 769 were built to new drawings and were not dissimilar to the last generation of 8 NHP chain drive traction engines. They were fitted with the 120 PSI type KG boiler used on the 12 NHP single cylinder long chain ploughing engines built in the 1870s. These three engines were the first Thetford-built traction engines built with the hind axle arranged behind the firebox which permitted a larger footplate to be built and the front steerage was discarded. This allowed both the driver and the steersman to be accommodated on the footplate and for their added comfort the footplate floor was spring mounted. The hind wheels measured 5 ft 8 ins dia × 20 ins wide and the front wheels were 4 ft 0 ins dia × 16 ins wide. No 734 was provided with water tanks under both the footplate and the boiler and No 769 had a winding drum stud attached to the underside of the boiler. This enabled the engine to work cable hauled cultivating machinery as well as fulfilling its duties as a haulage and threshing engine.

Fig 30 The same engine as shown in fig 29 after conversion to a geared drive engine threshing at West Row in Suffolk.

No 498 was the first Burrell built crane engine. It had 6½ ins dia × 10 ins stroke duplex cylinders and was built for J Duncan of Kilomen in Argyllshire and used mainly for timber haulage. Unfortunately no details of the design and construction of the crane gear have survived.

So far as can be traced only three 12 NHP chain drive traction engines were built and these carried the following works numbers:

12 NHP DUPLEX CYLINDER CHAIN DRIVE TRACTION ENGINES

No	Built
No 328	1863
395	1867
442	1868

No 328 was a 6 ins pitch single chain engine; the other two had double chain drive, all had 7⅝ ins dia × 12 ins stroke duplex cylinders. This engine is believed to have been the first to be fitted with Sharp Stewart's patent water lifter, which soon became standard on all Thetford-built engines. The front wheels were of wooden construction, probably as those used on the larger size portable engines of the day. The hind wheels were wrought iron measuring 6 ft 0 ins dia × 12 ins wide.

No 442 was a greatly improved engine incorporating all the design improvements evolved for the 8 NHP chain engines. It had a 5 sq ft grate and forty-one 7 ft 3 ins long × 2 ins dia smoke tubes giving a heating surface to grate area ratio of 33.8. It was fitted with a copper firebox and brass smoke tubes in accordance with the best railway locomotive practice of the day. The engine was exhibited at the 1869 Attleborough Show and for over 20 years was engaged upon haulage work in Norfolk and Suffolk in the ownership of John Tingay. The engine is almost certainly that depicted in a run-away accident shown in Ronald Clark's classic *Chronicles of a Country Works*.

In 1877 a unique road locomotive was built to the order of Richard Sargent, haulage contractor of Market Lavington in Wiltshire. The engine was allocated works No 770 and weighed in working order 14 tons 5 cwt, which must have severely limited its use on the common road due to the continued imposition of penal legislation affecting the gross weight and usage of such engines. It had a single cylinder measuring 10 ins dia × 12 ins stroke and double chain drive to the hind axle, but unlike all previous chain drive engines the drive shafts incorporated a differential or compensating gear to facilitate turning corners. All drive shaft bearings were increased by 2 ins in length for continuous working. Two speed gearing was retained having ratios of 22.1 to 1 slow speed and 13.1 to 1 fast speed. Cast iron wheels were fitted, the hind wheels

Fig 31 No. 857 the final design of 8 NHP chain drive engine built in 1879 for Cammell & Baker, threshing contractors of Hopton in Suffolk.

measuring 5 ft 11½ ins dia × 18 ins wide and the front wheels 4 ft 1½ ins dia × 10½ ins wide. The flywheel was 4 ft 0 ins dia × 5½ ins wide and a new type of screw-down brake was fitted to the chain spur ring. The boiler was unique and fitted with raising and lowering gear for maintaining a constant water level over the crown of the firebox when climbing and descending hills. The boiler dimensions were given as follows:

Working pressure	100 PSI
Diameter	2′9¾″
Inside firebox – length	2′6½″
– width	2′2½″
– depth	3′1″
Smoke tubes – length × dia.	6′11″ × 2¼″
No. tubes	40
Grate area	5.6 sq ft
Heating surface – firebox	32 sq ft
– tubes	155 sq ft
– total	187 sq ft

A second unique road locomotive was built in 1883 to the special order of Edward Box of Walton, near Liverpool, one of the pioneers in heavy haulage and the transportation of large indivisible loads. It remains an interesting speculation as to why this already acknowledged expert should have selected a four shaft chain-driven engine so many years after the successful introduction by other manufacturers of heavy duty geared engines. Possibly the answer lies in Box's desire to have a spring mounted engine with a greater free vertical movement of the hind axle than was then permissible on a geared engine, for one of the several unique features of this engine was the long, fully elliptical rear axle springs specially manufactured by Spencer & Company of Newcastle-Upon-Tyne.

In 1877 Box's father, William, was an engineer at a brick and tile works at Market Lavington in Wiltshire and almost certainly would have been familiar with Richard Sargent's Burrell engine. He built an experimental road engine himself, incorporating a novel method of transmitting the drive from the third motion shaft or jackshaft to the hind wheels by means of connecting rods and friction straps. The connecting rods permitted a considerable degree of vertical movement on the axle springs and the friction straps acted as a compensating gear when turning corners. William Box patented his idea and with his son's help demonstrated the engine in Liverpool during the RASE Show held in the city that year. Both Fowells of St Ives, a company founded by a former trusted employee at St Nicholas Works, and Robeys of Lincoln manufactured several engines incorporating this system. It seems highly probable that a relationship existed between Box and Joseph Fowell whilst the latter was still employed by Charles Burrell, for the separation occurred during the trials of Box's engine.

Edward Box's 1883 engine, named 'Oregon' and carrying works No 1061, was largely based upon Burrell's C type 8 NHP geared traction engine introduced in 1881.

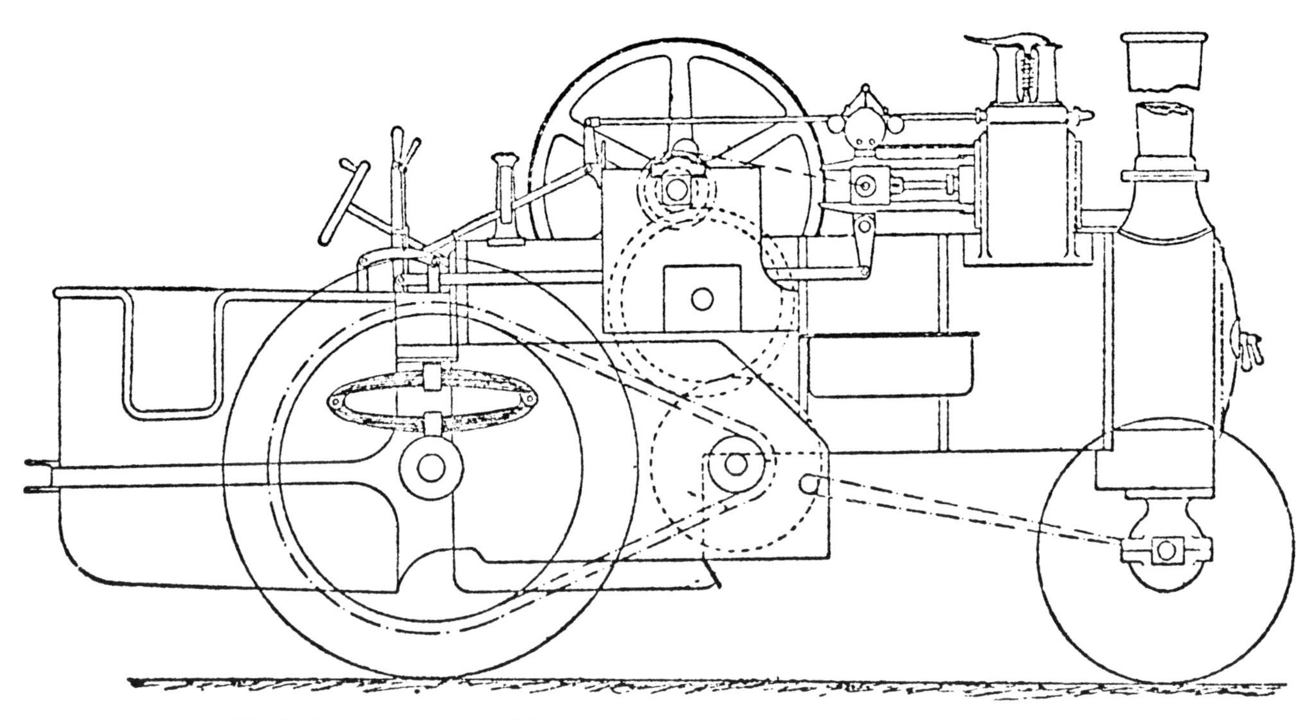

Fig 32 No. 1061 'Oregon' special 8 NHP chain drive road engine built for Edward Box in 1883.

It had a 9 ins dia × 12 ins stroke single cylinder and the 'C' class boiler described in Chapter 6. The wrought iron hind wheels measured 5 ft 8 ins dia × 15 ins wide and the front wheels 3 ft 10 ins dia × 9 ins wide. The spoked flywheel was 4 ft 4 ins dia × 6 ins wide. The crankshaft with special long bearings was carried in a plate frame attached to the boiler shell adjacent to the firebox, the second motion shaft was carried on stub axles attached to the boiler and the third motion shaft ran the full width of the engine and incorporated compensating gear mounted underneath the boiler in front of the firebox and in line with the hind axle. Chain sprockets were attached to each end of the third motion shaft such that each chain did an equal amount of work, whether the engine was travelling in a straight line or turning corners. Standard pinions and spur wheels were used throughout and the two road speeds had ratios of 23.9 to 1 slow speed and 14 to 1 fast speed. A conventional tender was used, with the water tank mounted under the footplate and drawbar gear was spring-loaded giving a greatly increased starting performance when handling a heavy load. A cable winding drum, so often used by the haulage contractor for unloading and positioning his load, was bolted to the near side chain spur wheel and specially designed vertical rollers were attached to the tender. Screwdown brakes were built into each chain spur wheel and the engine was fitted with Burrell's patent high speed governor. After many years heavy haulage duty in north-west England, the engine finished its useful working life in the ownership of Edward Mornement, a well known East Anglian drainage contractor.

During the 1890s many of the Burrell general purpose chain engines were rebuilt as geared engines. Tenders replaced the original manstand and the front steerage was replaced by conventional footplate steering gear. Some, like the example illustrated in Fig 29, were partially rebuilt, retaining the cylinder over the firebox and employing a chain of gear wheels to drive the hind axle; others like No 748, illustrated in Fig 30, were competely rebuilt, with the cylinder adjacent to the chimney and with a conventional three shaft drive to the hind axle. Like their predecessors, the Burrell-Boydell engines, the chain drive engines had virtually disappeared by the turn of the century.

CHAPTER FOUR

Early Ploughing Engines and Portable Engines

On December 19th 1861 Charles Burrell signed an agreement with John Fowler which gave him access to twenty patents filed by the latter in the years 1856 to 1860. The supremacy of the Fowler system of land cultivation employing steam engines working along the headland with cable-hauled implements was indisputable following his triumph at the RASE Chester Show held in 1858. The direct traction systems proposed by Burrell, Boydell and others, the rotary system of Ricketts and the alternative cable-hauled systems of William Smith and the brothers James and Frederick Howard demonstrated at Chelmsford, Salisbury and Chester had all been found wanting for one reason or another. Indeed such was Fowler's success that he dominated the scene for the next fifty years and his subsequent achievements were often treated almost with disdain by the public and the technical press.

Clayton and Shuttleworth of Lincoln and Ransomes and Sims of Ipswich were also signatories to the agreement, which remained valid until the patents expired in 1874. Originally it was intended that J & F Howard should also participate, but for reasons unknown they withdrew at the last moment. The fascinating story of Fowler's subsequent long and often bitter dispute with William Smith and the patent infringement litigation with Howards belongs elsewhere.

The agreement stipulated that the participants should pay Fowler royalties on all balance ploughs, ploughing engines and cultivating apparatus applied to ordinary portable engines manufactured and sold by them, which contained any of the features described in the twenty listed patents. The amount of royalty payable varied from £15 for a small balance plough to £50 for a ploughing engine having a nominal horse power in excess of 8 NHP. Each licencee was required to pay Fowler £5,000 upon the completion of the agreement, which was set off against future royalty earnings without any right of refund. If upon the expiration of the agreement, the individual licencees had paid less than a total of £22,500 in royalties, Fowler retained the right to a minimum payment of £7,500 from each participant. Additionally he retained the right to licence one other manufacturer and in the event of any of the existing licencees objecting they were given the option of paying an additional £5,000 with the minimum payment due upon expiration being increased to £10,000. Fowler, for his part, agreed to defend vigorously his patents against infringement and to bear all the costs arising. Although it seems unlikely that any of the licencees sold sufficient to avoid the minimum royalty clause, the agreement must have proved very advantageous to the John Fowler concern.

We know that the Steam Plough Works supplied Charles Burrell with a 12 NHP Kitson & Hewitson type ploughing engine and tackle in March 1862. We know also that Burrell exhibited a set of 14 NHP Fowler type engines at the Great Exhibition held at Battersea in 1862. The first ploughing engines to be built at St Nicholas Works were probably Nos 296 and 297. We know that these 14 NHP engines were Thetford built because Fowler's slanting shaft drive was replaced by a pitch chain drive to the hind axle and they incorporated Burrell's 7 ins × 12 ins duplex cylinders and motion parts. They were built to the 'FE' series of drawings which probably designates 'Fowler Engines' and were fitted with Fowler's patent clip drum. The flywheels originally had curved spokes but these were eventually abandoned because of the great difficulties they caused in the foundry.

In 1864 at least three 14 NHP single chain drive engines were built to the 'A' series drawings. Initially they were fitted with Fowler's vertical shaft driven clip drum, although it is recorded that in 1878 the works replaced these with conventional winding drums and coiling gear. Later at least two 14 NHP engines, one of which carried works No 456, were built to the 'AW' series drawings. Apparently the main differences between the 'A' and the 'AW' series was that the 'A' series were three shaft engines with a single countershaft between the crankshaft and the hind axle and were single chain driven, whereas the 'AW' series were four shaft engines with a double chain drive. No 456 featured prominently at the 1869 Smithfield Show and was priced at £600 ex-works.

In the years 1864-1867 several smaller ploughing engines were built to the 'PE' series drawings. They were rated 10 NHP, had 10½ ins dia × 12 ins stroke single cylinders and were essentially based upon the 10 NHP chain-driven traction engines of the period. Variations of this series were the 'WE' series introduced circa 1866 and the 'PEB' series with four-shaft drive.

In 1867 two engines, Nos 397 and 398 were built to the 'PEW' series drawings. Although retaining the same cylinders as the 'PE' series they had enlarged fireboxes, giving an increased total heating surface and were rated 11 NHP. All the variations of the 'PE' series were fitted with Fowler's clip drum.

It was not until 1868 that the long chain ploughing engine design became anything like stabilised, although the specific requirements of the individual customer always took precedence over all other considerations. In the 10

Fig 33 An early Thetford built Fowler type 14 NHP ploughing engine with clip drum having a pitch chain drive to the hind axle – circa 1862.

years to 1877 twenty-four 12 NHP single cylinder long chain engines were built and allocated the following works numbers.

12 NHP SC LONG CHAIN PLOUGHING ENGINES

No	Built		No	Built	
No 413	Built	1868	No 446	Built	1869
416	"	1868	447	"	1869
421	"	1868	453	"	1869
422	"	1868	454	"	1870
423	"	1868	541	"	1871
424	"	1868	582	"	1873
425	"	1868	659	"	1875
426	"	1868	660	"	1875
435	"	1869	687	"	1875
436	"	1869	688	"	1875
438	"	1869	761	"	1877
439	"	1869	762	"	1877

The majority were fitted with Fowler's clip drum, but Nos 425/426; 435/436; 659/660 and 761/762 were fitted with conventional winding drums and coiling gear. All except Nos 413 and 416 had 10½ ins dia × 12 ins stroke cylinders and used 'F' type chains in the long drive to the hind axle.

Up to and including No 454 the type 'KG' boiler as used on some larger sizes of chain driven traction engine was employed. The majority of these boilers had locomotive type steam domes mounted on the first ring of the boiler incorporating a spring safety valve. The final eight engines in the series had considerably enlarged fireboxes. The leading dimensions of the 'KG' boiler were:

Working pressure	100 PSI
Diameter	2′9¾″
Inside firebox – length	2′6″
– width	2′2¼″
– depth	3′0½″
Smoke tubes – length × dia.	8′6″ × 2¼″
No. tubes	40
Smokebox – length × dia.	1′3½″ × 2′9¾″
Grate area	5.5 sq ft
Heating surface – firebox	32 sq ft
– tubes	189 sq ft
– total	221 sq ft

Design ratios expressed per NHP:

Grate area	0.458
Firebox heating surface	2.66
Tubes heating surface	15.84
Total heating surface	18.5
Ratio heating surface to grate area	40.1

A number of interesting innovations and developments were incorporated in some of the engines in this series,

Fig 34 An early 12 NHP long chain ploughing engine as depicted in Burrell's catalogue – circa 1869.

most of which went to East Anglian agriculturists. Engine No 582 which went new to Phipps of Northampton was fitted with an exhaust steam feed water heater, a spark arrester was fitted in the smokebox and the engine was provided with a Hortings patent steam water lifter for filling the tanks from external sources. A similar engine, No 541, went new to Count Knut, an influential Danish landowner. Engine Nos 446 and 447 represented a landmark in the firm's history because they were the first ploughing engines to be exported to Germany through the Shutt & Ahrens agency in Stettin in 1869. They were the precursors of 150 ploughing engines and road rollers supplied to German customers in the years preceding the First World War.

Engine Nos 659 and 660 were fitted with special enormously strong three bearing crankshafts and the Giffard steam injector. Almost certainly these were the very first Burrell engines to be fitted with this latter feature. Invented by Henri Giffard, a pioneer French aeronaut in 1859, this inspired invention dispensed with the need for mechanically driven boiler feed pumps which only operated when the crankshaft was in motion. At first the injector's ability to impel feed water into the boiler by utilising a high velocity jet of steam taken from the boiler was received with some scepticism. Engineers at the time claimed that the idea of boiler steam feeding water against its own pressure was against all the laws of nature. However, it was soon accepted that an injector in good condition and properly installed and operated was capable of supplying 10 lbs of feed water for 1 lb of steam used.

Four engines in this batch, Nos 659/660 and 761/762, went to Percival Everitt who had established a small agricultural engineering workshop at Great Ryburgh near Fakenham in Norfolk. A close working relationship developed between the Burrell family and Everitt in the years 1875-1882 which resulted in the patent side drum ploughing engine with the winding drum mounted vertically on a stub shaft attached independently of the boiler shell known as the 'Universal' type ploughing engine. This design formed the basis of the bulk of Burrells' production of geared ploughing engines in the years 1880-1914, the majority of which were exported to Germany.

In 1878 Everitt took into partnership William John Adams, a younger son of the celebrated locomotive engineer, William Adams. Adams Snr had recently relinquished the post as locomotive superintendent of the Great Eastern Railway based at their Stratford works to take up a similar position at the London and South Western Railways Nine Elms works, a post which he filled with great distinction until his retirement in 1895. The Great Ryburgh concern was renamed Everitt, Adams and Company until the partnership was dissolved in 1880. Eventually Adams Jr emigrated to Australia where he founded his own company, William Adams & Company which successfully held the Sentinel Steam Waggon franchise in Australia for many years.

Everitt was a prolific inventor and in the six years to 1882 he filed eighteen patents dealing with a variety of subjects ranging from smokers' requisites, agricultural and threshing machinery, workshop and measuring equipment to steam engines and vacuum brakes. In 1880 Everitt and Charles Burrell II jointly filed patent No 5433 describing a novel fairground roundabout and two years later he and Charles Burrell I filed patent No 698 entitled 'Transport over Rivers,' confirming Burrells' renewed interest in matters related to the development of navigation upon East Anglian waterways, but both patents belong elsewhere in

Fig 35 No 660 12 NHP SC long chain ploughing engine, built 1875 with three bearing crankshaft.

our story. About this time Everitt sold his Great Ryburgh business to Tommy Cooper of Kings Lynn. Renamed the Farmers' Foundry the company survived well into the 20th century.

Nos 761/762, which in all major respects were similar to No 769, a 10 NHP chain-driven traction engine described elsewhere in Chapter 3, were fitted with experimental equilibrium slide valves. The engine power lost in overcoming the friction of a conventional slide valve was not inconsiderable and Trick of Esslingen in Germany and Alexander Allan in England proposed modifications to the simple slide valve which reduced the valve travel for the same port opening, thereby reducing the frictional losses. We do not know who was reponsible for this Thetford design. It could have been Charles Burrell I or any of his three sons who were by this date all employed by the firm, or, as is most likely, it could have been Robert Edwards, the then chief draughtsman. Edwards played a major role introducing the geared traction engine in 1876, designed to replace the outmoded chain driven engine, confirming that the little Thetford concern were up to date with contemporary innovations.

It was a great loss to the company when Edwards left Burrells to take up a similar position with Ruston's of Lincoln. Fortunately young Frederick Burrell, Charles Burrell I's youngest son then aged 22 years, was beginning to demonstrate his flair for mechanical engineering and draughtsmanship and was on the threshold of taking over control of the design office.

The great length of the driving chains on the early Thetford built ploughing engines clearly caused problems in service due to the chains stretching and excessive wear on the pins. The improved short chain engine was introduced in 1875, the cylinders being placed adjacent to the chimney and the crankshaft on top of the firebox. The double chain drive to the hind axle was taken from chain pinions carried on the outer ends of the second motion shaft, which was mounted forward of the crankshaft. A vertical shaft with bevel gears at its upper end engaged with similar gears on the second motion shaft to drive the ploughing gear mounted under the boiler.

These engines were manufactured in 12 NHP and 14 NHP sizes, the former having 10½ ins bore × 12 ins stroke single cylinders and the latter 11¼ ins bore × 12 ins stroke single cylinders. Charles Burrell was learning the wisdom of Thomas Aveling's adage that engines should be made as simple as possible and that duplex cylinders should not be used where a single cylinder would suffice. The works Nos and building dates were as follows.

12 NHP SC SHORT CHAIN PLOUGHING ENGINES

No	Built	No	Built
No 726	Built 1876	No 729	Built 1876
727	" 1876	730	" 1876
728	" 1876	731	" 1876

14 NHP SC SHORT CHAIN PLOUGHING ENGINES

No	Built	No	Built
No 689	Built 1875	No 757	Built 1877
690	" 1875	778	" 1878
723	" 1876	779	" 1878
724	" 1876	801	" 1878
756	" 1877	802	" 1878

All sixteen engines were fitted with winding drums and Fowler's patent coiling gear, with a single speed drive to the drum having a ratio of 10.5 to 1. Marriott's 30-strand best quality wire ropes were supplied as standard

Fig 36 No 728 12 NHP SC short chain ploughing engine, built 1876.

equipment. The 12 NHP engines employed the same boiler as the last batch of 12 NHP long chain engines and a re-designed boiler to the 659 series of drawings was used on the 14 NHP engines, both types having a working pressure of 120 PSI. Engine Nos 730 and 731 were demonstrated at the RASE Birmingham Show in 1877 working as a double engine tackle before going to B W & D P Hill of Stone, Gloucestershire.

During the life of the agreement with John Fowler, St Nicholas Works factored a variety of balance ploughs and other cultivating implements incorporating various Fowler patents. During the same period they also produced four-wheel living vans fitted out with six berths, a table, benches and a cooking stove. It was customary for agricultural contractors to purchase a living van and a two or four wheel water cart with each set of plouging tackle because during the busy season their men often lived away from home for several weeks at a time. Typically each set of double engine tackle employed a foreman, two engine drivers, a ploughman and a cook boy, who was responsible for watering the engine and providing the men with hot meals. They were a unique breed of men, who understood the land. They were often good mechanics and like those who went to sea in ships, were close to nature and philosophical in their attitudes to life.

In the twenty-five years preceding 1880, the period in which St Nicholas Works were busy developing the self-moving engine to meet the ever growing needs of the haulier and the agriculturist, production of the ordinary portable engine remained an important sheet anchor activity. Although the works records are incomplete, it is clear that the ratio of portable engines to self-moving engines sold was of the order of three to one. The following table lists portable engines built in the period 1868 to 1880:

YEAR BUILT	NOMINAL HP							TOTAL
	6	7	8	9	10	12	16	
1868	–	1	9	–	2	1	–	13
1869	–	–	10	–	–	–	–	10
1870	–	2	13	–	2	–	–	17
1871	–	–	18	–	2	–	–	20
1872	–	–	18	–	1	–	–	19
1873	–	–	21	–	7	–	–	28
1874	–	1	27	–	15	1	–	44
1875	3	1	24	–	6	5	1	40
1876	–	1	10	–	2	–	–	13
1877	–	2	14	–	1	–	–	17
1878	–	–	19	–	5	–	–	24
1879	–	–	8	–	14	–	–	22
1880	–	–	11	1	–	1	–	13
TOTALS	3	8	202	1	57	8	1	280

Production reached its peak in the period 1874–75 and thereafter declined as the great agricultural depression, which was to last until 1884, took its toll. The majority of

Fig 37 A typical portable engine of the period as depicted in Charles Burrell's 1876 catalogue with steam jacketted cylinders.

portable engines built were rated 8 NHP, all had single cylinders and were ideal for driving a threshing machine or performing the many other day-to-day duties required on the farm. Basic designs were little altered since the days of the Great Exhibition in 1851, but points of detail were improved, especially the boiler performance, and gradually working pressures were more than doubled. Cylinder castings were strengthened and machined to closer tolerances, ensuring greater steam tightness and a longer working life, and steam jacketing became standard practice. Wooden wheels were employed until the mid-1870s and then replaced by wrought iron. Improved governors and boiler feed pumps were developed and the boiler shells were lagged and covered with sheet metal cleading which was usually painted and beautifully lined-out.

Originally the 8 NHP engines had 9 ins bore × 12 ins stroke cylinders. An improved design was introduced in 1871 and the cylinder bore was increased to 9¼ ins but in 1873 the works reverted to 9 ins dia bore. The boilers used on the majority of engines built after 1871 had the following dimensions:

Boiler diameter	2′6⅝″
Inside firebox – length	2′1⅜″
– width	2′6⅝″
– depth	2′9¾″
Smoke tubes – length × dia.	6′6½″ × 2½″
No. tubes	28
Smokebox – length × dia.	1′7½″ × 2′9⅛″
Grate area	5.39 sq ft
Heating surface – firebox	31 sq ft
– tubes	105 sq ft
– total	136 sq ft

Some engines were fitted with enlarged fireboxes for wood burning and others were adapted for burning straw, reeds, cotton and maize stalks, megass and other vegetable refuse. In the period under review the R & T Elworthy patented straw-burning system became popular. Elworthy were a British-owned company whose factory was established in Russia and they offered a cheap and simple system which could be readily adapted to any standard type coal-burning firebox. A tubular mouth-piece was inserted in the fire-hole for manually feeding the straw, and a cast iron frame was attached to the lower part of the inner firebox, which incorporated a set of rocking grate-bars operated by a lever extending to the front of the firebox. A set of baffle plates were fixed diagonally across the upper part of the firebox to throw the flames onto the sides of the box, preventing the smoke tubes clogging. The ashpan rested upon the ground and could readily be taken to pieces when the engine was moved. It was said that the average consumption of straw was four times the weight of coal used and that eight to ten sheaves of straw were required to thresh one hundred sheaves of wheat.

The majority of the Thetford built 10 NHP portable engines were exported, most going to John Sandalgi, Burrell's Russian agent based in Odessa. Robert Burrell, Charles I's second son travelled extensively in Europe seeking business and visited Russia in 1875, 1879 and 1881. He established a close relationship with Sandalgi and when his father converted the company into a limited liability company in 1884, Sandalgi became a major shareholder.

With two exceptions, all the 10 NHP engines had 10$\frac{1}{2}$ ins dia × 12 stroke single cylinders. Engine No 500 built in 1871 had an unusually long 15 ins stroke and No 581 built in 1873 had duplex cylinders measuring 7 ins dia × 12 ins stroke. Improvements incorporated in the 8 NHP engines in 1873 were also incorporated in the 10 NHP engines in the same year and one of each size was exhibited at the 1874 RASE Show held in Bedford. The leading boiler dimensions of these engines were:

Boiler diameter	2′9$\frac{5}{8}$″
Inside firebox – length	2′5$\frac{5}{16}$″
– width	2′9$\frac{5}{8}$″
– depth	3′0$\frac{1}{4}$″
Smoke tubes – length × dia.	6′6$\frac{1}{4}$″ × 2$\frac{1}{2}$″
No. tubes	32
Smokebox – length × dia.	1′8$\frac{3}{4}$″ × 3′0″
Grate area	6.7 sq ft
Heating surface – firebox	33 sq ft
– tubes	133 sq ft
– total	166 sq ft

The majority of the engines exported were supplied with Elworthy's straw-burning apparatus but engine No 669 built in 1875 was specially ordered with Ruston's patent apparatus which unlike the former system was arranged so that the straw was manually fed under the engine firebox. This system ensured that the new fuel thoroughly stirred up the burning straw as it was forced under the fire and avoided the damping down effects inherent in the Elworthy system.

Eight powerful 12 NHP engines were supplied for a variety of special duties in the period, the three single cylinder engines having 11$\frac{1}{2}$ ins dia × 14 ins stroke cylinders, the remaining five having duplex cylinders measuring 7$\frac{3}{4}$ ins dia × 12 ins stroke. The boiler dimensions were as follows:

Boiler diameter	3′0$\frac{3}{4}$″
Inside firebox – length	2′7$\frac{3}{8}$″
Smoke tubes – length × dia.	7′0$\frac{1}{2}$″ × 2$\frac{1}{2}$″
No. tubes	34
Smokebox – length × dia.	1′9$\frac{1}{2}$″ × 3′3$\frac{3}{4}$″
Grate area	6.5 sq ft
Heating surface – firebox	38 sq ft
– tubes	137 sq ft
– total	175 sq ft

One of the single cylinder engines, No 682 built in 1875, was fitted with a unique slotted eccentric expansion gear. Nos 683 to 686, built with duplex cylinders, had Stephenson link motion reversing gear and special grooved pulleys for working roundabout system cultivating machinery. Several other portable engines supplied for

Fig 38 R. & T. Elworthy's patent straw burning apparatus as adapted to the portable engine.

driving a fixed windlass had a universal joint fitted to the end of the crankshaft giving a direct shaft drive to the coiling gear. No 889, built in 1880, was supplied to the Lakenheath Fen Commissioners for pumping duties. This engine had a special cylinder, a special boiler and a 5 ft 6 ins dia × 7$\frac{1}{2}$ ins wide spoked flywheel. Later St Nicholas Works built a large replacement Lancashire type boiler for the commissioners to provide steam for their old Butterley beam engine at the Lakenheath pumping station which was originally installed in 1845 and operated continuously until the mid-1930s. The boiler was 16 ft 0 ins long × 5 ft 6 ins dia, had a working pressure of 80 PSI and clearly from the surviving drawings was a splendid example of Victorian boilermaking at its best. Many other diverse and interesting items were produced by the works throughout the history of the company, but these are reviewed elsewhere in our story.

Charles I continued to manage the company almost single-handed until three of his surviving sons were old enough to join him in the works. Throughout his married life he and his wife Elizabeth resided in a large comfortable house in the Bury Road known as St Mary's House. In due course Elizabeth presented Charles I with five sons and two daughters. The eldest, Charles II was born in 1847, Robert George was born in 1849 and Joseph, who was drowned in an accident on the Little Ouse aged 9 years, was born in 1851. The fourth son, William, born in 1850 was destined to become a solicitor and resided in Richmond, Surrey for many years. Following the failure of his own business and the untimely death of his brother Robert in 1904, he was made a director of Charles Burrell.

The youngest son, Frederick John, was born in 1855. He showed a remarkable flair for mechanical engineering at an early age and in the 1880s became the company's Technical Director and head of the Drawing Office. In 1885 he became a member of the Institution of Mechanical Engineers but always remained the 'apple of his mother's eye' and was spoilt and indulged by her to his ultimate detriment.

The eldest of the two girls, Ellen Elizabeth, remained a spinster and lived most of her adult life at Ventnor in the Isle of Wight. In 1914 both she and Robert Burrell's widow, Ellen Alborough Burrell, were elected members of the Board of Directors of Charles Burrell & Sons Ltd. The youngest daughter, Fanny Elizabeth, married Frederick Houchen, an Attleborough solicitor, and pre-deceased her father by seven years.

Little is know about the Burrell children's childhood other than that they enjoyed the life of a typical small East Anglian country town. They appeared to have been a united family and on good terms with their neighbours and many cousins living in the area. The boys attended Thetford Grammar School and Charles II, Robert and Frederick went straight into the works at the age of fourteen. We know that subsequently Charles II received some further technical education at King's College in London. British agriculture was fast approaching its peak of prosperity which culminated in the 1870s and Thetford was undoubtedly a pleasant place in which to grow up in the mid-Victorian years. Charles I was by this time a highly respected figure in the community and the largest employer in the town. Later in 1877 he became a Justice of the Peace, having for some years participated in the aristocratic social system mainly centred around field sports which farmers, local employers and professional people were allowed to share with the gentry living in the district. These associations existed only out of doors on a footing of understood inferiority. For many years Charles I employed a butler and boot boy and a coachman named Nunn, who was a familiar sight driving a carriage and pair about the town.

Charles I was undoubtedly an entrepreneur in the best tradition. He understood that nobody owed him a living and he appreciated the full implications of the responsibilities he shouldered. Naturally he took steps to ensure that his values and standards were passed to his children. Charles, Robert and Frederick each went through every department of the works and acquired not only many of the skills of the craftsmen employed on the shopfloor, but a thorough knowledge of the firm's products and the duties they were required to perform. Perhaps most important of all, they understood and gained the respect of the men they were to lead in the most successful and formative years of the company. To many in the present age of the bureaucratic welfare state, Charles I would have seemed to be a hard taskmaster, but he gave his sons the priceless gift of a sense of responsibility and a feeling of duty and service, which served them so well in adult life and greatly benefitted the small community over which they later presided.

With the passage of time the individual strengths and weaknesses of the boys manifested themselves. Charles II was schooled to be the leader and eventually took over the day to day management of the works. Robert, an extrovert, admirably fulfilled the role of salesman. He travelled extensively and attended all the major agricultural shows, and as early as 1870 we find old Gustav Toepffer, John Fowler's German agent, reporting to Robert Fowler, "Met young Burrell from Thetford, who was installing a threshing machine on an estate near here (Stettin) and he told me that his firm has received an order from the English Government for a road locomotive with rubber tyres" – a reference to the Thomson Road Steamer which we shall learn about in the next chapter. Frederick was the innovator and he quickly established himself as the chief draughtsman. After 1880 he was responsible for the majority of the inventions originating in St Nicholas Works and it remains a great tragedy that his subsequent unsuccessful marriage and mode of living led to a complete physical and mental breakdown.

The other brothers had happy marriages. In 1873 Charles married Sarah Annie Thomas of York and nine years later, in 1882, Robert married Ellen Cockayne, the daughter of an old established and influential family living in Dunmow, Essex. She became known affectionately by the employees at St Nicholas Works as 'The Duchess' and for many years led the Primrose League in Thetford. Charles and Sarah produced three children, two boys and a girl, and Robert and Ellen had seven daughters and an only son, but we shall learn more about them as our story unfolds.

Rarely do people accept change without some difficulty. When the three Burrell boys began to flex their muscles and establish their authority in the works there was almost inevitably some unhappiness amongst a section of the older, long serving employees. Joseph Fowell, a native of Thetford and an employee of St Nicholas Works since Charles I took over control of the company, was just such a person. In 1878 he was said to be the most highly paid employee earning £5 per week, but some dispute arose and he left St Nicholas Works together with his three sons and established his own steam engine building company at the Cromwell Iron Works at St Ives in Huntingdonshire.

Joseph's eldest son, George, was a leading draughtsman in the drawing office at St Nicholas Works and in 1871 was co-patentee with Charles I of an invention entitled "Improvements in Elastic Wheel Tyres". We must now examine the era of the road steamer and Burrells' brief but fascinating association with R W Thomson, the inventor of the pneumatic tyre, which, had we had a more enlightened Legislature at the time, might have revolutionised road transport in the 1870s.

CHAPTER FIVE

The Age of the Road Steamer

Robert William Thomson, a full-bearded, six feet tall Scot was twenty-three years old when he filed the first of his many patents in 1845. His invention proposed the application of india rubber tyres filled with air to ordinary carriage wheels and invalid chairs, anticipating the patents of Dunlop and Michelin by over 40 years. Thomson fitted his pneumatic tyres to several horse-drawn vehicles and established a liaison with the well known carriage builders, Whitehurst & Company, whose works were in Oxford Street, London, and with Croall the Edinburgh carriage hirers. May and Jacob of Guildford also supplied a brougham to Lord Loraine of Albury Park fitted with his tyres.

The inner tube was made from a fabric material and rendered airtight by vulcanising a rubber solution onto its outer surface. The outer cover was of leather laced on in sections, the whole being riveted to the wheel rim or felloe. The tyres were inflated to 25 PSI. Fig 40 illustrates a cross-section of the arrangement: F is a part of the wheel spoke; E is the felloe; C is the india rubber inner tyre and A is the hooped outer covering of leather, laced together and riveted or bolted to the wheel rim.

Whitehurst attempted to market the invention under the trade name 'Ariel Wheels' and a public demonstration was given in London's Regent's Park in March 1847. The makers claimed spectacular savings in draught of between 60 and 300 per cent, depending upon the surface being traversed. Unfortunately, the high cost of the rubber and the difficulties encountered in manufacturing the inner tubes resulted in the wheels exceeding half the cost of a conventional carriage. It was found also that the smooth tyre treads tended to cause slipping on the stone sett city roads in wet weather and the project was abandoned. Croall's brougham plied the streets of Edinburgh for six months and its smoothness and silence pleased the fare-paying passengers, but the street urchins apparently preferred the rattle of the conventional iron tyres and mobs of lads continually stoned the driver and occupants until Croall was forced to withdraw the vehicle. The tyres were returned to Thomson after covering some 1700 miles without giving trouble of any sort.

Thomson was born on 29th June 1822 in the little Scottish port of Stonehaven, fifteen miles south of Aberdeen, the eleventh child of a family of twelve. Although his father was the owner of a prosperous woollen mill, it was always the family's intention that Robert should enter the Church, but as a teenage boy he had other ideas, coupled we are told with 'a complete inability to master Latin'. In 1836 a compromise was agreed and he was despatched to an uncle living in Charleston, USA, with the object of serving an apprenticeship with a merchant in the town. Apparently commerce also proved unattractive to young Robert and two years later he returned home. However, during his stay in America he established contacts which were to prove of great value to him in the future and in the years 1870–1876 his friend D D Williamson of New Jersey built under licence more Thomson road steamers than all the United Kingdom manufacturers in the same period.

Upon his return to Scotland, Robert's family and friends regarded him as an unpromising youth, but they misjudged his real character and ability. With the aid of a local mathematics teacher he set about mastering elementary chemistry, electricity and astronomy and in later life often recalled how he had used an old stone ball topping a farmyard gate post for his astronomical studies. Whilst still only sixteen, he rebuilt his mother's heavy old mangle so that the wet linen could be passed through the rollers in either direction, without the need to carry it round to the front of the machine after each pass. An example of his first invention is to be found today in the Aberdeen Regional Museum. At seventeen he designed and built a successful ribbon saw and later he completed his first working model of the elliptic rotary steam engine, which he perfected in later life. Such was Robert's new found industry, he had no difficulty in persuading his father to set aside a room in his factory for him to continue his innovative activities.

Following a workshop apprenticeship in Aberdeen and Dundee and a spell in a civil engineer's office in Glasgow he was given employment by his mother's brother, who had earlier built the elegant Dean Bridge in Edinburgh and was the contractor responsible for the blasting operations which had accidentally partly demolished Dunbar Castle. Thomson seized this mishap as an opportuntiy to develop his ideas for detonating explosive charges by electricity. At the age of nineteen and with only £6 in his pocket he set out for London, intending to exploit this invention and hopefully to make his fortune. He called upon Michael Faraday, the famous physicist, who gave him a letter of introduction to Sir William Cubitt, a former partner in Ransomes of Ipswich and at that time engaged as the consulting engineer responsible for extending the South Eastern Railway to Dover. Cubitt immediately offered young Thomson a job and set him over 500 men engaged upon blasting operations on the chalk cliffs near Dover. In 1843 the face of Round Down Cliff was successfully blasted by a single charge weighing 18,000 pounds, the gunpowder being detonated by Thomson's electrically operated device. Similar techniques were employed on the 1,387 yards long Shakespeare Cliff tunnel outside Dover.

In 1844 Thomson left Cubitt, who had recently become the consulting engineer to the Great Northern Railway, and passed into the employment of the Stephensons, but very shortly afterwards he put up his plate and went into business on his own account, in order to take advantage of the enormous opportunities offered the engineer by the short lived railway mania. He secured a contract for surveying a proposed line in the eastern counties and within a year triumphed against the Stephensons before a parliamentary committee, getting their rival line set aside in favour of his own project. The subsequent financial panic affecting most railway projects prevented the line being completed as planned, but the route he had chosen was ultimately adopted.

Forced by the crisis to close his promising consultancy business, he turned his fertile mind to other matters and, as we have seen, secured patent No 10990 in 1845,

Mechanics' Magazine,
MUSEUM, REGISTER, JOURNAL, AND GAZETTE.
No. 1233.] SATURDAY, MARCH 27. [Price 3d.
Edited by J. C. Robertson, 166, Fleet-street.
THOMSON'S PATENT AERIAL WHEELS.
Fig. 1.
Fig. 2.
Fig. 3.
Fig. 4.

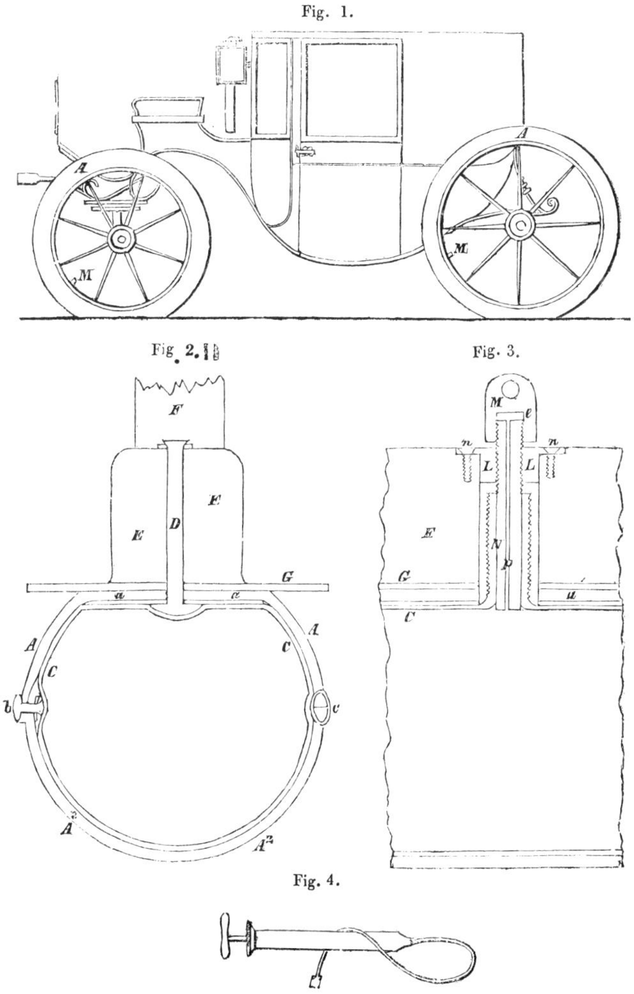

Fig 40 R W Thomson's patent pneumatic tyre of 1845 as portrayed in the Mechanics Magazine.

describing his india rubber pneumatic tyre. Another of his early inventions was the fountain pen. His original model, still extant, comprised a glass tube, tapered at one end to form the nib, the other end being open such that the ink could be drawn down the tube by capilliary action to feed the nib. Exhibited at the Great Exhibition in 1851, it aroused considerable public interest. It appears that financial considerations compelled him to sell his invention with little or no lasting benefit to himself.

In 1852 he accepted an appointment as agent for a British-owned engineering company on the island of Labuan situated off the North Borneo coast. The island had been occupied by the British Government in 1847 and Thomson was made responsible for the erection of a new sugar refinery. The island was rich in minerals including coal, gold, iron and manganese but the area was held in exceedingly bad repute at the time owing to the playful way its inhabitants had of organising head-hunting expeditions and similarly improper methods of passing the time when life became dull and other pleasures palled.

Thomson soon proved his worth and without capital he was made a partner in a firm designing plant and machinery for the manufacture of sugar which proved superior to anything previously seen in the area. Whilst home on leave he designed a large steam crane, but the authorities refused permission for the erection of waterside cranes unless they could readily be removed at night claiming paternally that "the natives might stumble over them in the dark and fall in the water." Robert commissioned the Glasgow engineering firm Alexander Chaplin & Company to manufacture the crane and, although it was realised that the design met a pressing worldwide need, he took no steps to secure patent protection for his invention. Subsequently Chaplin built

Fig 41 The Thomson Pneumatic tyre as fitted to Lord Loraine's Brougham in 1846.

Fig 42 Robert William Thomson (1822–1873). Photographed in his declining years in Edinburgh.

two large factories on Clydeside devoted to the manufacture of steam cranes.

In 1859 he returned home to superintend the building by Randolph & Elder of a dry dock of novel design. Previously proposals for large structures of this kind had involved their erection in the United Kingdom, with the alternative of a hazardous tow across the ocean or taking the structure to pieces for re-erection at the ultimate destination. Thomson designed the dock such that it consisted entirely of a few types and sizes of plates, each plate being interchangeable with any other plate of its class, resulting in great savings in cost. Unfortunately the first dock was assembled in Surabaya during Thomson's absence and an inexperienced young engineer allowed the structure to be lowered into the water without first ensuring the sides had been properly caulked and it sank. Two other docks of the same design were built at the same time, one for the French in Saigon and the other for Callao in Peru and they proved entirely satisfactory.

In failing health due to a disease contacted in Labuan, Thomson retired home to Scotland in 1862 but his mind remained fertile and active. Whilst in Labuan he married a Bohemian lady, Clara Hertz, who bore him two sons and two daughters. She was a lady of outstanding personality and charm and possessed a remarkable brain. It was said she could multiply ten numbers by ten numbers in her head. She provided Robert with constant encouragement as he became increasingly incapacitated, assisting him with his work and charming his many new found friends and associates.

Each of the Thomson children achieved distinction in their various ways, although sadly all died without heirs. The eldest, Harold Lyon Thomson, born in Java in 1861, inherited his father's mechanical flair and played an important part in the organisation of mechanical road transport in the Army Service Corps during the First World War. He never married but in the years 1912–13 served as Mayor of Westminster. It is on record that as a boy living in Stonehaven, he often played with J B Dunlop and that their favourite toy was a small, four-wheel, pneumatic-tyred carriage built by young Thomson's father.

The second child, Elspeth, married Kenneth Grahame, author of the great children's classic *Wind in the Willows*. Elspeth, described as strange and imperious, was an intellectual and named amongst her closest friends Tennyson, Thomas Hardy and Theodore Roosevelt. They had an only son, Alastair, who suffered from physical and mental congenital deformities inherited from Elspeth's side of the family. Tragically at the age of 19, whilst an undergraduate at Oxford, Alistair took his own life.

Winifred Hope, the third child, was a gifted miniaturist whose work was exhibited at the Royal Academy. She enjoyed a close friendship with the late King George V's sisters, Princess Helena Victoria and Princess Marie Louise, who shared her love of sketching and painting.

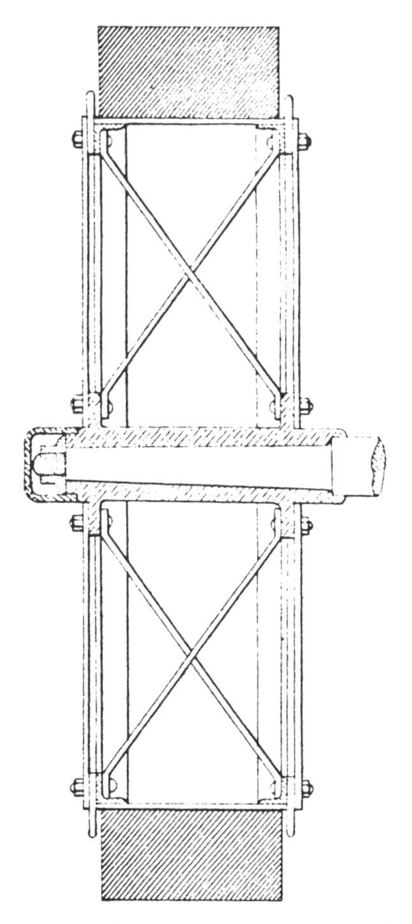

Fig 43 Section through Thomson's road steamer wheel as described in his patent 2986 of 1867.

Fig 44 An early Tennant built road steamer clearly showing Thomson's smooth rubber tyred wheels.

The fourth child, Courtauld, born in 1865, subsequently became Lord Courtauld Thomson. He was educated at Eton and Magdalen, Oxford, and he became a member of the Inner Temple, High Sheriff of Buckinghamshire and was chairman of several important City companies. He left his magnificent home, Dorney Wood in Buckinghamshire to the nation to be used for entertaining distinguished overseas visitors.

Like so many men of science, Thomson was not commercially minded and many of his potentially remunerative inventions were sacrificed to satisfy some more immediate financial need. In the four years following his return from Labuan he filed the following patents:

No 512 – 1863 "Improvements in obtaining and applying motive power, which improvements or parts thereof are applicable for raising, forcing and measuring fluids."
No 1493 – 1864 "Dividing hard substances, such as rock, stone and coal."
No 401 – 1865 "Steam Boilers."
No 1006 – 1866 "Improvements in steam gauges and applicable to other pressure indicators."

The improvements he proposed to the pressure gauge were suggested to him by a piece of ornamental twisted brass, but its success was forestalled by a French engineer's prior patent. In 1867 he exhibited the final form of his rotary steam engine at the Paris Exhibition, but his claim to patent rights failed, it being found that Hornblower, the original patentee of the compound steam engine, had established a claim to the idea many years earlier. Thomson then devoted his whole attention to the application of solid india rubber tyres to road engines and he filed his celebrated patent No 2986 in 1867 which was entitled, "An improved wheel for steam carriages to be used on the common roads." The quaint wording of the patent specification is perhaps worth recalling:

"To all to whom these presents shall come, I Robert Thomson of Edinburgh, in the County of Mid-Lothian, North Britain, Civil Engineer, send greeting. Whereas Her most Excellent Majesty Queen Victoria, by Her Letters Patent, bearing date twenty-fourth day October, in the year of our Lord one thousand eight hundred and sixty seven, in the thirty-first year of Her reign did of Herself, Her Heirs and Her Successors, give and grant unto me . . . and should make, use, exercise and vend within the United Kingdom of Great Britain and

Fig 45 R W Thomson's first road steamer with corrugated rubber tyres on test before shipment to Labuan.

Ireland, the Channel Islands and the Isle of Man an invention for an improved wheel for steam carriages to be used on Common Roads."

Undoubtedly Thomson understood the relationship between the weight of an engine bearing upon the driving wheels and the tractive effort produced and appreciated that this could be substantially increased by employing a resilient material on the periphery of the wheels. He based his design on the premise that india rubber would permit him to build a lightweight prime mover capable of hauling pay loads comparable with the much heavier conventional traction engines of the day. In a paper read before the British Association he commented:

"The question of traction engines or steam locomotives to work on common roads is a very old one, being of much more ancient date than railways. The attempt to construct a steam engine to run on a common road is probably the most difficult enterprise that mechanical engineering has ever attempted. They had to produce an engine which would work with perfect accuracy and at the same time have the faculty of adapting itself to the most varying circumstances. It would have to run over a hard, now over a soft road; over wet, dry and slippery roads. It would have to climb hills and descend them; pick its way over obstacles, to endure severe shocks and to take a firm hold of all kinds of surfaces. When it was found that the rough roads broke the machinery, the engine was made so heavy that it destroyed the road. When it was found that the surface of the ground would offer no hold to the wheels, the wheels in revenge, as it were, were provided with claws which gripped the ground, but tore it woefully.

"At last Mr Boydell once more thought of dealing with the question from a scientific point of view – that is to say, he endeavoured to produce a certain uniformity of conditions under which the engine was to work and to this end provided the wheels with wooden blocks, which laid themselves down in a kind of Endless Railway. But although theoretically he had been working in the right direction, practically his invention was not a success, as it was impossible to keep the appendages to the wheels from breaking. More years went by and it occurred to the inventor of the road steamer to surround the wheels of his engine with a thick tyre of india rubber. By this means he sought and obtained a very considerable degree of uniformity of condition, because he had as it were, spread under his wheel a thick carpet of solid india rubber 4 inches or 5 inches in depth. Not only does this india rubber carpet or cushion completely prevent all hard shocks to the machinery – shocks which, passing over paved streets, are quite destructive to the ordinary traction engine – but it further saves the road from the grinding action of the iron wheels, which are so terribly injurious to the pathways over which they travel."

Two forms of construction of the wheels were envisaged in Thomson's patent. In the simpler form of construction, the metal wheels were provided with flanges which formed a shallow circumferential groove on the periphery of the wheel; into this groove the solid india rubber tyre was moulded and vulcanised in the form of a complete ring. Provision was made also for the circumference of the tyre to be corrugated to assist the passage of an engine over soft ground. Thomson claimed that ordinary springs could be dispensed with when fitting an engine with his invention, thus enabling the power of the engine to be transmitted to the driving wheels through simpler gearing mechanism than was possible on a conventional road engine.

The second arrangement proposed dispensed with the flanges and employed linked steel chips to hold the vulcanised wheel rim. Although this system minimised the tendency of the smooth rubber tyre to slip on wet surfaces, experience proved that it required a great deal of maintenance and considerably reduced the working life of the rubber tyre. We shall see shortly that this system was greatly improved by the modifications proposed in Burrell and Fowell's patent filed in 1871.

It is clear that Thomson retained close ties with the United States throughout his adult life. One of his nephews, Robert Woods, became a pastor in the Southern States and much of the correspondence between the two men has survived. His pot-boiler seems to have been based on the work of Joseph Fawkes, who exhibited an interesting road engine at the Illinois State Fair held in Chicago in 1864. The three-wheel layout of his engine seems to have been inspired by the Larmanjar system developed in France for the Compagnie Générale des Messageries à Vapeur.

Thomson rented premises in Coatfield Lane, Leith, and during 1868 manufactured five engines of unique design. The first engine, named 'Enterprise' and illustrated in Fig 45, went to the Island of Labuan and the engine and its four wagon train were used for coal haulage. It had a single horizontal cylinder measuring 5 ins dia × 8 ins stroke mounted between the frames forward of a vertical pot-boiler, the drive to the hind axle being through a two-speed gear train. The pedestal-mounted steering wheel was directly over the single front wheel and the driver's seat was arranged on top of the totally enclosed cylinder and motion. Water tanks were fixed either side of the main frame, and the rear platform behind the boiler was flanked by fuel bunkers. The rubber tyres on the hind wheels were 12 ins wide × 5 ins thick. The weight of the engine was a little over 5 tons.

The engine was extensively tested in the Edinburgh area before shipment to Java and although the surviving reports of those early trials indicate that a satisfactory performance was achieved on the roads, it is apparent that adhesion was poor on soft ground, especially upon wet grass. The durability and mechanical strength of the india rubber tyres also proved disappointing. It was found that at speeds over 12 mph over-heating of the rubber occurred, which was initially thought to be due to friction between the inner surface of the rubber and the outer surface of the metal wheel. Experiments were carried out, polishing the steel rim of the wheel and drilling holes in the rim to permit a degree of air cooling between the steel and the rubber. Powdered graphite was also introduced between the rim and the rubber but eventually Thomson discovered that the overheating was due to the rapid and repeated changes in shape as the rubber rolled over the road surface. Expressed in practical terms, he had discovered the hysteresis of vulcanised rubber, the factor which, when multiplied by the speed, gives the total work or heat developed within the rubber itself by continued change of form. Throughout this experimental stage Thomson was greatly assisted by the North British Rubber Company. The original tyres each weighed 750 pounds and were the largest single pieces of the material ever produced, costing 10p per pound.

In 1869 due to his worsening physical condition Thomson handed over his designs and patterns to T M Tennant & Company of Bowershall Iron & Engine Works, Leith. They were established in the 1850s as mechanical engineers and manufacturers of railway rolling stock. Their chief draughtsman eventually became the distinguished consulting engineer and academic, Professor Sir Alexander Kennedy. The company went into liquidation in 1871 and shortly before his death Thomson admitted that his decision to entrust Tennants with the manufacture of his engines had been a grave error of judgement upon his part, due to the gross mismanagement of the concern. Although he had been made a director, ill-health precluded Thomson's active participation in the affairs of the company.

It is clear that by the end of 1869 Thomson appreciated the need to convince other traction engine builders of the

Fig 46 R E Crompton's 'Bluebell' built by him whilst serving as a young lieutenant in India in the 1860s.

Fig 47 A Burrell-Thompson road steamer built for the Turkish Government with the notorious vertical 'pot' boiler.

merit and potential of his road steamer, in order to retain his initiative and to fully capitalise upon his invention. His old friend D D Williamson of New Jersey was probably the first to be granted a licence giving him sole rights for the North American Continent, and he commenced production in early 1870. Robey and Company of Globe Works, Lincoln, who had been established steam engine builders since 1852, were the first English licencees and they exhibited two Thomson engines at the RASE Show held in Oxford in 1870. They were closely followed by Charles Burrell and Ransomes, Sims and Head, who both exhibited road steamers at the 1871 Royal Show held at Wolverhampton. There is also extant a photograph of a smart-looking Road Steamer with Thomson wheels, built by Ruston and Proctor of Lincoln, but the building date is not known. Throughout this difficult period, Thomson's wife actively assisted her ailing husband, travelling extensively calling upon suppliers, potential licencees and customers. Her charm and professionalism earned her many new friends and admirers.

Early in 1869 a young army lieutenant who was serving in India noted Thomson's work in the technical press. Rookes Evelyn Crompton had been fascinated by steam since he was taken to the Royal Show at Armley, Leeds, in 1861, and he started building his first steam carriage whilst still at Harrow. Later when serving on the Staff at Simla he built a second steam carriage which he called 'Bluebell' and he wrote to Thomson to enquire whether he would supply a set of rubber tyres for the vehicle. Although the tyres proved too expensive, a correspondence developed between the two men which Crompton eventually placed before his superiors.

As an Aide-de-Camp to the Commander-in-Chief he had access to the right people and it was agreed that an engine should be purchased for trials by the Indian postal authorities, who were anxious to replace the slow cumbersome bullock trains used for transporting the mail in areas where there were no railways. Lord Mayo, the Viceroy, gave his blessing to the project and an 8 NHP engine was ordered from Thomson in September in 1869.

Crompton was officially appointed Superintendent of the Government Steam Train and the Tennant-built engine, which he had named 'Prima', arrived in Calcutta in March 1870. Subsequent events are well documented in Ronald Clark's presidential address before the Road Locomotive Society in 1973, in Crompton's own paper before the Institution of Mechanical Engineers in 1879 and in John Head of Ransomes' paper before the Institution of Civil Engineers in 1873. Unfortunately, due to Thomson's inability to supervise the manufacture of the engine personally, the workmanship and attention to mechanical detail in the Tennant-built engine was found to be quite unsatisfactory, the pot-boiler proving especially troublesome and inadequate. However, after some modifications and adjustments had been carried out in the local government workshops, the subsequent trials proved encouraging and it was decided that Crompton should return home to negotiate the supply of a further four powerful engines of improved design for use in the Punjab on the Grand Trunk Road between Rawalpindi and Jhelum, a distance of 68 miles.

He arrived in Edinburgh in October 1870 only to find Thomson a complete invalid, more or less permanently confined to a couch in his study. In spite of this enormous handicap his mind remained very active and his wife deliberately arranged frequent dinner parties, such that the house in Moray Place became a well-known meeting place for cultured and scientific people from all over the world. A great friendship developed between the two men and Crompton and his assistant, Richard Muirhead, moved into the Thomson home, where they stayed for more than two months. Without doubt this proved to be a very formative interlude for Crompton, having a great influence upon his later achievements with mechanical road transport, both in South Africa during the Boer War and later in France during the First World War.

Even before Crompton's arrival in the United Kingdom, Thomson had opened negotiations with Ransomes, Sims & Head for the construction of the Indian engines and they promptly sent a brilliant young German engineer, Gustav Bremme, to Edinburgh to assist with the preparation of the working drawings. In spite of the pleasant social and professional environment offered by Moray Place, Crompton found Thomson dogmatic and persistent in many of his opinions. It says a lot for the character of the two men, that regardless of the gap in their ages and their quite fundamental differences of opinion, especially with regard to the type of boiler to be employed and the strength of the reciprocating machinery, the drawings were completed and in Ransome's possession by December 1870. Undoubtedly Bremme also played a major role in bringing this stage of the project to a speedy and satisfactory conclusion. In the years following the road steamer era Bremme gained professional recognition and patented an elastic wheel for application to traction engines and an ingenious radial valve gear which was used extensively on marine engines.

It was during Crompton's stay in Edinburgh that Charles Burrell became associated with the road steamer. Thomson had received an enquiry from the Turkish Government for three engines and he included Charles Burrell amongst the firms invited to tender. Their offer was successful and they completed the engines ready for shipment during the first quarter of 1871. Your author having spent the last forty years in various branches of the engineering industry never ceases to be amazed by the speed with which the Victorians were able to execute customers' requirements, often calling for entirely new, untried products involving the production of new patterns and tools. During 1871 St Nicholas Works completed a total of seven Thomson road steamers, the works numbers and building dates being as follows:

THETFORD BUILT VERTICAL BOILER ROAD STEAMERS

No 491	Built 1871		No 509	Built 1871
492	" 1871		512	" 1871
493	" 1871		513	" 1871
494	" 1871			

Nos 491, 493 and 494 were shipped to Constantinople for the Turkish Government and were fitted with large grate pot-boilers for burning inferior wood fuel. No 492 was supplied suitable for burning coal and went to Lord Egerton of Sketchwood Park, near Newmarket. No 509, another wood-burning engine, was demonstrated and tested at the RASE Wolverhampton Show before despatch to Ricotta in Brazil. The engine had been specially commissioned by the President of Bahia to operate a passenger service between Alagoenhas and Jacu. Nos 512 and 513 were coal-burning engines and went to the Newcastle industrialist Sir W G Armstrong and the Earl of Craysfort of Elton Hall, near Peterborough, respectively. In 1875 No 513 was sold to the Harrogate Gas Company who became important and enthusiastic users of Burrell engines for many years.

All seven engines were rated 8 NHP and had two vertical cylinders mounted behind the pot-boiler measuring 6 ins dia × 10 ins stroke. The RASE judges described the boiler submitted for trial at Wolverhampton in the following terms:

"The boiler consists of a plain vertical cylinder, containing at its lower end an internal cylinder of lesser diameter forming the firebox. In the centre of the crown plate of the firebox there is a circular opening about 13½ ins dia to which is joined the neck of the copper pot. Below the neck the pot swells out into spherical form and is of such size as to nearly fill the firebox, leaving a space of approximately 1½ ins between its outer shell and the inner shell of the firebox. Up this space the products of combustion pass and escape through 36 vertical tubes 1⅞ ins dia × 3 ft 10½ ins long which are inserted in the crown plate of the firebox, in the space left between its sides and the neck of the pot. These tubes extend through the upper part of the cylindrical case of the boiler to the top tube plate; they being surmounted by a short cylindrical casing or drum which raises the funnel. At the ordinary working height of the water about 1 ft 6 ins of the tubes are immersed in the water, while 2 ft 3½ ins of the upper part of the tubes are in the steam space thus drying and superheating the steam.

"The ashpan is hinged at the back end and is provided with a hinged bottom at the front. The pan and the door are each upheld by chains and by means of these chains the pan and the door can be shaken and the ashes cleaned out. There is an iron wire grate in the base of the funnel to arrest the ignited fuel.

"The mode in which the joint between the pot and the boiler is made is a bold one. The upper pot has a brass neck riveted and brazed to it, which is turned to fit the central opening in the crown of the firebox, the sides of which opening are formed by a flanging upwards of the crown plate. This opening is bored to take the turned neck of the pot. On the top of the neck of the pot there is secured by 18 ¾ ins steel bolts, with close-ended brass nuts, a gun metal flange. This is faced and overlies the thickness of the turned-up crown plate round the hole. The top of this thickness is also faced and is bevelled inwards and into the sink thus formed an india rubber ring is put, upon which the brass ring bears, being kept hard down on it by the pressure of the steam."

The pot-boiler was carried on a wrought iron frame extending fore and aft, but more fore than aft. The ends of the frame were upheld by two wrought iron inclined stays or truss rods, the upper ends of which were attached to two stays secured to the boiler case. Immediately behind the boiler the wrought iron frame carried four inclined wrought iron standards on which the two cylinders were supported. The cylinders, un-jacketed, were mounted across the engine. The solid forged crankshaft, with four integral eccentrics between the throws was mounted 3 ft 10½ ins above ground level.

At each end of the crankshaft were sliding pinions to engage on internal spur wheels bolted onto the inner side of the driving wheels, which, when engaged, gave the high speed or top gear drive. To engage the second or low gear drive the crankshaft pinions were slid to engage with gears on the second motion shaft. The sliding pinions were controlled by levers joined on the ends of the shafts which extended lengthways of the engine. The four levers were placed two on each side of the engine, convenient to the driver, and there was an ingenious arrangement of stops whereby the driver could not inadvertently engage both gears simultaneously. This system enabled the drive on one wheel to be disengaged when turning corners, as no differential gear was provided, as well as providing a quick means of changing gear. The reversing gear and steam regulator were on the driver's left side. No brake was provided.

The driving wheels were 5 ft 0 ins dia and the india rubber tyres were 11½ ins wide × 4⅛ ins thick and surrounded by a chain of steel shoes as described in Thomson's 1867 patent. The spindle on the front wheel fork passed upwards through a heavy domed shape casting and was rotated by a worm wheel keyed to the shaft and driven by a worm pinion on the horizontal steering spindle. Water tanks mounted either side of the wrought iron frame carried 250 gallons of water and the feed pump, controlled by the firemen, was eccentric driven off the second motion shaft. No feed water heater was provided but surplus exhaust steam was fed into the water tanks. A set of belt driven governors were provided for regulating the steam to the cylinder when working as a stationary engine. The drive to the band wheel for driving stationary machinery was of a novel design necessitating the left-hand driving wheel being located in a particular position relative to the frame. Holes in the inner and outer wrought iron wheel discs were brought into line with the end of the crankshaft, enabling an extension shaft to be fitted to the crank keyways. An extra bearing was bolted to the driving wheel outer disc to support the extension shaft and the band wheel or belt driving pulley was attached to the end of the shaft. The extension shaft was only 3 ft 4½ ins above ground level which was a great inconvenience in practice.

The vital statistics of the boiler were:

Heating surface	– firebox	– 38	sq ft
	– pot	– 15	sq ft
	– tubes	– 68	sq ft
	– total	– 121	sq ft
Grate area		– 5.41	sq ft

Only 32.5 sq ft of the tube heating surface was in contact with the water, with the gauge glass half full; the remainder was in the steam space, in theory providing some degree of superheat to the steam. The boiler was 2 ft 10 ins dia. The engine was tested on the RASE dynamometer brake and developed 24 BHP at 150 RPM and 130 PSI boiler pressure. The best gross indicated horse power achieved was 31.4 IHP. Best Llangennech steam coal was used throughout the trials and 4.63 lbs coal was consumed per IHP per hour. Water evaporated amounted to 5.95 lbs per pound of coal burnt per hour.

The Royal Agricultural Society's engine trials in 1871 were undoubtedly a very important series of tests at a critical stage in the evolution of steam road haulage. It was the first occasion in which the Society had attempted to pass judgement on self-moving haulage engines, for in previous years engines had been judged solely in relation to their ability as agricultural machines. Although interest had been centred upon ploughing engines and their associated tackle, there now appeared no valid reason why locomotive engines should not provide the motive power required by farmers for general haulage duties. With this objective in view the Society offered a prize at the Wolverhampton show for "The best agricultural locomotive engine applicable to the ordinary requirements of farming."

The engines submitted for trial were firstly tested on the Society's dynamometer, then they were tested drawing loads at the nearby Barnhurst Farm, the course being laid over various types of natural terrain including a short incline of 1 in 9. Road tests on the Stafford Road over a 16 miles course followed, each of the engines hauling its own road train. The test culminated on a stretch of the Wolverhampton to Shrewsbury road at Tettenhall, the course being 2,000 ft long with the start and finish on the level and intermediate gradients varying from 1 in 35 to 1 in 18. By modern standards the tests may appear unambitious, but the trial conditions proved exacting and informative, and the judges' subsequent report undoubtedly crystallised design criteria for the next forty years.

Thirteen engines were entered for the tests of which four were entered by Aveling & Porter of Rochester, one by Ashby, Jeffery & Luke of Stamford, one by Tuxford & Sons of Boston, one by Maude & Walker of Tewkesbury, one by James & Frederick Howard of Bedford, one by

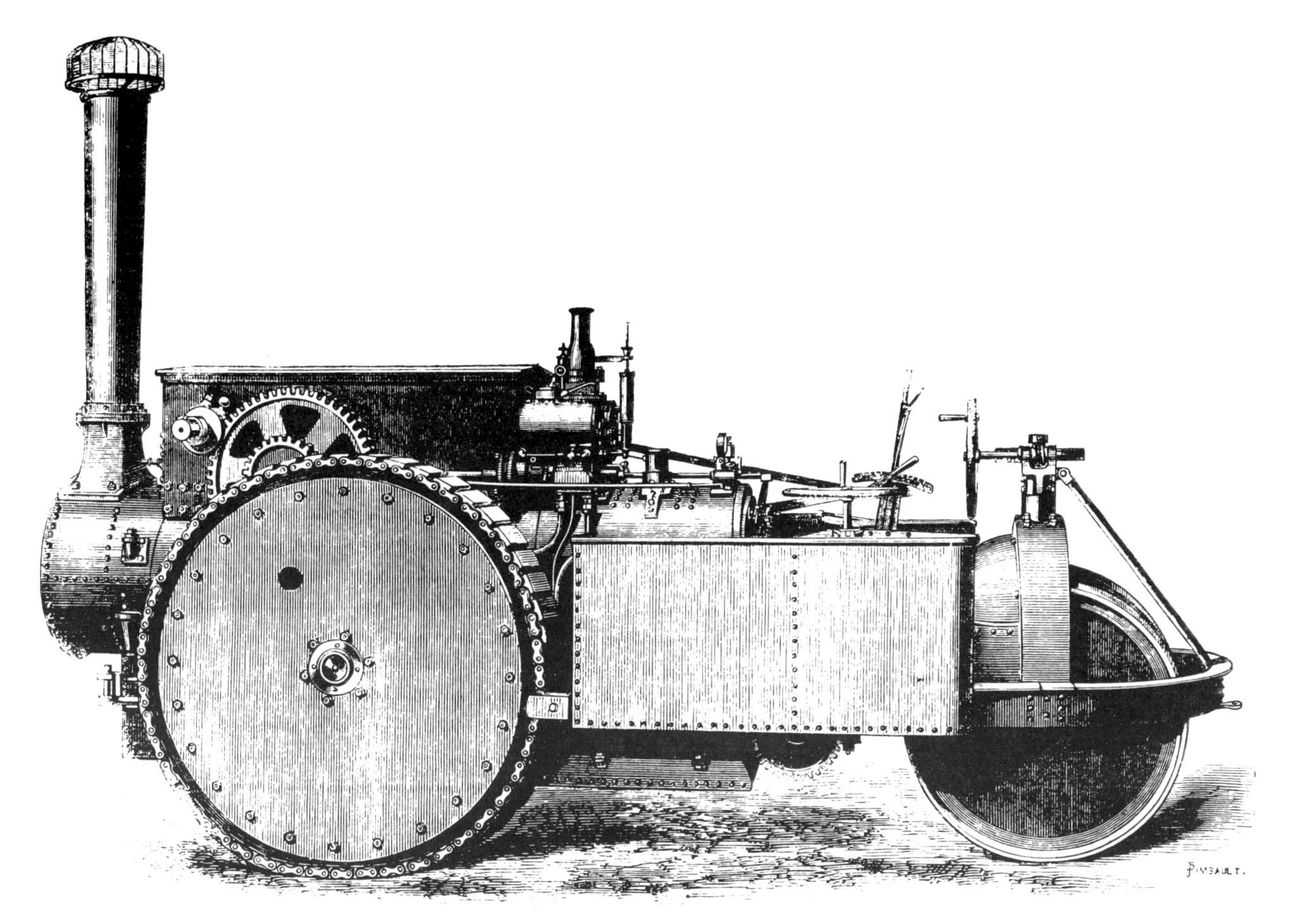

Fig 48 No 510 the first Thetford road steamer as exhibited at RASE Wolverhampton 1871 in an unfinished state.

Robey & Company of Lincoln, two by Ransomes, Sims & Head of Ipswich and two by Charles Burrell. Ransomes' entry in fact referred to a single 8 NHP version of the Thomson-Crompton road steamer with the facility to change the wheels from either Thomson type with rubber tyres to conventional traction engine type iron wheels with cross-strakes. One of the Burrell engines was the Thomson design road steamer No 509, the other was a conventional 8 NHP geared traction engine No 495. Ashby, Jeffery & Luke, Maude & Walker and Robey withdrew from the contest and Thomas Aveling failed to present his 12 NHP traction engine.

The first prize was awarded to the Aveling & Porter 10 NHP traction engine. The judges, one of whom was Mr J F Bramwell, who had been apprenticed to Walter Hancock, the steam carriage pioneer, at his Stratford Works in the 1830s, commented, "Whether considered in point of economy as a driver of machinery or of efficiency for traction upon a farm, Mr Aveling's 10 NHP engine no doubt was far ahead of any of its competitors and was awarded the first prize of £50. The only point on which it was surpassed was that of its adhesive powers upon a high road; here no doubt it was not equal to the Thomson system, and we felt that the merits of the india rubber tyres were such as to award a silver medal to that inventor."

The judges made three criticisms of a general nature in their report. Firstly the low rate of evaporation of the boilers submitted to test, the best performance being only 7.76 pounds of water per pound of coal burnt. Secondly the apparent lack of appreciation by many manufacturers of the importance and benefits to be gained by steam jacketing the cylinder, affecting substantially both the efficiency and economy of an engine. Only Aveling & Porter's and Tuxford's engines were fitted with brakes and the judges stated that they were strongly of the opinion that no traction engine was really safe without the ability to apply brake power to the supporting wheels of the engine itself. No doubt this latter comment was especially emotive at the time for a fatal accident had occurred during the trials, due to a driving chain breaking and the engine running away out of control killing a spectator.

The modern traction engine owner who spends many summer week-ends driving to and from the rally field will perhaps enjoy the RASE judges' description of the Burrell-Thomson road steamer's trial on the Wolverhampton to Stafford road, on 6th July 1871.

> "Burrell's 8 NHP engine with pot-boiler and india rubber tyres left the show yard at 5.46 am. The weight of the engine with a full tank of 250 gallons of water and 11 cwts of coal was about 8 tons 17 cwts. The weight drawn was 12 tons composed of one wagon with its load and one lorry with its load. The engine reached Stafford in 7 hours 11 minutes; but this requires explanation, as so far from this engine being the slowest of the lot, it was, when travelling, one of the fastest, as is shown by the fact that at about the fifth mile it came up to Aveling & Porter's 10 NHP engine which had started 21

Fig 49 No 514 an 8 NHP Thetford Road Steamer complete with insulated meat van supplied to a Russian customer in 1871.

minutes before it, although in the first three miles there had been a stoppage to replace some of the pigs which had fallen off the lorry and also to secure the ashpan which had become loose. At the first stopping place there was a delay of 9 minutes to allow for Aveling's watering; then water was taken by the Burrell engine which consumed a further 13 minutes. There was then a stoppage of 17 minutes to allow the men to take breakfast. Shortly after this a bad place in the road was passed and the engine took its load over it without difficulty and without having to resort to the use of a chain. Between the eighth and seventh mile from Stafford, the distance was done in about 8 minutes, being at the rate of 7½ mph, but the result of this speed was that a bearing got hot and it became necessary to stop the engine to oil; 5 minutes were consumed by this. The engine then stopped at Penkridge to take a second quantity of water. In this operation, owing to the engine being uncoupled from its load and going away to a watering place different to that used by some of the other engines, 45 minutes were consumed. At 11.30 am, when within one mile of Stafford, a linch-pin came out of the common road lorry which formed part of the load of this engine. A wheel came off and 13 minutes were occupied in endeavouring to rectify the matter. The result was however, that the lorry had to be left behind. This took 4 tons from the load of the engine, leaving it to haul 8 tons into Stafford. At 11.50 am a waggon was passed, which the waggoner had backed into a ditch in his desire to get out of the way of the preceding engine. A stoppage took place to assist him getting out of the ditch and 33 minutes were occupied in this. A little water was taken in. The stoppages together amounted to 2 hours 15 minutes, making the actual running time 4 hours 57 minutes. The coals consumed were 8 cwt 1 qr 22 lbs; the ashes were shaken out on the road so that there were none taken back. This is a very large consumption of coal. No doubt a great deal of it was due to what was being burnt while the engine was not running. It is impossible to make an accurate allowance for this, and therefore, the economic duty of this engine upon the trial cannot be ascertained. The water consumed was 579 gallons, being 6.12 pounds of water evaporated for 1 pound of coal. The ordinary working pressure of the steam during the run was from 120 PSI to 160 PSI, but on two or three occasions the steam fell and the engine was stopped for a minute or two until a pressure of 130 PSI was obtained."

Obviously Charles Burrell experienced the shortcomings of Thomson's pot-boiler during the initial trials with the three Turkish engines in the early part of 1871 and in May that year he decided to manufacture a road steamer of his own design. Whereas Lieut Crompton opted for the Field type vertical boiler manufactured by his friend Lewis Olrick, Burrell designed a horizontal locomotive type boiler, with the smokebox and chimney facing aft. The crankshaft was carried in brackets attached to the boiler shell adjacent to the chimney and the cylinders were mounted on top of the firebox. The motion and gear train to the hind axle was totally enclosed. Generally known as Thetford road steamers the first of six engines built in the three years 1871–1873 was exhibited at Wolverhampton. It was presented in an unfinished state, without boiler cleading and painted in grey undercoat and although the engine did not participate in any of the trials it was commented upon favourably by both the RASE judges and the technical press. It was a powerful engine rated 12 NHP, having duplex cylinders measuring 7¼ ins dia × 10 ins stroke and the total heating surface was 231 sq ft, nearly twice that of the original Burrell built pot-boiler. The crankshaft was of forged iron construction with integral eccentrics. The steel second motion shaft carried pinions at each end giving two road speeds, the gears being cast in McHaffies' best malleable iron. An eccentric driven feed pump was mounted horizontally beside the off-side cylinder. The driving wheels were 6 ft 0 ins dia and the rubber tyres were 16 ins wide × 4 ins thick. The same arrangement for driving stationary machinery as incorporated in the Thomson engines was provided with the added facility that the extension shaft could be fitted to either side of the engine. The original Thomson engines were inclined to steer erratically and Burrell used twin front wheels, 4 ft 2 ins dia mounted close together either side of the vertical steering shaft. The water tank which carried 250 gallons was suspended under the boiler behind the rear axle and a 4 cwt fuel bunker was arranged on the driver's right.

One of the arguments Thomson used for the continued

Fig 50 No 510 12 NHP Thetford road steamer built for the Turkish government for operating a bus service on the island of Crete.

employment of the pot-boiler was the ease with which the water level could be maintained in the boiler when the engine was ascending or descending hills. Burrell arranged his horizontal boiler such that it was balanced on the driving axle and capable of being manually raised or lowered at the firebox end by means of a gun metal rack and pinion operated by the driver.

The first Thetford road steamer was allocated works No 510 and was supplied to the Turkish Government upon the recommendation of a group of British engineers who were building a new fifty mile long road in Crete. The engine was supplied complete with a forty-seat double deck omnibus built in the carpenter's shop at St Nicholas Works.

Two months later another Thetford road steamer was completed for a Russian customer, a Mr Kleburg, who had a contract for supplying the military authorities with fresh meat. Allocated works No 514 and named 'Erimus' the engine was rated 8 NHP and had duplex cylinders measuring 6 ins dia × 10 ins stroke. A standard 2 ft 9 ins dia traction engine boiler without the raising and lowering gear was fitted, having a heating surface of 168 sq ft and a working pressure of 130 PSI. The driving wheels were 5 ft 0 ins dia, the rubber tyres being 12 ins wide 4 ins thick. The leading pair of wheels were 3 ft 6 ins dia and mounted on helical springs. Like its bigger predecessor it had two road speeds and the facility for easily disengaging the pinions on the second motion shaft when turning corners. Also like its predecessor, it had a large spark arrester chimney. The outfit was supplied complete with a smart four wheel, well ventilated meat van.

Early in September 1871 the two engines underwent extensive tests on the Croxton Road, on the northern outskirts of Thetford, in the presence of senior Turkish officials. It seems probable that the earlier Thomson designed boilers had proved disappointing in service and that the officers had been sent over by their government with the dual task of negotiating a solution to the shortcomings of the pot-boiler and to ensure the suitability of the new engine ordered for Crete. The event was fully reported in the *Engineer* in the following terms:

> "About 3.00 pm a train was made up consisting of the engine (No 510) which weighed with coal and water 10½ tons, one wagon on springs loaded with pig iron, a portable engine, a coprolite mill on wheels and a lorry loaded with pig iron. The train weighed with the engine 25 tons 12 cwt, the gross load being 36 tons 2 cwt. With a boiler pressure of 130 PSI the engine and train left the yard for a run round the town. The average pace maintained was about 5 mph, estimated from the fact that it was impossible to keep up with the train without running now and then. Thetford and the district round it is very flat, but one incline was found a couple of hundred yards long and rising to about 1 in 18, up which the engine proceeded without the slightest difficulty or the least approach to slipping; she could have taken another five tons with ease. The whole distance round was accomplished in thirty-five minutes, but a good deal of time was wasted in waiting for horses and in taking a baffle plate out of the chimney that had been put in a few days previously for experimental

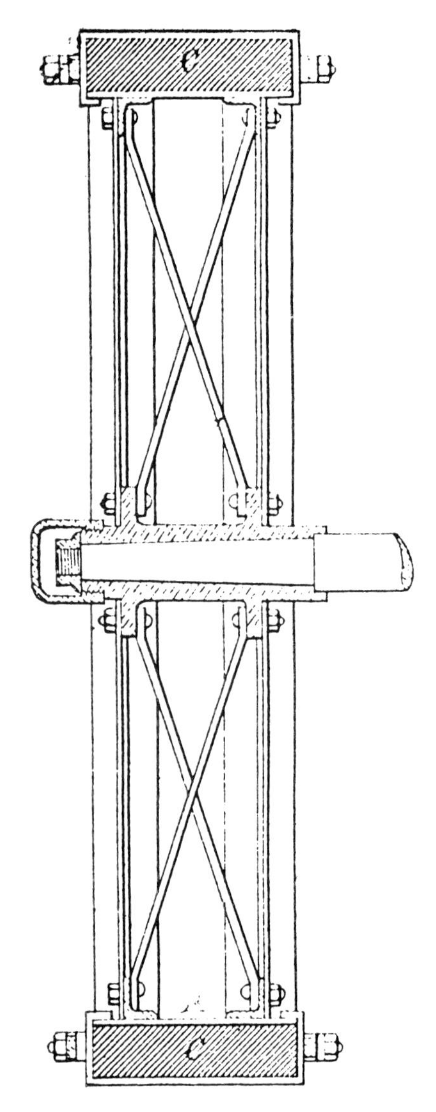

Fig 51 Burrells' improved road steamer wheel as described in patent 3105 of 1871 showing the rubber tyre retaining clips.

purposes and had been forgotten. The train was accompanied by a second 8 NHP engine (No 514) built for service in Russia.

"In the evening, both engines were again brought out. The 12 NHP engine being attached to the omnibus had fourteen or fifteen persons inside and outside men and boys from the works swarmed all over it like bees, every available spot being occupied. The average speed uphill and downhill was 9 mph but several stops for horses had to be made, not for more than a few seconds duration it is true, but still reducing speed. Part of the run was done at least at 12 mph; steam was easily kept at 150 PSI during the whole time and those who have had most experience with traction engines will agree with us that, if under such circumstances the steam can be kept up for a quarter of an hour, it can be kept for a day. No trial could be more satisfactory and it was specially so in the fact that the speed was constant, or very nearly so uphill and downhill. No very steep inclines were met it is true but the road undulated nevertheless. The only difference was the sharper beat when ascending an incline."

At the end of the run the smaller engine was attached to the omnibus, the larger one being taken off, and this although a slow speed engine ran back to Thetford at a speed greater than could be got from horses in regular service. It may be decided, we think, that no difficulty whatever exists in applying steam on common roads for the purposes of passenger traffic."

The Russian engine failed to satisfy its owners, due one suspects to the uneconomic performance associated with the short life of the Thomson tyres. It appears that the patent clip shoes proved especially troublesome and the engine was returned to Thetford. Clearly Charles Burrell had already appreciated the shortcomings of the latter feature, for in November 1871 he filed patent No 3105 linking with it the name of his chief draughtsman, George Fowell. Entitled "Elastic Wheel Tyres", the patent described an improved design of clip shoe to retain the india rubber tyre in such a manner that the tread followed exactly the undulations of the road surface. The arrangement is clearly illustrated in Fig 51.

Burrell's clip shoes were fitted to 'Erimus', some modifications were made also to the layout of the front steering and the engine was exhibited at the RASE Cardiff Show in July 1872, but did not find a buyer. In the following month it was again demonstrated before an invited audience and showed its paces on the Thetford, Barnham, Euston road hauling 10½ tons of pig iron loaded into two wagons. A Mr Duncan, the owner of an experimental sugar beet factory at Lavenham in Suffolk purchased the engine for hauling the beet harvest, but he insisted that the Thomson wheels be removed and the engine was fitted with 5 ft 2 ins dia conventional iron traction wheels.

The first engine to be built new with Burrell's patent clip shoes was a single cylinder Thetford type road steamer, completed in October 1871 and allocated works No 511. It was supplied to Lord Amherst, who had a large estate in the Thetford area, after appearing at the Smithfield Club Show in December 1871. Rated 8 NHP, the cylinder measured 9 ins dia × 12 ins stroke and a standard traction engine boiler with raising and lowering gear was fitted. Unlike its predecessors, the cylinder was aft adjacent to the chimney and the crankshaft was carried in brackets mounted on top of the firebox. The rubber tyred driving wheels were 5 ft 0 ins dia and the single leading wheel was of wrought iron. In 1881 having been found too heavy for direct traction ploughing, the engine was converted to a semi-portable type engine and spent the rest of its life driving a threshing machine. The Thomson type road steamer supplied to Sir W G Armstrong, to which we have already referred, also left St Nicholas Works now fitted with Burrell's patent clip shoes and is believed to have spent its entire useful life on Armstrong's magnificent estate at Craigside in Northumberland.

The fourth and fifth Thetford Road Steamers, allocated works Nos 540 and 542, were similar to Lord Amherst's engine. They had single cylinders, 9 ins dia × 12 ins stroke, an 8 NHP traction engine boiler and the cylinder adjacent to the chimney. Both engines were fitted with raising and lowering gear. The drive to the rubber tyred hind wheels was through a four shaft gear train, the two road speeds having ratios of 18 to 1 and 9.75 to 1. No 540

Fig 52 No 511, Lord Amherst's engine, fitted with Burrell's patent wheel on a road test with Robert Burrell driving.

Fig 53 No 574 the final Thetford road steamer completed in April 1873 being driven by George Fowell, shortly before leaving Thetford.

went to Steinmüller in Germany and No 542 went to Stone Bros, General Haulage Contractors of Bath. Engine No 540 fortunately survives today in preservation at Steinmüller's boiler works at Gummersbach in Westphalia. Apparently they encountered problems with the boiler raising and lowering gear and they removed the wheels and used the engine for driving stationary plant until 1928. This historic engine minus gearing and drive shafts has now been restored as a road engine. Following periods of duty with several owners, including Henry Boys of Walsall, the present day manufacturers of the Boys heavy duty commercial vehicle axle, No 542 was returned to St Nicholas Works in 1889 and fitted with conventional iron wheels, ending her days with a Leicestershire agricultural contractor.

The final Thetford Road Steamer was completed in April 1873 and allocated works No 574. It was probably built as a speculation, for Charles Burrell exhibited it at both the 1873 and 1874 Royal Shows before finding a buyer. Rated 10 NHP, the boiler and four shaft drive to the hind axle were based on their first geared traction engine introduced in December 1872. No 574 had duplex cylinders measuring 7 ins dia × 12 ins stroke. Fig 53 illustrates the engine being driven by George Fowell, with

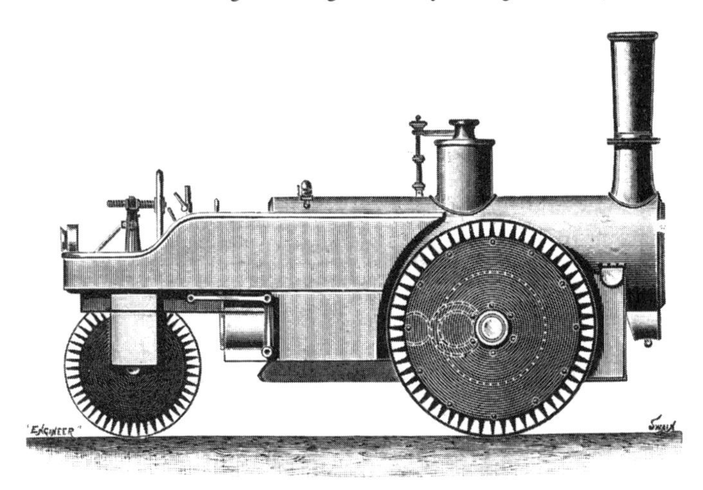

Fig 54 Charles Burrell's proposed high speed road steamer of 1872. Allocated works No 554 but never built.

the erecting shop foreman acting as his fireman. Conventional iron straked driving wheels 5 ft 10 ins dia × 18 ins wide and single 3 ft 7 ins wrought iron front wheel were fitted and the reader will note the totally enclosed motion, the large Watt type governors and the pair of Salter type safety valves. The engine was eventually sold to a Mr George Jeeves of Hilton in Huntingdonshire, but shortly afterwards, in October 1874, it was returned to St Nicholas Works and nothing more is known of its history.

During 1871 and 1872 the technical press devoted much space to articles and correspondence regarding the merits and shortcomings of the rubber-tyred road steamer. Lieut R E Crompton made his historic journeys from Ipswich to Wolverhampton and Ipswich to Edinburgh with one of the Ramsomes-built engines and received tremendous publicity. The third Duke of Sutherland, a well-known mechanical pioneer, purchased a road steamer and concurrently further development work was taking place in both Europe and the United States. In 1873 the technical press paid a great deal of attention to the need for high speed road engines. The editor of the *Engineer* commented that in his opinion "a light road locomotive designed for running at quick speeds, both silently and smoothly with an under-type engine, was the most practical solution to a real need requiring traction engine designers' early attention."

In fact Charles Burrell had already reacted to this challenge and designed a neat, rubber tyred, high speed, duplex cylinder engine, with the cylinders mounted between the frames, which he intended to exhibit at the Cardiff Royal Show in 1872 and later, in 1873, at the Vienna International Exhibition. It was said publicly that the engine could not be got ready in time, although there is now considerable doubt as to whether it was ever completed, in spite of it being allocated works No 554 in the company's engine register. The following advantages were claimed for the design, which was probably the work of George Fowell and young Robert Burrell. A proper distribution of the weight was more easily achieved and the engine could be made lighter; the counter shaft and hind axle were on the same horizontal centre line, permitting a simple arrangement of the road springs; the boiler was a steam generator only and no engine parts were bolted to it, the side frames taking all the hauling strain; the copper steam pipe in the smokebox dried the steam and the cylinders could be well lagged to prevent condensation; the blast pipe could be placed in the best possible position for ensuring a good blast; a large steam dome could be provided, obviating any tendency to prime; and all the moving parts were neatly enclosed, giving a simple, well-engineered appearance.

Although Charles II subsequently stated that the principal reason for abandoning the project was that the engine had been intended for one-man operation, which necessitated the driver having his back to the road when attending to the fire, it seems more probable that the company ran into some patent infringement problems. John Fowler had filed his patent No 980 in April 1871 describing a novel under-type engine with a unique epicyclic gearbox incorporated in the hind axle and both Tennants of Leith and Alexander Chaplin had built prototype under-type engines, pre-dating Burrell's design.

Poor Robert Thomson, now totally paralysed, died at his home in Moray Place in March 1873 in his fifty-first year and the age of the solid rubber-tyred road steamer effectively died with him. He had made a great and fascinating contribution to the evolution of road haulage, but he was perhaps ahead of his time. None of the licencees brought his invention to a real state of mechanical perfection, the economies of the rubber tyre were unattractive, legislation at home remained punitive and no ready market could be found for the Road Steamer. We must now devote our attention to the evolution of the general purpose traction engine.

CHAPTER SIX

The Single Cylinder Geared Traction Engine

In the years following the 1871 Engine Trials held at Wolverhampton the single cylinder general purpose traction engine virtually eclipsed the portable type steam engine as the main source of power on the farm and soon became the principal 'bread-and-butter' product of most established agricultural steam engine builders. Attempts to develop the large scale use of steam on the common roads, both for passenger carrying and heavy haulage duties had failed due to the penal legislation in force and to the established supremacy of the railways in these fields. In urban areas the horse continued to provide feeder services for the railway and it was only in country districts where the power and versatility of the self-moving traction engine made significant progress. It was equally at home whether hauling or driving a threshing drum; working in wooded areas hauling timber or driving a saw bench or providing the power to drive a corn mill or other stationary machinery. General haulage duties were often incidental to its main tasks, but as a tool of trade it became indispensable to the Victorian agriculturist, just as the modern farm tractor has become to its twentieth century counterpart. Only in the fields of land cultivation was the comparison with the present day different. Direct traction ploughing was out of favour due to the great weight and high axle loading of the traction engine causing severe compaction of the sub-soil and the steam driven, cable-hauled implement reigned supreme until after the First World War.

In 1865 John Fowler & Company adapted their range of four-shaft ploughing engines as traction engines, listing 8, 10 and 14 NHP engines in their catalogue, but they sold comparatively few because of their weight and relatively high cost. Other makers, including Charles Burrell, offered the chain-driven traction engine, developed from the portable engine, and did rather better. It was not until 1870 that designs for a three-shaft geared traction engine began to emerge as an economic and reliable proposition.

In 1869 a Mr P Edwards, partner in a small Grantham engineering works trading as Ford & Edwards, designed what was soon to become the conventional three-shaft engine layout. There is no evidence that this engine was ever built and Edwards apparently made no effort to make his ideas public, although details of the engine and a general arrangement drawing subsequently appeared in the *Engineer*. The essential features of this design were that the cylinders were mounted on the boiler barrel adjacent to the chimney, the crankshaft was carried in cast iron brackets affixed to the side walls of the outer firebox and the intermediate motion shaft was arranged the full width of the engine, supported in a canon bracket mounted behind the firebox. A large flywheel was fitted to the nearside end of the crankshaft and a pinion gear wheel engaging with a spur wheel on the intermediate motion shaft, was carried on the off-side end of the crankshaft. Another pinion wheel on the intermediate shaft engaged with a second spur wheel attached to the off-side hind wheel. The engine was unsprung and no differential or compensating gear was provided; the near-side hind wheel rotating freely on the axle, enabling the engine to negotiate corners without wheel slip. On soft ground, a pin was inserted through the wheel hub, locking the wheel to the wheel centre attached to the axle, enabling the engine power to be transmitted to both wheels.

The first patent giving protection to the three-shaft arrangement was filed by Thomas Aveling in 1870. In the same year he filed his famous 'Hornplates' patent and engines incorporting this feature were exhibited at the RASE Oxford Show in 1870. Aveling found that the accepted practice of mounting the crankshaft in brackets bolted to the boiler or firebox casing was a source of trouble. Inevitably sooner or later the bolts were shaken loose, caused by the engine trundling over rough ground, and by the stresses set up by the reciprocating motion, resulting in excessive wear in the bearings and damaging the boiler structure. Rivets were tried with little better results. The patent described how the outer side walls of the firebox could be extended upwards and backwards to carry the crankshaft, intermediate shaft and hind axle bearings in a very rigid box structure. This feature was prominently displayed in the Aveling & Porter engines tested at the RASE Wolverhampton engine trials and its merit was quickly appreciated by both the Judges and Aveling's competitors. Fortunately an early example of one of these engines survives today in the London Science Museum, donated by the Road Locomotive Society.

Thomas Aveling was a remarkable man, as well as an extremely competent engineer and innovator. He was almost certainly the first person to propose adapting the ordinary portable engine to become self-moving in the early 1850s although the earliest patent protection went to John Fowler's friend and associate, John Allin Williams. Whilst hiring out his own portable engine to his neighbours, Aveling was struck by the absurdity of having to haul the ponderous machine by horses when it possessed the ability to generate ten times the power of the horses struggling to move it. He was born in 1824 at Elm, near Wisbech in Cambridgeshire, where his grandfather had been High Sheriff. Upon his father's untimely death

Fig 55 No 532 the first geared traction engine built at St. Nicholas Works in 1872.

the family moved to Kent and young Thomas eventually secured employment on Robert Lake's farm near Canterbury. Lake fully appreciated the potential of steam power as an aid to the farmer and was one of the original shareholders of the Steam Plough Royalty Company Limited, formed by John Fowler to finance the development of his cultivating machinery patents. At the age of twenty-five Aveling married Lake's niece and took a farm on his own account at Ruckinge on Romney Marsh. In 1856 in partnership with his former employer he acquired a small millwright's business at Rochester on the Medway, thus laying the foundations of the once great firm, Aveling & Porter Limited.

Aveling's first patent, filed in 1859, described the pitch chain driving gear, including the chain tightening pulley described in Chapter 3. He exhibited the first self-moving traction engine entirely of his own manufacture at the 1861 Royal Show. He invented the system of pilot wheel steerage employed on some of the Burrell-Boydell engines. He was the pioneer of simplicity and strength in engine design and he never employed two cylinders where one would suffice. By placing the crankshaft over the firebox and the cylinder forward he secured two advantages which other engine builders all adopted. Firstly he ensured dry steam when the engine was pulling uphill and secondly the flywheel was within easy reach of the driver, should the engine stop on dead centre. He was one of the pioneers of the steam jacketed cylinder which greatly improved engine efficiency and overall performance minimising condensation. He pioneered the steam road roller as we know it today and was one of the first engineers to appreciate the importance of hydraulic riveting, such that by 1872 his boiler shop was the most modern and best equipped in the trade.

Although involved in some patent litigation in 1881 in an abortive attempt to protect his hornplate invention, Aveling remained popular and highly respected by his professional colleagues. An especially close and practical relationship existed with John Fowler and his successors for many years. He became also a local benefactor and philanthropist and his name is still revered in the Rochester area. In middle life he became a keen yachtsman and derived much pleasure from sailing in the Thames Estuary. Unfortunately, as the result of a thorough soaking whilst out in his boat, he contracted pneumonia and died a few days later at his home, Boley Hill House, at the comparatively early age of fifty-eight.

The Wolverhampton Engine Trials could be described as a Thomas Aveling benefit, for the judges' report applauded and rewarded the manner in which he had brought together his many inventions. Charles Burrell was compelled to re-assess his own position and, although

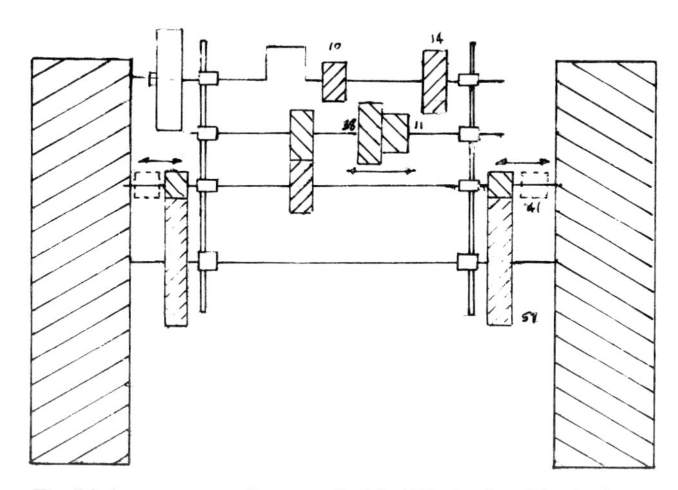

Fig 56 Arrangement of gearing for No 532 the first Thetford built geared traction engine.

perhaps somewhat slow to adopt all Aveling's successful design features, a new breed of traction engine began to emerge from St Nicholas Works and by 1914 the company had justifiably earned the reputation as builders of the Rolls Royce of traction engines.

The first geared traction engine built at Thetford was rated 10 NHP, one of a batch of four, all built in 1872 and allocated works Nos 532, 533, 552 and 553. They had 10 ins dia × 12 ins stroke steam-jacketed cylinders and the KG type boiler, which was later used on the chain-driven crane engine mentioned in Chapter 3. The boiler barrel was 2 ft 9¾ ins dia, the forty 2¼ ins dia smoke tubes were 7 ft 5 ins long and the inner firebox measured 2 ft 2¼ ins long × 2 ft 2¼ ins wide × 3 ft 1 ins deep, giving a total heating surface of 195 sq ft. The grate area was 4.8 sq ft. The two-speed gearing to the unsprung hind axle was through a four-shaft transmission system as shown in Fig 56. No differential or compensating gear was fitted and the pinions on each end of the third motion shaft could be readily disengaged from the footplate when turning corners. The hind wheels were 5 ft 6 ins dia × 18 ins wide with cast iron naves and wrought iron spokes and wheel rims, each wheel being fitted with a screw-down hand brake. Steerage was from the footplate by means of worm, wormwheel and chain barrel. Water was carried in large belly tanks mounted under the boiler and the feed pump was eccentric-driven from the crankshaft. The 5 ft 0 ins dia flywheel had curved spokes, as used on the earlier chain engines; Salter type spring balance safety valves were fitted to the domed cylinder casting; and a tall stove pipe chimney completed the ensemble. The first engine in the batch, No 532, was exhibted at the Royal Show held in Cardiff in 1872, at the Bath & West Show in Dorchester and at the Devon Show, driven upon each occasion by George Fowell. Eventually at the end of the show season the engine was purchased by a Devon farmer. No 533 went to the Ravensthorpe Plough Company, an offshoot of the Ravensthorpe Engineering Company, who played a notable part in the development of early steam cultivating machinery, recently having acquired Fisken Brothers, the original patentees of Fowler's balance plough. About this time Ravensthorpe employed a young man, who in later life established a considerable reputation as a traction engine builder. John McLaren, who later received a knighthood, established his works in partnership with his brother Henry in 1876 on land adjoining John Fowlers's works at Hunslet, Leeds.

Obviously there were deficiencies in the design of these engines and perhaps it is not surprising that only four were built. The crankshaft assembly lacked rigidity; the overhang on the off-side or gear side of the shaft was excessive in order to accommodate the two-change speed pinions outside the bearing bracket; the second motion shaft was a short shaft, supported by the outer firebox wall and lacking the benefit of bearings on both sides of the engine; the system of disengaging the pinions when turning corners became outdated as the differential gear came into more general use; and a three-shaft drive would have been preferable on an engine of this type, avoiding the loss of power due to the added friction associated with four shafts.

A further five 10 NHP engines and one 12 NHP engine were built in the period 1875–1879. Each was different from the others and it would be true to say none represented a milestone in the company's history. No 674, completed in August 1875, had the same gearing and transmission as No 532 and a heavy 4 ft 6 ins dia flywheel grooved for Fisken's plough rope, with guide pulleys attached to the steerage shaft. No 725 completed in December 1875, was the same as No 532, except that it was fitted with a differential gear on the third motion shaft, dispensing with the need for disengaging pinions; also, it had the added facility of water tanks under both the footplate and the boiler. In later life this engine enjoyed the distinction of being the earliest Burrell engine to be owned by a travelling showman. Purchased second hand by Savages of King's Lynn, the fairground machinery manufacturers in 1880, it was supplied to William H Marshall, a well known Yorkshire showman, together with a brand new set of Savage's Galloping Horses. It was fitted with an extra large water tank and 6 ft 0 ins dia hind wheels, giving it greater speed on the road. In 1891 the engine was taken in part exchange by John Fowler, who supplied Marshall with one of his new class B1 road engines which he named 'Sunny Boy No 1'.

Number 735 completed in August 1876 was as No 674, except that it was supplied with a copper firebox and brass smoke tubes to satisfy French boiler regulations then in force and, so far as can be traced, it was the first Burrell engine to be supplied to a French customer. Ploughing rope pulleys were attached to the front water tank and the tender back was altered for the attachment of a plough windlass. No 841, completed in April 1879, was built to a completely new design, having the N type boiler as fitted to the 14 NHP geared drive ploughing engine. The proportion of the heating surface to the grate area was reduced to 31.1 to 1, indicating that the engine was primarily intended for road haulage work. The engine was provided with road springs and differential gear, but unfortunately no record of the method of maintaining the correct mesh of the gear teeth as the axle rose and fell due to the action of the springs has survived. The engine was supplied to R G Wilberforce of Woolavington in Somerset, a kinsman of Charles II's second wife, whom he married in 1912. The above engines all had the 10 ins dia × 12 ins stroke single cylinder but in October 1878 St Nicholas Works completed their last duplex cylinder engine. No 800 had two cylinders measuring 7½ ins dia × 12 ins stroke and was generally similar to a 10 NHP road engine No 789 supplied to Woods of Brandon in 1878, which we shall discuss in a later chapter.

No 708, completed in October 1875, was the only early geared traction engine to be rated 12 NHP. The single cylinder measured 10½ ins dia × 12 ins stroke and in every other respect it appears to have been similar to No 674, with the transmission shafts and gearing as No 552.

The years 1871 to 1876 were difficult years for St Nicholas Works. The road steamer had failed to secure a worthwhile market, they were lagging behind several of their competitors in the introduction of a reliable general purpose traction engine and worldwide business was moving towards a serious economic recession. Charles I and his three sons, now trading as Charles Burrell & Sons, realised that something had to be done quickly if they were to retain their reputation and share of the market. They were all working partners, very much dependant upon the success of the business for their livelihood. In 1876 they introduced new designs of 6 and 8 NHP traction engines and the position improved until 1879, when the whole industry began to feel the full effects of the Great Agricultural Depression, which was to last until 1884. Thereafter, as we shall see, they went from strength to strength and, apart from a period of recession in the years 1902 to 1905 , sales increased annually to reach an all-time peak in 1909.

The first of the new engines, Works No 691, made its debut at the Smithfield Club Show in December 1875. Described as a light 6 NHP traction engine, it weighed only 5 tons 17 cwts in working order. It had a new cylinder measuring 8 ins dia × 10 ins stroke, a new boiler having a working pressure of 120 PSI and a total heating surface of 115 sq ft. The three-shaft drive to the hind wheels gave a choice of two road speeds and the pinions on the ends of the intermediate motion shaft engaged with internally toothed spur rings attached directly to the driving wheels. Differential gearing was incorporated in the intermediate motion shaft and provision was made for the differential to be locked in the event of the engine getting into difficulty and requiring the whole power of the engine to be applied to both wheels. The driving wheels were 5 ft 6 ins dia × 12 ins wide, with cast iron naves and flat section wrought iron spokes and wheel rims. The front wheels were 3 ft 9 ins dia × 9 ins wide. The water tank was mounted under the footplate having a capacity of 110 gallons and the feed pump was eccentric driven from the crankshaft. A belt-driven Watt type governor was supplied, but no brakes were fitted to the engine.

Reaction to this engine appears to have been unfavourable; it was considered to be too light, the boiler too small and the final drive arrangement having the

Fig 57 No 691, the first 6 NHP gear driven traction engine built by St Nicholas Works in 1875.

internally toothed spur ring bolted to the hind wheels was not popular. In July 1876 a new design of 6 NHP engine was completed and total of twenty-one engines were built.

It is an indication of the concern felt by the partners that the new design was introduced in stages, rather than waiting for all the proposed new features to be available for incorporation in a single engine. However, there is no doubt that in its final form this series, together with the larger 8 NHP engines introduced more or less concurrently, set the seal on Charles Burrell's future success as traction engine builders.

All twenty-one engines had boilers to drawing 732/10 having the following dimensions:

Boiler barrel dia	2′7½″
Firebox – length	1′10½″
– width	2′0″
– depth	2′9″
Smokebox – dia.	2′7½″
– length	1′2″
– dia. × length	2′¼″ × 5′6″
Number of tubes	33
Working pressure	120 PSI
Grate area	3.75 sq ft
Heating surface – firebox	24 sq ft
– tubes	101 sq ft
– total	125 sq ft

All had steam-jacketed cylinders measuring 8 ins dia × 10 ins stroke, 2-speed gearing, 5 ft 2 ins dia × 18 ins wide hind wheels and 4 ft dia spoked flywheels, but there the similarity ended. Engine Nos 732 and 733 were obviously completed before the proposed new transmission

SECOND GENERATION 6 NHP SINGLE DRIVE, UNSPRUNG TRACTION ENGINE

No 732 Built 1876	No 760 Built 1877	No 784 Built 1878	No 827 Built 1879
733 " 1876	763 " 1877	785 " 1878	828 " 1879
741 " 1876	764 " 1878	806 " 1878	829 " 1880
742 " 1877	765 " 1878	807 " 1878	830 " 1880
758 " 1877	783 " 1878	808 " 1879	831 " 1880
759 " 1877			

Fig 58 A second generation 6 NHP geared traction engine as depicted in Burrell's catalogue.

arrangements were available for they were built with a rigid drive to the hind axle, the pinions on each end of the intermediate shaft being arranged such that they could be readily disengaged by the driver to facilitate turning corners. In 1877 both were rebuilt with 2-speed gearing and winding drums. No 732 was exhibited at the RASE Show held in Birmingham in 1876 and the following year in its rebuilt state became the prize-winning engine at the Diss Agricultural Show in Norfolk. No 741 which was exhibited at Smithfield in December 1876 was the first engine to be built with Burrell's now famous single drive 3-shaft geared drive which was similar to Aveling & Porter's early arrangement which dispensed with the need for the unpopular spur wheels attached to the hind wheels of the engine.

No 759 was the first engine to be built with Burrell's patent differential or compensating gear combined with a winding drum and a brake drum, the subject of Robert Burrell's patent No 4432 sealed in April 1877. This patent represented a major technical breakthrough for the partners and variants of the single drive arrangement described was utilised on many types of engine for the remainder of the firm's existence. In the following year both John Fowler & Co of Leeds and W Marshall & Sons of Gainsborough became licensees, paying Burrell a royalty of five shillings on every engine they built incorporating this system, the engines by arrangement carrying a Royalty Plate. The patent also provided for the compensating gear and brake drum to be optionally mounted on the second motion shaft. Engine No 760 was also fitted with belly tanks and worked as the works yard engine from 1877–1886.

Spring wheels claimed a great deal of engine designers' attention at this time. Thomas Aveling, John Fowler, Charles Burrell and several other gentlemen all filed patents in their search for better adhesion and starting performance under load and all adopted the idea of interposing springs between the wheel rim and the nave. Charles Burrell II and Robert Edwards's patent No 4812 dated 1877 referred to their objective as being to 'effectively hang the engine upon springs'. It now seems doubtful if any of the proposals really justified the extra initial cost or the added weight and maintenance involved, for the majority were soon discarded. The main claim for the various systems was that, upon starting kinetic energy was stored in the wheel springs giving the trailing loads motion similar to pulling a cork out of a bottle thereby serving the same purpose as a drawbar spring. Four systems of springing were described in the patent, but unfortunately we do not know which options were used on engines Nos 764 and 784.

Patent No 4812 also described a crane engine provided with a crane tower as an extension of the firebox side plates with a jib and lifting gear. The crane barrel took its motion from a geared drive to the engine crankshaft. The whole was so arranged that the weight when lifted by the crane

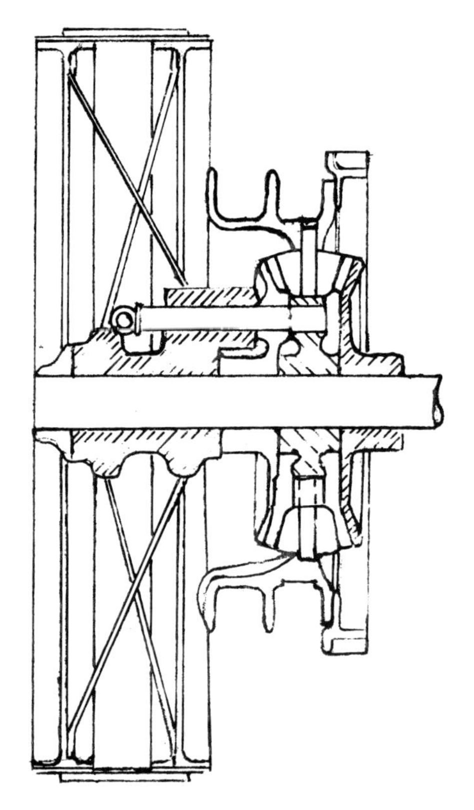

Fig 59 The combined compensating gear and winding drum described in Robert Burrell's famous patent No 4432 of 1877.

could be swung round to the other side of the engine in either direction. When it was desired to use the crane for lifting purposes the road gearing could be disconnected by sliding pinions on the crankshaft. Engine No 764 was provided with such a crane and was employed in the works' yard for 12 months before being sold to Tippler's of Takeley in Essex. The first 8 engines in this series were supplied without governors, the majority of the remainder were fitted with Burrell's high-speed governor. Six of the latter engines were acquired by J Myers of Leeming in North Yorkshire, an important agricultural machinery merchant who widely demonstrated the engines to potential customers in the area.

Another extremely important innovation was built into engine No 808 and incorporated in all subsequent production. It was the subject of Burrell's patent No 2881 dated July 1878 and filed jointly in the names of Charles I and Robert Edwards. It described amongst other things, the method of selecting the two-speed drive pinions mounted on the off-side end of the crankshaft, by means of forks and a single gear shift lever, to give fast, slow and neutral drive to the intermediate shaft. The selector mechanism was so arranged that it was impossible for both sliding pinion wheels to be put in gear at the same time. The arrangement of this clutch gear is illustrated in Fig 62 and it will be noted that the fast speed pinion was located next to the crankshaft bearing and recessed such that it partly passed over it, minimising the unsupported overhang of the crankshaft, a feature which became

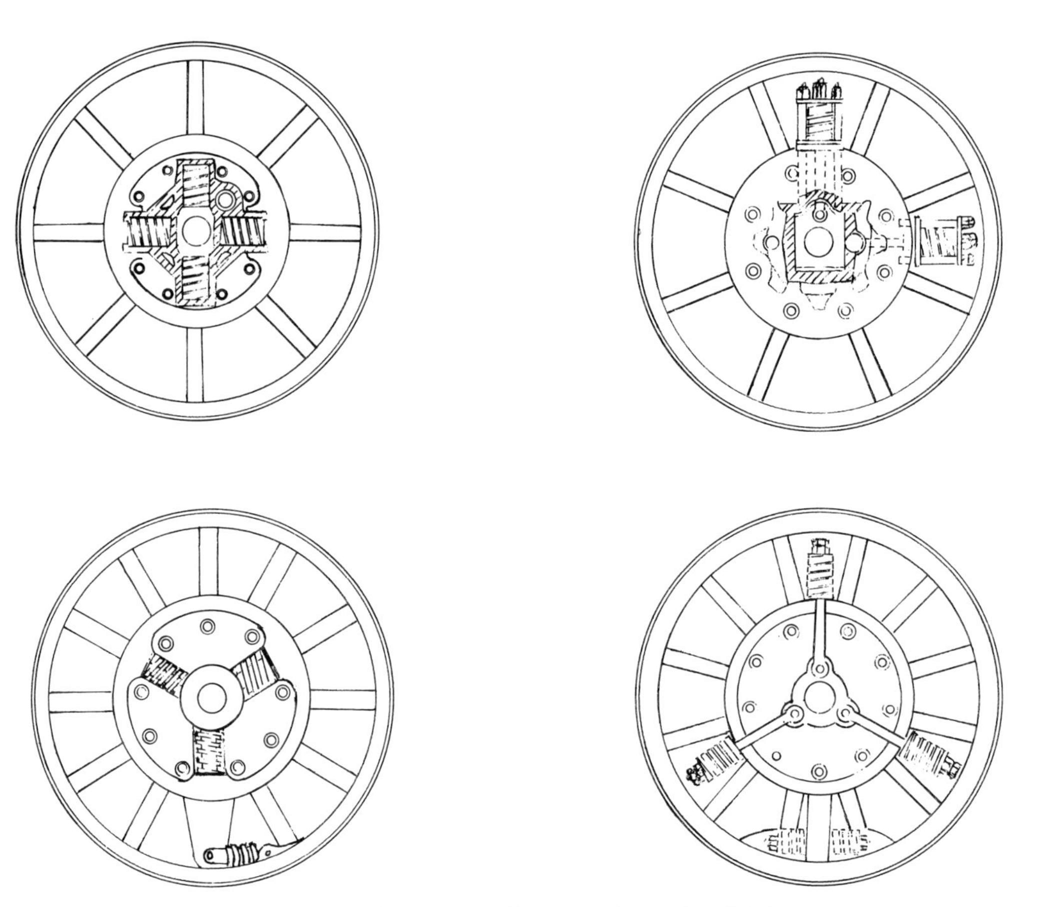

Fig 60 Spring wheels proposed by Charles Burrell and Robert Edwards in their patent No 4812 of 1877.

especially significant when three-speed gearing became popular. This engine was exhibited at the Smithfield Club Show in 1879 and received wide publicity in the technical press.

A great deal of the credit for this clever design must go to Robert Edwards who had succeeded George Fowell as chief draughtsman in 1876. Edwards's efforts were rewarded by being awarded half the royalties received during the first seven years of the patent's life. Unfortunately shortly afterwards he left St Nicholas Works to take up a similar appointment with Richard Hornsby & Sons in Grantham.

A further batch of six 6 NHP engines were built in 1881. They appear to have been identical in all respects to their predecessors, except that they were fitted with a redesigned cylinder, measuring 8½ ins dia × 10 ins stroke, having a flat top circular dome on the top of the casting and the boiler barrel was extended by 2 ins.

THIRD GENERATION 6 NHP SINGLE DRIVE, UNSPRUNG TRACTION ENGINE

No	Built	No	Built
No 890	Built 1881	No 905	Built 1881
891	" 1881	906	" 1881
892	" 1881	907	" 1881

Engine Nos 890 and 892 were the first Thetford built engines sold through the Burnell et Cie agency in Paris. Originally the firm traded as Waite and Burnell and this agency was subsequently instrumental in securing orders for forty-six Burrell engines of various types including ploughing engines, traction engines, 5 ton steam tractors, road rollers and three showmen's type engines. A close personal friendship developed between Burnell and members of the Burrell family and Charles II and Robert soon discovered the joys of combining business with pleasure in the French capital.

In the middle of the Great Agricultural Depression Charles Burrell introduced their now famous type 'T' 6 NHP single drive general purpose traction engine. Twenty-one unsprung engines were built in the five years to 1886 although later production including double geared and spring mounted versions were produced until 1920.

'T' TYPE 6 NHP SINGLE DRIVE, UNSPRUNG TRACTION ENGINE

No	Built	No	Built
No 930	Built 1881	No 977	Built 1883
931	" 1881	978	" 1883
932	" 1882	1143	" 1884
951	" 1882	1144	" 1884
952	" 1883	1154	" 1885
953	" 1883	1155	" 1885
954	" 1882	1156	" 1885
955	" 1882	1182	" 1886
956	" 1882	1183	" 1886
975	" 1883	1184	" 1886
976	" 1883		

Nos 954, 955, 956, 976, 977 and 978 had 8½ ins dia × 10 ins stroke single cylinders, the remainder had 8 ins dia × 10 ins stroke cylinders. The type T11 boilers were slightly larger than their predecessors and had a working pressure of 125 PSI. The grate area was 4.2 sq ft and the total heating surface 128 sq ft of which 27 sq ft came from the firebox and 101 sq ft from the forty-one 4 ft 9 ins long

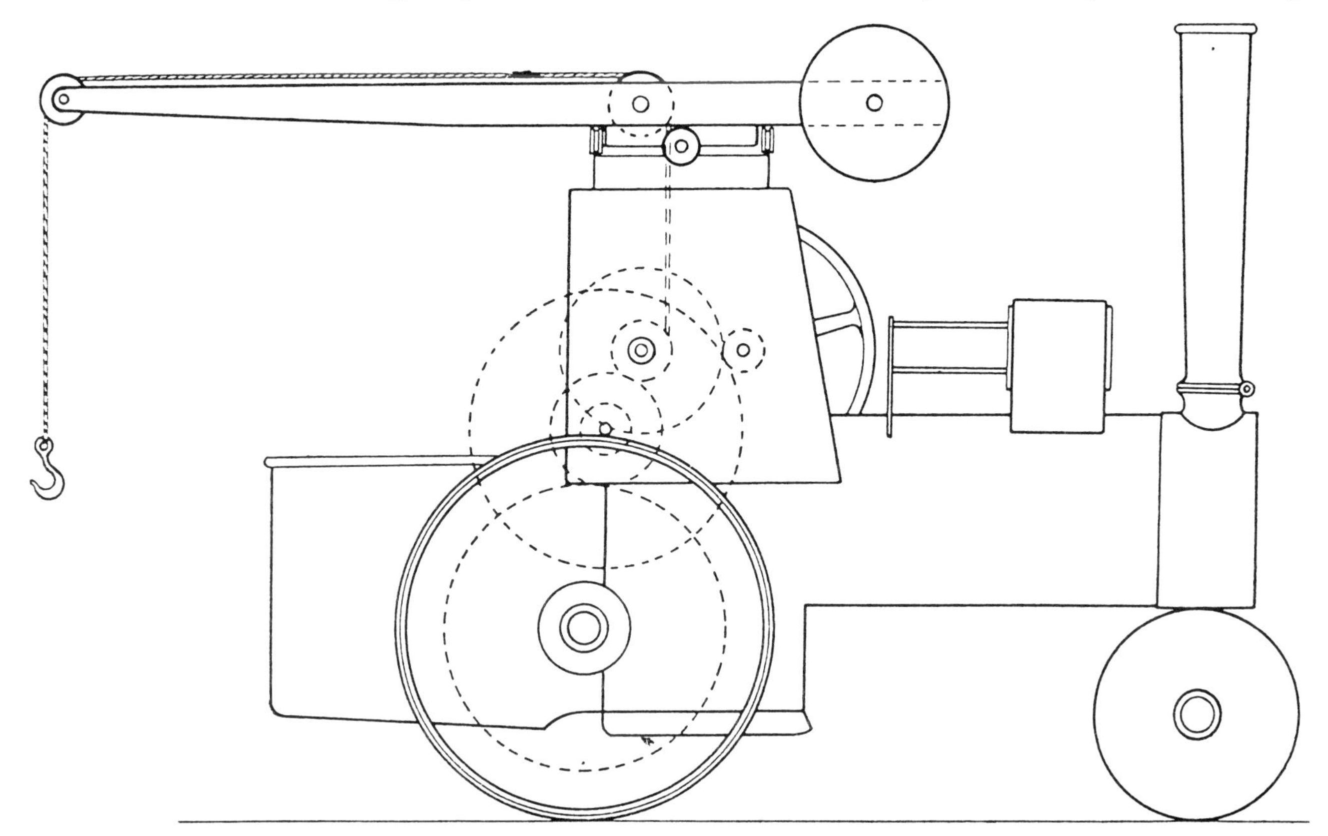

Fig 61 Engine No 764, the first Burrell crane engine built in 1878.

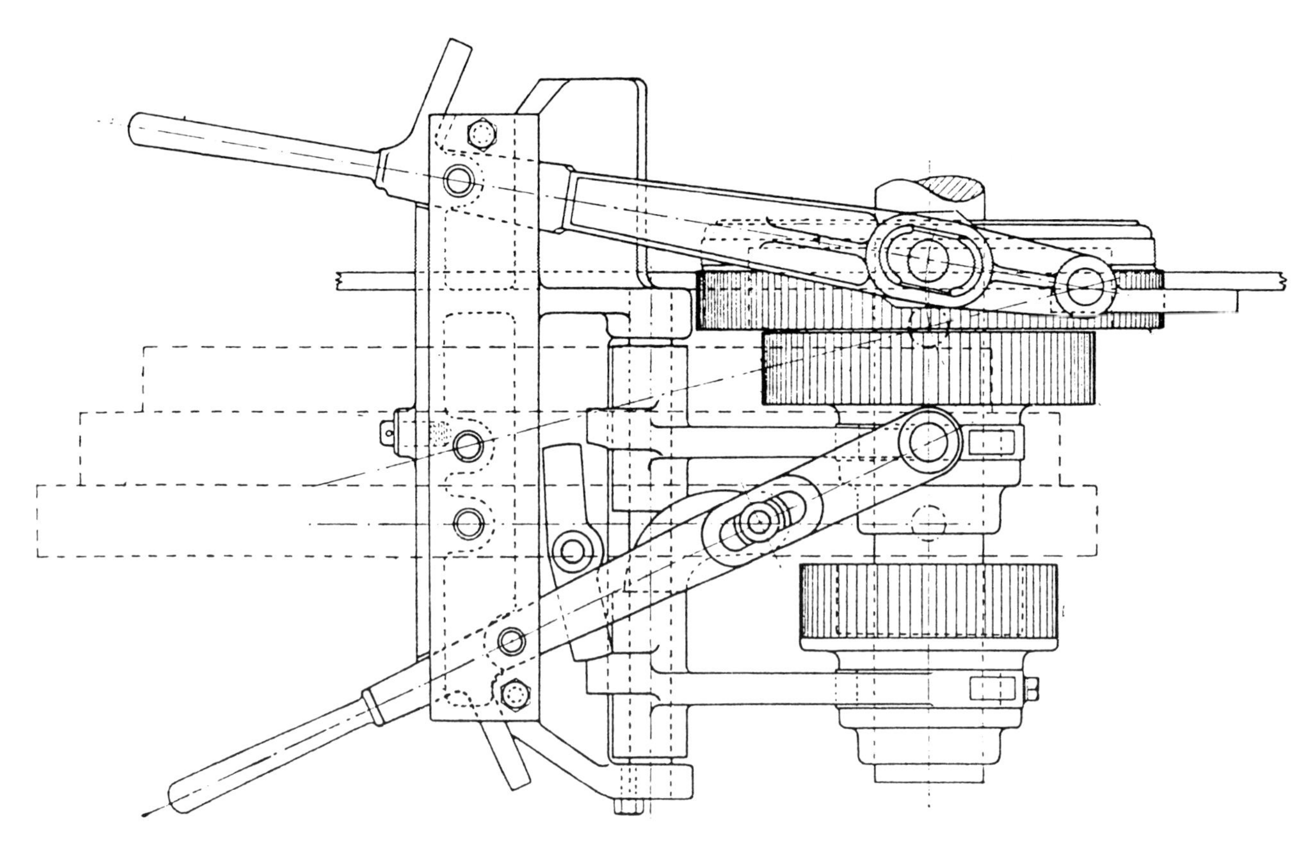

Fig 62 Charles Burrell's & Robert Edwards' 3-speed gear selector mechanism developed from their patent No 2881 of 1878.

Fig 63 No 890. A third generation 6 NHP traction engine supplied to a French customer in 1881.

× 2 ins dia smoke tubes. No 975 went to a customer in Manila in the Philippines fitted with 22 ins wide wheels, the firebox was lengthened by 4 ins and suitable for burning inferior fuel. No 1184's boiler was experimentally fitted with steel rivets in place of the conventional iron rivet and No 930 was probably the first Burrell engine to be fitted with Ramsbottom type safety valves. Patented by the famous locomotive engineer, John Ramsbottom in 1856, they were widely used on railway locomotives by 1880 and comprised a coil spring-mounted between two short vertical pipes, connected to the steam space pulling down on a beam arranged above the pipes and closing valves in their outer ends. Ramsbottom also patented the split piston ring, which greatly improved the steam tightness of the piston as it worked in the cylinder bore; and the displacement type lubricator which was used for lubricating engine cylinders prior to the introduction of the mechanically operated lubricator.

All this batch of engines were fitted with the type T23 eccentric driven boiler feed pump and engine Nos 1182 and 1184 were additionally fitted with Sharp Stewart No 4 injectors. Shart Stewart & Co, the Manchester-based locomotive builders, were the sole British licensees of Giffard's patent until it expired in 1872. Later, in 1886, Holden and Brookes took over the manufacturing rights and by the turn of the century a wide choice of makes were available to the engine builder, but they always remained a specialist bought-out component at St Nicholas Works.

Engineers had long tried to reproduce mechanically the action of the spade for cultivating the land and achieved varying degrees of success. As our story unfolds we shall learn that Charles Burrell were involved at various times in the later part of the 19th century with the development of mechanical diggers. They supplied engines to the principal protagonists, Frank Proctor, Thomas Darby and Thomas Cooper. Cooper acquired Percival Everitt's business at Great Ryburgh when William Adams left the partnership, renaming it the Farmers Foundry Co Ltd. By 1899 Cooper also had a factory in King's Lynn where in addition to the Cooper Steam Digger Co Ltd, he established the now renowned Cooper Roller Bearing Company. In 1883 Burrell supplied No 978 to Edward Cobham of Stevenage in Hertfordshire for conversion to a digging engine. No road wheels, axles, transmission shafts, water tanks or steerage were supplied and the crankshaft was lengthened on the gear side. Digging gear was attached to the rear of the engine in acordance with Cobham's patent No 515 filed in January 1883. The engine was demonstrated at the RASE Show held in York later that year, but as far as can be traced this was the only engine built with Cobham's digging gear.

The first Thetford built 8 NHP geared drive engines were completed in December 1876 and a batch of twenty engines were produced in the period to August 1881.

Basically, they were an enlarged version of the 6 NHP engines, having 9 ins dia × 12 ins stroke single cylinders and boilers of the following dimensions:

Boiler barrel – dia	2′9¾″
– length o/a	9′10½″
Firebox – length	2′2⅜″
– width	2′2⅛″
– depth	2′11″
Smokebox – dia.	3′0½″
– length	1′6⅜″
– dia. × length	2′¼″ × 5′10″
Number of tubes	36
Working pressure	120 PSI
Grate area	4.8 sq ft
Heating surface – firebox	30 sq ft
– tubes	120 sq ft
– total	152 sq ft

The unsprung transmission arrangements were as described in patent No 4432 and the layout of the gear train was as illustrated in Fig 65, the two-speed gear ratios being 20.9 to 1 and 13.8 to 1. The wrought iron hind wheels measured 5 ft 8 ins dia × 16 ins wide and the front wheels 3 ft 9¾ ins dia × 9¾ ins wide. Some were fitted with screw-down hand brakes operating on the near-side hind wheel, others operated on the off-side wheel. The spoked flywheels were 4 ft 6 ins dia × 6 ins wide. The weight in working order was about 9 ton 10 cwts. All had eccentric driven feed pumps and No 782 was fitted additionally with Hall's patent injector.

Sixty per cent of the batch went to customers in East Anglia and No 848 went to Russia fitted with a long wood burning firebox. The series made its debut at the 1877 Royal Show held in Liverpool. No 750 was exhibied at the Bath & West Show in 1877 and No 782 appeared at the Smithfield Club Show in 1878. Traditionally many big landowners and farmers continued to purchase their new engines at the showground, knowing that the exhibits often recieved that extra bit of care and attention in the erecting shop and especially in the paint shop. Most agricultural engines were painted Quaker Green at this time although the customer continued to have the final choice.

Following the successful introduction of the 8 NHP series it was found that there was a market for an engine having a power output and performance mid-way between the 6 and 8 NHP engines for driving 5 ft threshing drums. Four first generation 7 NHP engines were built in 1879 and 1880.

FIRST GENERATION 7 NHP SINGLE DRIVE, UNSPRUNG TRACTION ENGINES

No	Built	No	Built
No 869	Built 1879	No 886	Built 1880
885	" 1880	887	" 1880

FIRST GENERATION 8 NHP SINGLE DRIVE, UNSPRUNG TRACTION ENGINE

No	Built	No	Built	No	Built	No	Built
No 744	Built 1876	No 753	Built 1877	No 782	Built 1878	No 871	Built 1881
745	" 1876	754	" 1877	804	" 1878	872	" 1880
746	" 1877	755	" 1878	805	" 1878	881	" 1881
750	" 1877	780	" 1878	848	" 1878	882	" 1881
752	" 1877	781	" 1878	870	" 1878	883	" 1881

Fig 64 No 744 8 NHP single cylinder general purpose traction engine introduced in 1876.

They were fitted with an entirely new pattern cylinder measuring 8½ ins dia × 12 ins stroke and the same new type C1 boiler was employed as fitted to the successful 8 NHP type 'C' engines introduced in 1881. They had 5 ft 8 ins dia × 16 ins wide hind wheels and the overall width of the engines was only 7 ft 3 ins which appealed to many farmers. All four engines were supplied with Burrell threshing drums. The first of the four engines was exhibited at Smithfield in 1879 and the fourth at the RASE Show at Carlisle in 1880.

By this time the designs of Burrell general purpose (GP) traction engines had been consolidated and all the features recommended by the Judges at the 1871 Wolverhampton Engine Trials had been incorporated. The excellence of Burrell products was now widely recognised by the agricultural fraternity as being compatible with the best of the other established steam engine manufacturers.

We shall now deal with the remaining single cylinder GP traction engines built at St Nicholas Works in the halcyon years to 1914 in order of size and we start with the diminutive 4 NHP engines introduced in 1884.

'R' TYPE 4 NHP DOUBLE-GEARED, UNSPRUNG TRACTION ENGINES

No	Built	No	Built
No 1082	Built 1884	No 1189	Built 1886
1187	" 1885	1248	" 1886
1188	" 1887	1272	" 1887

The single cylinders measured 6½ ins dia × 9 ins stroke and a new R38 type boiler was fitted, having a working pressure of 150 PSI, a grate area of only 3.3 sq ft and a total heating surface of 80.8 sq ft. The drive to the hind axle was double-geared, that is, unlike the single drive arrangement described in patent 4432 of 1876, the intermediate shaft had pinion wheels on each end, which engaged with large spur wheels arranged on both sides of the engine. The spur wheels were attached to wheel centres mounted on the hind axle and the drive to the hind wheels was transmitted through removable driving pins passing through the wheel hubs into the driving centres. The differential gear was fitted to the gear-side end of the intermediate motion shaft. The arrangement which eventually came into common usage on many types and sizes of engine was first publicly demonstrated on an 8 NHP road locomotive No 1068 exhibited at the 1883 Smithfield Club Show. Two-speed gearing was provided having ratios of 22.4 to 1 and 13.2 to 1 and the hind wheels were 5 ft 0 ins dia × 12 ins wide. A winding drum was fitted to the hind axle on the flywheel side; the flywheel was 3 ft 6 ins dia × 5½ ins wide; a water tank mounted under the boiler carried 72 gallons of water; no brakes were fitted and the overall width of the engine was only 5 ft 8 ins.

Engine Nos 1187, 1188 and 1189 went to West Country farmers for light haulage duties on hill farms in Devonshire and Nos 1248 and 1272 were built as digging engines. In 1886 Frederick Burrell, who was now established as the company's chief designer, and Frank Proctor, an independent consulting engineer, jointly filed patent No 9059 describing such an engine and the novel drive to the three sets of digging forks is shown in Fig 67. The final drive pinions on the intermediate shaft were arranged such that they could be moved sideways to engage with either the spur wheels on the hind axle for

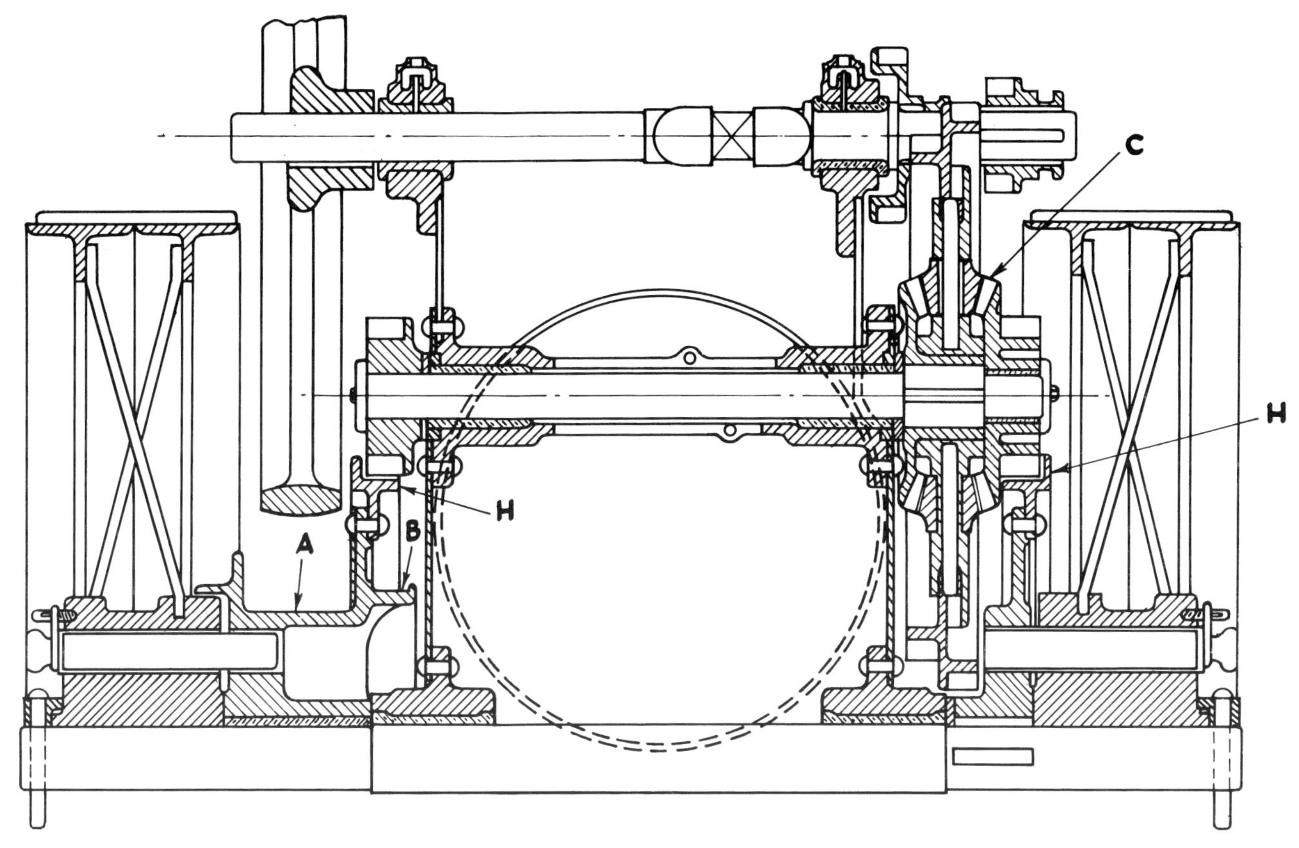

Fig 65 General arrangement of the double geared drive to the hind axle introduced in 1884.

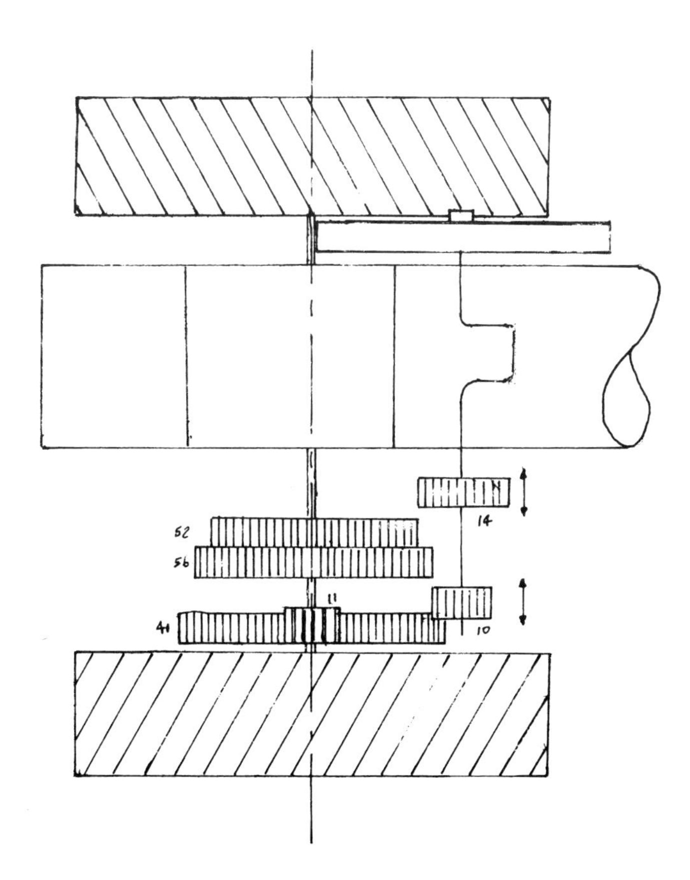

Fig 66 Layout of transmission shafting and gearing of the early 8 NHP traction engine.

normal road work or with the digging wheel, which was eccentrically mounted on the stub axle such that it could be rotated in or out of gear. A smaller pinion was combined with digging wheel and meshed with an annular toothed ring which was integral with the road spur, this giving a very low road speed gear ratio when the digging gear was engaged. Motion for the three throw digging crank was derived from the spur wheels on the intermediate motion shaft driving through the idler wheel which was also eccentrically mounted for disengagement when not in use, to the final drive digging wheel mounted on the crankshaft. Each of the three sets of forks was fitted with six hardened steel tynes, which were given an oscillating and scooping motion by the combined action of the crank and the radius links attached to the engine frame. A woodcut engraving of the engine, appearing in the *Engineer* in 1886 is reproduced in Fig 68.

Engine No 1248 was originally ordered by the Marquis de la Laguma for use on his estates in Spain, but for some unknown reason the order was frustrated and the engine went to the Waghausel sugar estate in southern Germany, where on December 4th 1886, it was demonstrated before the Grand Duke of Baden. We learn from the company's records that in 1890 it was returned to Thetford and that after removal of the digging gear the engine was resold as an ordinary 4 NHP traction engine to a Devonshire farmer. The second Proctor digging engine, No 1272, supplied originally to a customer in the Isle of Wight, was similarly returned to the works in 1892 and again the digging gear was removed. After extensive rebuilding, including the fitting of single crank compound

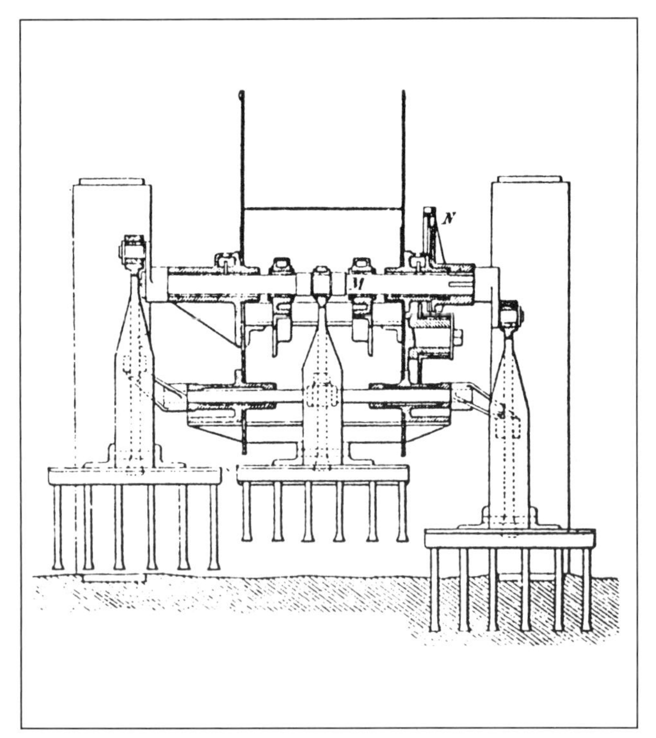

Fig 67 Frederick Burrell's & Frank Proctor's digging machine as shown in patent specification No 9059 of 1886.

cylinders, the engine went for a brief period to the East Anglian drainage contractors, Edward Mornement, and then passed to a succession of Cornish farmers. Perusing the company's records it is interesting to note the number of instances in which the original buyer returned his engine to the works, and one wonders what commercial arrangements were made in such circumstances. The implications to be drawn from the records are that Charles Burrell always went to extremes in his efforts to satisfy his customers.

In 1887 a slightly enlarged version of these double geared engines was introduced. The cylinder was increased to 7½ ins dia × 9 ins stroke and the engines were rated 5 NHP.

'R' TYPE 5 NHP DOUBLE-GEARED, UNSPRUNG TRACTION ENGINES

No	Built	No	Built
No 1314	Built 1887	No 1502	Built 1890
1322	" 1888	1543	" 1891
1325	" 1888	1941	" 1896

A larger type R64 boiler was fitted, but the working pressure was reduced from 150 PSI to 140 PSI. The grate area was 4.0 sq ft and the total heating surface was 108 sq ft. The first three had Lowmoor iron fireboxes and the last three were fitted with steel boxes. The transmission shafting and gear ratios were basically as the 4 NHP engines, but the hind wheels were increased by 1½ ins dia. Screw-down hand brakes operated on the flywheel side main spur ring. All six engines went to customers in the West Country.

A seventh 5 NHP engine, No 1336, was built in 1888 and fitted with a Proctor Digger. Unlike its contemporaries the cylinder size was reduced to 7¼ ins dia × 9 ins stroke and it was fitted with single drive gearing on the hind axle, the differential being incorporated on the second motion shaft. The engine was supplied new to a Dorset farmer, but in 1896 it passed to James Graven & sons of Ely who were secondhand dealers in traction engines. They removed the digging gear and sold the engine to the Caterham Traction Company in Surrey for general haulage duties.

Jumping ahead of our story by over 20 years, Charles Burrell produced a neat little 5 NHP unsprung double-geared single crank compound traction engine, No 3092 for a Leicester farmer which became known as the 'Irish' type. In 1911 the works received orders for two similar, but single cylinder versions of the engine from Limerick County Council for the use of the Highways Department. Limerick became good customers and purchased a total of 10 engines of various types over the next 13 years. Later in 1913 the original order was repeated.

'IRISH' TYPE 5 NHP SINGLE CYLINDER, UNSPRUNG DOUBLE-GEARED ENGINE

No	Built	No	Built
No 3344	Built 1911	No 3565	Built 1914
3345	" 1911	3566	" 1914

The engines which weighed only 7.5 tons were painted emerald green with red wheels and had motion side plates and 3 ft 3 ins dia solid flywheels. The boilers and fireboxes were both by now constructed of steel and pressed to 200 PSI. They were fitted with two injectors and Pickering type governors and were fitted with special valves for operating steam driven rock drills. They had two-speed gearing (22.5 to 1 and 13.2 to 1) the compensating gear and brakes were mounted on the intermediate motion shaft and the hind wheels were 5 ft 0 ins dia × 14 ins wide.

We must now consider the remaining 6, 7 & 8 NHP engines built in the period under review. The type T68 boiler was introduced in 1886 and twenty-seven 6 NHP engines were built in the years to 1893 and a further nine engines were subsequently built with the type T194 boiler having the firebox outer side plates extended upwards to form hornplates to accommodate the crankshaft bearings and transmission shafts.

Fig 68 The 4 NHP 'R' type SC traction engine of 1886 as depicted by the 'Engineer' fitted with Proctor's digger.

Fig 69 No 3344 5 NHP SC traction engine, one of 10 Burrell engines supplied to Limerick County Council.

Fig 70 No 1222 6 NHP SC single drive unsprung crane traction engine built in 1887. St Nicholas Works yard engine 1887–1895.

'T' TYPE 6 NHP SINGLE DRIVE, UNSPRUNG TRACTION ENGINE WITH T68 BOILER

No 1221 Built 1886	No 1288 Built 1887	No 1401 Built 1889	No 1596 Built 1892
1222 ” 1887	1307 ” 1888	1435 ” 1889	1601 ” 1892
1251 ” 1886	1310 ” 1888	1482 ” 1890	1620 ” 1892
1261 ” 1887	1311 ” 1888	1508 ” 1890	1641 ” 1892
1267 ” 1887	1349 ” 1888	1514 ” 1891	1643 ” 1892
1285 ” 1887	1362 ” 1888	1531 ” 1891	1690 ” 1893
1286 ” 1887	1378 ” 1889	1555 ” 1891	

Fig 71 No 1840 6 NHP 'T' type SC single drive unsprung traction engine purchased new at the 1895 Bath & West Show by Mr W C Mitchell of Merriot, Somerset.

The majority had steel fireboxes which were then coming into general use following the pioneering work done at the Steam Plough Works by David Greig and Max Eyth in the period 1868–1879. Their work culminated in an important paper given before the Institution of Mechanical Engineers in June 1879. They proposed the substitution of wrought iron plates by mild steel for locomotive type boiler shells. British and German steel manufacturers were now able to offer a homogeneous rolled material, free from laminations and having a superior tensile strength and for fireboxes they recommended special ductile steels having a high percentage elongation. The T68 boiler was pressed to 140 PSI, the grate area was 4.5 sq ft and the total heating surface 126.4 sq ft.

Most engines had 5 ft 7½ ins dia × 16 ins wide hind wheels and two-speed gearing having ratios 23.6 to 1 and 10.9 to 1. All were fitted with cross-arm type governors and type T91 boiler feed pumps but none were fitted with injectors. No 1222 had the Burrell-Kircaldy patent water heater and several were provided with the now somewhat dated lock-up type Salter's safety valve mounted on top of the cylinder dome.

No 1221 was exhibited at the 1886 Royal Show held in Norwich, fitted with a front axle mounted crane jib, the drive being through a bevel wheel on the end of the crankshaft and worm drive on the crane drum, having a 14 to 1 gear ratio. Immediately after the show the crane gear and jib were removed and fitted to No 1386 an 8 NHP SCC traction engine which was exported to France. The second crane engine in this batch No 1222 served for eight years as the works crane engine, then the crane gear and jib were transferred to No 1876, a 10 NHP SCC road locomotive which remained the works crane engine for many years.

The nine type 6T single drive unsprung engines with the type T194 boiler incorporating hornplates were as follows. Thereafter upon the expiration of Aveling's patent their use became standard on all Thetford engine production.

'T' TYPE 6 NHP SINGLE DRIVE UNSPRUNG TRACTION ENGINES WITH HORNPLATES

No		Built	No		Built
No 1714	Built	1893	No 1851	Built	1895
1731	"	1894	1866	"	1896
1759	"	1894	1951	"	1896
1811	"	1894	2016	"	1897
1840	"	1895			

They conformed generally with their predecessors, some being fitted with the increasingly popular American designed Penberthy injector. All were originally fitted with Burrell's cross-arm governor but most were later exchanged for the American Pickering type patented by R H Pascall of Portland, Connecticut in the early years of the 20th century.

Generally these engines were purchased by farmers and agricultural contractors for driving threshing machines, straw elevators and general duties on the farm in scattered locations throughout the United Kingdom. Fig 71 shows engine No 1840 hauling a Burrell threshing machine and straw elevator. The outfit was purchased by W C Mitchell of Merriott in Somerset at the 1895 Bath & West Show. The unusual spectacle plate and the arrangement of the hornplates will be noted. Fig 73 depicts a delightfully typical Edwardian scene, showing one of these engines providing transport for the Annual Sunday School Outing, in the village of Stanton, near Bury St Edmunds.

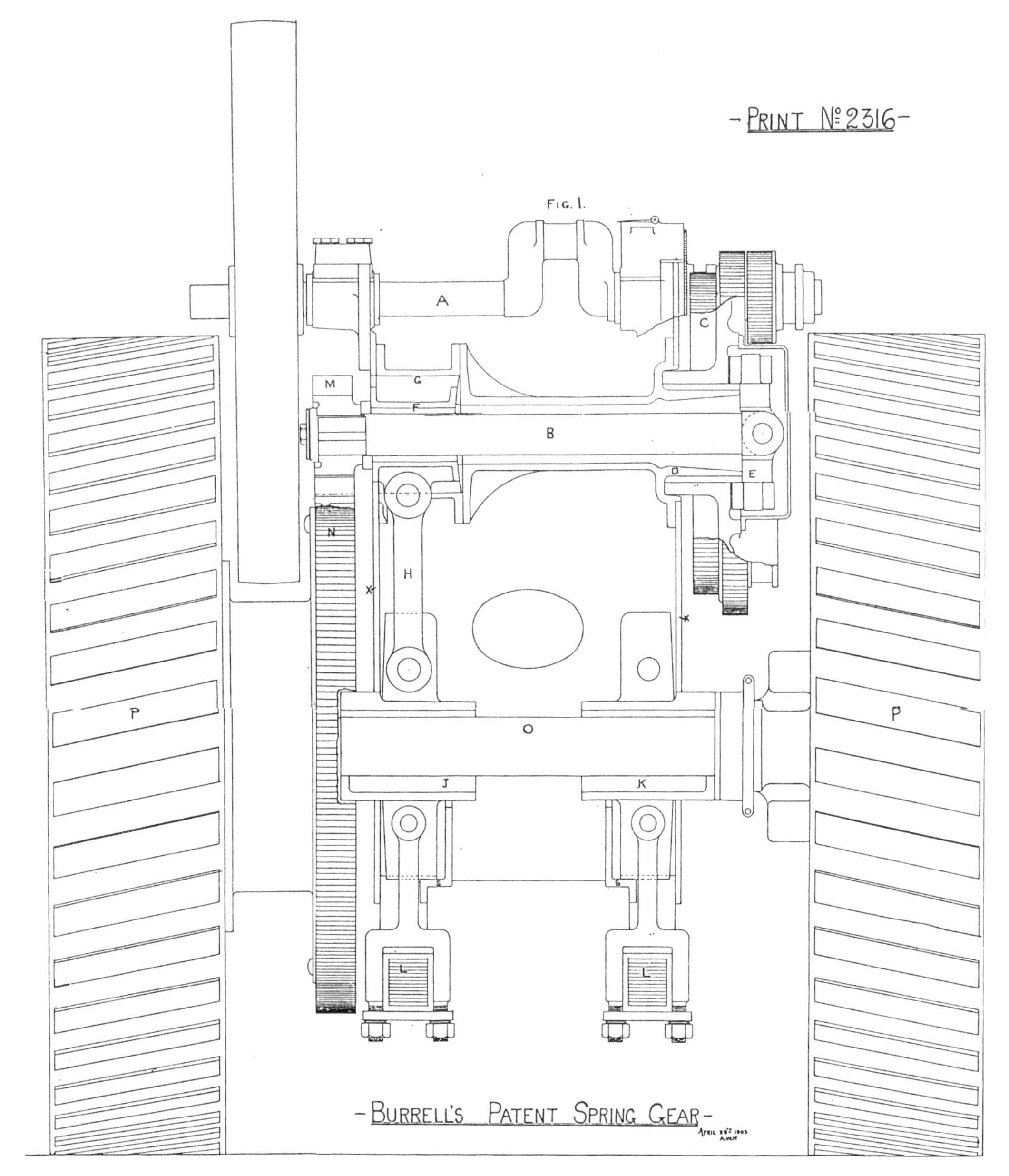

Fig 72 Layout of the hind axle spring gear described in Frederick Burrell's patent No 5747 of 1887.

In 1888 the spring mounted 6 NHP single cylinder single drive traction engine was introduced and apart from this batch of engines built in the period 1888 to 1906 all subsequent 6 NHP engines, whether sprung or unsprung, had double-geared drive to the hind axle.

'T' TYPE 6 NHP SINGLE CYLINDER, SINGLE DRIVE SPRING-MOUNTED ENGINES

No	Built	No	Built
No 1335	Built 1888	No 1561	Built 1891
1351	" 1888	1567	" 1891
1395	" 1889	1604	" 1892
1432	" 1889	1705	" 1893
1471	" 1890	1863	" 1895
1489	" 1890	1954	" 1896
1509	" 1890	2002	" 1897
1545	" 1991	2848	" 1906

The main constraint upon the introduction of spring gear on the hind axle of geared traction engines had always been the difficulty of maintaining the gear teeth on the transmission shafts in correct mesh as the axle rose and fell under the influence of the springs. In April 1887 Frederick Burrell filed his famous patent No 5747 entitled 'Improvements in Traction and Tramway Engines', which described a very efficient means of overcoming the problem. The first engine to be publicly exhibited incorporating this feature was in fact a 7 NHP engine, No 1309, which appeared at the Royal Show held in Newcastle in 1887, and the general layout of the system is shown in Fig 72. It will be noted that the crankshaft A communicates its motion to the intermediate shaft B by means of the two-speed pinions engaging with the spur wheel C which rotates on the fixed steel tube D. The countershaft B is connected to the spur wheel C through the universal joint E. The other end of the countershaft is

Fig 73 A Sturgeon's of Stanton SC Burrell providing transport for the local Sunday School outing.

carried in the bearing F and is free to move up and down in the box G. A vertical link H connects the bearing F to the hind axle box J, which is also free to slide up and down in hornblocks S, such that both the hind axle and the flywheel end of the countershaft rise and fall together upon the springs L. Originally volute springs were employed, but later these were substitued for other types. It will be seen from the drawing that not only did the arrangement ensure the maintenance of the correct pitch circles on the spur wheel driving gear, but the rise and fall of the axle did not interfere with the correct action of the differential gear, nor was the action of the springs influenced by the transmission of the engine power through the gearing.

Later in 1892 Frederick filed a further patent No 1572 which described improvements to patent No 5747 whereby the hind wheels of the engine could be brought closer to the hornplates. Hornplates were introduced as a standard feature in 1893 and the arrangements enabled the engines to be constructed narrower than previously. Volute type springs were generally replaced by the helical type.

Later somewhat similar arrangements were applied to double-geared engines, but the rise and fall of the engine on the springs was restricted to about ¾ ins. The long travel spring gear associated with the single drive transmission system, which had a rise and fall on the springs of approximately 1½ ins, remained popular with many users, especially the heavy haulage contractors.

The sixteen engines in this batch, the first twelve having the T68 boilder and last four having hornplates and the T194 boiler, were scattered across the kingdom from Scotland to Devonshire and from Wales to East Anglia. No 1545 was one of seventeen Burrell engines owned by John Charlton & Sons, the Dumfries contractors and flour millers. At various times they had 6, 7 and 8 NHP traction engines, both single cylinder and compound, as well as three one-man operation 5-ton tractors, and they were always treated by the works as especially important customers.

A total of thirty-one 6 NHP single cylinder double geared unsprung GP traction engines were built in the period 1897 to 1914. They all had 8 ins dia × 10 ins stroke solid end cylinders in which the steam was passed through the motion bar end and under the steam chest.

All had variants of the type T194 boiler pressed to 140 PSI with chain-riveted double flange plates. Some had cross-arm governors, others Burrell's high-speed pattern and models built after 1904 were fitted with the Pickering type. The majority had Pemberthy type injectors in

6 NHP SINGLE CYLINDER, DOUBLE-GEARED UNSPRUNG GP TRACTION ENGINES

No	Built	No	Built	No	Built	No	Built
No 2046	Built 1897	No 2208	Built 1899	No 2441	Built 1901	No 2782	Built 1905
2112	" 1898	2211	" 1899	2517	" 1902	2817	" 1906
2115	" 1898	2214	" 1899	2540	" 1902	3055	" 1908
2121	" 1898	2251	" 1899	2594	" 1903	3271	" 1911
2128	" 1898	2314	" 1900	2613	" 1903	3438	" 1912
2142	" 1898	2365	" 1901	2685	" 1904	3461	" 1913
2172	" 1899	2406	" 1901	2718	" 1905	3520	" 1913
2203	" 1899	2412	" 1901	2741	" 1905		

addition to eccentric-driven boiler feed pumps, but Nos 2718 and 2782 were fitted with Moores steam pumps. This feature became popular in the early part of the 20th century, although it had a comparatively short life as injectors became more reliable. The eccentric driven boiler feed pump could only be operated when steam was admitted to the main cylinder and the engine was running, whether in gear or not. This was not always convenient and the Moore's steam pump had its own separate small cylinder for activating the pump. The pump could easily be regulated to provide the right amount of feed water when driving in heavy traffic without distracting the driver. Moreover it could operate with hotter and dirtier water than the injector. Less steam was discharged to atmosphere, it was quicker than the injector and no water was wasted; but it could not be used with the same facility for reducing the boiler pressure. Generally most drivers preferred to have both a feed pump and an injector.

Two-speed gearing (25.3 to 1 and 14.1 to 1 ratio) was fitted to all the batch except No 3438 which had three-speed gearing first introduced in 1901. The majority of hind wheels were 5 ft 7½ ins dia × 16 ins wide and the flywheels were 4 ft 4 ins dia × 6 ins wide, the engines

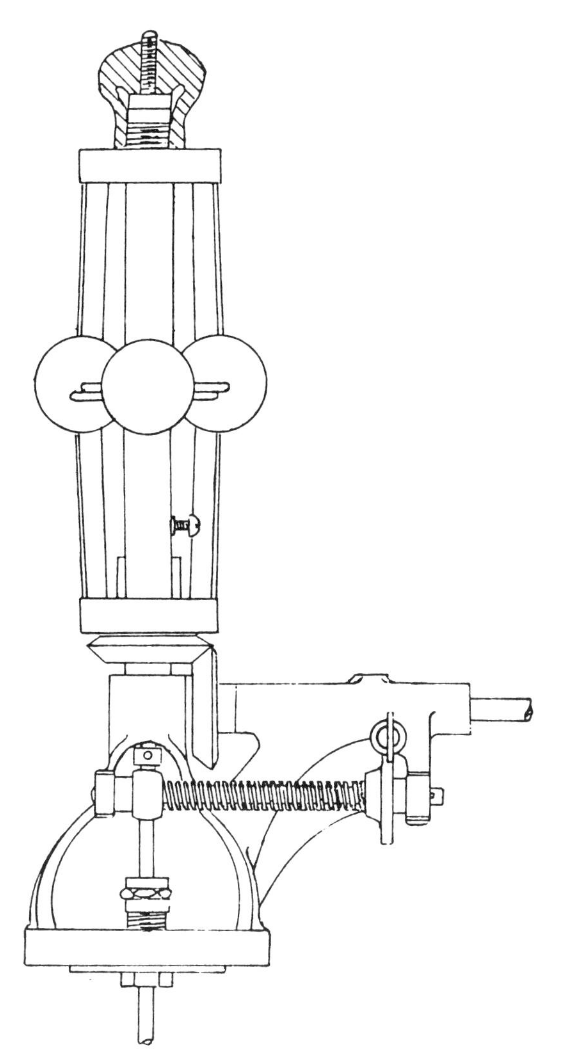

Fig 74 Layout of the American Pickering governor extensively used by Charles Burrell after 1903.

having an overall width across the hind wheels of 6 ft 10½ ins. The normal engine speed for threshing, the speed at which the governors were set, was 165 RPM.

A batch of five similar 6 NHP double-geared engines were built in the period 1905–1916, but all were spring mounted on the hind axle only.

6 NHP SINGLE CYLINDER SPRING-MOUNTED, DOUBLE-GEARED GP TRACTION ENGINES

No	Built	No	Built
No 2774	1905	No 3536	1913
2775	1905	3730	1916
3042	1908		

Engine Nos 2774 and 2775 went to New Zealand customers through the Reid & Gray agency fitted with Moore's steam feed pumps, BP 'F' injectors and Pickering governors. Large square headlamps were fitted on the top of the smokebox, a characteristic feature of engines sold in New Zealand.

Production of the 7 NHP single cylinder GP traction engine continued concurrently with their smaller 6 NHP counterparts and a total of 33 single drive unsprung engines were built in the period 1881–1887 with 8½ ins dia × 10 stroke cylinders.

Half the batch went to farmers in East Anglia; three went to Scotland; No 914 went to New Zealand and the remainder were scattered as far afield as Lancashire in the north, Devonshire in the West Country and Sussex in the south.

'7T' TYPE 7 NHP SINGLE DRIVE UNSPRUNG TRACTION ENGINE

No	Built	No	Built
No 908	1881	No 1159	1885
909	1881	1179	1885
910	1881	1180	1885
912	1881	1181	1885
913	1881	1200	1885
914	1882	1201	1886
979	1883	1202	1886
980	1883	1225	1886
1080	1883	1229	1886
1086	1884	1236	1886
1087	1884	1243	1886
1088	1884	1246	1886
1126	1884	1250	1886
1127	1884	1268	1887
1128	1885	1275	1887
1157	1885	1278	1887
1158	1885		

These were followed by a batch of 30 with enlarged cylinders measuring 8½ ins dia × 12 ins stroke. With the availability of steel boilers having increased working pressures, farmers were finding the 7 NHP engine could provide adequate power for driving their threshing machines whereas previously they had more or less automatically specified a 8 NHP engine for threshing and general farm duties. Also, competition from Burrell's leading competitors necessitated that their engines produced a greater I.H.P., especially for overseas markets.

'T' TYPE 7 NHP SINGLE DRIVE UNSPRUNG TRACTION ENGINE

No 1297 Built 1887	No 1422 Built 1889	No 1560 Built 1891	No 1630 Built 1892
1312 ” 1888	1491 ” 1890	1564 ” 1891	1640 ” 1892
1317 ” 1888	1499 ” 1890	1570 ” 1891	1649 ” 1892
1321 ” 1888	1511 ” 1890	1580 ” 1891	1660 ” 1892
1350 ” 1888	1519 ” 1891	1595 ” 1892	1691 ” 1893
1363 ” 1888	1527 ” 1891	1605 ” 1892	1703 ” 1893
1367 ” 1888	1533 ” 1891	1610 ” 1892	1704 ” 1893
1383 ” 1889	1557 ” 1891		

The boilers were pressed to 140 PSI and had grate areas of 4.9 sq ft and a total heating surface of 143 sq ft. The 33 2¼ ins dia smoke tubes were generally 5 ft 8 ins long. All had two-speed gearing, but in other respects there were many detailed variations. The introduction of the various new innovations patented in the 1870s and 1880s followed very much the pattern of the 6 NHP engines. Landore-Siemens steel fireboxes were introduced in 1886. Ramsbottom safety valves were fitted from 1881, but some engines continued to use the old Salter's lock-up safety valve. Some boilers were fitted with manholes, some had equilibrium throttle valves, others the old butterfly type throttle valve. Initially many engines were fitted with Burrell's patent high-speed governor, but in most cases these were replaced. No 908 was fitted originally with spring wheels but these were removed a year later.

Single drive 7 NHP engines built after 1893 had Aveling type hornplates. The type T192 140 PSI boiler was used having an enlarged grate area of 5.375 sq ft and the boiler barrel diameter was increased to accommodate forty-one 2 ins dia smoke tubes which were shortened in length by 7 ins. Engine No 1936 and subsequent engines were fitted with a new pattern 8½ ins dia × 12 stroke solid end cylinder.

Nos 1294 and 1300 were probably the first engines fitted with Burrell's beautifully proportioned flared copper chimney top. For reasons now unknown No 1433 was supplied with a 6 ft long chimney instead of the standard 4 ft long pattern indicating that the engine was intended to spend much of its life working as a stationary engine. Engines up to and including No 1396 had unsprung front axles, thereafter the sprung forecarriage became more or less standard practice. The road gear was as for the

Fig 75 No 1433 'Bambridge Pet' a 7 NHP SC single drive spring mounted traction as modified by Alfred Bartlett of Fordingbridge for use in the fairground during the First World War.

7 NHP SINGLE CYLINDER, SINGLE DRIVE UNSPRUNG GP TRACTION ENGINES WITH HORNPLATES

No 1762 Built 1894	No 1847 Built 1895	No 1923 Built 1896	No 1992 Built 1897
1778 ” 1894	1855 ” 1895	1925 ” 1896	2015 ” 1897
1793 ” 1894	1856 ” 1895	1936 ” 1896	2074 ” 1898
1804 ” 1894	1864 ” 1895	1970 ” 1896	2098 ” 1898
1808 ” 1894	1875 ” 1895	1976 ” 1897	2100 ” 1898
1827 ” 1895			

Concurrently with the three types of 7 NHP single drive unsprung GP traction engine listed St Nicholas Works built 28 similar sprung engines fitted with 6 ton volute type springs. Nos 1881 to 2421 were built with hornplates.

'T' TYPE 7 NHP SINGLE CYLINDER, SINGLE DRIVE, SPRING-MOUNTED TRACTION ENGINES

No 1294 Built 1887	No 1366 Built 1888	No 1453 Built 1889	No 1634 Built 1892
1300 ” 1887	1389 ” 1889	1458 ” 1889	1881 ” 1895
1309 ” 1887	1396 ” 1889	1473 ” 1890	1988 ” 1897
1330 ” 1888	1408 ” 1889	1504 ” 1890	2039 ” 1897
1331 ” 1888	1426 ” 1889	1552 ” 1891	2063 ” 1898
1332 ” 1888	1433 ” 1889	1572 ” 1891	2397 ” 1901
1355 ” 1888	1440 ” 1889	1592 ” 1892	2421 ” 1901

Fig 76 An unidentified works photograph of a 7 NHP single cylinder, double geared, 2-speed, unsprung general purpose traction engine circa 1905.

unsprung engines but the two-speed gear ratios were altered to 27.9 to 1 and 12.9 to 1. Nos 1309 and 1366 were finished as show engines and exhibited at Smithfield in 1887 and 1888 respectively and the majority of the series went to farmers, agricultural contractors and firms concerned with the haulage of agricultural produce.

No 1988 is of special interest as the first Burrell traction engine supplied to the War Office. It was a heavy engine and weighed 13 tons 15 cwt. The WD specification called for a special fusille plug in the firebox roof, a special manhole in the top of the firebox, a plate over the firedoor and an inspection gauge cock between the cylinder and the governor bracket.

Similarly, as with the 6 NHP GP traction engine, most 7 NHP engines built after 1899 had the double-geared drive to the hind axle. Forty-one such engines were built in the period 1899–1914.

The first seventeen engines had variants of the T194 boiler pressed to 140 PSI with 4.9 sq ft grates, a total heating surface of 118.0 sq ft and thirty-four 2 ins dia smoke tubes 5 ft 1 ins long. The next five engines had lengthened boilers fitted with thirty-eight 1¾ ins dia × 5 ft 8 ins long smoke tubes increasing the total heating surface to 125 sq ft. In 1907 a new design of boiler was introduced, pressed to 160 PSI and fitted with thirty-five 2 ins dia × 5 ft 8 ins long smoke tubes.

7 NHP SINGLE CYLINDER, DOUBLE-GEARED, UNSPRUNG GP TRACTION ENGINE

No	Built	No	Built	No	Built	No	Built
No 2158	Built 1899	No 2582	Built 1903	No 2918	Built 1907	No 3324	Built 1911
2159	" 1899	2598	" 1903	2951	" 1907	3326	" 1911
2197	" 1899	2614	" 1903	2953	" 1907	3332	" 1911
2298	" 1900	2664	" 1904	2963	" 1908	3391	" 1912
2313	" 1900	2673	" 1904	3068	" 1909	3405	" 1912
2402	" 1901	2743	" 1905	3111	" 1909	3422	" 1912
2507	" 1902	2751	" 1905	3154	" 1909	3427	" 1912
2509	" 1902	2772	" 1905	3208	" 1910	3491	" 1913
2525	" 1902	2784	" 1905	3231	" 1910	3503	" 1913
2567	" 1903	2820	" 1906	3310	" 1911	3607	" 1914
2581	" 1903						

Fig 77 No 3068 7 NHP single cylinder double geared unsprung traction engine of 1909.

Between 1906 and 1912 only nine spring mounted versions of the double-geared engine were produced although a further eight engines were built during and after the First World War.

7 NHP SINGLE CYLINDER, DOUBLE-GEARED, SPRUNG GP TRACTION ENGINES

No	Built		No	Built	
No 2833	Built	1906	No 3157	Built	1909
3005	"	1908	3249	"	1910
3025	"	1908	3254	"	1910
3100	"	1909	3430	"	1912
3124	"	1909			

No 2833 had the 140 PSI boiler with thirty-five 2 ins dia × 5 ft 8 ins long tubes and the remainder of the batch had 160 PSi boilers with the firebox plates thickened to $\frac{7}{16}$ ins. As on all other types and sizes of Burrell engine a multitude of variations were incorporated in these engines in accordance with individual customers' requirements. Most had 6 ft 0 ins dia hind wheels × 16 ins or 18 ins wide. The two-speed gear ratios were 24.4 to 1 and 13.6 to 1 making them fast engines on the road. Some had solid flywheels but the majority were spoked. Some later models had asbestos-lagged boilers and solid drawn steel smoke tubes were introduced in 1910.

We now come to Burrell's famous type 'C' 8 NHP single cylinder traction engine introduced in 1881. More 8 NHP single cylinder engines were built than any other type or size of Thetford built general purpose traction engine. Their evolution from the first generation of 8 NHP geared engines followed closely that of the 6 and 7 NHP engines already described, the class 'C' being entirely contemporaneous with the smaller class 'T' engines. These engines soon became well known and respected by agriculturists in many parts of the world and the demand for them continued long after the introduction of compounding, especially in the Antipodes.

CLASS 'C' 8 NHP SINGLE CYLINDER, SINGLE DRIVE UNSPRUNG TRACTION ENGINE

No	Built		No	Built		No	Built		No	Built	
No 896	Built	1881	No 973	Built	1882	No 1083	Built	1884	No 1176	Built	1885
897	"	1881	974	"	1882	1084	"	1884	1177	"	1885
901	"	1881	1000	"	1882	1085	"	1884	1178	"	1886
902	"	1881	1003	"	1882	1102	"	1884	1212	"	1886
903	"	1881	1004	"	1883	1103	"	1885	1216	"	1886
915	"	1881	1005	"	1883	1104	"	1885	1223	"	1886
916	"	1881	1007	"	1883	1133	"	1885	1230	"	1886
917	"	1882	1008	"	1883	1134	"	1885	1240	"	1886
918	"	1882	1027	"	1883	1135	"	1885			

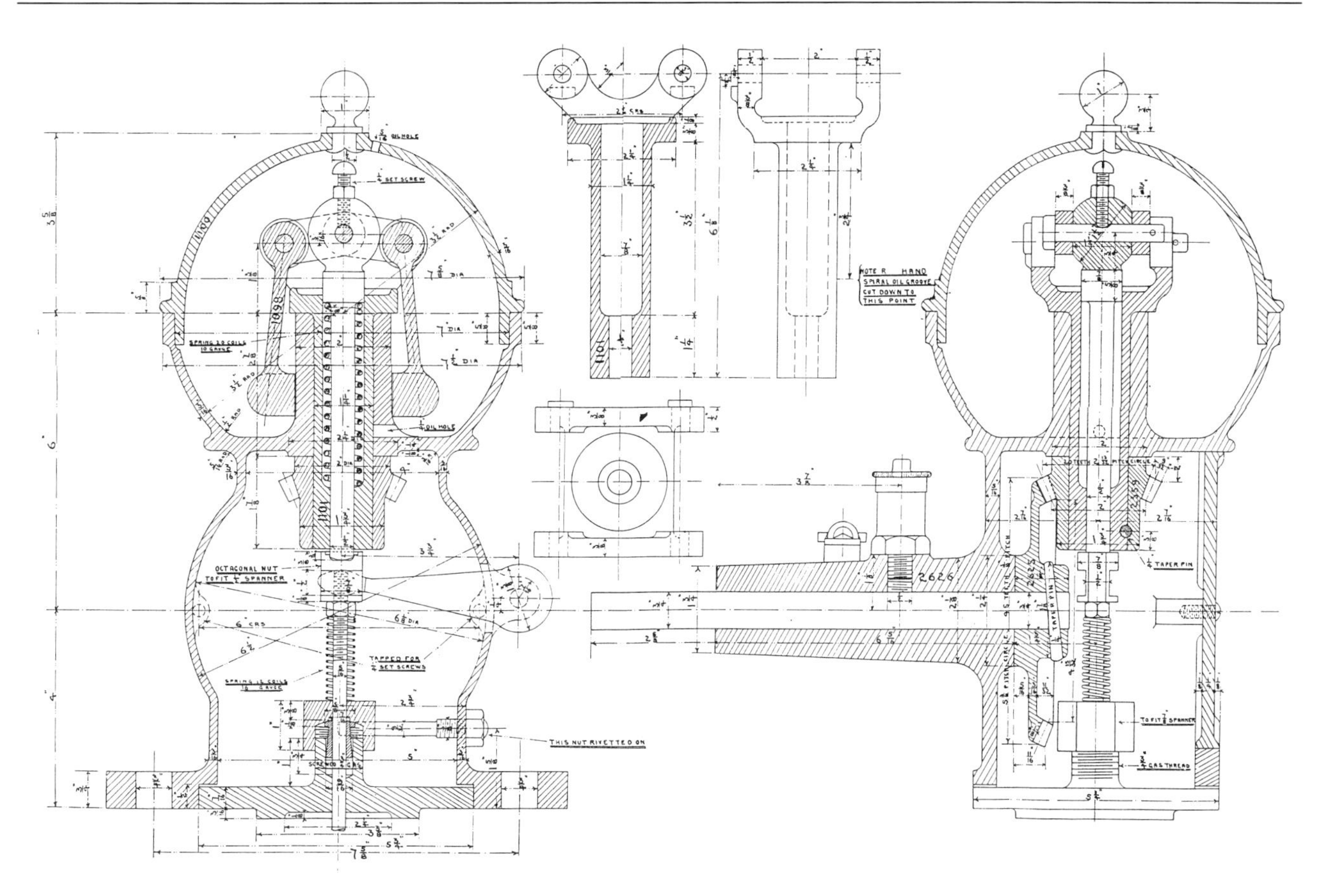

Fig 78 Frederick Burrell's totally enclosed dust proof centrifugal governor. In theory a good idea, but disappointing in practice and soon discarded.

The various innovations introduced in the 1870s, the subject of patents filed by Charles, Robert and Frederick Burrell and Robert Edwards were progressively incorporated in these engines all of which had 9 ins dia × 12 ins stroke cylinders. The first five engines had the type C1 short smoke tube boiler pressed to 120 PSI, having a grate area of 4.2 sq ft and a total heating surface of 143 sq ft. Subsequent engines had the type C60 boiler with 5 ft 8 ins long smoke tubes which increased the grate area to 5.375 sq ft and the total heating surface to 151 sq ft. The boiler working pressure in the last five engines was increased to 140 PSI. Steel fireboxes were installed in No 902 and all subsequent engines in the series, which individually continued to incorporate a host of lesser variations specified by the customer such as Salter lock-up safety valves, suet cylinder lubricators and blowers, which were not yet fitted as standard equipment.

After an experimental period, the three shaft unsprung transmission system with two-speed gearing having gear ratios of 24.0 to 1 and 13.0 to 1 became standard. Initially the hind wheels were 5 ft 7½ ins dia × 16 ins or 18 ins wide. No 1004 onwards were fitted with stronger road wheels and the wheel size was increased to 6 ft 0 ins dia. All winding drums were supplied with 100 yds of best quality wire rope and generally the screw-down brake acted on the left hand driving disc, although the earlier models had the brake on the left hand axle. The spoked flywheels were 4 ft 6 ins dia × 6 ins wide and the tender water tank carried 140 gallons. Belly tanks increasing the water carrying capacity to 230 gallons were an optional extra. Nos 896 to 1104 were fitted with high-speed governors, thereafter the remainder of this series were fitted with Frederick Burrell's own design of totally enclosed high-speed governor. These proved unsatisfactory and were later replaced with the well proven cross-arm pattern. The governors were set to give an engine speed 140 RPM for working on the belt. None of this series were fitted with injectors, all having the type C52 boiler feed pumps. Generally the engines weighed 9 ton 17 cwt in working order.

Nos 916, 1004 and 1102 were prepared as show engines and exhibited at Smithfield in 1881, 1882 and 1884 respectively. The majority of the engines went to farmers in East Anglia and the southern counties, but No 916, supplied to Conyer & Davidson of Dunedin in New Zealand's South Island, marked a milestone in the firm's history. It was the first of eighty-four 8 NHP GP traction engines shipped to New Zealand customers. Concurrently a 7 NHP single cylinder engine went to J Shortt in Auckland. Nos 1176, 1177 and 1230 also went to New Zealand customers and the latter was the first Thetford built engine supplied through the highly successful Reid & Gray agency with offices in Dunedin. In total this agency sold 192 Burrell engines of all types. Initially engines were shipped through the forwarding agents McEwan & Company of London, but later, from 1904, the business was transferred to P Gardiner & Company. Throughout the thirty years to the outbreak of war in 1914 there was intense competition between Burrells, J & H McLaren of Leeds and Marshalls of Gainsborough. F A Manning,

James Marshall's brother-in-law, established his successful agency in Dunedin and in the same period supplied 155 Marshall engines and an even greater number of Marshall threshing machines to New Zealand customers. McLaren are reputed to have supplied 165 engines to this market. In view of the importance of the market it is somewhat extraordinary that there is no record of any member of the Burrell family ever visiting the Antipodes.

The great majority of 8 NHP single cylinder GP traction engines built after 1886 were double-geared, only five being built with unsprung single drive gearing. No 1304 described in the works registers as a 7/8 NHP single-drive engine was built in October 1887 with the 'T' type cylinder bored out to 9 ins dia × 10 ins stroke, the type T116 boiler pressed to 160 PSI having forty-one 2 ins dia × 5 ft 8 ins long smoke tubes and 5 ft 9½ ins dia hind wheels. It was supplied new to a Yorkshire agriculturist.

The remaining four single-drive engines were as follows.

Fig 79 A typical 8 NHP SC double geared unsprung GP traction engine built between 1886 and 1893 as exhibited at RASE Windsor in 1889.

LATER 8 NHP SINGLE CYLINDER, SINGLE DRIVE UNSPRUNG TRACTION ENGINE

No	Built	No	Built
No 1998	Built 1897	No 2443	Built 1901
2169	„ 1899	2469	„ 1902

No 2169 was supplied new to Barnes & Sons, saw millers and timber hauliers of Swindon in Wiltshire who at various times owned eight Burrell engines.

From 1886 the type 'C' engines were predominantly double-geared.

These engines were fitted with a redesigned cylinder having a cast iron liner in the bore giving a finished size 9 ins dia × 12 ins stroke. The earlier models had the type C224 boiler pressed to 140 PSI and some later models had the working pressure increased to 175 PSI, but all had the same grate area and heating surface as their single drive counterparts. After 1888 the majority were fitted with steel fireboxes. The compensating gear was mounted on the countershaft and the winding drum was on the hind axle. The majority had two-speed gearing with ratios 24 to 1 and 13 to 1 and 6 ft 0 ins dia hind wheels. Cross-arm type governors were fitted and Greshams No 4 injectors were supplied when the customer called for an injector in addition to the standard boiler feed pump. Experimentally a two-speed governor was fitted to No 1274. No 1273 was fitted with Aveling & Porter's spring wheels in which the outer ends of the flat spokes were riveted to an inner tyre which in turn was connected to the wheel tyre by a series of coil springs. This arrangement not only carried the weight of the wheel but provided a form of cushioned drive which assisted the engine to attain its maximum tractive effort before wheel slip occurred. This engine was one of the few Burrell engines fitted with a special steam water lift which by means of a butterfly valve enabled the water being lifted to be diverted from the engine belly tank to an external container such as an independant water cart. No 1501 which was supplied to the order of W Brooks of Northwich in Cheshire was fitted with a special 10 ins dia flange plate on the gear side end of the crankshaft. To this was added a 15 ins long extension shaft presumably intended for mounting an additional pulley wheel for driving stationary machinery.

Nos 1549 and 1611 were built in accordance with then current German boiler regulations and were fitted with a baffle plate in the smokebox to protect the top of the tube

'C' TYPE 8 NHP SINGLE CYLINDER, DOUBLE-GEARED UNSPRUNG TRACTION ENGINE

No	Built	No	Built	No	Built	No	Built
No 1244	Built 1886	No 1320	Built 1888	No 1490	Built 1890	No 1587	Built 1892
1253	„ 1887	1329	„ 1888	1501	„ 1890	1594	„ 1892
1266	„ 1887	1333	„ 1888	1505	„ 1890	1602	„ 1892
1273	„ 1887	1340	„ 1888	1512	„ 1890	1611	„ 1892
1274	„ 1887	1361	„ 1888	1518	„ 1890	1614	„ 1892
1287	„ 1887	1421	„ 1889	1524	„ 1891	1615	„ 1892
1292	„ 1887	1427	„ 1889	1544	„ 1891	1636	„ 1892
1293	„ 1887	1438	„ 1889	1549	„ 1891	1648	„ 1892
1295	„ 1887	1443	„ 1889	1558	„ 1891	1658	„ 1892
1298	„ 1888	1446	„ 1889	1563	„ 1891	1686	„ 1893
1299	„ 1888	1450	„ 1889	1566	„ 1891	1694	„ 1893
1318	„ 1888	1461	„ 1890	1576	„ 1891	1712	„ 1893
1319	„ 1888						

Fig 80 No 1451 'Monarch' an 8 NHP SC single drive spring mounted traction engine. The first Burrell engine supplied direct to a travelling showman in 1889. Shown hauling Charles Byett's set of Gallopers.

plate as well as a wire mesh spark arrester. The cast iron clack box for the injector feed was fitted with a screw-down valve and Salter's lock-up type safety valves with a brass cage were fitted on the cylinder dome. A brass plate was attached to the cannon bracket stating the boiler working pressure in atmospheres. It is believed these engines were supplied to German customers through the Franz Schulte agency in Magdeburg.

Nearly half this batch of engines went to farmers and agricultural contractors in East Anglia and the southern counties and a further 10 engines went to New Zealand customers through the Reid & Gray agency. The majority were used for driving threshing drums as their main duty. It is unfortunte that no records have survived giving details of Burrell's threshing machine production, although it is known that at least three examples have survived in preservation. No 1587 went to a French customer and No 1694 went to the Stirling Steam Threshing Company who were well known contractors in the area in the 1890s and owned three Burrell engines.

No 1287 had an interesting career. Originally it was supplied to William Shipley, an agricultural contractor of Middleton-on-the-Wolds near Great Driffold in East Yorkshire. Shipley eventually gave up farming and travelled the fairgrounds with a set of three-abreast gallopers. Later the engine was converted to a traction centre engine by extending upwards the outer side plates of the firebox to carry a turret supporting the geared drive and top motion of the roundabout, thereby replacing the conventional heavy centre truck. The work was completed by Reynolds & King, the Leeds manufacturers of fairground rides having had earlier experience of an engine which was produced for them by John Fowler in 1886. No 1287 was then acquired by Morley Brothers of Castleford in Yorkshire who travelled a fine set of Galloping Horses lit by a mass of naphtha flare lamps which produced brilliant star-shaped lights. The engine survived until 1933 latterly driving Morley's Chair-O-Planes.

Concurrently with the type 'C' double-geared unsprung engines built in the period 1886–1893, St Nicholas Works built 16 single drive spring-mounted engines with volute type springs on the hind axle.

CLASS 'C' 8 NHP SINGLE CYLINDER, SINGLE DRIVE, SPRING-MOUNTED TRACTION ENGINE

No	Built		No	Built	
No 1341	Built	1888	No 1522	Built	1891
1352	»	1888	1538	»	1891
1411	»	1889	1556	»	1891
1428	»	1889	1574	»	1891
1436	»	1889	1606	»	1892
1451	»	1889	1635	»	1892
1479	»	1890	1642	»	1892
1483	»	1890	1659	»	1892

Historically the most important engine in this series was No 1451 because it was the first Thetford built engine to be supplied new to a travelling showman. The three brothers, Jacob, John and Henry Studt were pioneer users of the larger types of steam-driven fairground machinery and Jacob acquired No 1451 which he named 'Monarch' for hauling a set of Galloping Horses. Shortly afterwards he purchased an early set of the heavy Gondola Switchback ride and for many years he was a household name in South Wales, attending annually all the great fairs in the province. Mechanically 'Monarch' was a standard general purpose engine but it was specially fitted with a half-length canopy with ornamental sideboards, a flared, polished copper chimney top and brass axle caps. It was the precursor of the showman's type engine and their proud owners were soon vying with each other in their search for additional ornamentation, typified by twisted brass canopy supports, brass stars and rings and beautifully painted and lined out bodywork. Within a decade Travelling Showmen became a very important source of business for Charles Burrell. The fairground remained a bastion of steam power for some time after the internal combustion engine tractor took over on the farm and the petrol and diesel engine lorry dominated haulage on the public roads.

Eight engines in the series went to agriculturists in the southern counties and four went to East Anglian farmers. No 1522 went to Earl Cadogan who then resided at Culford Hall near Bury St Edmunds and No 1574 went to R Burrell, one of the Fornham Burrells who lived at Westley, near Bury St Edmunds. Trading as Burrell Bros they acquired four Thetford built engines at various times for their agricultural business.In 1894 the class 'C' designation was dropped and 133 8 NHP double-geared unsprung GP traction engines with hornplates were built in the 20 years to the outbreak of war.

This type of engine might well, with justification, have been called the New Zealand class, for of the 133 engines listed below, no less than 79 went to New Zealand customers and for ease of identification they are marked with an asterisk in the preceding table.

With two exceptions Nos 1766 to 2120 inclusive had the type C379 boiler pressed to 140 PSI. The exceptions were Nos 2032 and 2034 which were wood-burners having enlarged grates and 6 ft 0 ins long smoke tubes. Engines from No 2133 to No 2425 inclusive had the same C379 boiler but the working pressure was increased to 160 PSI by the use of chain riveting and 1 ins dia Whitworth thread stays. All the C379 boilers had a grate area of 5.375 sq ft and total heating surface of 151.0 sq ft. The forty-one 2 ins dia smoke tubes were 5 ft 8 ins long. In 1902 the works reverted to 140 PSI boilers but from 1907 pressures were again progressively increased to 160, 180 and finally 200 PSI. The latter all had six steel stay tubes.

The C379 boiler was superceded in 1902 and No 2530 and all subsequent engines were fitted with one of three alternative boilers having grate areas of 5.375 sq ft, 6.0 sq ft or 6.6 sq ft. These options were introduced primarily because of severe competition from Marshalls of Gainsborough and several orders received at the works from New Zealand customers had been cancelled. This situation accounts for engines originally allocated Nos 2672 and 2691 being renumbered Nos 2755 and 2749

8 NHP SINGLE CYLINDER DOUBLE-GEARED UNSPRUNG GP TRACTION ENGINES

No 1766	Built	1894*	No 2120	Built	1898*	No 2501	Built	1902*	No 3001	Built	1908
1779	"	1894*	2133	"	1898	2502	"	1902*	3011	"	1908
1781	"	1894	2135	"	1898*	2503	"	1902*	3032	"	1908
1791	"	1894	2136	"	1898*	2530	"	1902	3039	"	1908
1797	"	1894	2140	"	1898*	2543	"	1902	3049	"	1908*
1807	"	1894	2153	"	1898	2554	"	1903	3051	"	1908*
1809	"	1894	2183	"	1899	2585	"	1903	3059	"	1908*
1826	"	1895	2186	"	1899	2608	"	1903*	3079	"	1909*
1833	"	1895*	2201	"	1899*	2610	"	1903*	3106	"	1909
1834	"	1895*	2202	"	1899*	2620	"	1903*	3114	"	1909
1838	"	1895*	2207	"	1899*	2627	"	1903*	3121	"	1909
1873	"	1895	2215	"	1899*	2629	"	1903*	3148	"	1909*
1882	"	1895	2216	"	1899*	2632	"	1903*	3151	"	1909*
1899	"	1896	2226	"	1899	2634	"	1903	3152	"	1909*
1917	"	1896*	2231	"	1899	2637	"	1903*	3153	"	1909*
1918	"	1896*	2260	"	1900*	2669	"	1904	3160	"	1909*
1920	"	1896*	2276	"	1900*	2694	"	1904*	3188	"	1910
1924	"	1896*	2277	"	1900*	2695	"	1904*	3235	"	1910*
1940	"	1896	2278	"	1900*	2745	"	1905	3237	"	1910*
1944	"	1896*	2295	"	1900*	2749	"	1907	3248	"	1910*
1946	"	1896	2296	"	1900*	2755	"	1905	3256	"	1910*
1956	"	1896	2297	"	1900*	2762	"	1905*	3259	"	1910*
2012	"	1897*	2306	"	1900	2763	"	1905	3260	"	1910*
2013	"	1897*	2331	"	1900*	2810	"	1906	3309	"	1911
2014	"	1897*	2332	"	1900*	2822	"	1906*	3316	"	1911*
2026	"	1897	2366	"	1901	2835	"	1906*	3329	"	1911*
2032	"	1897	2392	"	1901*	2840	"	1906*	3407	"	1912*
2034	"	1897*	2393	"	1901*	2855	"	1906	3410	"	1912*
2036	"	1897	2394	"	1901*	2910	"	1907	3467	"	1913
2043	"	1897*	2411	"	1901*	2926	"	1907	3511	"	1913*
2051	"	1897	2425	"	1901	2938	"	1907*	3528	"	1913
2093	"	1898	2482	"	1902*	2948	"	1907	3558	"	1914*
2106	"	1898	2485	"	1902	2956	"	1907*	3598	"	1914*
2114	"	1898*									

* Engines sold to New Zealand customers.

Fig 81 No 748 as rebuilt as a geared GP traction engine seen hauling a Robey semi-portable engine for the Bardon Road Saw Mills.

respectively when resold to UK customers. No 2694, the first of twenty-four engines built with 6.6 sq ft grates and 6 ft 2 ins long smoke tubes, all of which went to New Zealand, had a total heating surface of 162 sq ft. Nos 2620 and 2637 were fitted with special arched roof fireboxes and the barrel was rolled from a single plate. These became known in the works as Stevens boilers. No 2745 had an 11 ins × 14 ins manhole on the right-hand side of the boiler which was unusual on Burrell engines and, as far as has been traced, No 3011 was the first Burrell traction engine to be fitted with cast steel girder roof stay bars, which were then just coming into vogue. Generally after 1909 most engines in this series had 7/16 ins thick firebox plates. All engines built between 1903 and 1914 had a large gap in the box bracket which became a characteristic feature of Burrell engines built in this period. This eliminated the need to cut three separate apertures in the plate to accommodate the connecting rod, eccentric rods and regulator shaft.

Although all the cylinders measured 9 ins dia × 12 ins stroke, Nos 1882 to 2260 inclusive had the solid end type cylinder casting. The compensating gear was mounted on the second motion shaft and the winding drum was carried on the hind axle. The flywheels, mostly spoked, remained 4 ft 6 ins dia × 6 ins wide and the hind wheels generally were 6 ft 0 ins dia × 18 ins wide. A few 20th century New Zealand engines were fitted with Moore's steam feed pumps but the majority relied upon injectors to complement the eccentric driven feed pumps. High-speed governors were fitted until 1903; thereafter all had Pickering governors.

No 2810 was supplied to a French customer in Paris and No 3114 was supplied to B Sadullah, a Turkish customer in Constantinople (Istanbul). This engine may well be the Burrell engine with its wheels removed reported to be still at work driving stationary machinery in a marble quarry on the island of Marmora. Thirty-one of the engines were supplied to agriculturists and contractors in East Anglia and the Home Counties, three went to Irish customers and two went to good homes in Scotland.

The final type of single cylinder GP traction engine built prior to the First War was a batch of 13 8 NHP double geared spring-mounted engines.

8 NHP SINGLE CYLINDER, DOUBLE-GEARED SPRING-MOUNTED GP TRACTION ENGINES

No		Built	No		Built
No 2985	Built	1908*	No 3247	Built	1910
3026	”	1908	3255	”	1911*
3132	”	1909*	3328	”	1911
3144	”	1909*	3597	”	1910
3149	”	1909	3668	”	1914
3236	”	1910*	3690	”	1915
3242	”	1910			

* Engines sold to New Zealand customers

Five of the engines in this series went to New Zealand customers having 6.6 sq ft grates and forty 2 ins dia × 5 ft

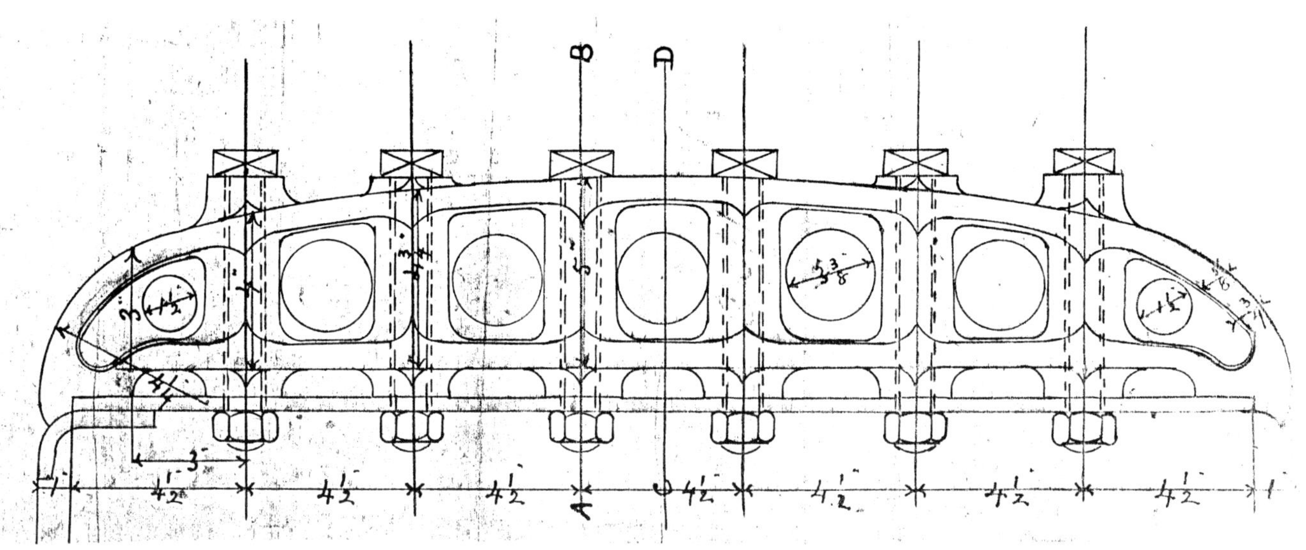

Fig 82 Cast steel firebox roof stay introduced in 1908.

8 ins long smoke tubes, the remainder all had 6.0 sq ft grates. The principal innovation incorporated in these engines was the substitution of volute type springs by 17 plate leaf springs which were generally employed in road locomotives after 1902. It had been found that the friction between the plates of laminated springs reduced vibration after a jolt, eliminating the noticeable roll caused when using the softer volute and helical type springs. The hind wheels were 6 ft 6 ins dia x 18 ins wide and the two-speed gearing gave ratios of 24.4 to 1 and 13.6 to 1. The addition of a third speed on Nos 3144 and 3255 gave an added ratio of 8.3 to 1.

Four of this batch of engines went to East Anglian customers, No 3247 went to the Hampshire landowner, Capt Sir Frederick Carden and three were sent to Scottish customers. Nos 3328 and 3668 were regular sights on the roads in south west Scotland in the years prior to the Great War. J Charlton & Sons, Flour Millers of Dumfries had 17 new Burrell engines at various times and J Wyllie also of Dumfries had 8 new Burrell engines between 1902 and 1921.

In this chapter reference has been made to 596 single cylinder general purpose traction engines built between 1872 and the First World War ranging in size from 4 NHP to 12 NHP. We have traced their evolution from the days when the rigid geared drive replaced the unsatisfactory chain drive engine (1872); the large cast iron spur wheel bolted to the spokes of the hind wheel was replaced by a spur wheel attached directly to the hind axle (1876); compensating gear was introduced (1877); Charles Burrell's famous single drive gearing and Robert Edwards's patent gear change mechanism was adopted (1878). This was followed by the brief era of the spring wheel; single drive gearing was substituted by double gearing (1886) and Frederick Burrell introduced his patent spring gear (1888). In the 1880s materials available were greatly improved and wrought, malleable and cast iron were replaced by steel for many items such as boiler plates, fireboxes, motion shafts and gear wheels. Boiler pressures were progressively increased from 120 PSI to 200 PSI and boilers became much more efficient. We must now turn our attention to compounding and the introduction of Frederick Burrell's famous single crank compound arrangement in 1887.

CHAPTER SEVEN

The Single Crank Compound Traction Engine

The benefits of using the expansive properties of steam by passing it successively through two cylinders of differing sizes, allowing the steam to expand twice before discharging to atmosphere had been appreciated by engineers for a hundred years before the leading railway locomotive and traction engine builders of the day applied their minds to the problem and developed the idea for application to their own products. Greatly to James Watt's consternation, Jonathan Hornblower took out a patent describing the compound beam engine in 1781 and he built his first successful engine for the Radstock Colliery near Bath in the following year. The idea was developed further by Arthur Woolf in 1803 and by 1850 it had become quite common practice to place a second cylinder on the opposite side of the beam, provided with a second set of parallel motion and employing boiler pressures of up to 150 PSI.

Anatole Mallet, the distinguished French locomotive engineer, and the indomitable Francis Webb, chief mechanical engineer of the London and North Western Railway, worked more or less concurrently upon the idea. Mallet exhibited a compound tank engine at the 1878 Paris Show and in the following year Webb converted one of the diminutive Trevithick-Allan 2–2–2 engines to a two-cylinder compound, launching the much debated 'Compound Era' in British locomotive history. Most traction engine builders experimented with the semi-portable under-type engine before attempting to apply the system to self-moving traction engines. John Fowler exhibited such an engine at the Royal Show held at Kilburn in 1879, claiming a saving in water consumption of thirty per cent. Although the technical press were sceptical, most other leading manufacturers quickly followed suit. Fowler maintained his initial lead and exhibited an 8 NHP compound cylinder traction engine at the Royal Show held in Derby in July 1881; his first compound cylinder ploughing engine appearing at the Smithfield Club Show the following December. A great deal of experimentation was necessary in the early stages of development in order to determine the correct relationship required between the diameter of the high pressure cylinder and that of the larger second stage low pressure cylinder. It was important to ensure that each piston did an equal amount of work in order to maintain a balanced load on the crankshaft bearings, whilst at the same time preserving sufficient energy in the steam exhausted to the chimney to provide an adequate draught in the boiler smoke tubes to maintain proper combustion in the firebox.

Frederick Burrell, well and truly established as the company's chief designer, monitored these developments very closely and St Nicholas Works' first compound cylinder engine of which we have reliable details was completed in 1884. Rated 14 NHP and allocated works No 1009 it was a semi-portable, under-type engine having 7 ins dia high pressure (HP) × 12½ ins dia low pressure (LP) × 14 ins stroke cylinders mounted horizontally side by side under the smokebox, with double cranks set at 90 degrees to each other. Following a period of extensive testing in the works the engine was sold to a Russian customer in December 1886. A second engine, No 1186, rated 20 NHP and having 9 ins dia HP × 14 ins dia LP × 16 ins stroke cylinders was completed in July 1885.

An earlier patent, No 1124 filed in March 1881, indicates that Frederick had been applying his mind to the problems of compounding for some time. Entitled 'Improvements in Steam and Other Motive Power Engines and Steering Engines', the patent was presented in two parts. The first part described the operation of a rotary valve engine suitable for propelling launches or steering ships or heavy road engines, the precursor of powered steering as we know it today. The proposed arrangements were shown to be adaptable to either simple expansion or compound engines. The second part described a tandem compound horizontal engine, the HP cylinder being double acting and the LP cylinder single acting, the rotary valves being operated by a unique ring governor.

Frederick's co-patentee was Thomas Tank Burall, then works manager at St Nicholas Works. Burall was born at Devoran in Cornwall in 1847 and was brought up steeped in the Trevithick tradition by an uncle who was employed by Harveys of Hayle. Earlier his father had spent some time at Wisbech erecting a pumping engine where he met and married his wife, Catherine Tank. Thomas, their eldest son learned his trade at a Perran Wharf foundry in Cornwall before accepting a position at St Nicholas Works where he gained rapid promotion. An article written at the turn of the century by F J Gardiner, a Fellow of the Royal Historical Society has the following to say about Burall:

> "Tom Tank Burall was an ingenious mechanical expert, with an inventive turn of mind and his employers soon realised his value by making him manager of their Thetford engineering works. He was always devising some new improvement in agricultural and marine machinery or labour saving schemes in the works. Amongst other brilliant ideas he invented the compound steam traction engine (sic) which was reported upon in the *Engineer* of July 15th 1881. At the

Royal Agricultural Show at Derby in that year, Messrs Burrell exhibited what is described as a novel engine, a 10 NHP traction engine with a Landore steel boiler. It was said to be a curious type of compound engine, very simple, with a new steam steering gear which was the invention of Mr Burall. This gear was stated to be adaptable for steering ships and for marine engines, to which it has since been widely applied (sic). The engine was said to be the most noteworthy in the showyard. A silver medal was awarded to it at the Worcester Agricultural Show. Unfortunately this clever expert's career was but a short one. Constantly overworking himself, the strain proved too great and one day while in his office he fell down dead, the result of heart trouble."

During the period 1878 to 1880 Burall's assistant was a former Marshall's of Gainsborough apprentice named William Fletcher. He is best remembered today as the author of two classic books, *Steam on the Common Roads* and *English and American Steam Carriages and Traction Engines*.

Burall was succeeded by Thomas Lumley who came from Tangye's of Smethwick near Birmingham, another famous engineering firm with Cornish origins. Although less extrovert than Burall he proved to be a good manager and brought many sound ideas with him. Until Lumley's arrival the manager had lived in St Nicholas House, a splendid early Victorian house adjoining the works. It was vacated in 1885 to enable Robert Burrell and his growing family to live near the works.

The engine referred to in Gardiner's article does not appear to have been allocated a works number and unfortunately we have only sketchy details of its construction. The tandem cylinder, based on Kingdon's earlier patent was developed originally by the Dartmouth boatbuilders, Simpson & Denison, for use in their steam launches. On the Burrell engine the double acting HP cylinder was adjacent to the crankshaft and the end of the connecting rod was pivoted directly on the HP piston. There was a single slide valve controlling the steam to and from both cylinders, but it seems unlikely that the rotary valve described in the patent was used in the engine. Steam was admitted first to the small HP cylinder. At the end of the stroke the steam was exhausted into the opposite end of the small HP cylinder and into the space behind the larger LP piston. At the next stroke steam was admitted to the opposite or crank side of the small HP cylinder and the process was repeated.

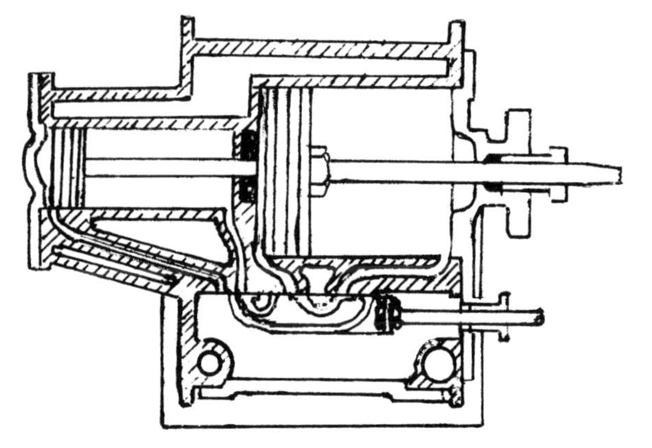

Fig 83 Simpson & Denison's tandem compound cylinder similar to that employed on Burrell's 10 NHP experimental traction engine exhibited at the RASE Show, Derby.

This engine was one of two built at St Nicholas Works in 1881 fitted with David Joy's patent valve gear, the other being the 'F' type road locomotive No 911 described in a later chapter.

Leeds born, Joy started life as a pupil at Fenton, Murray & Jackson's works and later he became a protégé of E B Wilson at the famous Railway Foundry in Leeds. He was appointed chief draughtsman at an early age and was largely resonsible for the Railway Foundry's most famous locomotive design, the 'Jenny Lind' introduced in 1847. Joy patented his radial valve gear in 1879. It provided a very accurate and advantageous distribution of the steam, but also had the attractive feature of requiring no eccentrics which enabled the main bearings and crankshaft webs to be lengthened and strengthened. The required oscillating and rotational motion was obtained by a link attached to the connecting rod at near the mid-point between the big end and the gudgeon pin, necessitating an enlargement of the connecting rod in the area of the pin joint. Many engineers took objection to this feature claiming it weakened the rod, although the system was widely adopted by Francis Webb at the London and North Western Railway's Crewe works.

The unique steering engine consisted of two small vertical double acting cylinders bolted to the side of the front water tank mounted under the boiler. The crankshaft carried a worm wheel which engaged with the traditional chain steerage shaft. The admission and exhaust of steam was controlled by an ingenious rotary slide valve as described in the patent. One end of the valve was attached to a threaded collar or nut which could be revolved by the steersman turning the traditional engine steering wheel. Each complete turn given to the nut caused the steering engine to make one complete revolution which was transmitted to the steering shaft. Immediately the steersman stopped turning the steering wheel the rotary valve screwed itself endways into the nut shutting off the steam and stopping the steering engine. In this manner the steering engine always followed the hand of the steersman trying to overtake him. Because the rotary valve was double acting the steering engine would run in either direction always following the hand of the steersman. It could not overrun itself and when left to itself always stopped having shut off the steam supply.

With every justification the inventors claimed the system could be easily adapted for steering ships and operating the link motion of large marine or stationary steam engines. The editor of the *Engineer* commented upon those who claimed that the added complication was a retrograde step, adding that any attempt to stop progress would be as, 'judicious as trying to keep back the tide with a pitchfork.' Although power steering became a common feature on 20th century vehicles, there is no evidence that any other traction engines were built incorporating this feature.

In the early stages of development of the compound engine, with the HP and LP cylinders mounted side by side, probably the greatest difficulty facing the traction engine designer was the restricted space on top of the firebox. The overall width of the firebox rarely exceeded 3 ft 6 ins and the designer had to accommodate two

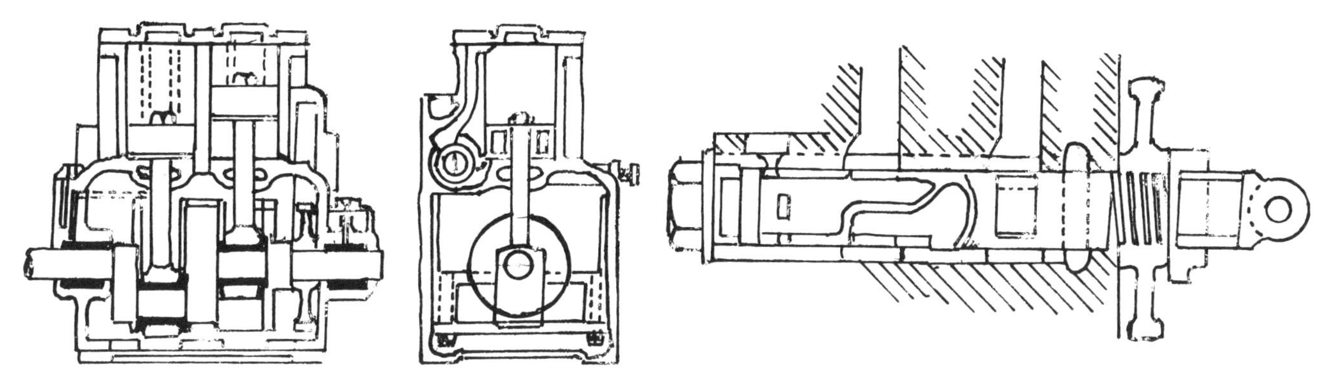

Fig 84 Frederick Burrell's & Thomas Tank Burall's steering engine as described in their patent No 1124 of 1881.

cranks, spaced to coincide with the centre lines of the two cylinders of differing diameter, four eccentrics and to provide crankshaft bearings of sufficient length to suit the duty required of the engine.

Undoubtedly the great contribution made by Frederick Burrell was to conceive the idea of placing both cylinders in a single casting with the smaller HP cylinder arranged diagonally above the larger LP cylinder, linking the two piston rods together in a common crosshead and using one connecting rod and crank. it then became logical to link together the two valve rods such that they were driven through a single set of link motion. Apart from simplicity and the space saving considerations, Frederick had in mind the provision of a facility that would enable the ordinary single cylinder engine to be converted to a compound cylinder engine, by simply exchanging the cylinder castings, without having to raise the centre line of the crankshaft or making other extensive alterations. Several engines, including some Fowler ploughing engines, were sucessfully converted on this principle by the works in subsequent years.

It is interesting to note that although Frederick produced his first single crank compound engine in 1887, he did not apply for patent protection until February 1889. This late application was no doubt prompted by his discovery that similar ideas were being developed in the United States. Samuel Vauclain, a leading American locomotive engineer and later president of the giant Baldwin Locomotive Works in Philadelphia, produced his famous four cylinder compound design in 1889, in which the HP and LP piston rods on both sides of the engine were connected to common crossheads, driving two cranks.

The first single crank compund engine (SCC) built in accordance with Frederick Burrell's patent No 3489 filed in February 1889 was a 8 NHP engine allocated No 1290. It had 6 ins dia high pressure (HP) × 10½ ins dia low pressure (LP) × 12 ins stroke cylinders and was fitted with an 8 ft 6 ins Proctor digger similar to that fitted to the 4 NHP engines described in the last chapter. Both engines went to Mrs Harvey in the Isle of Wight in the summer of 1887. A second identical 8 NHP compound digging engine, No 1387 completed in August 1889 went to W Farmer of Coworth Park in Berkshire, but all three had a short life as digging engines. No 1387 finished its useful working life with Coupe Bros, the Sheffield heavy haulage contractors after being fitted with larger, heavier wheels and belly tanks in 1907. Type CD2 boilers, similar to the

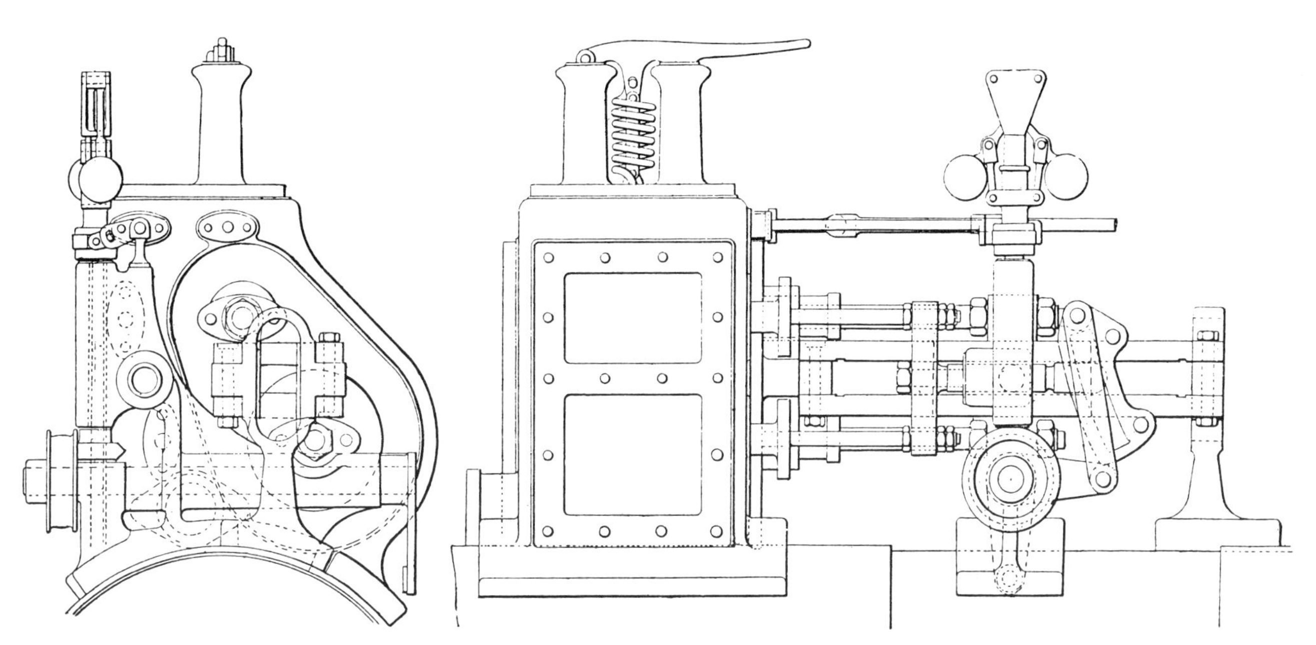

Fig 85 Layout of Burrell's now famous single crank compound cylinder & motion constructed in accordance with Frederick Burrell's patent No 3489 of 1889.

type T116, were fitted, having a working pressure of 140 PSI, a grate area of 4.9 sq ft and a total heating surface of 143 sq ft. The engines were unsprung with single drive two-speed gearing. The compensating gear was on the flywheel side and the winding drum on the gear side of the engine. They weighed 15 tons in working order. In 1893 a third similar engine, No 1708, was supplied to the Société Général Mercantile in Paris, but its fate remains unknown.

One of the earliest problems with compound cylinders was the difficulty of starting should the HP piston stop in the dead centre position and it became necesary to supply steam at boiler pressure into the LP receiver enabling the engine to be started by the action of the LP piston. As early as July 1886 Frederick Burrell filed his patent No 9842 describing a starting valve mechanism. Later this was developed and applied to both single and double crank compound engines. The patent also provided for steam at boiler pressure to be used in both the HP and LP cylinders in order to obtain maximum power for starting heavy loads and ascending hills. The arrangement also acted as a safety valve and allowed the steam in the receiver to blow-off when a predetermined critical pressure was reached. The device became known to enginemen as the Simpling Valve.

Concurrent with these digging engines the works built seven 8 NHP SCC single drive spring-mounted compound traction engines with differing sized cylinders. Between 1887 and 1893, Charles Burrell experimented with varying HP and LP cylinder diameters in their search for correct proportions and optimum performance. In those early days of compounding very careful measurements were taken of fuel and water consumption and one can imagine Frederick Burrell and his assistants spending much time studying steam indicator diagrams. We shall see as this chapter unfolds that the ratio between the cylinder bores was progressively reduced from approximately 1.75 to 1 and 1.67 to 1.

No 1386, the first of the seven experimental engines, was exhibited at the 1889 RASE Windsor Show and in December 1890 the editor of the *Engineer* commented upon these engines in glowing terms following their subsequent appearance at the Smithfield Show.

> "Here we have an exceedingly compact compound engine, very simple and very efficient and economical. The engine exhibited is called an 8 NHP engine and the boiler has only 150 sq ft of heating surface, but running at 200 RPM with 160 PSI boiler pressure it has indiated over 80 IHP, and as the safety valves were blowing off all the time, there is reason to believe that if the load had been augmented and the boiler forced, the engine would have indicated 100 IHP or 1 HP for every 1.5 sq ft of heating surface. Even at 80 IHP, however, the actual bears to the nominal power a greater proportion than we have before met with, 50 IHP being about the most that can be got out of a nominal (single cylinder) 8 NHP engine."

The boilers, transmission shafting arrangements and other mechanical features corresponded closely with the contemporary single cylinder engines. The first two engines had a working pressure of 140 PSI, the remainder were pressed to 160 PSI and all had steel fireboxes. Volute springs were used, the hind wheels were 6 ft 0 ins dia and the two-speed gearing gave ratios of 27.9 to 1 and 14.9 to 1.

8 NHP SINGLE CRANK COMPOUND, SINGLE DRIVE, SPRING-MOUNTED TRACTION ENGINES

No	Built	Month	Year	Cylinders	Size
No 1386	Built	February	1889	Cylinders	6×10½×12 ins
No 1409	"	June	1889	"	6×10½×12 ins
No 1513	"	December	1890	"	6¼×11×12 ins
No 1523	"	March	1891	"	6×10½×12 ins
No 1559	"	August	1891	"	6¼×11×12 ins
No 1578	"	November	1891	"	6¼×11×12 ins
No 1683	"	June	1893	"	6¼×11×12 ins

No 1386 had the forward mounted jib and crane gear originally fitted to No 1221, as mentioned in chapter 6, and was sold to Pécard Frères of Nevers in France as a stablemate to the 6 NHP traction engine No 892. The remaining six engines went to widely scattered customers in the United Kingdom. Similarly, five 7 NHP SCC single drive engines with varying size cylinders were built in the period 1887 to 1893.

7 NHP SINGLE CRANK COMPOUND, SINGLE DRIVE, TRACTION ENGINES

No	Built	Month	Year	Cylinders	Size
No 1291	Built	September	1881	Cylinders	6×10½×12 ins
No 1494	"	August	1890	"	6×10¾×12 ins
No 1632	"	August	1892	"	6×10×12 ins
No 1652	"	November	1892	"	6×10×12 ins
No 1710	"	August	1893	"	6¼×10×12 ins

The first four engines were spring-mounted on volute type springs; the fifth engine was unsprung. No 1291 had the type 'T' 6/7 NHP boiler and the other four engines had the class 'C' 8 NHP boilers. All five engines went to agriculturists in various parts of England, No 1494 being supplied with a fine set of copper cooking utensils mounted on the side of the boiler manufactured by Sabertons of Norwich. 1892 saw the introduction of a circular cast nameplate on the smokebox door inscribed 'The Burrell Compound'. Variations of this became a feature of Burrell engines of all types for the remainder of the firm's existence.

We shall deal with the remaining 594 SCC GP traction engines built prior to the First War in order of size. Principal design features of Burrell boilers, transmission shafting and many other mechanical details had become established by 1890 and have already been dealt with in chapter 6. Material specifications continued to improve as new alloys and methods of production became available and these were incorporated in all later types of Burrell engine. Individual customer preferences and requirements continued to receive close attention by the works.

The majority of single cylinder GP traction engines built were rated 8 NHP, but following the advent of the compound cylinder combined with steadily increasing boiler pressures, the 6 NHP engine became the most popular size after 1890. Two basic types were offered by St Nicholas Works for the remainder of the steam era, the light type weighing on average 8 tons and the standard type weighing approximately 10 tons 5 cwt. The light type gave a power output of 24 IHP and had a hauling power of 20 tons on a 1 in 18 incline and the latter produced 28 IHP hauling 24 tons on a similar incline. The light compound was introduced with the needs of the farmer primarily in mind, whose main requirement was for an economic, reliable engine for driving and hauling a 4 ft 6 ins threshing drum often in moderately hilly country.

The introduction of the light type single crank compound traction engine caused quite a stir at both the agricultural shows at which it was exhibited and in the technical and agricultural press of the day. St Nicholas Works were very busy at this time and the indications are that had they had more capacity they would have sold more of these excellent engines to UK farmers.

Towards the end of 1893 St Nicholas Works had adopted Aveling's patent hornplates as standard and this feature was progressively incorporated in all new production. Until this time separate plates had been riveted to the outer firebox shell to accommodate the crankshaft and drive shaft bearings but in future the firebox outer shell was extended upwards and backwards to give this facility in a single integrated unit, thus greatly increasing the rigidity of the whole assembly. Prior to this date St Nichoals Works had produced only one engine, a 12 NHP single cylinder road locomotive, No 884 with this feature. It is not known for certain whether they obtained a licence from Thomas Aveling for this construction or whether it was adopted to test the strength of Aveling's patent. In any event Burrell's interpretation of the Aveling hornplate was not very successful upon this occasion for after a few weeks the engine was returned to the works for major alterations, the wrought iron plates having sprung, causing difficulties with the drive shafts. In February 1881 Aveling challenged J & H McLaren in the High Court for alleged infringement of his patent but the verdict went

6 NHP SINGLE CRANK COMPOUND, DOUBLE GEARED, UNSPRUNG TRACTION ENGINE

No	Built	No	Built	No	Built	No	Built
No 1503	Built 1890	No 1684	Built 1893	No 1772	Built 1894	No 1830	Built 1895
1540	" 1891	1685	" 1893	1785	" 1894	1831	" 1895
1599	" 1892	1706	" 1893	1789	" 1894	1850	" 1895
1607	" 1892	1724	" 1893	1795	" 1894	1862	" 1895
1656	" 1892	1750	" 1894	1805	" 1894	1871	" 1895
1663	" 1892	1752	" 1894	1813	" 1894	1919	" 1897
1671	" 1893	1756	" 1894	1823	" 1894	1922	" 1897
1678	" 1893	1761	" 1894	1828	" 1895	1927	" 1896

All had 5 ins dia HP × 9 ins dia LP × 9 ins stroke cylinders and derivatives of the 'R' type boiler originally fitted to the 5 NHP single cylinder traction engines introduced in 1887, pressed to 160 PSI. The grate area was 4.0 sq ft and the total heating surface was 110 sq ft. Forty 1¾ ins dia × 4 ft 9½ ins long smoke tubes were employed. Six engines, Nos 1684 to 1752, had large manholes in the boiler side and No 1756 and successive engines in the series had Aveling type hornplates.

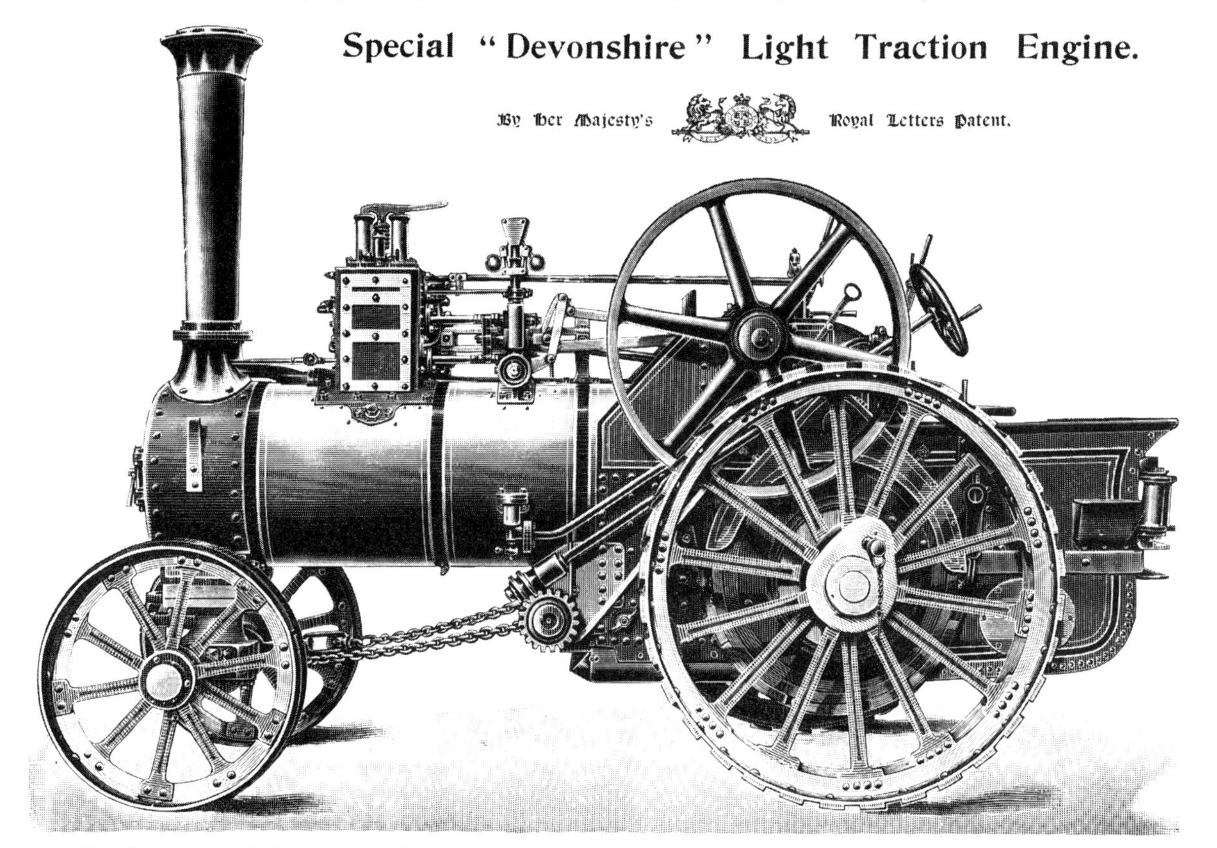

Fig 86 The 6 NHP 'Devonshire' light pattern SCC double geared unsprung traction engine introduced in 1890.

against the defendants. Be that as it may, Charles Burrell deferred the universal adoption of this important feature until the final expiration of the patent.

The two-speed gearing on these engines gave ratios of 25.6 to 1 and 15.1 to 1, the hind wheels were generally 5 ft 4½ ins dia × 4 ins wide and the flywheels were 4 ft 0 ins dia × 5½ ins wide.

Whereas in all previous batches of GP traction engines the majority of engines went to Burrell's traditional customers in Eastern England the majority of this batch went to farmers in Devon and Cornwall. Only three engines went to East Anglia, five went to Scottish customers and one went to Ireland. No 1828 named 'El Angel' was built as a special wood-burner with the firebox lengthened by 3 ft 0 ins to give a grate area of 5 sq ft and a large spark arrester was fitted in the enlarged smokebox. It was sold to the Chatteris Engineering Company in Cambridgeshire and subsequently exported to South America. Nos 1656 and 1772 were prepared as show engines, the former appearing at Smithfield in 1892 and the latter at the RASE Show held in Cambridge in 1894. After service with a Scottish contractor No 1772 was purchased by Hives Bros, travelling showmen of Gateshead who extensively travelled the north of England fairs with a china stall until 1925. Always in pristine condition it was a pretty little engine with a half length canopy and decorated sideboards.

Special mention must be made of No 1599 which in 1899 was repossessed by Burrell, rebuilt and fitted with road springs. It was then sold to the War Office together with two new engines, Nos 2262, and 2267, to become a part of a special searchlight unit, The Electrical Engineers RE Volunteers commanded by Major R E Crompton of road steamer fame. Fuller details of these three engines are given later in this chapter.

The second generation of light SCC compound GP traction engines appeared in 1897.

The principal difference between the first generation light compound traction engines and the second generation introduced in 1897 was that the cylinders were increased to 5½ ins dia HP × 9 ins dia LP × 10 ins stroke. The first sixteen had solid end cylinders having the end adjacent to the motion bracket cast as an integral part of the cylinder, to drawing 542–547, the remainder were conventionally open ended. They continued to use variants of the 'R' type boiler and all except the first three, which had lengthened boilers, retained the 4 ft 2 ins long smoke tubes. Nos 2512 and 2513 had boiler shells rolled from a single plate. The average weight of this series was increased to 8 ton 5 cwt.

Once again the majority of the batch went to west country farmers although six did go to Ireland. Two went to Robert Robinson & Son, contractors of Annan in Dumfries who owned five Burrell engines at various times and two went to Isaac Ball, contractors of Wharles in Lancashire. They became confirmed Burrell enthusiasts and purchased no less than 18 Burrell engines between 1881 and 1921 including traction engines, road locos, road rollers and a 5 ton tractor.

A short paragraph in the *Daily Mail* dated 6th March 1900 read:

> "The active service contingent of fifty-one officers and men of the Electrical Engineers RE Volunteers are leaving very shortly for South Africa. They were entertained at dinner of Saturday night at the Prince's Restaurant. Lord Kelvin, Honorary Colonel of the corps presided. Major R E Crompton mentioned that the men would take with them steam traction engines, electric searchlights and field telephones of the pattern used by foreign armies, but hitherto never employed by this country."

This elite corps was formed some years previously following an initiative by R E Crompton whom we first

6 NHP SINGLE CRANK COMPOUND, DOUBLE GEARED, UNSPRUNG TRACTION ENGINES

No	Built	No	Built	No	Built	No	Built
No 2031	Built 1897	No 2262	Built 1900	No 2318	Built 1900	No 2465	Built 1902
2033	" 1897	2267	" 1900	2333	" 1900	2480	" 1902
2091	" 1898	2275	" 1900	2388	" 1901	2486	" 1902
2094	" 1898	2282	" 1900	2407	" 1901	2506	" 1902
2152	" 1898	2294	" 1900	2408	" 1901	2512	" 1902
2185	" 1899	2307	" 1900	2422	" 1901	2513	" 1902
2196	" 1899	2309	" 1900				

Fig 87 No 1772 6 NHP SCC double geared unsprung traction engine whilst in the ownership of Hives Bros of Gateshead. Engine was built in 1894 and exhibited at RASE Cambridge Show.

encountered in chapter 5 as superintendent of the government steam road train in India. The unit formed for service in South Africa comprised three Burrell light pattern 6 NHP single crank compound traction engines. Reference has already been made to No 1599 built originally in 1892, the other two were Nos 2262 and 2267. They were painted khaki and carried War Office Nos EE1, EE2 and EE3. All had long awnings and Nos 2262 and 2267 were fitted with dynamo platforms on top of the smokebox. Additionally No 2262 was fitted with a novel condenser and fan on the smokebox. Exhaust steam was discharged into the fan-cooled box structure mounted on a sideways extension of the dynamo platform. The 2 ft 6 ins dia fan was driven by a pitch chain from a sprocket wheel mounted on the flywheel boss. The condensate was returned from the bottom of the condenser to the tender water tank by a copper pipe mounted on the gear side of the engine. Each engine hauled a train comprising a tender and store wagon, two light gun carriages, a searchlight projector and a two-wheeled carriage carrying a drum of electric cable. The unit was also equipped with twenty bicycles to facilitate laying telephone wires. No 2267 arrived in South Africa some weeks after the other two engines acompanied by Major Crompton and was initially employed assisting with the repair of vital bridges destroyed by the Boers.

Concurrent with the batch of 26 double geared unsprung engines the works built six similar SCC single drive spring-mounted engines. Five of the six engines went to West Country farmers.

6 NHP SINGLE CRANK COMPOUND, SINGLE DRIVE SPRING-MOUNTED TRACTION ENGINES

No	Built	No	Built
No 1995	Built 1897	No 2424	Built 1901
2312	" 1900	2579	" 1903
2390	" 1901	2909	" 1907

By 1902 the popularity of the 6 NHP light traction engine in the West Country had become so well established that the marque became universally known as 'Devonshire' engines. The name was also applied to comparable road locomotives and class 'B' road rollers. A total of sixty-five SCC compound, double-geared drive, unsprung traction engines were built between 1902 and 1914 and a further six engines were built in the post-war years. Concurrently twelve similar engines but spring mounted were built in the pre-war years. The now well-proven 5½ ins dia HP × 9 ins dia LP × 10 ins stroke SCC cylinder was maintained throughout the life of the series. Most of these engines built after 1904 carried a smokebox door ring inscribed 'The Devonshire Engine'.

6 NHP SCC 'DEVONSHIRE' TRACTION ENGINES, DOUBLE-GEARED, SPRING-MOUNTED

No	Built	No	Built
No 2942	Built 1907	No 3179	Built 1910
2944	" 1907	3196	" 1910
3027	" 1908	3230	" 1910
3029	" 1908	3342	" 1911
3054	" 1908	3516	" 1913
3082	" 1909	3578	" 1914

Engines built prior to 1909 had boilers pressed to 160 PSI; thereafter working pressures were progressively increased to 200 PSI. Most engines had 4.6 sq ft grates although nine engines supplied to Australia had enlarged 5.76 sq ft grates suitable for burning inferior fuels. Several of these engines also had lengthened smokeboxes fitted with large spark arresters. Fifty-two of the unsprung engines had 4 ft 9½ ins long smoke tubes; the remainder had 4 ft 2 ins tubes. The engines with enlarged grates had thirty-four 1¾ ins dia smoke tubes whereas the remaining engines in the series had forty 1¾ ins tubes. After 1912 all engines in the series had thirty 2 ins dia tubes. Engines built in 1902/03 except No 2534 had boiler shells made in one piece. The average weight of the engines was 8 ton 5 cwt. For reasons which are now obscure, but probably resulting from New Zealand order cancellations Nos 2807, 2838 and 3108 were originally allocated Nos 2754, 2828 and 3044 respectively. No 2604 was supplied to an Irish customer whom one suspects was left-handed because the steering was on the right-hand side of the engine and the reversing lever was on the left-hand side.

6 NHP SCC 'DEVONSHIRE' TRACTION ENGINES, DOUBLE-GEARED, UNSPRUNG

No	Built	No	Built	No	Built	No	Built
No 2534	Built 1902	No 2706	Built 1904	No 2950	Built 1907	No 3216	Built 1910
2539	" 1902	2715	" 1904*	2964	" 1907	3243	" 1910
2560	" 1903	2731	" 1905	2995	" 1908	3262	" 1910
2572	" 1903	2735	" 1905	2999	" 1908	3286	" 1911
2577	" 1903	2739	" 1905	3010	" 1908*	3296	" 1911
2587	" 1903	2785	" 1905*	3031	" 1908	3304	" 1911
2599	" 1903	2795	" 1906*	3035	" 1908	3317	" 1911
2604	" 1903	2807	" 1906	3071	" 1909*	3321	" 1911
2606	" 1903	2816	" 1906	3108	" 1909	3331	" 1911
2609	" 1903	2838	" 1906	3116	" 1909	3367	" 1912
2611	" 1903	2846	" 1906	3117	" 1909	3382	" 1912
2617	" 1903	2864	" 1906*	3135	" 1909	3396	" 1912
2624	" 1903	2872	" 1906*	3146	" 1909	3403	" 1912
2644	" 1904	2893	" 1907	3155	" 1909*	3460	" 1913
2645	" 1904	2905	" 1907*	3176	" 1910	3479	" 1913
2666	" 1904	2908	" 1907	3189	" 1910	3541	" 1914
2671	" 1904						

* Engines fitted with the enlarged 5.76 sq ft grates supplied to the E Coulson Agency in Melbourne, Australia.

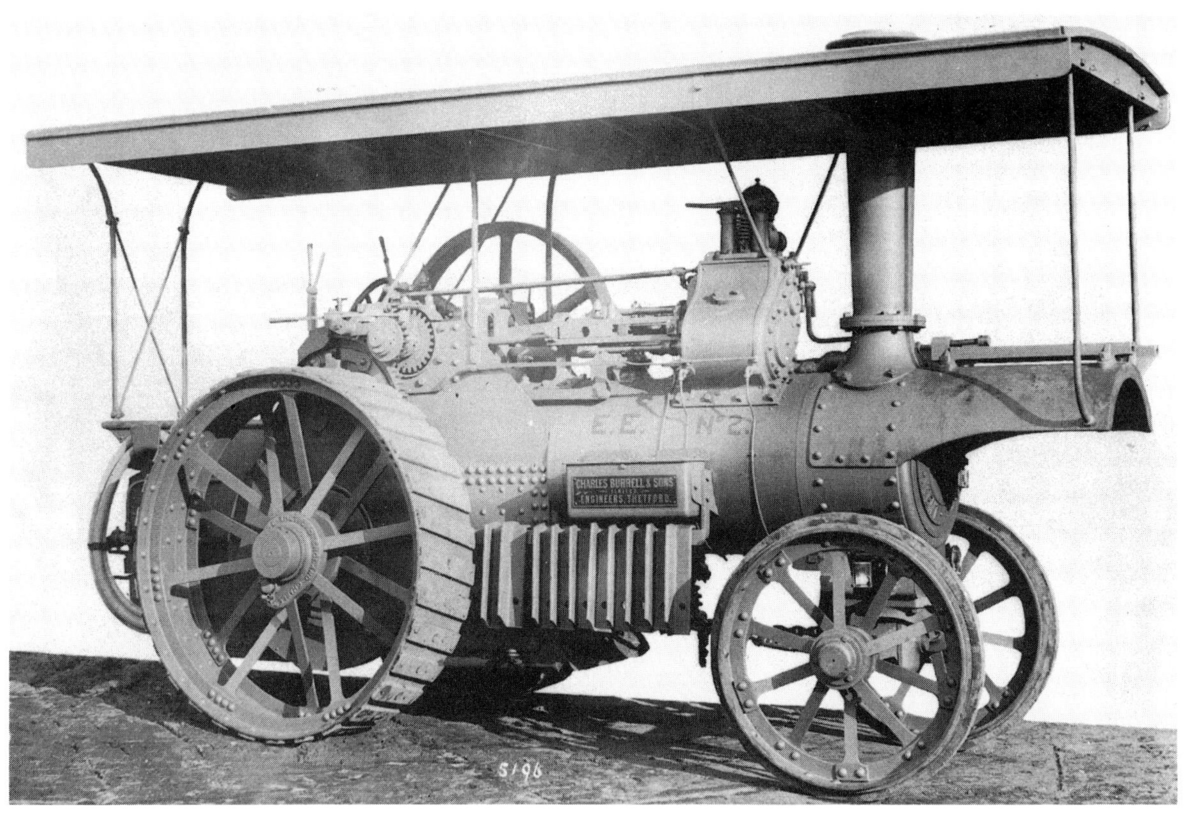

Fig 88 No 2262 6 NHP SCC double geared unsprung traction engine showing the addition of a dynamo platform and full length canopy.

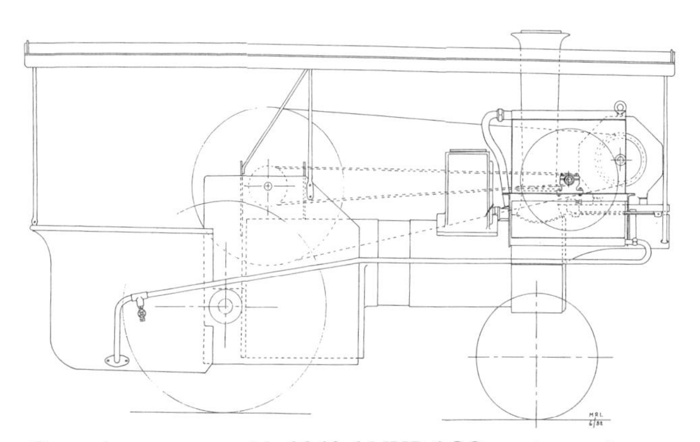

General arrangement No 2262 6 NHP SCC traction engine built for Colonel R E Crompton's Corps of Electrical Engineers in 1900 showing novel belt driven condenser.

By the turn of the century the importance of the Irish market was apparent and twenty-five per cent of these Devonshire engines went to the Emerald Isle. The company had exhibited annually at the great Ball Bridge Agricultural Show in Dublin for many years and the attention paid to this market was now paying a dividend.

Nineteen engines in this series went to West Country customers and nine went to the E Coulson Agency in Melbourne, Australia. Although a serious attempt was made to obtain a larger share of this growing market at the beginning of the 20th century, it has to be said that Burrells were never as successful in Australia as they had been in New Zealand. In a large measure this was due to competition from Walter Maplesden Noakes, a former Aveling & Porter apprentice who represented John Fowler & Co in Australia for many years. We shall see later that the first Burrell engine sent out to Australia in 1891 was a fine big 10 NHP crane engine. Initially the firm was represented by J Howard of Sydney, NSW. In total 38 engines were sent to Australia direct from St Nicholas Works and it is understood that at least two more were acquired second-hand from South Africa after the Boer War. No 3082 was one of three Burrell engines shipped to customers in Rhodesia (Zimbabwe) and No 3230 went direct to a sugar beet factory Sucrerie de Fontaine le Dun.

Before considering the 182 6 NHP standard duty engines with 6 ins dia HP $\times$ 10 ins dia LP $\times$ 10 ins stroke SCC cylinders, it is necessary we make mention of two 'Irish' type engines rated 5 NHP built in the early years of the 20th century. Both had 5 ins dia $\times$ $8\frac{1}{2}$ ins dia $\times$ 9 ins stroke SCC cylinders and both were double-geared to the hind axle. No 3092 built in 1909 was unsprung and weighed 7 tons 5 cwt; No 3195 built in 1911 was spring mounted on 15 leaf type springs and weighed 7 tons 19 cwt. They were only 6 ft $5\frac{1}{2}$ ins wide, the hind wheels were 5 ft 0 ins dia $\times$ 14 ins wide and the spoked flywheels were 3 ft 9 ins dia $\times$ 5 ins wide. No 3092 went to an Irish customer and No 3195, named 'Country Girl', gave many years service in northern fairgrounds in the ownership of Mr A Palmer of Rowlands Gill in County Durham before being acquired for preservation. The engine had a full length canopy but it was not fitted with twisted brass canopy supports or other adornments associated with the fairground, nor was it fitted with motion side plates.

Fig 89 A new SCC 'Devonshire' engine complete with threshing machine and straw elevator about to leave St Nicholas Works – circa 1904.

6 NHP SCC 6 × 10 × 10 ins STANDARD DUTY SINGLE DRIVE UNSPRUNG GP TRACTION ENGINES

No 1577	Built 1891	No 1751	Built 1894	No 1822	Built 1894	No 1916	Built 1896
1617	" 1892	1763	" 1894	1829	" 1894	1928	" 1896
1646	" 1892	1773	" 1894	1832	" 1895	1930	" 1896
1647	" 1892	1780	" 1894	1837	" 1895	1933	" 1896
1651	" 1893	1782	" 1894	1843	" 1895	1945	" 1896
1669	" 1893	1786	" 1894	1846	" 1895	1950	" 1896
1676	" 1893	1787	" 1894	1858	" 1895	1962	" 1896
1677	" 1893	1792	" 1894	1860	" 1895	1963	" 1896
1687	" 1893	1799	" 1894	1861	" 1895	1966	" 1896
1698	" 1893	1800	" 1894	1872	" 1895	1968	" 1896
1699	" 1893	1806	" 1894	1874	" 1895	1977	" 1897
1711	" 1893	1812	" 1894	1879	" 1895	1983	" 1897
1715	" 1893	1815	" 1895	1885	" 1895	1991	" 1897
1739	" 1894	1816	" 1895	1891	" 1895	2003	" 1897
1742	" 1894	1818	" 1895				

6 NHP SCC single drive standard duty GP traction engines, both sprung and unsprung versions were introduced in 1891. A total of forty-nine of the former and fifty-eight of the latter were produced and we will deal firstly with the unsprung version.

A remarkable degree of standardisation was achieved on these engines after some teething troubles with the crossheads and eccentrics had been resolved. The T68 type boiler as fitted to the 'T' type single cylinder traction engines with 5 ft 1 ins long smoke tubes was used until the introduction of hornplates in 1893 and thereafter the T194 boiler pressed to 160 PSI with 5 ft 1 ins long smoke tubes was employed. All had steel fireboxes; all had cross arm type governors and a minority were fitted with injectors, which resulted in a thoroughly reliable and economic general purpose engine to meet the basic needs of the UK farmer.

Both Nos 1816 and 1891 were specially prepared as show engines complete with Saberton's cooking apparatus and exhibited at Smithfield. Rumour has it that the older threshermen continued to show a preference for their coal shovels when preparing their bacon and eggs and few of these additional luxuries appear to have been purchased. No 1782 was shown at the RASE Cambridge show in 1894 and other engines were exhibited at Darlington, Ball Bridge Dublin, Ayr, Nottingham and Grimsby Agricultural Shows. In the 1890s the company's sales effort headed by the energetic Robert Burrell was fast approaching a climax made possible by the greatly improved methods of production at St Nicholas Works initiated by Frederick Burrell and Thomas Tank Burall. They had for some time appreciated the benefits of batch production and the standardisation of parts in order to keep down costs.

It is not surprising to find that the majority of these engines went to East Anglian farmers. No 1933 was supplied to Lord Iveagh, the head of the Guiness brewing family for working on his recently acquired 10,000 acre estate at Elvedon on the outskirts of Thetford. Once described as one of the more exotic phenomena of East

Fig 90 No 3071 6 NHP SCC 'Devonshire' type double geared unsprung traction engine with enlarged firebox, smokebox with spark arrester and Australian pattern fuel bunker. Built in 1909.

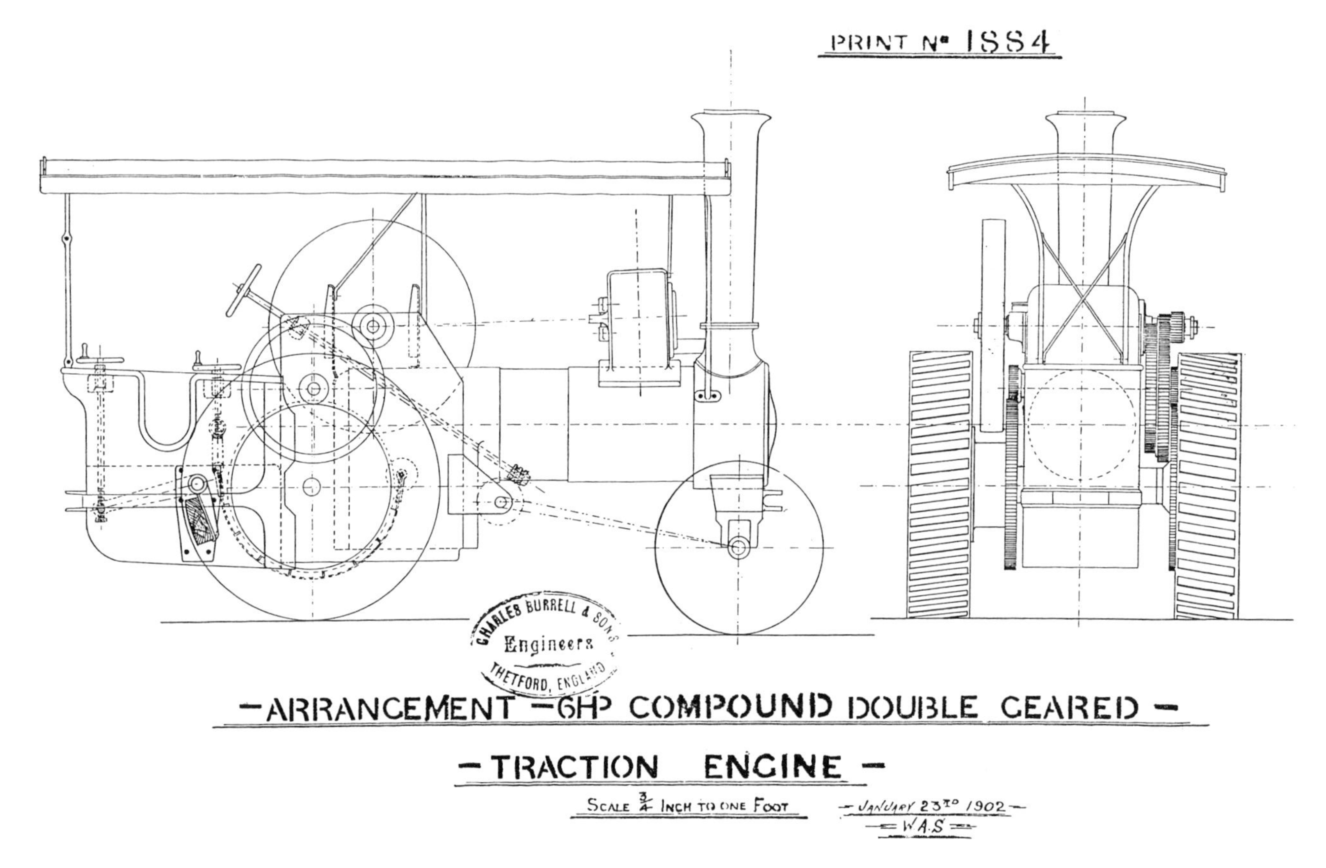

Fig 91 Works' outline drawing of a 1902 6 NHP SCC double geared traction engine.

Fig 92 No 1676 6 NHP SCC single drive unsprung GP traction engine exhibited at the RASE Show Chester in 1893. One of the last Burrell engines built before the universal adoption of hornplates.

Anglia, Elvedon had for many years been the home of Maharajah Duleep Singh, a former leader of the Sikh nation. He had been banished from India by Queen Victoria for his part in the bloody Sikh wars and making the best of a bad situation he employed his great wealth to out-squire the English Gentlemen in the area. Many stories of his extravagant lifestyle have survived. It is said that in one year over 19,000 pheasants were slaughtered by his guns; others have commented that at one period many of the young men employed in St Nicholas Works bore a remarkable likeness to him. He is remembered also as an erudite local archaeologist. Today this vast Sikh-Irish palace lies unoccupied and gone is all trace of the four Burrell engines which worked on the estate at various times.

Another engine worth mentioning is No 1818 which was acquired second-hand by George Soame, an agricultural engineer and contractor of Perseverance Works at Marsham in Norfolk. In the 1860s he made a small portable steam engine for belt-driving an early fairground roundabout. It is said that the idea so impressed Frederick Savage, the proprietor of the already renowned agricultural engineering business in King's Lynn that he resolved there and then to develop further the idea. The final engine in the series, No 2003, survives today as a fine example of the breed in preservation.

These engines were popular also with Scottish farmers and contractors and thirteen went to homes north of the border, including two to the Stirling Steam Threshing Company. Eight engines went to farmers in Yorkshire, but only two went to the West Country and one to Ireland. The remaining twelve engines were widely scattered throughout the United Kingdom.

The standard duty single drive spring-mounted engines were the first type of Thetford built engine in which the spring-mounted version approximated the number of unsprung engines built confirming the growing popularity of this feature with all types of user. Engine Nos 1565 to 1662 were fitted with spiral type springs which obviously gave some trouble and the remainder of the batch reverted to volute type springs. Similarly, as with the unsprung engines, there were some initial problems with the crossheads and eccentrics and revised, heavier duty components were quickly substituted. It was fashionable at the turn of the century to use the solid end type cylinder casting with the steam passing through the motion bar and engines built in the period 1898-1900 had this feature. Another feature incorporated in 1898 was a mudhole over the crown of the firebox. This enabled the area around the roof stays to be scraped and thoroughly cleaned when washing out the boiler. No 1744 and successive engines in the batch had Aveling type hornplates and the same 'T' type boilers as used on the unsprung engines. Engine Nos 2573, 2575 and 2612 had their boiler barrels made in one piece. On average these engines weighed 10 tons and the 5 ft 9½ ins dia × 14 ins wide hind wheels were retained. The two-speed gear ratios were 25.5 to 1 and 13.6 to 1.

6 NHP SCC 6 × 10 × 10 ins SINGLE DRIVE, SPRING-MOUNTED TRACTION ENGINES

No 1565	Built	1891	No 1622	Built	1892	No 1765	Built	1894	No 2221	Built	1898
1569	"	1891	1623	"	1892	1771	"	1894	2264	"	1900
1573	"	1891	1662	"	1893	1798	"	1894	2290	"	1900
1581	"	1891	1672	"	1893	1801	"	1894	2340	"	1900
1584	"	1891	1675	"	1893	1848	"	1895	2426	"	1901
1589	"	1891	1679	"	1893	1931	"	1896	2495	"	1902
1590	"	1891	1680	"	1893	1949	"	1896	2523	"	1902
1597	"	1892	1696	"	1893	1978	"	1897	2573	"	1903
1603	"	1892	1732	"	1894	2087	"	1898	2575	"	1903
1609	"	1892	1738	"	1894	2102	"	1898	2612	"	1903
1612	"	1892	1744	"	1894	2122	"	1898	2770	"	1905
1618	"	1892	1758	"	1894	2147	"	1898	2903	"	1907
1621	"	1892									

Fourteen of this batch went new to customers in East Anglia. In 1895 No 1801 was returned to the works and converted to a traction engine-cum-road roller convertible engine for William Arnold & Sons of Branbridge, near Paddock Wood in Kent. Arnold's business was originally based at Peckham in South London, but as it grew and prospered was removed to Kent. He employed nine Burrell engines at various times and around the turn of the century undertook many interesting road haulage assignments in the area, as well as general haulage and road rolling work of a more mundane character. The first four engines built as convertibles left St Nicholas Works in 1895/1896 and the second in the batch went to William Arnold. The conversion of No 1801 took place more or less simultaneously and this necessitated manufacturing a new smokebox with a forward extension to accommodate the roller forked forecarriage and a set of rollers to be interchangeable with the traction engine wheels.

No 2495 supplied originally to Burrell Bros of Great Barton, Bury St Edmunds, was returned to the works in 1917 for conversion to a Showman's type engine for Alfred E. Gadd, Sussex travellers. It was fitted with a dynamo platform on top of the smokebox, belly tanks for carrying additional water, a full length awning, the traditional twisted brass canopy supports and brass stars and rings so much beloved by fairground people.

In total a further eight engines in this batch went to West Country customers, eight went to Scotland and five went to Ireland. No 1584 was given a show finish and exhibited at Smithfield in 1891 where it was sold to a French farmer. The remaining thirteen engines went to customers widely scattered throughout the United Kingdom.

After 1897 all 6 NHP standard duty unsprung SCC engines built employed the independent double geared drive to the hind axle. Eighty-seven of these engines were built in the period to the First World War and the marque became very much the 'bread and butter' of works activity.

These engines followed closely the various detailed design changes incorporated in other types and sizes of contemporary GP traction engines. Those built in 1897 and 1898 had the solid end type cylinder; thereafter most had conventional cylinders with detachable cylinder end

6 NHP SCC 6 × 10 × 10 ins DOUBLE-GEARED, UNSPRUNG TRACTION ENGINE

No 2008	Built	1897	No 2219	Built	1899	No 2474	Built	1902	No 2767	Built	1904
2021	"	1897	2229	"	1899	2487	"	1902	2811	"	1905
2024	"	1897	2241	"	1899	2492	"	1902	2821	"	1905
2029	"	1897	2254	"	1900	2499	"	1902	2843	"	1906
2044	"	1897	2286	"	1900	2500	"	1902	2906	"	1907
2047	"	1897	2299	"	1900	2504	"	1902	2952	"	1907
2056	"	1897	2300	"	1900	2508	"	1902	2965	"	1907
2066	"	1898	2308	"	1900	2518	"	1902	3003	"	1908
2079	"	1898	2319	"	1900	2536	"	1903	3017	"	1908
2086	"	1898	2329	"	1900	2538	"	1903	3034	"	1908
2092	"	1898	2330	"	1900	2544	"	1903	3036	"	1908
2113	"	1898	2376	"	1901	2545	"	1903	3125	"	1908
2131	"	1898	2383	"	1901	2586	"	1903	3134	"	1909
2143	"	1898	2391	"	1901	2590	"	1903	3143	"	1909
2149	"	1898	2405	"	1901	2615	"	1903	3145	"	1909
2155	"	1899	2409	"	1901	2662	"	1904	3205	"	1910
2156	"	1899	2415	"	1901	2663	"	1904	3209	"	1910
2167	"	1899	2418	"	1901	2665	"	1904	3224	"	1910
2181	"	1899	2449	"	1902	2684	"	1904	3233	"	1910
2188	"	1899	2451	"	1902	2700	"	1904	3240	"	1910
2198	"	1899	2453	"	1902	2732	"	1904	3385	"	1912
2206	"	1899	2454	"	1902	2737	"	1904			

covers. In 1902 several engines were built with the boiler barrel in one piece. Engines built after 1903 had a large gap in the front box bracket instead of individual cut-outs for the connecting rod and eccentric rods. Until 1906 the boiler working pressure was 160 PSI, thereafter progressively increasing to 200 PSI. The double-geared transmission shafting and other mechanical details were as already described. A grate area of 4.5 sq ft and a total heating surface of 116 sq ft was maintained and all had thirty-four 2 ins dia × 5 ft 1 ins long smoke tubes. Most hind wheels were 5 ft 7½ ins dia × 16 ins wide and the two-speed gearing gave ratio of 25.7 to 1 and 14.1 to 1. The first twelve engines were fitted with cross-arm governors; then high speed type governors were fitted until 1903 and thereafer all were fitted with Pickering governors set at 155 RPM. The great majority had Penberthy type injectors. On average the engines weighed 9 tons 10 cwt.

Thirty engines in this group went to East Anglian customers and eleven went to the West Country. No 2021 was delivered new to Squire Weller Poley of Boxted Hall, then High Sheriff of Suffolk, on July 6th 1897, and was employed for many years on his 2000 acre farm driving a threshing drum. Your author's study window overlooks the very yard where this activity took place and is now replaced at harvest time by an apparently endless stream of noisy diesel engine tractors en route to the grain dryer. Eventually the engine joined Sturgeon Bros' large fleet of engines at Stanton, near Bury St Edmunds. Eight of these engines went to Scotland, Nos 2544 and 2545 joining J Wyllies' fleet of Burrell engines at Dumfries; four went to Yorkshire farmers and sixteen went to a variety of customers scattered throughout the country.

A special mention must be made of engine No 3145 which started its working life with a Lancashire farmer. In 1954 it was spotted on Walney Island near Barrow-in-Furness with its boiler, cylinder and motion installed on a rail mounted steam crane chassis in the ownership of the Piel & Walney Gravel Company. This is the only record we have of a Burrell engine ever being rail-mounted.

Nineteen of this series were exported, thirteen going to New Zealand customers. No 2538 was obviously a repeat order for it had a special boiler with a special arched firebox roof, four stay tubes and a barrel rolled in one piece as fitted to some earlier 8 NHP single cylinder traction engines. All were fitted with the locally favoured large rectangular headlamp on top of the smokebox.

Engine Nos 2181, 2229, 2451 and 2454 were sold through the Charles Ludt & Co agency whose office was in the Rue Crimée in Paris. The steam chest covers of these engines carried a special plate embossed 'Brevet Burrell Frères.' The use of the term Burrell Brothers is of interest because the word 'Brothers' never formed any part of the company's registered name. It is more likely to be a reference to the fact that the several patents incorporated in these engines were all filed in one or other of the Burrell brothers' names. We shall learn in a later chapter that the financial structure of the firm was altered to that of a Limited Liability Company, trading as Charles Burrell & Sons Ltd from July 1st 1884. The relationship between Jean Burnell and Ludt is not now known, but both agencies appear to have operated in parallel, although a score of engines appear to have been sold direct to French customers. An example is No 3240 which went direct to the Lyonese Manaccan Company in 1910. Herbert Burrell, Charles II's eldest son, received part of his education in Paris under Jean Burnell's supervision, attending a Lycée at Batignolles in the northern suburbs of the city. Correspondence between Robert Burrell and young Herbert remains extant, indicating that both were keen stamp collectors at the time and that Robert was a frequent visitor to Paris.

One of the Ludt engines, No 2284, was returned to the works, renumbered 2451 and resold to a Scottish customer. No 2454 was provided with a full length canopy and given the added refinement of a spring mounted footplate floor. At the turn of the century electro-plating was coming increasingly into use and No 2499 and several subsequent engines were fitted with nickel-plated axle caps. Chromium plating was never used at any time on Burrell engines. It is believed No 2155 went to Brown & McKenzie of Port Elizabeth in South Africa and spent its working life with a Burrell road roller engaged on public works contracts.

A spring-mounted version of the 6 NHP double-geared standard duty traction engine was introduced in 1905 and universally became known as the 'Aberdeenshire' engine, although only the last of the seven engines built ever went anywhere near Aberdeen.

6 NHP SCC 6 × 10 × 10 ins DOUBLE-GEARED, 'ABERDEENSHIRE' ENGINE

No	Built		No	Built	
No 2742	Built	1905	No 2860	Built	1917
2798	"	1906	2933	"	1907
2799	"	1906	3014	"	1907
2834	"	1907			

All seven engines carried a ring on the smokebox door inscribed 'The Aberdeenshire Engine'. They had 160 PSI boilers similar to their unsprung equivalents, but with 5 ft 8 ins long smoke tubes. All except No 2860 had three-speed gearing giving ratios of 25.0 to 1, 17.4 to 1 and 10.2 to 1; 6 ft 0 ins dia × 18 ins wide hind wheels and long travel spring gear with 15 plate leaf springs on the hind axles. Nos 2798 and 2799 named 'Vedette' and 'Eureka'

Fig 93 No 2003 the last of the fifty-eight 6 NHP SCC single drive unsprung standard duty GP traction engines built between 1891 and 1897.

were built as Showman's type engines and supplied to M Anderson, a Parisian showman who painted them a deep crimson. They were supplied with full length awnings, six twisted brass canopy supports, motion side plates and Crompton dynamos, with a sheet iron guard between the chimney and the dynamo. Both engines were fitted with Moore's steam feed pumps and the front belly tanks carried 140 gallons of water giving a total carrying capacity of 260 gallons. They appear to have had a comparatively short life as Showman's engines and in 1911 both were returned to the works for conversion to road rollers on the Jean Bonhoure system which we shall learn more about in a later chapter.

More or less concurrently with the introduction of the Aberdeenshire engines the works built eighteen 6 NHP SCC standard duty spring-mounted engines, similar in most respects to their unsprung equivalents. The main difference from the Aberdeenshire engines was that the boilers were shortened and fitted with thirty-five 2 ins dia × 5 ft 1 ins long smoke tubes. The volute and spiral springs fitted on earlier engines were replaced by 17 plate leaf springs and the compensating gear was fitted with Burrells' patent differential locking device operated from the footplate which enabled the driver to override the action of the differential gear in order to give a positive drive to both hind wheels. This feature was of great value when operating on soft muddy ground. Six of these engines were spring mounted on the hind axle only and the 6 ft 0 ins dia hind wheels were retained.

6 NHP SCC DOUBLE-GEARED, SPRING-MOUNTED STANDARD DUTY TRACTION ENGINES

No	Built	No	Built
No 2621	Built 1903	No 3126	Built 1909
2853	" 1906	3136	" 1909
2857	" 1906	3215	" 1910
2927	" 1907	3299	" 1911
2930	" 1906	3323	" 1911
2931	" 1907	3327	" 1911
3066	" 1908	3402	" 1912
3107	" 1909	3500	" 1913
3123	" 1909	3587	" 1914

Nos 2621 and 2853 went to the Reid & Gray Agency in New Zealand. No 2621 had three-speed gearing and the special arched firebox, one-piece boiler barrel, four-stay tube boiler previously referred to. Four engines went to Scottish customers, Nos 2927 and 2930 joining J Wyllie's fleet. Two engines went to East Anglian customers and two went to the West Country, one of which, No 3299, had a long awning and motion side plates, a feature usually reserved for road locomotives and intended primarily to conceal the reciprocating motion from passing horses.

The evolution of the 7 NHP SCC traction engine followed closely that of the equivalent single cylinder engines, but because they were not produced in any quantity until 1897 no single drive unsprung engines were produced apart from the original five largely experimental

Fig 94 A line-up of six Burrell traction engines at the 1904 Suffolk Show. The engine on the left of the picture is No 2674 7 NHP SCC TE supplied to Sir Richard Lacon of Ormesby with polished brass boiler cladding.

engines already discussed. The majority of 7 NHP SCC unsprung engines built were double-geared in accordance with then current fashion, although thirty-two single drive spring-mounted engines were built concurrently. One suspects the majority of road users preferred the longer travel springs provided by the single drive gearing. It is interesting to note that whereas the number of 6 NHP SCC engines built was two and a half times greater than their single cylinder equivalents the number of 7 NHP SCC engines produced was 20 per cent less and 8 NHP SCC engines 60 per cent less than their single cylinder equivalents. Such was the increased performance and utility of the 6 NHP SCC engines that farmers in particular preferred the smaller engines.

Seventy-six 7 NHP SCC double-geared unsprung engines were built between 1897 and 1914. The first twenty-six engines had 6¼ ins dia HP × 10½ ins dia LP × 12 ins stroke cylinders, thereafter all had 6 ins dia HP × 10 ins dia LP × 12 ins stroke cylinders.

Five of the six engines produced with the 6.11 sq ft grates – Nos 2738, 2791, 2873, 3065 and 3067 – were supplied to the Coulson agency in Melbourne fitted with spark arresters in their extended smokeboxes making them suitable for wood burning. Additionally these engines were fitted with special 4 ft 3 ins between centres connecting rods. The sixth engine built of this type was only given seven rows of stays in the firebox due to an error in the boiler shop and was sold off cheaply to a Yorkshire farmer.

The drive shafts, gearing and wheels, pumps, injectors and governors all remained as fitted to the equivalent vintage 6 NHP engines. A new innovation introduced in the series was the tubular front axle replacing the rectangular forged faggotted iron axle.

Thirty-five of these engines went to customers in East Anglia, ten went to customers in Lancashire and Yorkshire and three went to Scottish customers. Already mentioned are the five wood-burners which went to Australia and No 2442 went to New Zealand. Many of these engines gave long and continuous service and fortunately several remain in preservation.

7 NHP SCC, DOUBLE-GEARED, UNSPRUNG TRACTION ENGINES

No	Built	No	Built	No	Built	No	Built
No 2027	Built 1897	No 2292	Built 1900	No 2531	Built 1903	No 2947	Built 1907
2061	" 1898	2310	" 1900	2578	" 1903	2961	" 1907
2089	" 1898	2311	" 1900	2597	" 1903	3000	" 1908
2108	" 1898	2317	" 1900	2605	" 1903	3048	" 1908
2119	" 1898	2322	" 1900	2607	" 1903	3052	" 1908
2124	" 1898	2324	" 1900	2630	" 1903	3065	" 1908
2129	" 1898	2335	" 1900	2674	" 1904	3067	" 1908
2144	" 1899	2341	" 1901	2693	" 1904	3112	" 1909
2148	" 1898	2386	" 1901	2699	" 1904	3133	" 1909
2162	" 1899	2399	" 1901	2707	" 1904	3137	" 1909
2191	" 1899	2400	" 1901	2738	" 1905	3138	" 1909
2212	" 1899	2420	" 1901	2766	" 1905	3139	" 1909
2218	" 1899	2439	" 1901	2776	" 1905	3164	" 1909
2233	" 1899	2442	" 1901	2786	" 1905	3221	" 1910
2236	" 1899	2476	" 1902	2791	" 1906	3241	" 1910
2244	" 1899	2505	" 1902	2826	" 1906	3280	" 1911
2246	" 1899	2511	" 1902	2836	" 1906	3498	" 1913
2256	" 1900	2514	" 1902	2873	" 1906	3611	" 1914
2257	" 1900	2521	" 1902	2914	" 1907	3629	" 1914

Nos 2027 to 2335 had the solid end pattern cylinders. Nos 2341 and successive engines had the conventional open-ended cylinders with the bores reduced by ½ ins dia to drawing T2101. Engines Nos 2027 to 2119 had the smaller type 602 boiler pressed to 160 PSI as fitted to many 6 NHP engines. These had 4.5 sq ft grates and 5 ft 1 ins long smoke tubes. Thereafter Nos 2124 to 2707 had hornplates and variations of the larger type T194 boiler pressed to 160 PSI with a 4.9 sq ft grate. The thirty 2 ins dia smoke tubes remained 5 ft 1 ins long. The majority of the earlier engines in this series had a mud-hole over the steel firebox crown and the hornplates were chain riveted. Later engines built between 1905 and 1914 were fitted with either 4.9 sq ft or 6.11 sq ft grates. All had longer boilers with thirty-eight 1¾ ins dia × 5 ft 8 ins long smoke tubes. Boiler pressures were progressively increased to 185 PSI. After 1903 the majority had the large gap in the front box bracket previously referred to and for a period the boiler shells were rolled in one piece. This was made possible by the very high quality steel plate then being purchased from Krupps of Essen.

We next consider the 32 TNHP SCC single drive spring mounted traction engines built between 1897 and 1906.

The cylinders of the first thirteen engines measured 6¼ ins dia HP × 10½ ins dia LP × 12 ins stroke. The remainder had 6 ins dia × 10 ins dia × 12 ins stroke cylinders. This class represented in many respects a half way stage between GP traction engines and road locomotives. In accordance with the vogue established at St Nicholas Works, those built up to No 2475 had the solid end type cylinder. The boilers were all based on the type T194 employed on the contemporary 6 NHP standard duty engines pressed to 160 PSI. The majority had thirty-four 2 ins dia × 5 ft 1 ins long smoke tubes, but the last five engines in the series had lengthened boilers with thirty-eight 1¾ ins dia × 5 ft 8 ins long smoke tubes. The majority had 5 ft 9½ ins dia hind wheels and in all other major respects they were similar to the 7 NHP unsprung engines already described.

7 NHP SCC, SINGLE DRIVE, SPRING-MOUNTED TRACTION ENGINES

No	Built	No	Built	No	Built	No	Built
No 2042	Built 1897	No 2243	Built 1899	No 2416	Built 1901	No 2520	Built 1902
2139	” 1898	2250	” 1899	2423	” 1901	2592	” 1903
2163	” 1899	2263	” 1900	2433	” 1901	2682	” 1904
2180	” 1899	2301	” 1901	2459	” 1902	2728	” 1905
2189	” 1899	2302	” 1901	2462	” 1902	2750	” 1905
2190	” 1899	2348	” 1901	2475	” 1902	2781	” 1905
2220	” 1899	2361	” 1901	2488	” 1902	2819	” 1906
2227	” 1899	2380	” 1901	2496	” 1902	2856	” 1906

Although strictly speaking a spring-mounted traction engine, No 2462 was built new as a Showman's type road locomotive with a dynamo platform, full length canopy with twisted brass supports and other traditional showman's adornments. It was the first of seven fine Burrell engines supplied new to Charles Thurston, the well known Norwich traveller who named her 'Alexandra'. The engine had a solid flywheel, motion side plates and 6 ft 0 ins dia × 18 ins wide hind wheels all of which were more usually associated with road locomotives. In 1909 the engine was sold to John Jones, a Bristol showman.

A similar engine No 2263 having the smaller size cylinder gave four years service in commercial ownership with Wood & Nesbet before being returned to the works and similarly converted to a Showman's type engine for Mrs Susan Woolgar, a popular London area traveller who named her 'Romulus'. Later it was sold to James Cole of Yate, near Bristol; who at various times owned six Burrell Showman's engines including No 2072 the oldest showman's type engine to survive in its original condition. Finally the engine finished its working life with Tom Smith, a Sussex showman from Shoreham-by-Sea.

No 2781, built to the order of John Powell of Liverpool, was built to perform the duties of a road locomotive. The boiler working pressure was increased to 180 PSI. Strengthened 12 leaf spring gear was fitted and a short awning was provided, although the traction engine transmission shafting, gearing and bearing sizes were retained. The engine was a familiar sight around Liverpool Docks for many years. Twelve of the remaining engines in the batch went to East Anglian customers, six went to Scottish customers and the rest went to customers in the rural shires. Three of the Scottish engines, Nos 2139, 2437 and 2488 went to Charlton & Wyllie of Dumfries, the third important Burrell owner in the area to use his engines primarily for road haulage duties.

The final type of 7 NHP SCC traction engines built were a batch of twenty-one double-geared, spring-mounted engines similar in most respects to the single drive engines just discussed.

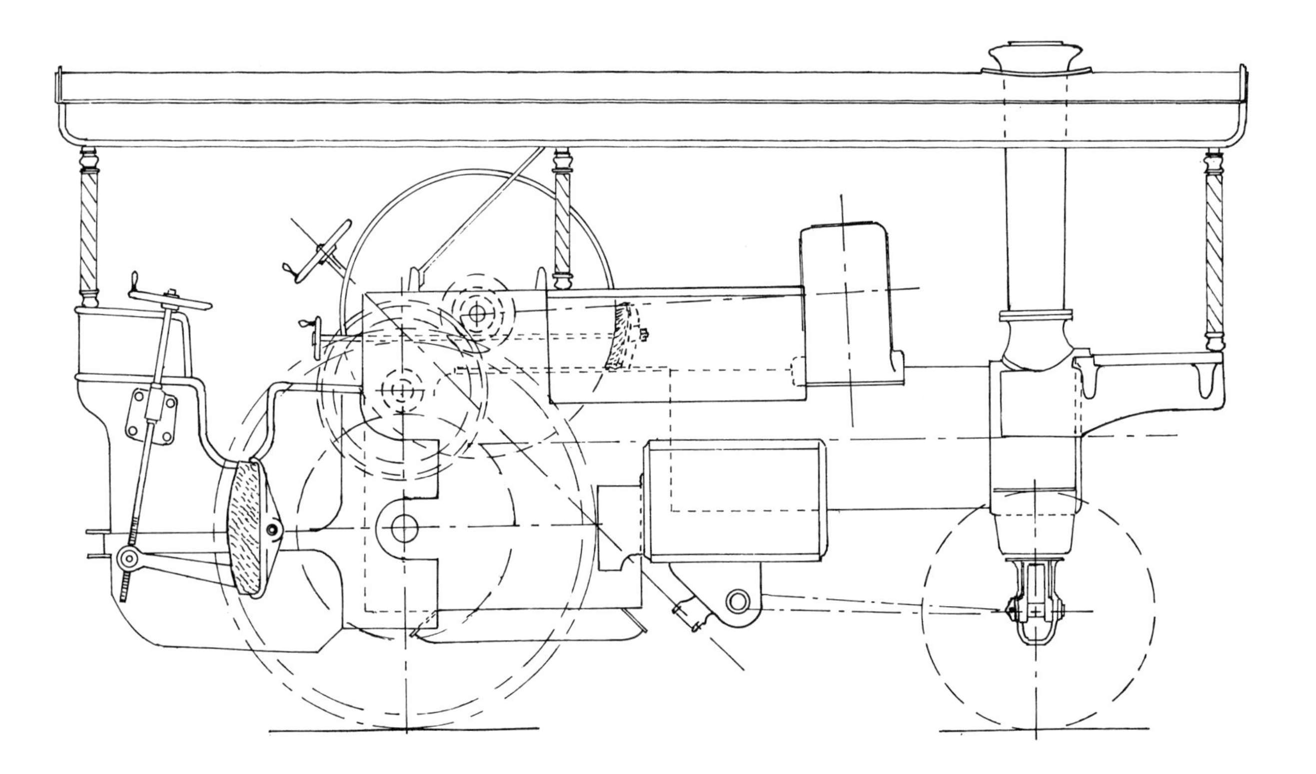

Fig 95 Reproduction of works drawing illustrating No 2798 6 NHP 'Aberdeenshire' type Showman's traction engine supplied to a French Showman in 1906.

7 NHP SCC, DOUBLE-GEARED, SPRING-MOUNTED TRACTION ENGINES

No 2635 Built 1903	No 2959 Built 1908	No 3184 Built 1910	No 3399 Built 1912
2659 " 1904	3002 " 1908	3201 " 1910	3420 " 1912
2901 " 1907	3024 " 1908	3218 " 1910	3432 " 1912
2921 " 1907	3043 " 1908	3263 " 1910	3586 " 1914
2943 " 1907	3087 " 1909	3307 " 1911	3702 " 1915
2946 " 1907	3158 " 1909		

The first seven engines had boilers pressed to 160 PSI and thereafter the working pressure was increased to 185 PSI. All had 5 ft 8 ins long smoke tubes, boiler feed pumps, type BP 'F' injectors and Pickering governors. All had 17 leaf spring gear. Some, but not all, were fitted with differential locking gear.

Nos 2659 and 2901 were shipped to the Coulson agency in Melbourne, Australia. As with the earlier unsprung engines supplied to this agency, the grate area was increased from 4.9 sq ft to 6.11 sq ft, spark arresters were fitted in the extended smokeboxes and special guard rail type extensions were fitted to the tender in order to increase their fuel-carrying capacity. The two Australian engines had three-speed gearing, their main duty being the transportation of bales of wool from the homestead to the railhead for shipment.

Ten of the engines in this series went to East Anglian customers, two went to Scottish customers and three went to J L Penfold of Barnham, near Arundel in Sussex, who employed six Burrell engines at various times in his haulage business. The remainder went to customers in the rural shires. So far as can be traced all these engines spent most of their useful lives transporting wool, flour and other agricultural produce.

8 NHP SCC traction engines went into regular production in 1893, although as we have already seen, three largely experimental engines were built in the years 1887–1893. Compared with the omnipotent 6 NHP engines only one-third as many 8 NHP engines were built and 20 per cent of these were exported. The evolution of the marque followed closely the pattern set by the smaller size engines and three basic types were built. Firstly, double-geared unsprung engines; secondly and concurrently, single drive spring-mounted engines; and thirdly a batch of twenty-seven double-geared spring-mounted engines.

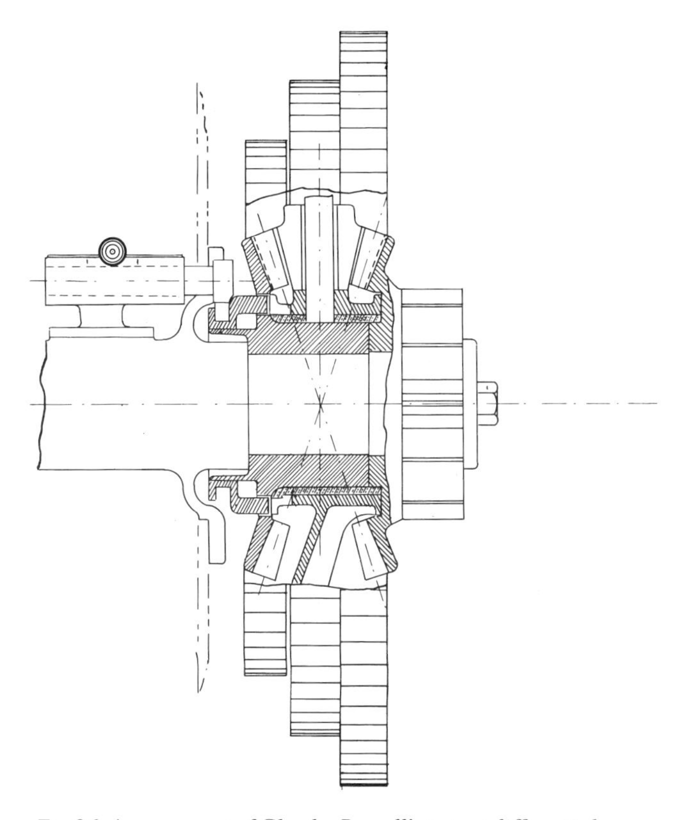

Fig 96 Arrangement of Charles Burrell's patent differential locking gear showing the clutch mechanism described in patent No 24978/1905.

Fifty-three 8 NHP SCC unsprung engines with double gearing were built. All except two had 6¼ ins dia HP × 10½ ins dia LP × 12 ins stroke cylinders and the solid end type cylinder taking steam up the motion bar end was introduced in 1896.

8 NHP SCC DOUBLE-GEARED UNSPRUNG TRACTION ENGINES

No 1668 Built 1893	No 1859 Built 1895	No 2178 Built 1899	No 2419 Built 1901
1689 " 1893	1865 " 1895	2179 " 1899	2429 " 1901
1693 " 1893	1883 " 1895	2182 " 1899	2435 " 1901
1695 " 1893	1921 " 1896	2217 " 1899	2473 " 1902
1720 " 1893	1929 " 1896	2248 " 1899	2479 " 1902
1722 " 1893	1959 " 1896	2255 " 1900	2481 " 1902
1730 " 1893	2054 " 1898	2271 " 1901	2483 " 1902
1760 " 1894	2060 " 1897	2321 " 1901	2484 " 1902
1768 " 1894	2071 " 1898	2326 " 1901	2510 " 1902
1775 " 1894	2082 " 1898	2336 " 1901	2546 " 1903
1814 " 1894	2099 " 1898	2375 " 1901	2583 " 1903
1835 " 1895	2107 " 1898	2378 " 1901	2622 " 1903
1844 " 1895	2171 " 1899	2396 " 1901	2761 " 1905
1854 " 1895			

Fig 97 No 2263 7 NHP SCC single drive spring mounted traction engine as built before conversion to a Showman's type engine.

The majority of the boilers fitted to these engines were as the type C379 fitted to their single cylinder contemporaries except that the working pressure was increased to 160 PSI. All except the five engines supplied to the Howard agency in Sydney had 5.375 sq ft grates, giving a total heating surface of 151 sq ft and most had forty-one 2 ins × 5 ft 8 ins long smoke tubes. No 1854 and the succeeding six engines had double-riveted, double flange plates. Engines Nos 2510, 2622 and 2761 had special one-piece boiler shells and arched roof fireboxes with large flanges to drawing 1828. These boilers were fitted with 20 per cent fewer smoke tubes. The Australian engines, Nos 1959, 2071, 2082, 2107, 2217 and 2375 had 6.0 sq ft grates, spark arresters in their extended smokeboxes and enlarged fuel bunkers. The smoke tubes remained 5 ft 8 ins long.

In addition to the six engines which went to Australia, five, Nos 1768, 2419, 2483, 2484 and 2622, went to the Reid & Gray agency in New Zealand and two, Nos 2321 and 2326, went to the Jean Ludt agency in Paris. In accordance with French practice these engines were fitted with awnings, chimney dampers and spring-mounted footplates. Eighteen engines went to customers in East Anglia, five went to the southern counties and three went to Lancashire. No 2099 was supplied direct to the War Office where it underwent extensive proving trials in the Aldershot area and others went to customers in the Home Counties and the West Country.

Three of the Lancashire engines, Nos 1695, 2336 and 2761, were supplied to S T Rosbotham of Bickerstaff who operated a fleet of fifteen Burrell engines and road rollers over a long period of time. Two of the East Anglian engines, Nos 2473 and 2546, were specially adapted to take the tender-mounted Darby Digger and fitted with detachable rim flywheels to accommodate a pitch chain drive from the engine crankshaft to the digging machine countershaft. No 2182 was built as a special heavy duty scarifying engine for the Road Breaking Company in London. It was fitted with a Rutty 3-type scarifier, patented jointly by Frederick Burrell and Harry Rutty in July 1896. This device was attached directly to the engine hind axle, thereby removing all stresses from the tender. Subsequently it was fitted to many road rollers built at St Nicholas Works.

Nos 2054 was built as a full Showman's type engine for Mrs Susan Woolgar of Barnes who travelled the London area as Madame Linnet. No 2171 supplied originally to A G Stanborough, a contractor of Walmer in Kent, was acquired by H Dack of Deopham in Norfolk in 1907, converted to a full Showman's type engine and used for many years to haul his set of Galloping Horses. It is said that the full length awning and brasswork from his 8 NHP single cylinder engine No 1001 were utilised in this conversion.

Twenty-two 8 NHP SCC single drive spring mounted engines were built concurrently. Apart from the arrangement of the transmission shafts and spring gear the majority were similar to the double geared unsprung version.

8 NHP SCC SINGLE DRIVE, SPRING-MOUNTED TRACTION ENGINES

No 1725 Built 1893	No 2127 Built 1898	No 2343 Built 1900	No 2533 Built 1902
1770 " 1894	2130 " 1898	2367 " 1901	2574 " 1903
1776 " 1894	2252 " 1899	2377 " 1901	2600 " 1903
1938 " 1896	2270 " 1900	2389 " 1901	2616 " 1903
1957 " 1896	2289 " 1900	2532 " 1902	2648 " 1904
1975 " 1896	2327 " 1900		

All except Nos 1770 and 1776 had 6¼ ins dia HP × 10½ ins dia LP × 12 ins stroke cylinders. The two exceptions had 6½ ins × 11 ins × 12 ins stroke cylinders which were more usually associated with road locomotives. Solid end cylinders taking steam up the motion bar end were introduced in 1898. All the boilers except Nos 2327, 2532 and 2533 were based on the 'C' type with 5.375 sq ft grates and 5 ft 8 ins long smoke tubes. No 2327 was built similarly to the 7 NHP engines with a 4.9 sq ft grate and 5 ft 1 ins long smoke tubes and Nos 2532 and 2533 were fitted with a special boiler described in the company's records as a Stevens boiler. The firebox crown had special stays to drawing 1867, additional special stays were arranged between the hornplates and the one-piece boiler barrel carried five stay tubes. Both these engines went to the Reid and Gray agency and it is assumed that this specification was laid down by the New Zealand customer.

These engines performed a wide variety of general haulage duties and, with the exception of Nos 2532 and 2533, were widely scattered throughout the United Kingdom. Most had 6 ft 6 ins dia × 16 ins wide hind wheels and two-speed gearing with 27.9 to 1 and 14.9 to 1 ratios making them fast engines on the road. No 1770 went to James Reid at Bridge of Dee for timber haulage in the lovely country around Balmoral Castle. Eventually No 1938 became one of eight Burrell engines in the Bath & Portland Stone Firms fleet used for hauling large blocks of quarried stone. Nos 1975 and 2127 eventually found their way into James Graven's possession. This well-known East Anglian dealer had twenty-six Burrell engines in his possession at various times. No 2289 went new to the War Office for hauling animal fodder in the Aldershot area and then passed to the London based Steam Wagon & Tractor Company. No 2327 was one of twelve Burrell engines owned by Devonshire contractor Fred Payne of Red Ball, near Culmstock, and No 2343 went to John Henton, a threshing contractor of Hopwas, near Tamworth in Staffordshire. He owned five Burrell engines at various times, including the two famous Bostock & Wombwell Showman's engines 'Rajah' and 'Nero'. No 2574 went to the Brynamman Silica Company in Carmarthenshire and was used for belt-driving a crushing machine and for general haulage duties in the area.

Only one of this series saw service in Showland. In 1904 No 2389 was purchased by Arthur Crighton of Nayland in Suffolk and he named her 'Kitchener'. Although fitted with a dynamo platform and full length awning with twisted brass supports, the spoked flywheel was retained.

Fig 98 No 3024 7 NHP SCC double geared spring mounted traction engine. Photographed at Mildenhall, Suffolk in 1908 at the start of its first day's work on Favor Parker's Beck Row farm.

8 NHP SCC DOUBLE-GEARED, SPRING-MOUNTED TRACTION ENGINES

No	Built	No	Built	No	Built	No	Built
No 2601	Built 1903*	No 2688	Built 1904*	No 2845	Built 1906†	No 3050	Built 1908*
2602	" 1903*	2689	" 1904*	2851	" 1906*†	3213	" 1910†
2603	" 1903*	2697	" 1904*	2859	" 1906	3474	" 1913†
2628	" 1903*	2711	" 1904†	2869	" 1906*	3522	" 1913*†
2681	" 1904*	2747	" 1906†	2875	" 1906	3625	" 1914*†
2686	" 1904*	2757	" 1905	2897	" 1907	3737	" 1916
2687	" 1904*	2800	" 1906†	3046	" 1908		

* Engines sold to New Zealand customers † Engines fitted with three-speed gearing

The final type of 8 NHP SCC traction engine had double gearing and was spring-mounted. These engines were more akin to road locomotives than traction engines, although they retained traction engine transmission shafting and bearing sizes.

Engines Nos 2601 to 2698 had the standard 8 NHP SCC traction engine cylinders measuring 6¼ ins dia HP × 10½ ins dia LP × 12 ins stroke, the remainder, except Nos 2845 and 2875, had road locomotive cylinders measuring 6¾ ins × 11¼ ins × 12 ins stroke. Three variations of boiler were fitted to this class of engine. The first four engines, all of which went to New Zealand, had the large flange, arched roof type firebox with 5.375 sq ft grates, 5 ft 8 ins long smoke tubes and a one-piece boiler barrel. The twelve succeeding engines which also went to New Zealand plus the special Showman's engine No 2845 had 6.6 sq ft grates and 6 ft 2 ins long smoke tubes giving a total heating surface of 162.0 sq ft. The remaining ten engines had 6.0 sq ft grates and 5 ft 8 ins long smoke tubes. Boiler pressures were progressively increased from 160 PSI in 1903 to 200 PSI in 1913. Engines built between 1906 and 1908 had the large gap in the front box bracket to give greater clearance and improved access to the connecting rods and eccentrics. An unusual feature specified for engines Nos 2601 to 2603 was that the boiler cleading should be supplied in a burnished blue steel finish.

Most of the engines sent to New Zealand were fitted with a Moores steam pump which had a greater output than the mechanically driven pump. Penberthy injectors were widely used but some little known alternatives, the Natham, Strübe and Antopositive, were also specified and all the batch were fitted with Pickering type governors. The hind wheels were 6 ft 6 ins dia × 18 ins wide giving an overall engine width of 7 ft 11 ins. The flywheels were 4 ft 6 ins dia × 6 ins wide and on average the engines weighed 12 tons 15 cwt. Nine of the engines were fitted with three-speed gearing having ratios 24.4 to 1 and 8.3 to 1.

The special Showman's engine, No 2845 was supplied new to the self-styled 'President', G H Kemp of Leicester, one of the greatly loved characters of the Edwardian

Fig 99 A typical Australian scene at the turn of the century transporting bales of wool from the homestead to the railhead.

Fig 100 A typical 8 NHP SCC double geared unsprung GP traction engine built between 1893 and 1903.

Fig 101 No 3522 8 NHP SCC double geared spring mounted traction engine built in 1913 with the large smokebox mounted headlamp characteristic of engines supplied through the Reid & Gray Agency photographed in preservation in New Zealand.

Fig 102 Favor Parker's 7 NHP SCC Burrell engine threshing at Willow Meadow Farm, Mildenhall – circa 1910.

fairground scene. Starting life as a solicitor's clerk he extensively travelled throughout the United Kingdom for nearly thirty years and included visits to America and Canada. His three fine Bioscope shows, precursors of the cinema, were always popular with the public wherever they appeared. He acquired three Burrell engines, No 2789 'Lord Kitchener', No 2845 'The President' and No 2984 'Premier'. He was immensely proud of these engines and always ensured that they were turned out in immaculate condition.

No 2845 was supplied new with a dynamo platform, full length awning and the traditional adornments specified by the showman. It was painted crimson with yellow wheels. Its SCC cylinder was bored oversize and measured 6¾ ins dia × 11¼ ins dia × 12 ins stroke and it had the same large grate, long boiler as fitted to the engines sent to New Zealand. The hind wheels were 6 ft 6 ins dia × 22 ins wide giving an overall engine width of 8 ft 6 ins. It was one of the few traction engines built with brakes operating on the hind wheel rims and on the rim of the flywheel. Motion side plates were fitted and the spoked flywheel was covered by a sheet metal disc giving a tout ensemble of a Showman's road locomotive. In 1912 the engine passed into the ownership of Marshall Hill, another well-known amusement caterer of Bedminster near Bristol. No 2875, the second Showman's type traction engine in the series, was supplied to the Northampton travellers, Relph and Pedley. At one time it was used to generate for their scenic railway.

No 2859 was the only Burrell traction engine supplied to the Meissner & Dietlein agency of Magdeburg in Germany which operated between 1896 and 1914. Magdeburg, an old fortress town and an important centre of communcations on the river Elbe, had become the hub of the German traction engine and agricultural machinery industry. The Machinenfabrik R Wolf and A Hencke, as well as John Fowler and Garretts of Leiston, had important factories in the area. Robert Burrell is known to have made several visits to Magdeburg. In total this agency secured orders for forty-two Burrell ploughing engines, twenty-eight road rollers and one traction engine.

We end this chapter with mention of the only 10 NHP single crank compound traction engine listed in the company's records. No 2334 was completed in October 1900 and supplied to Rabling & Company of Camborne in Cornwall, near the birthplace of Richard Trevithick. It is by no means clear why the works designated this as a 10 NHP engine, for it had 8 NHP cylinders measuring 6½ ins dia HP × 11 ins dia LP × 12 ins stroke and the type C379 8 NHP boiler with a 5.375 sq ft grate and 41 2 ins dia × 5 ft 8 ins smoke tubes. The single drive gearing had the differential mounted on the hind axle integral with the winding drum and the long travel spring gear was mounted on volute springs. Two road speeds were provided having ratios of 27.3 and 15.0 to 1, the hind wheels were 6 ft 6 ins dia × 18 ins wide. Belly tanks were fitted giving a total water carrying capacity of 258 gallons. It had a short awning over the footplate and weighed 13 tons in working order. The fate of this engine is unknown to your author, but it seems probable that it was employed hauling china clay in the Redruth area.

Inevitably this chapter has contained a great deal of statistical data, identifying and cataloguing some 600 engines built at St Nicholas Works in the years between 1887 and the First World War. Some personalities involved in their design and manufacture have emerged as the story has unfolded and some details of the owners and usage to which the engines were put has been given, but a great deal more remains to be written about the Herculean tasks performed by both the engines and the men who drove them. For over half a century, when steam power dominated the agricultural scene in the United Kingdom, a splendid breed of man, the general purpose traction engine driver, went philosophically and competently about his daily task. His praises have remained largely unsung, but his considerable contribution to the well-being of his fellow men is undeniable.

CHAPTER EIGHT

Final Designs of Ploughing Engines and Portables

The story of the double crank compound (DCC) general purpose traction engine belongs to the 20th century and we must firstly consider other developments which took place at St Nicholas Works during the latter part of Queen Victoria's reign. In the 1860s the stewards of the Royal Agricultural Society pronounced, "A careful examination of the improved machinery now brought into use will show that advances have been made sufficient to prove that steam cultivation is now becoming a fact." However, the strength of John Fowler's cultivating machinery patents, coupled with the bonanza he had enjoyed as a result of the Egyptian 'Cotton Boom' precluded any of his competitors from securing more than a small corner of the existing world market for ploughing engines. We have seen in chapter 4 that throughout the 1860s Charles Burrell maintained a small output of chain-driven ploughing engines, most of which went to local farmers, but these represented a mere fraction of the sales achieved by Fowler's Steam Plough Works. Although the situation at St Nicholas Works began to change in the 1870s when Charles Burrell's three energetic sons became established in the business, a further twenty years elapsed before they achieved any significant successes with ploughing engines.

In the interim period the three brothers made their mark as thoroughly competent engineers and managers, in spite of some of the older employees finding it difficult to accept inevitable changes. Young Charles concentrated upon the works, Robert upon sales and Frederick upon the design office, although at all times they showed great respect for their father's judgement and experience. Undoubtedly the quartet made an excellent team. There is no evidence that Charles I ever travelled abroad in search of business, but from an early age Robert made frequent visits to France, Germany and Russia. Having a good ear for music, he found languages comparatively easy and he understood the importance of personal contact with overseas agents and customers. One suspects that he had the ability to work hard and play hard and combine business with pleasure during these visits. In this formative period the partners spent considerable sums of money participating in the leading agricultural shows and exhibitions and increasingly became involved in the work of various professional bodies, such as the Institution of Mechanical Engineers. Undoubtedly they benefited greatly from a widening of their horizons. During this period the company gained three silver medals awarded by the Royal Agricultural Society of England; they won gold and silver medals in France, Germany and Sweden and received numerous other prizes presented by leading United Kingdom agricultural societies.

Although neither the Boydell endless railway nor the Thomson road steamer era could be described as unqualified successes, the company had obtained an enormous amount of publicity and these factors contributed greatly to the creation of a new image. Perhaps most important of all, St Nicholas Works built an excellent reputation for quality, reliability and service. Gone for ever was the image of a small country engineering workshop and although never as large as some in terms of sales and numbers employed, by 1880 St Nicholas Works were able to compete upon equal terms with their major competitors.

At this time the United Kingdom was, as already noted, in the throes of a serious agricultural depression which lasted until 1884, but fortunately Robert Burrell had discovered the great potential of the German and Central European markets. Vast acreages of formerly virgin land were being brought into cultivation for growing cereals and beet and there was clearly a case for the company to develop new heavy duty ploughing engines. Although the Burrell team applied themselves to the problem, it was not until the 1890s that they secured a share of this lucrative market.

Their first gear-driven ploughing engine was introduced more or less concurrently with the geared traction engine and nine 8 NHP engines were produced in the period 1877–1882.

8 NHP SINGLE CYLINDER, 4-SHAFT PLOUGHING ENGINES

No	Built		No	Built
No 766	Built 1877		No 861	Built 1879
767	" 1877		862	" 1879
775	" 1878		1015	" 1882
776	" 1879		1016	" 1882
777	" 1879			

With the exception of No 766 which was sold without a cable winding drum, all the batch were sold to English farmers for use with double engine tackle with the engines working on opposite headlands drawing the implement backwards and forwards across the land. No 767 was exhibited at the 1877 Smithfield Club Show, but clearly the discerning buyers did not regard the design as having any great merit. Fitted with a single cylinder measuring 9 ins × 12 ins stroke, the engines utilised the type M7 boiler having a working pressure of 120 PSI. The grate area was 5.25 sq ft and the total heating surface 157 sq ft.

Fig 103 No 767 8 NHP geared ploughing engine fitted with Fowler's epicycloidal coiling gear as exhibited at the Smithfield Show in December 1877.

The arrangement of the geared drive to the hind wheels and to the ploughing drum is shown in the accompanying sketch, the drums being fitted with Fowler's patent epicycloidal coiling gear, enabling the cable to be coiled neatly, one coil upon another. Two road speeds were provided having ratios of 21.1 and 12.5 to 1, but in order to change speed it was necessary to remove physically one crankshaft pinion and replace it with another. The hind wheels were 5 ft 2 ins dia × 20 ins wide. In working order, the engines weighed 12 tons 3 cwt.

These were followed in early 1879 by a single pair of 'N' type 14 NHP engines having $11\frac{1}{4}$ ins dia × 12 ins stroke cylinders. They were similar in most respects to the 8 NHP engines, but the grate area was increased to 7.3 sq ft and the diameter of the boiler barrel increased from 2 ft $7\frac{1}{2}$ ins dia to 3 ft $1\frac{1}{4}$ ins dia. The wheels also were substantially increased in diameter to 6 ft 6 ins dia × 21 ins wide. Allocated works Nos 814 and 815 they went to a Gloucestershire farmer, but nothing is known of the subsequent working life.

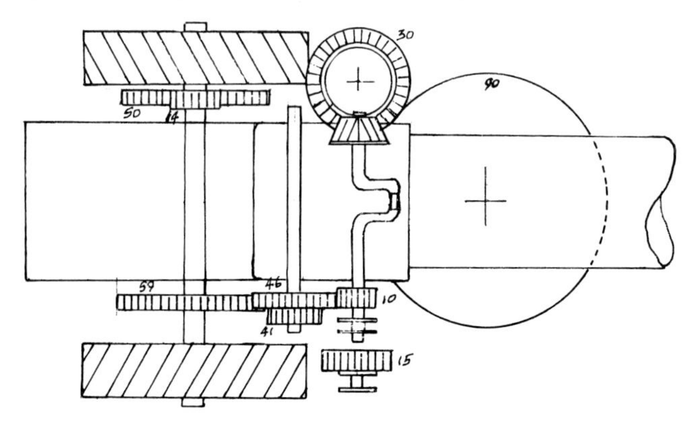

Fig 104 Diagram of 8 NHP ploughing engine 3-shaft gearing.

Mention has already been made of the small Norfolk engineering company, Everitt, Adams & Company of Great Ryburgh. In 1879 they exhibited an entirely new and novel design of ploughing engine at the RASE Kilburn Show. Instead of the winding drum being mounted horizontally under the boiler as the Fowler system, the engine had two 6 ft 6 ins dia drums carried on short stub axles either side of the boiler, each drum carrying 800 yards of $\frac{3}{4}$ ins steel plough rope. The arrangement was the subject of patent No 3553 filed in February 1879 in the joint names of Percival Everitt and Thomas Cooper, later the well known founder of the Cooper Steam Digger Company. The patent described a complete cultivating system, including details of an improved snatch block, a self-moving anchor carriage and the arrangement of the vertical winding drums mounted on the engine boiler shell. In operation the engine was positioned at the corner of the field to be cultivated and a rope was led diagonally from one of the winding drums to the snatch block positioned at the far end of the opposite headland. It was then passed around a sheave on the anchor carriage which was

Fig 105 An 8 NHP geared ploughing engine, probably No 777, at work in Essex at the turn of the century.

positioned directly opposite the engine and attached to one end of the cultivating implement. The rope from the second winding drum on the engine was passed round a large sheave mounted under the engine tender and attached to the other end of the implement. The anchor carriage possessed several novel features; it was made self-moving to move along the headland at the end of each pull or 'bout' of the implement by the action of the plough rope; the carriage frame was fitted with coulters which ploughed the headland as the carriage advanced along it; the plough rope operated a semaphore signal mounted on the anchor carriage to tell the engine driver when the implement had completed its 'bout'; and both the anchor carriage and the snatch block were fitted with travelling wheels for use on the road.

Immediately following the Kilburn Show, Everitt concluded an agreement with Charles Burrell, whereby the latter undertook to manufacture and sell ploughing engines incorporating the patent drum, paying a royalty of £5.00 on each engine sold and the first engine to be produced by St Nicholas Works was presented at the RASE Carlisle Show in July 1880. Allocated works number 888 it was an 8 NHP engine having a 9½ ins dia × 12 ins stroke single cylinder and the type X1 boiler having a working pressure of 150 PSI. The boiler was 2 ft 7½ ins diameter, had a grate area of 5.5 sq ft and a total heating surface of 170.8 sq ft, of which 138.8 sq ft was contributed by the thirty-three 2¼ ins dia × 7 ft 0 ins long smoke tubes. Due to the heavy stresses imposed upon the boiler by the attachment of the two winding drums the shell was rolled from steel plates. The drum stub axles were in reality the ends of a strong axle bent in the middle to half encircle the underside of the boiler and attached to angle irons riveted to the boiler shell.

Four transmission shafts to the hind wheels were employed and the drive to the winding drum was taken from a pinion mounted on the end of the crankshaft. The

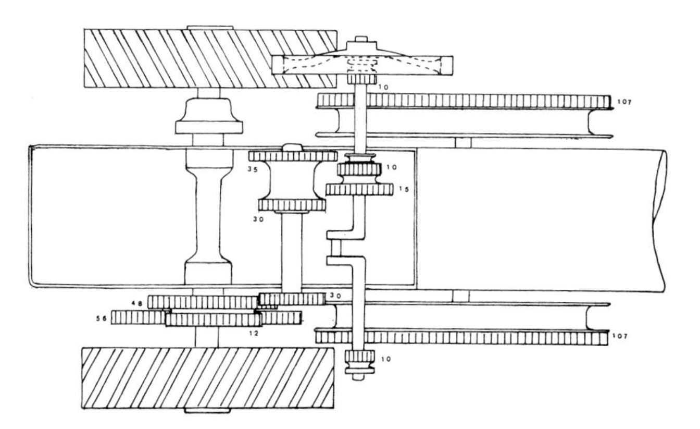

Fig 106 The twin drum 4-shaft universal ploughing engine gear train.

Fig 107 No 888, the first Burrell built universal side drum ploughing engine exhibited at the RASE Show, Carlisle in 1880.

layout of the shafts and the two speed gearing is shown in the accompanying sketch. All the gears were produced from steel but the brackets, road wheels and fabricated winding drums were of wrought iron, the drum spur rings being cast iron. Unlike the earlier ploughing engines the change speed gears were fork clutch operated, the gear ratios being 26.1 and 14.9 to 1. No differential gearing or winding drum was fitted to the hind axle, the final drive to the wheels being transmitted through pins. The sixteen spoke hind wheels were 5 ft 7½ ins dia × 18 ins wide and the front wheels 4 ft 0½ ins dia × 14 ins wide. The flywheel was 4 ft 0 ins dia × 6 ins wide and the tender water tank carried 150 gallons of water, sufficient for about two hours working.

Like the Everitt prototype the winding drums were 6 ft 6 ins dia and each carried 800 yds of ¾ ins plough rope. A self-acting brake was fitted to each winding drum consisting of a steel hoop lined with wooden blocks encircling a sheave fixed to the drum. A small ratchet wheel was fixed to the drum stub axles and an arm provided with a click was attached at its outer end to the adjustable brake strap, the other end revolving upon the stub axle. When the drum was winding-in the plough rope the brake strap carried the arm around with it, the click running over the ratchet wheel; but when the drum was paying-out the plough rope, the click engaged with the ratchet wheel, the arm then preventing the brake strap revolving with the drum, and in this manner the tail rope was kept tight. With the engine running at 150 RPM when hauling, the drum revolved at 15½ RPM which gave an equivalent implement speed across the land of 310 ft per minute. When cultivating light land where a higher rate would be permissible, the engine speed was increased to 250 RPM. Later, in 1895, when Fowler commenced the manufacture of vertical side drum ploughing engines or the 'Universal' type engine as it became known, they drove the drum spur ring from the second motion shaft giving the drum two geared speeds, which was found to be a great advantage. The RASE judges appear to have had reservations about the merits of the Everitt system of

LEFT-HAND ENGINE.

RIGHT-HAND ENGINE.

Fig 108 Left-hand & right-hand SCC ploughing engines with single universal rope drums.

Fig 109 An artist's impression of a double-engine set of Everitt's universal drum ploughing tackle at work.

cultivation but of the Burrell engine they said, "The workmanship of this engine, we need hardly add leaves nothing to be desired."

A second double drum Universal ploughing engine was completed in September 1882 and allocated works number 894. The cylinder was increased to 10 ins dia × 12 ins stroke and the boiler was lengthened to 7 ft 4½ ins, increasing the total heating surface to 201.7 sq ft, otherwise it was almost identical to its predecessor. Perhaps the most significant improvement was the replacement of the original fabricated wrought iron drums with much stronger cast steel drums.

Clearly, there were some difficulties working the engine as a single engine set of tackle and within two months of delivery to W C Cazalet of Dorking in Surrey, the right hand side drum was removed and the steering and flywheel were repositioned on the right hand side of the engine. Cazalet ordered a second single drum engine, No 895, which was delivered in March 1883. The discarded drum from No 894 was used on this engine and the steering and all the gearing was put on the left hand side enabling the pair to work as double engine tackle. The new system appears to have been successful, for after this date only four sets of ploughing engines were built at St Nicholas Works with the conventional winding drum mounted under the boiler.

The method of working is shown in the above engraving. The two engines worked opposite headlands, each alternately drawing the implement towards itself, the engine not working paying out its plough rope, whilst moving forward along the headland into position for the return pull. Any kind of implement could be used and one of the principal advantages of this system was the facility with which the tackle was set to work and removed from one site to another. They were able to remove themselves and the whole of the apparatus to fresh fields without any delay or additional labour and it was claimed that they were able to cultivate from thirty to fifty acres a day on light soils. Perhaps their greatest disadvantage was that the engines had to be paired, one with the drum on the right hand side of the engine, the other with the drum on the left hand side; whereas the conventional ploughing engine with the drum mounted under the boiler was completely interchangeable.

Although the company advertised the Universal Ploughing Engine as being available in 10, 12, 16 and 20 NHP sizes, it was not until 1893, a decade after its apparently successful introduction, that they received further orders. Initially, they emanated from the Schulte agency in Magdeburg and reflected Robert Burrell's strenuous selling efforts in this area, but before considering these, mention must be made of the four sets of conventional ploughing engines built at St Nicholas Works in the period 1881 to 1886.

The first of two pairs of 16 NHP engines, Nos 849 and 850 were completed in January 1881, having the same

Fig 110 A works' photograph of a 16 NHP single cylinder 4-shaft ploughing engine built in 1881 minus its winding drum.

11¼ ins dia × 12 ins stroke single cylinders and type 'N18' boiler fitted to the 14 NHP engines built in 1879, but with the working pressure, grate area and total heating surface suitably enlarged. They were fitted with the same drive shafts and steel gearing as the earlier engines and weighed in working order 18 tons 10 cwts. The second pair, completed in September 1883, were shipped to a farmer in Dirschan in Germany, carrying works numbers 1071 and 1072. They were similar in all respects to the earlier pair, except that the hind wheels were fitted with eighteen spokes and the width was increased to 24 ins.

The next pair of engines were rated 18 NHP, completed in December 1886 and carried works numbers 1257 and 1258. They were especially interesting for they were the first self-moving engines built by St Nicholas Works having double crank compound cylinders. Basically they had the same cylinder layout as the 20 NHP undertype engine built in 1885. The cylinders mounted side by side, measured 8½ ins dia HP × 14⅛ ins dia LP × 12 ins stroke and the cranks were set at 90 degrees to each other. The same type N18 boiler as used on the 16 NHP engines was employed, but the firebox was copper and the 2¼ ins dia × 8 ft 4½ ins long smoke tubes were produced from 11 SWG brass to meet current French boiler regulations. The four drive shafts, gearing and wheels were as the 16 NHP German engines, and the winding drum mounted under the boiler was cast iron with a steel spur ring and fitted with Wicksteads' patent coiling gear. These were the first engines supplied through the Burnell agency and went to a contractor in the ancient Roman town of Nimes in Southern France. Clearly, these were very much experimental engines for they appear to have had more than their fair share of teething troubles. No doubt it was largely due to the after sale service and attention to detail given by the works that enabled the Burnell agency to blossom as it did in later years. In 1887 the cast iron drums were replaced by ones of cast steel, specially produced by Firths of Sheffield. Apparently, the customer had managed to break no less than four iron drums in the first six months of working. Later, the crankshafts and connecting rods were replaced by an improved and stronger design. In 1890, after only three years' service, the front tube plate required replacement. The low pressure cylinder pistons also had to be renewed with a stronger, internally ribbed pattern. Apparently the injectors proved unreliable, but this was probably caused by the brackish water in the area and they were replaced by Worthington steam feed pumps. Finally, in 1893, redesigned malleable iron forecarriages were fitted. Needless to say, no more engines of this design were built.

In November 1889, T Clark of Chalford in Gloucestershire, who had purchased a pair of the 1879 type 14 NHP engines, took delivery of a pair of single cylinder engines rated 9 NHP. They carried works numbers 1161 and 1162 and had cylinders measuring 9¼ ins bore × 12 ins stroke. An improved and lengthened version of the 'M' type boiler was used with the working pressure increased to 140 PSI. Their grate area was 5.2

Fig 111 The 12 NHP single crank compound universal drum ploughing engine introduced in 1893.

sq ft and the total heating surface 176.0 sq ft, all other details being substantially as the 8 NHP engines built in 1882.

In 1890 a pair of Fowler's 20 NHP duplex cylinder ploughing engines were rebuilt by St Nicholas Works. The engines were built originally in 1868 for Robert Campbell, a wealthy Australian gold trader who owned a 3500 acre estate at Buscot Park in Berkshire and pioneered the large scale production of sugar beet in the United Kingdom. The engines originally carried Fowler numbers 1024 and 1025 but after conversion were re-numbered Nos 1487 and 1488 by Charles Burrell. The full story behind this unusual exercise remains obscure, but upon completion they were shipped to Nimes through the Burnell agency to the purchaser of the two ill-fated 18 NHP engines. Double crank compound cylinders, exactly as fitted to engine numbers 1257 and 1258 and an enlarged 'M' type boiler with copper firebox and brass tubes were supplied. The grate area was increased to 9.0 sq ft which together with the forty-six 2¼ ins dia × 7 ft 11 ins long smoke tubes gave a total heating surface of 261.0 sq ft. New Burrell built transmission shafts and gearing were fitted, but the old Fowler crankshaft, tender, boiler feed pump and winding drum were retained. Wicksteads patent coiling gear was added to the winding drum. Presumably, these conversions proved satisfactory, for there is no further mention of them in the works' records.

In October 1893, four 12 NHP Universal type ploughing engines suitable for double engine working and fitted with Everitt's patent winding drum were supplied to the recently established Franz Schulte agency in Magdeburg.

12 NHP SCC UNIVERSAL PLOUGHING ENGINES

No	Built		No	Built	
No 1716	Built	1893 (LH)	No 1718	Built	1893 (LH)
1717	"	1893 (RH)	1719	"	1893 (RH)

They had 7¼ ins dia × 12 ins dia × 12 ins stroke single crank compound cylinders and the type X83 boiler constructed in accordance with the German Boiler Regulations, which included a baffle plate and spark arrester in the smokebox and Salter type screw-down safety valves. The working pressure was 175 PSI, the grate area 8.0 sq ft and the firebox heating surface of 42.0 sq ft together with the forty-six 2 ins dia × 6 ft 7 ins long smoke tubes, giving a total heating surface of 196.5 sq ft. They were fitted with the type X95 boiler feed pumps, Penberthy type injectors and cross-arm governors. Two road speeds were provided having ratios of 27.9 and 17.7 to 1. No differential gearing was fitted and the final drive to the 6 ft 6 ins dia × 20 ins wide hind wheels was through driving pins engaging with wheel centres attached to the hind axle. The single 6 ft 6 ins dia steel winding drums were handed, one engine in each pair having the drum on the left hand side of the boiler, the other engine having it on the right hand side. Steel spur rings were bolted onto a cast iron drum centre, the drum gear ratio being 10.7 to 1. Screw-down brakes operated on the winding drum only. The flywheels were 4 ft 6 ins dia × 7 ins wide; the tender water tanks had a capacity of 190 gallons, sufficient for approximately two hours working; and the overall width of the engines was 8 ft 8 ins.

These were followed in 1894 by six similar engines but rated 14 NHP. The SCC cylinder and boiler details and the working pressure were identical and the decisions to uprate the nominal power rating was presumably either an arbitrary one, or based upon better than anticipated performance on the dynamometer brake.

14 NHP SCC UNIVERSAL PLOUGHING ENGINES

No	Built		No	Built	
No 1745	Built	1894 (RH)	No 1748	Built	1894 (LH)
1746	"	1894 (LH)	1754	"	1894 (LH)
1747	"	1894 (RH)	1755	"	1894 (RH)

The only significant variations in mechanical details were that the flywheels had grooved rims and the width of the hind wheels was increased from 20 ins to 22 ins giving an overall engine width of 9 ft 0 ins. All six engines were sold through the F Schulte agency in Magdeburg, although in 1895, for reasons now unknown the agency was transferred to another Magdeburg firm, Meissner & Dietlien who continued to represent Burrells' interests until 1914.

The year 1894 saw also the introduction of the 20 NHP Universal Ploughing engine. Thirty-four of these splendid engines were built in the twenty-one years to the outbreak of the First World War.

The breed evolved year by year and many improvements and modifications were incorporated in each pair of engines built. All had single crank compound cylinders measuring $8\frac{1}{2}$ ins dia × 14 ins dia × 12 ins stroke; the first four engines built had cylinders based upon Frederick Burrell's original design; Nos 2018 to 2372 had the solid end type casting, which was in vogue at the turn of the century; and the remainder had the final design of cylinder casting, introduced in 1901, having detachable covers at each end of the cylinder. Engine No 2568 and all

20 NHP SCC UNIVERSAL PLOUGHING ENGINES

No 1783	Built	1894 (LH)	No 2305	Built	1900 (LH)	No 2568	Built	1903 (RH)	No 3022	Built	1908 (LH)
1784	"	1894 (RH)	2371	"	1901 (LH)	2569	"	1903 (LH)	3023	"	1908 (RH)
1802	"	1894 (RH)	2372	"	1901 (RH)	2814	"	1906 (RH)	3094	"	1909 (LH)
1803	"	1894 (LH)	2381	"	1901 (LH)	2815	"	1906 (LH)	3095	"	1909 (RH)
2018	"	1897 (LH)	2382	"	1901 (RH)	2911	"	1907 (RH)	3487	"	1913 (LH)
2019	"	1897 (RH)	2413	"	1901 (LH)	2912	"	1907 (LH)	3488	"	1913 (RH)
2204	"	1899 (LH)	2414	"	1901 (RH)	2992	"	1908 (RH)	3580	"	1914 (RH)
2205	"	1899 (LH)	2477	"	1902 (RH)	2993	"	1908 (LH)	3581	"	1914 (RH)
2304	"	1900 (RH)	2478	"	1902 (LH)						

Fig 112 No 1746 14 NHP single crank compound universal drum ploughing engine built in March 1894 photographed in the works yard outside the old original paint shop prior to shipment to Magdeburg.

Fig 113 No 1783 the first of the thirty-four 20 NHP SCC universal drum ploughing engines built between 1894 and 1914 undergoing test in the works' yard.

subsequent engines in the batch were fitted with a centre bearing on the crankshaft, giving an immensely robust and rigid assembly.

The type N137 boiler was a development of that used on the pair of Fowler engines re-built in 1890, having originally a working pressure of 175 PSI. In 1908 the pressure was increased to 180 PSI and in 1909 it was further increased to 185 PSI. The grate area was 8.95 sq ft and the total heating surface was 240.3 sq ft with 45.2 sq ft contributed by the firebox and 195.0 sq ft by the fifty-seven 2 ins dia × 6 ft 7 ins long smoke tubes. In 1906 six stay tubes were added having the effect of reducing the total heating surface to 224.42 sq ft and from this time, the boiler shells were double riveted on the circumferential seam and treble riveted on the longitudinal seam, the side horns having double flanges, double riveted. Later engines in the batch were fitted also with mud-holes in the sides of the firebox to ease the cleaning of the firebox crown. Engine Nos 3487 to 3581 employed German made Krupp's steel boiler plates, then acknowledged as the finest steel plate available in the world. Additionally, they had 11 ins × 14 ins manholes on the left hand side of the boiler, facilitating washing-out, cleaning and inspection.

The majority of engines were fitted with the type X95 eccentric driven boiler feed pump and with the German Strübe type injectors. Only the first six engines in the batch had governors, since there was clearly little or no cause for these big engines to be used for belt driving work. The 5 ft long chimney was hinged at its base and arranged to lower forwards; and a 3 ft long extension chimney was supplied with each engine to aid steam raising. Tool boxes were supplied on top of the front axle and under the steerage step and special guards were fitted between the winding drum and the hind wheels. They looked and proved to be impressively large and powerful engines.

The four-shaft transmission system had two road speeds having ratios of 28.4 and 18.0 to 1 and a ploughing drum gear ratio of 10.7 to 1. The eighteen spoke hind wheels were 6 ft 6 ins dia × 22 ins wide. The spoked flywheels with a deep section rim were 4 ft 6 ins dia × 9 ins wide; the water carrying capacity was 200 gallons; and the engines had an overall width of 9 ft 5½ ins, later types increasing to 9 ft 8½ ins. The original engines weighed in excess of 20 tons in working order, but progressively the weight was reduced to 18 tons.

20 NHP UNIVERSAL PLOUGHING ENGINE GEARING

	FAST SPEED	SLOW SPEED
Crankshaft Pinions		
No Teeth	19	14
Pitch	1¾″	1¾″
Width	2¾″	2¾″
Spur Ring		
No Teeth	31	36
Pitch	1¾″	1¾″
Width	2¾″	2¾″

	No TEETH	PITCH	WIDTH
First Intermediate Shaft	21	2″	2¾″
Second Intermediate Shaft	57	2″	2¾″
Final Drive Pinion	13	3″	4″
Final Drive Gear	53	3″	4″
Plough Gear Pinion	10	2¼″	4″
Plough Gear Ring	107	2¼″	4″

Engine No 2477 and all subsequent engines were supplied without the winding drums, which were manufactured by Gruson & Company, a local Magdeburg foundry, and assembled by Burrells' agent before delivery to the customer. The first four engines in the batch were supplied through the Schulte agency and the remainder through Meissner & Dietlien, but unfortunately no records as to the engines' ultimate destinations have survived.

A topic widely discussed in the early years of the present century was the question of applying superheating to ploughing engines. Like compounding, the idea of superheating goes back to the very beginnings of the development of the steam engine. Both James Nasmyth and Richard Trevithick proposed schemes in the 1820s and 1830s but the first practical superheater for locomotive type boilers was devised in 1839 by R & W Hawthorn. In 1852 and 1859 James McConnell of the London and North Western Railway brought out two further types embodying various improvements. In 1902, following thirty years' work, Dr Wilhelm Schmidt of Kassel, successfully applied the smoke tube type superheater to railway locomotives. Other German designers were quick to apply the system to their then limited production of ploughing engines, claiming substantial improvements in both performance and efficiency. In 1902 Julius Kemna of Breslau built his first ploughing engine and in 1906 he fitted the Schmidt superheater as standard equipment. Such was his success that by 1914 his output reached 120 sets per annum and the dominance of British built engines in the European market was seriously threatened for the first time.

Precluded from using the smoke tube type superheater because of the strength of Schmidt's patents, John Fowler introduced a smokebox type in 1908. It would appear that the system was not satisfactory due to the elements cooling between bouts of working and they easily sooted up. Serious lubrication problems also arose due to the high temperature of the superheated steam carbonizing the oil and it became necessary to substitute the conventional slide valve with piston valves. In 1913 competition compelled Charles Burrell to design a superheater for application to their 20 NHP ploughing engines but the outbreak of war in 1914 seems to have prevented its development and so far as can be traced, no engines were

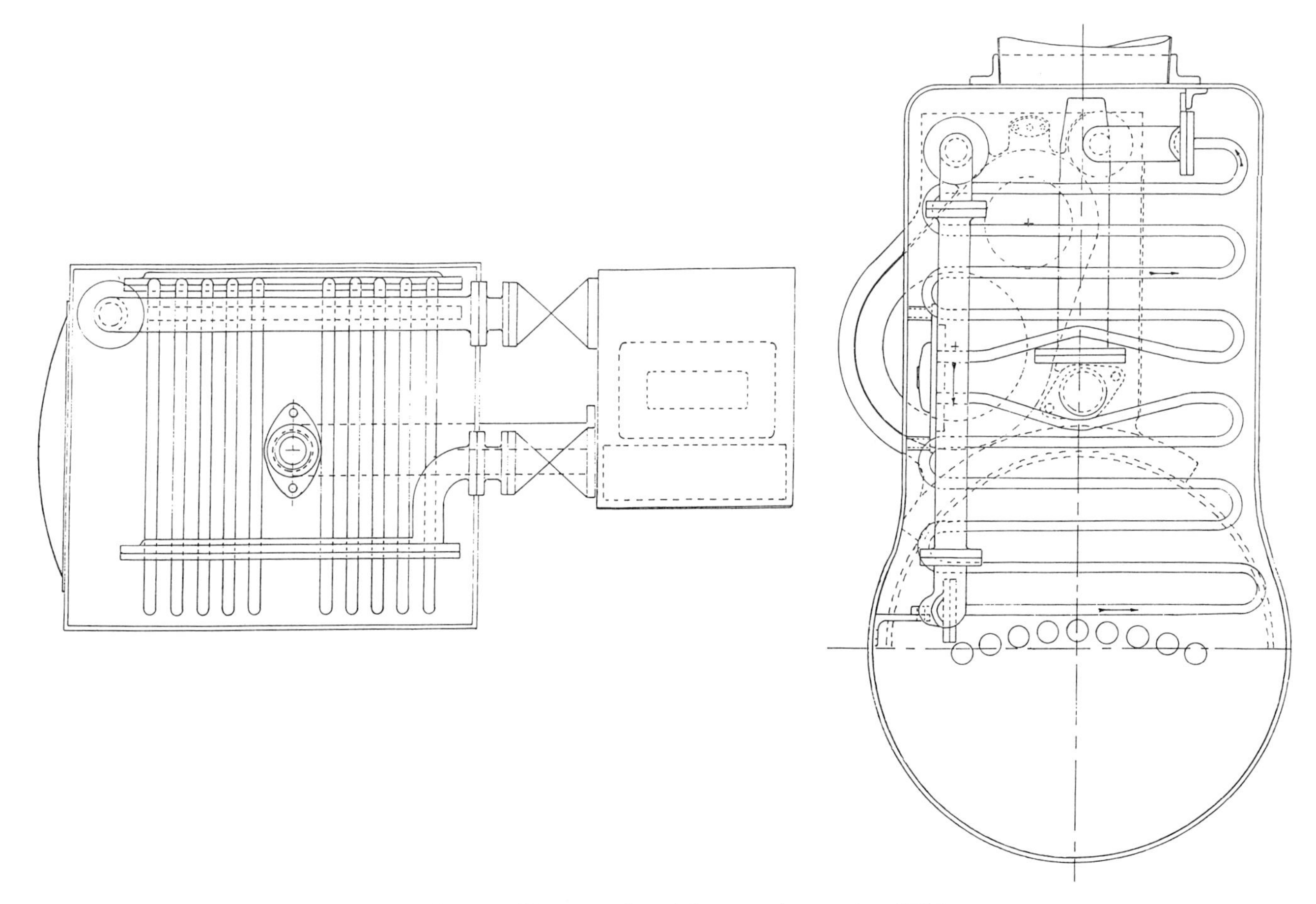

Fig 114 Burrell's proposed smokebox superheater circa 1913.

Fig 115 S Flack's 16 NHP SCC universal drum ploughing engine No 2889 at work in Cambridgeshire.

ever actually fitted with the device.

The proposed arrangement is shown in the attached drawing Fig 114. A box structure 34 ins high × 34 ins wide × 40 ins long was built on top of the smokebox, with the blast pipe mounted centrally, discharging the exhaust steam into the chimney. Live steam from the boiler was taken from the cylinder steam jacket into the top of the box structure, the main steam pipe passing downwards and connecting with a manifold arranged longitudinally on the right hand side of the smokebox. A bank of ten 1 ins dia pipes attached horizontally to the manifold were arranged to zig-zag upwards through the structure to another manifold arranged on its top left hand side. The second manifold was connected directly to the HP cylinder steam chest, the steam becoming superheated whilst passing through the honeycomb of 1 ins pipes which were exposed to the hot gases from the firebox en route to the chimney.

Two years after the introduction of the 20 NHP Universal ploughing engine, St Nicholas Works introduced a 16 NHP version which in all major respects was similar to the 14 NHP engines built in 1894 but having larger bore cylinders.

16 NHP SCC UNIVERSAL PLOUGHING ENGINES

No		Built	No		Built
No 1911	Built	1896 (RH)	No 2104	Built	1898 (RH)
1912	”	1896 (LH)	2287	”	1900 (RH)
1913	”	1896 (RH)	2288	”	1900 (LH)
1914	”	1896 (LH)	2678	”	1904 (RH)
2006	”	1897 (RH)	2679	”	1904 (LH)
2007	”	1897 (LH)	2889	”	1907 (LH)
2103	”	1898 (LH)	2890	”	1907 (RH)

The SCC cylinders measured 7½ ins dia × 12½ ins dia × 12 ins stroke. Nos 1911–2007 had the original design of cylinder block; Nos 2103–2288 had the solid end pattern; and the remaining engines had the final design of cylinder with loose end covers. All had the type X83 boiler pressed to 175 PSI and incorporating all the requirements of the German boiler regulations. The transmission shafting and wheel details were as the earlier 14 NHP engines and they weighed approximately 16 tons in working order.

Fig 116 J Sparks' 8 NHP Fowler ploughing engine, 'Princess' as re-built with Burrell single crank compound cylinders.

All except the last pair were shipped to Germany and sold through the Meissner & Dietlein agency. Nos 2889 and 2890 went to George Flack, a Cambridgeshire farmer who also owned a 7 NHP SCC traction engine and they are reputed to have given thirty years' continuous trouble free service cultivating his heavy land.

During the 1890s St Nicholas Works supplied several sets of SCC compound cylinders for converting Fowler single cylinder ploughing engines to compounds. The exact number of conversions is not known.

In chapter 4 we saw that the ratio of portable engines to self-moving engines built in the period 1868 to 1880 was of the order of three to one. In the succeeding twenty-six years the position was reversed and Charles Burrell built five times more self-moving engines than portable engines. The picture was the same throughout the industry and the majority of portable engines built in the United Kingdom were exported to European customers. Production at St Nicholas Works peaked in the years following the Great Agricultural Depression and rapidly diminished after 1900, the final pair of engines being completed in 1906. Between 1881 and 1906 they built a total of 396 portable engines ranging from a diminutive 1½ NHP engine built for the French market, to the big 20 NHP double crank compound engines introduced in 1883. The 8 NHP size, ideal for driving the standard 4 ft 6 ins threshing machine, accounted for fifty-six per cent of all production, followed by the 10 NHP and 6 NHP sizes in order of preference.

ORDINARY PORTABLE ENGINE PRODUCTION – 1881 TO 1906

YEAR BUILT	NOMINAL HP											TOTAL
	1	4	5	6	7	8	10	12	14	16	20	
1881	1	–	–	3	1	11	4	–	1	–	–	21
1882	5	–	–	–	–	18	11	1	–	–	–	35
1883	–	–	–	6	–	23	6	–	–	–	1	36
1884	–	–	–	2	–	18	8	–	–	–	–	28
1885	–	–	–	4	2	18	3	1	–	–	–	28
1886	–	7	1	4	–	27	3	–	–	–	–	42
1887	–	3	–	4	1	8	2	–	–	–	–	18
1888	–	2	–	7	1	14	6	–	–	–	1	31
1889	–	5	1	7	–	13	12	2	–	–	–	40
1890	–	1	–	3	–	15	4	1	–	–	–	24
1891	–	1	–	4	1	7	3	–	–	1	–	17
1892	–	1	–	4	–	13	–	–	–	–	–	18
1893	–	–	–	1	–	4	2	–	–	–	–	7
1894	–	–	–	1	–	3	–	–	–	1	–	5
1895	–	–	–	3	–	5	–	–	–	–	–	8
1896	–	–	–	1	–	1	–	–	–	–	–	2
1897	–	–	–	–	–	8	–	1	–	–	–	9
1898	–	–	–	1	–	5	–	–	–	–	–	6
1899	–	1	–	1	2	2	–	–	–	–	–	6
1900	–	–	–	–	–	3	–	–	–	–	–	3
1901	–	–	–	–	–	2	1	–	–	–	–	3
1902	–	–	–	–	–	1	1	–	–	–	–	2
1903	–	–	–	–	–	1	–	–	–	–	–	1
1904	–	–	–	–	–	–	1	–	–	–	–	1
1905	–	–	–	1	–	1	–	–	–	–	–	2
1906	–	–	–	1	–	1	–	–	–	–	–	2
	6	21	2	58	8	223	67	6	1	2	2	396

The 1½ NHP engines were designed for pumping and irrigation duties in the south of France and sold through the Burnell agency. The single cylinder measured 3¾ ins dia × 7 ins stroke, the boiler was 1 ft 8 ins dia and 3 ft 6 ins long between tube plates and contained twenty 1½ ins dia smoke tubes. The tiny grate had an area of 2.72 sq ft, the spoked flywheel was 2 ft 9 ins dia and all the batch were fitted with Tangye's type governors.

The 4 NHP engines introduced in 1886 had 7¼ ins dia × 10 ins stroke cylinders, Low Moor iron fireboxes and steel boiler shells constructed in accordance with current German boiler regulations having smokebox baffle plates and spark arresters. The working pressure was 80 PSI, the total heating surface 82 sq ft, of which 64 sq ft was provided by the twenty-four 2¼ ins dia smoke tubes and the grate areas measured 3.0 sq ft. The flywheel was 4 ft 0 ins dia × 6 ins wide and the carrying wheels were 3 ft 6 ins and 2 ft 6 ins dia × 4½ ins wide. One of the batch, No 1280 was specially adapted for burning wood and fitted with Dutch boiler mountings. The two 5 NHP engines, built in 1886 and 1889 were simply an enlargement of the 4 NHP design having 7¾ ins dia × 10 ins stroke cylinders. The grate area was increased to 3.5 sq ft and the total heating surface to 89.0 sq ft.

The majority of the 6 NHP engines had 8¼ ins dia × 12 ins stroke cylinders, some had a grate area of 4.36 sq ft suitable for burning coal, others had a grate area of 5.88 sq ft suitable for wood or other inferior fuels. Both types had 2 ft 5 ins dia boilers containing twenty-six 2½ ins dia smoke tubes 5 ft 5 ins long. Some boilers were built in accordance with the German boiler regulations, others conformed with the Dutch regulations. Nos 1429 to 1433, completed in 1889 were fitted with Elworthy's Patent Straw Burning apparatus. The comparatively small number of 6 NHP engines built for United Kingdom customers had 8½ ins dia × 12 ins stroke cylinders and a 2 ft 7¼ ins dia boiler fitted with thirty-two 2¼ ins dia smoke tubes 5 ft 5 ins long. British mined coal had a higher calorific value than the German brown coal used extensively in Central Europe enabling the engines intended for the United Kingdom market to utilise a smaller grate area and on the 6 NHP portable engines this was reduced to 3.75 sq ft.

In 1891 a 6 NHP 'Devonshire' type traction engine with single crank compound cylinders and allocated works No 1515 was adapted as a portable engine. It had 5 ins dia × 9 ins dia × 9 ins stroke cylinders, the type R64 boiler and a working pressure of 150 PSI. The grate area was 4.0 sq ft and the total heating surface was 113.0 sq ft, of which 90.3 sq ft was derived from the forty 1¾ ins dia smoke tubes. Additionally, it was supplied with the prototype Kircaldy-Burrell water heater fitted originally to the works crane engine, No 1222, together with a Hartnell-Turner type governor, belt driven from the crankshaft. The flywheel was 4 ft 0 ins dia × 6 ins wide and the carrying wheels 4 ft 0 ins and 2 ft 10 ins dia × 6 ins wide.

Engine No 904, the first 7 NHP portable engine built in the period under review had the same 8½ ins dia × 12 ins stroke cylinder as the contemporary 6 NHP engines but this was mounted on a new type V2 boiler. Built in 1881 this engine was one of the first Burrell engines supplied to a South African customer where it remained for many years in the ownership of Flower & Son of Cape Town.

Fig 117 The improved portable engine of the 1880s with patent straw burning apparatus.

The remaining 7 NHP engines built employed the same cylinder fitted to an enlarged type V17 boiler. They had a working pressure of 100 PSI, a grate area of 4.4 sq ft and a total heating surface of 115 sq ft of which 92 sq ft was derived from the twenty-six 2½ ins dia smoke tubes.

The first seventeen 8 NHP portable engines built in the period 1881–82 were fitted with the old 9¼ ins dia × 12 ins stroke single cylinder and a wrought iron boiler having a heating surface of 136 sq ft, and a grate area of 5.39 sq ft. The last of the batch, No 947, was fitted with Ruston's Patent Straw Burning Apparatus. Thereafter, all 8 NHP single cylinder portable engiens built by St Nicholas Works were fitted with a new pattern, fully steam jacketted cylinder measuring 10 ins dia × 12 ins stroke. The majority had the type W61 steel boiler and firebox having a grate area of 5.38 sq ft, although some were built with an enlarged 'Colonial' type firebox for burning wood and other inferior fuels. The total heating surface was 118 sq ft and the engines remained similar in appearance to the attached illustration, although some were fitted with Smith's Patent Chimney Raising and Lowering gear introduced in 1884. Beautifully made heavy duty wooden wheels made in the old wheelwright's shop were optionally available, although increasingly these were replaced by the cheaper wrought iron wheel. The first engine in the series, No 966, went to J S Vilimek in Austria in 1882, others in the same batch went to the Sandalgi Agency in Odessa, to Muscate in Danzig and to Schutte & Ahrens in Stettin, all friends of Robert Burrell and regularly visited by him during his Eastern European tours.

In the months following Fowler's successful introduction of the compound traction engine at the 1881 RASE Show held at Derby, St Nicholas Works carried out a number of experiments in the application of the compound principle to the ordinary 8 NHP portable engine. No 1089 was fitted with a double crank compound cylinder measuring 6½ ins dia × 10 ins dia × 12 ins stroke. No 1091 was built as a four cylinder single acting compound engine and No 1093 was fitted with tandem compound cylinders, both these engines incorporated the features described in Frederick Burrell's and Thomas Tank Burall's patent No 1124 filed in 1881. The tandem compound arrangement found little favour with users other than when applied to large stationary engines due mainly to its increased overall length and lubrication problems. The former engine was subsequently rebuilt with a 5½ ins dia × 10 ins dia × 12 ins stroke double crank compound cylinder and sold as No 1379 and the latter was fitted with the standard 10 ins dia × 12 ins stroke single cylinder and sold as No 1199. No further compound cylinder portable engines were built until 1895 when No 1852 was completed with 6½ ins dia × 10 ins dia × 14 ins stroke single crank compound cylinders. A new type CW41 boiler was developed having a working pressure of 140 PSI. The object of compounding was to achieve economies in both water and fuel consumption and already John Fowler & Company were claiming savings of up to 30 per cent. Charles Burrell had found that there was little if any advantage applying the compound principle to engines having a working pressure less than 140 PSI. No 1852 was designed for burning wood and was provided with a large 7.4 sq ft grate. The total heating surface was 135.2 sq ft of which 98.6 sq ft was derived from the forty-one 2 ins dia smoke tubes.

The only other 8 NHP SCC compound cylinder portable engines built by St Nicholas Works were Nos 2004 and 2059, completed in June and December 1897. Slightly smaller cylinder bores were employed in both the

Fig 118 An 8 NHP single crank compound portable engine circa 1890.

high pressure and low pressure cylinders, but the 14 ins long stroke was retained. Clearly a factor affecting the popularity of these engines was the difficulty of restarting when the crank had stopped in the dead centre position, with both pistons at the end of their stroke. They had no link motion or reversing gear and when belted up to a threshing drum or similar machine the single crank compound engines were difficult and heavy to turn over by hand.

Fig 119 No 2004 8 NHP SCC portable built 1897.

Until 1886 the 10 NHP portable engine was simply an enlargement of the 8 NHP machine. The single cylinder measured 10½ ins dia × 12 ins stroke. The boiler diameter was increased from 2 ft 6 ins to 2 ft 9 ins. The grate area was increased to 6.74 sq ft and the number of 2½ ins dia smoke tubes was increased from twenty-eight to thirty-two giving a total heating surface of 16.5 sq ft. Several were fitted with either the Ruston or the Elworthy straw burning apparatus. In 1883 engine No 983 was fitted in error with a maker's plate carrying the No 985, resulting in the ludicrous situation whereby two identical engines carried the same works number. In 1886 engine No 1254 was fitted with a 14 ins long stroke cylinder as a precursor of an entirely new design introduced in 1888.

The first of the new engines carried works No 1338. A redesigned cylinder to drawing S12/13 and having 11 ins dia bore × 14 ins stroke was employed in conjunction with the type S3 boiler having a working pressure of 80 PSI. The grate area was 6.8 sq ft and the total heating surface was 180 sq ft of which 140 sq ft was derived from the thirty-two 2½ ins dia smoke tubes. Clayton's patent

Fig 120 12 NHP portable engine No 1448 built in 1889.

smokebox baffle type spark arrester was fitted in the smokebox. The flywheel was 5 ft 6 ins dia × 9 ins wide and the iron carrying wheels were 4 ft 8 ins and 3 ft 6 ins dia.

Six only 12 NHP portable engines were built, each incorporating special features specified by the customer. No 999 completed in 1882 had duplex cylinders measuring 8½ ins dia × 12 ins stroke. It had a large 'Colonial' type firebox for burning cane trash, Dutch boiler mountings and spark arester and was exported to the Dutch East Indies. No 1070 completed in 1885 had 8¾ ins dia × 12 ins stroke duplex cylinders and Stephenson's link motion reversing gear. Nos 1448 and 1455 had 12 ins dia × 14 ins stroke single cylinders with the type U60 'Colonial' boiler having a 4 ft 1¾ ins long grate for burning cane trash and No 1476 had the same single cylinder but a 'continental' type boiler and Elworthy straw burning apparatus. The final 12 NHP engine, No 1989, built in 1897 had a boiler conforming with the German regulations and was fitted with locally made straw burning apparatus.

The sole 14 NHP portable engine No 923, built in 1881 and described in the works records as a 'Special Duplex' engine had 8¾ ins dia × 12 ins stroke cylinders and a large 'Colonial' type boiler having a grate area of 8.82 sq ft. The overall length of the boiler was given as 13 ft 1⅝ ins which was some 1 ft 4 ins longer than that fitted to the 12 NHP engines. Regrettably no information as to the power output or performance of these special big engines appears to have survived.

Two even bigger engine rated 16 NHP were built in the next decade. No 1547 was completed in 1891 and No 1769 in 1894. They appear to have been identical engines having 10 ins dia × 14 ins stroke duplex cylinders and a grate area of 10.42 sq ft. The big type F71 boiler had a working pressure of only 80 PSI and a total heating surface of 324 sq ft, of which 270 sq ft was derived from the sixty 2¼ ins dia smoke tubes. No details have survived as to the type of fuel used or how the big 'Colonial' type firebox was fed.

The first double crank compound engine built by St Nicholas Works, as mentioned in the previous chapter, was a 14 NHP semi-portable under-type engine allocated works No 1009. This underwent extensive tests in the works over a three year period and in 1886 was sold to a Russian customer. A total of 24 DCC under-type engines were built by St Nicholas Works in the period 1884 to 1893. Concurrently with the building of No 1009 the first of two 20 NHP portable engines was completed. Allocated works No 1079 it had 8 ins dia × 14 ins dia × 16 ins stroke DCC cylinders and the type P1 boiler. The working pressure was 140 PSI, the grate area 8.0 sq ft and the total heating surface was 282.2 sq ft of which 235.4 sq ft was derived from the forty-one 2¾ ins dia smoke tubes. It was fitted with two flywheels, one on each side of the engine, each 5 ft 0 ins dia × 9 ins wide. The carrying wheels were 5 ft 0 ins and 4 ft 0 ins dia × 8 ins wide and the engine went to Burton et Cie, a French customer based in Paris. The second engine started its life in 1884 as No 1094 but after four years testing in the works was completely refurbished and sold as No 1357 in 1888. All its leading dimensions were exactly as its predecessor, with the exception of a single flywheel 5 ft 6 ins dia × 10 ins wide.

The British demand for portable engines had virtually vanished by the turn of the century. A few firms like Marshalls of Gainsborough, who had produced many more and varied types than St Nicholas Works continued to meet the reduced demand from overseas markets until well into the 20th century. The majority were used for industrial rather than agricultural purposes in mines and quarries and for belt driving all types of stationary machinery, mainly in developing countries. Although fewer in number than those produced by their competitors the Burrell portable engine retained its reputation for quality and reliability and was comparable in all respects with their better known self-moving traction engine and road locomotive.

CHAPTER NINE

Miscellaneous Activities and Events in the 19th Century

Throughout the formative years of Charles Burrell & Sons the manufacture of threshing machines remained the most important of the firm's many and diverse miscellaneous activities. During this period St Nicholas Works produced between 30 and 40 threshing machines a year. We know that by 1890 the total number built exceeded 1,200 machines and that thereafter the numbers steadily declined. We do not know precisely when the last machine left the works, but undoubtedly competition in this field was very severe at the turn of the century. Firms like William Marshall, Clayton & Shuttleworth, Ransomes, and Fosters of Lincoln dominated the scene, the majority of machines built going to customers in the fast developing cereal growing areas in Eastern Europe. It was not an uncommon sight to see a whole train-load of new threshing machines and straw elevators leaving Lincoln and Gainsborough stations en route to the docks for shipment.

Although at least three Burrell threshing machines are in preservation we know remarkably little about their construction. A separate numbering system was employed by the works but no register of ownership has survived. It was in 1848 that Charles I built his first combined threshing and finishing machine and this was awarded a silver medal at the RASE Show held in York. Five years later an improved version won another prize at the Bath and West Show in Plymouth. By 1880 the company offered four basic types of machine with either 4 ft 6 ins or 5 ft 0 ins drums, together with Haynes patent 4-wheel straw elevators and a clover and trefoil seed drawing and dressing machines. The final version of their combined threshing, dressing and finishing machine is illustrated in Fig 121. Undoubtedly the longevity of these machines was due to the use of well seasoned oak timbers and heavy duty wrought iron fitments in their construction.

The class 'A' single blast threshing and chaff-bagging machine was basically as that exhibited in 1848. The chief feature of this machine was that the chaff and corn were thoroughly sifted together on a fine seive at the bottom of the machine and then carried to the top by buckets and the chaff coming before the wind fell direct into bags on one side and the corn into sacks on the other side. The straw was delivered at one end of the machine and the cavings or short straw at the other end. The stage and feeding boards were kept as near the ground as possible which was a great advantage.

The class 'B' combined double blast threshing, dressing and finishing machine was fitted with an adjustable rotary corn screen for finishing the corn in a single operation. This machine was the most sophisticated in the range and was the type generally recommended for export. It was fitted with an improved corn cleaner which also acted as a barley awner giving the grain a brightness which greatly increased its market value. Nalder's patent adjustable separating screen provided a larger screen than any other on the market; the meshes were fine at the feed end and gradually enlarged at the outlet end, the quantity of tail being regulated by slides fixed under the screen. This was much less liable to derangement than screens with shifting wires. When it was undesirable to pass wet corn through the second dressing apparatus the machine could be used as a single dressing machine. When dressing rape-seed a creeper could be applied allowing it to pass through the second dressing apparatus and separating screen without passing through the corn cleaner.

The class 'C' machine was similar to the class 'B' with the exception of the patent separating screen and finishing apparatus. The class 'D' single blast machine was also similar to those just described except that it had a single blast and the corn was delivered into the sacks as it fell from the buckets or after passing through the barley awner.

The clover huller was a simple apparatus enabling the husk to be stripped from the seed without injury. Introduced at the RASE Show in 1844 where it was awarded a prize, it continued in production for over 40 years. Three lengths of 4 ft 6 ins wide Hayes' patent straw elevator mounted on four wheels were offered. They would work in either direction up to a height of 24 ft and were said to be capable of replacing three men.

Fixed and portable corn mills and circular saw benches continued in production until the 1880s. The corn mill illustrated is shown having two pairs of stones in a single frame. Up to six pairs could be placed in a continuous line driven by one lay shaft thereby dispensing with overhead shafts, pulleys and driving belts. Any pair of stones could readily be thrown out of gear and remain stationary whilst the others were working. The distance between the stones could be regulated by a small hand wheel such that the mill could be used for producing the finest flour or for bruising or knibbling peas, beans, oats or similar. It is believed that several dozen of these machines, mainly the wheeled portable version, were exported to the colonies.

Adjoining St Nicholas Works in Minstergate Street a Mr Woods and his son occupied small premises manufacturing their patent grinding mill. Eventually Woods approached Robert Burrell suggesting that as he had more work in hand than he could cope with, the larger firm should take up the manufacture of his machine.

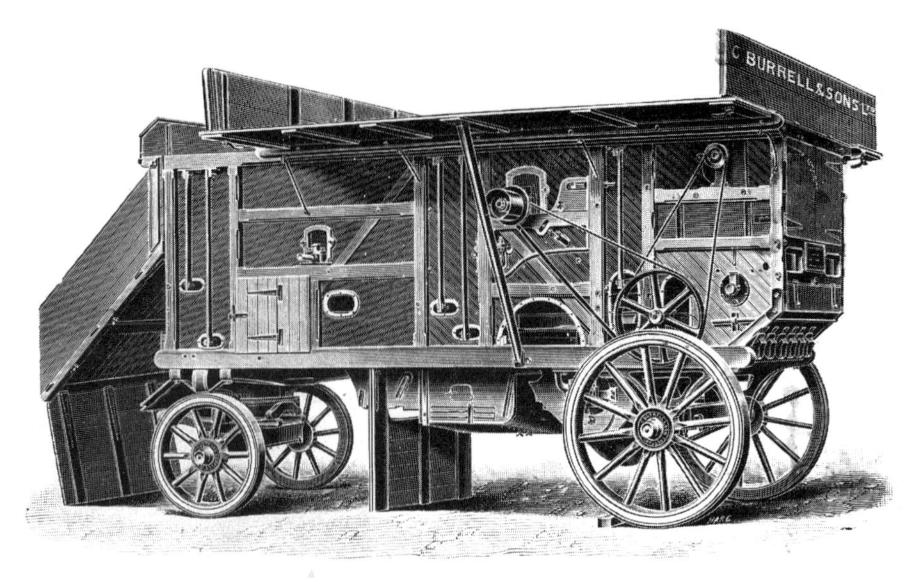

Fig 121 The final form of Burrell combined threshing, dressing and finishing machine.

Fig 122 Class 'A' single blast threshing & chaff bagging machine fitted with straw shakers, riddle, winnower, barley awner and sacking apparatus.

Fig 123 Class 'B' combined double blast threshing, dressing and finishing machine fitted with adjustable rotary corn screen for finishing the corn in one operation.

Fig 124 The 4 ft 6 ins wide belt driven Haye's patent straw elevator supplied in lengths up to 24 ft long.

Fig 125 The Burrell fixed corn mill extendable up to six mills placed in a continuous line. Any pair of stones could readily be disengaged whilst the others continue working.

Burrell's order book was full at the time but Robert saw the export potential and agreed to finance the extension of Woods' patent No 10595 of 1884 in certain specified foreign countries. Although a few machines were built in St Nicholas Works carrying a Burrell nameplate, an arrangement was concluded in 1885 with Hunt & Tawell (Later R Hunt & Co Ltd) of Earls Colne in Essex whereby they became the sole licensees of Woods' patent. They agreed to pay Burrell 5 per cent royalty on the catalogue price of all mills sold during the validity of the patent.

Another small item manufactured at this time was John Matthews' patent spirit level. This was a large level used when laying field drains and was of special value when draining the flat fen country. No example of this device appears to have survived but it was said to have been greatly improved by the firm.

Throughout the traction engine era St Nicholas Works produced 6, 8 and 10 ton traction waggons, bolster waggons and timber drags. They were extremely robust and constructed from well-seasoned oak with red deal drop sides. End and side tipping versions were available and a few steel waggons were produced in the 20th century. The bed and the frame were constructed such that the draw-bar could be taken through the whole length of the frame, enabling two or three waggons to follow the engine drawing them round any curve in each others' tracks. The front axles steered on a turntable type undercarriage and the wheels on later models were steel with fully floating bushes. Generally the waggons were spring mounted and fitted with screw-down brakes operating on the rear wheel rims. The firm also produced a heavy duty spring draw-bar for coupling waggons to the engine. This proved of great value in saving wear and tear caused by starting and stopping and the irregularities in the poor roads of Victorian England.

A close affinity between agricultural machinery and fairground machinery developed in the 1860s, although it was undoubtedly the steam engine which provided the catalyst. The first application of steam power for driving a fairground ride dates from 1865 when Sidney George Soame made a diminutive duplex cylinder portable engine to belt drive an existing hand-driven roundabout. Soame was the proprietor of a small foundry and general engineering shop known as Perseverance Works in the little village of Marsham on the Norwich to Cromer road and his engine made its first public appearance at a fair held at nearby Aylesham.

It is thought that Soame's engine was seen by Frederick Savage, a clever innovative engineer and a native of adjacent Hevingham. In 1860 he had set up his own engineering business at the St Nicholas Iron Works in Kings Lynn. Previously Savage had been employed for some time by Holmes & Sons in Norwich and had won

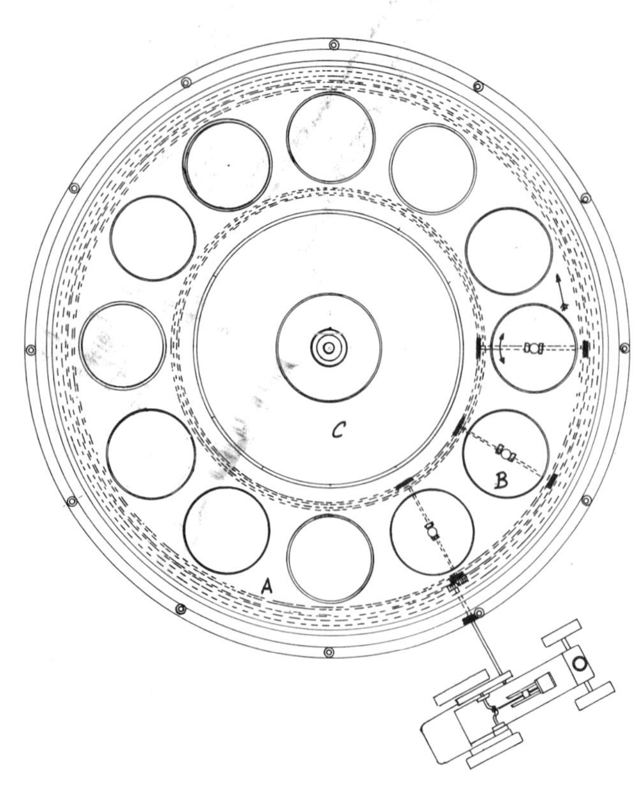

Fig 126 General arrangement of Charles Burrell's and Percival Everitt's roundabout patented in 1880.

considerable acclaim for a traction engine of his design exhibited at the RASE Show held in Bury St Edmunds.

It is thought that as early as 1861 Savage had built a hand-driven 'Velocipede' ride which comprised a series of velocipedes or early bicycles arranged about a circular grooved track for which the customer provided the motive power. Being better equipped than Soame, Savage set about exploiting the application of steam power in the fairground. In 1888 he patented his first Circular Switchback, a wonderfully ornate ride comprising two hills and two valleys with a 40 ft dia circular track and highly decorative gondola cars. His work culminated in the magnificent 'Scenic Railway' rides built in the early part of the 20th century.

Savage pioneered a new industry and Charles Burrell and his friends were well aware of the progress being made. In December 1880 Charles II and Percival Everitt of Great Ryburgh filed their patent No 5433 entitled 'Improvements in the construction of roundabouts.' The specification proposed a ride which would enable the patrons to perform gyrations in pairs in the manner of waltzers. The outer ring of the ride rotated in one direction and the smaller circular platforms located within the outer ring on which the riders stood, were made to rotate independently in either direction by depressing foot pedals operating the drive shaft clutches. The drive to the outer annular ring A and the bevel drives to the individual platforms B will be best understood by reference to the attached drawing. The centre of the ride C was stationary and suitable for accommodating either a fountain with running water provided by an engine driven pump or a steam centre engine and barrel organ as an alternative to the externally located traction engine and drive shafting shown in the drawing. The complete ensemble offered in the words of the patent specification, 'A picturesque and enlivening spectacle.' There is no evidence that this ride was ever built by St Nicholas Works or anybody else.

In March 1887 Frederick Burrell filed his patent No 3423 which claimed to give increased portability to steam roundabouts, enabling them to be more quickly and easily erected or dismantled for travelling. The lower part of the centre pole or chimney stack upon which the gearing for working the roundabout revolved formed a hydraulically operated cylinder making the pole telescopic. It was lowered for travelling or rigidly extended on the centre truck when the ride was erected and working. The hydraulic pressure was applied by a hand operated pump and the four corners of the centre truck were provided with jacks to take the weight and steady the heavy truck. The patent also made provision for the ram of the telescopic pole to be optionally located on the top of the boiler of a traction centre engine. We do not know if the patent was ever put to practical use, but it does confirm Burrells' continued interest in fairground machinery.

In 1889 St Nicholas Works formed an association with the Locomotive Merry-Go-Round Company Ltd and produced an elaborate Duo-Directional roundabout. The inner and outer portions of the ride rotated in opposite directions. The inner portion comprised a small railway with a steam locomotive hauling gondola shaped carriages. The outer portion consisted of a set of three-abreast galloping horses which were specially manufactured by Orton & Spooner of Burton-on-Trent. The central platform carried a brightly decorated fairground organ. Upon completion, the ride was erected in the works yard and the good people of Thetford were treated to free rides.

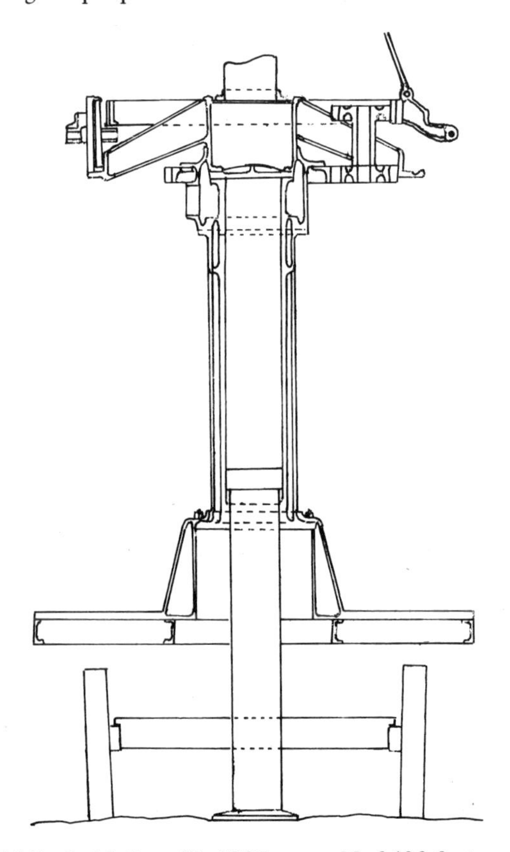

Fig 127 Frederick Burrell's 1887 patent No 3423 for improving the portability of roundabouts with telescopic centre pole.

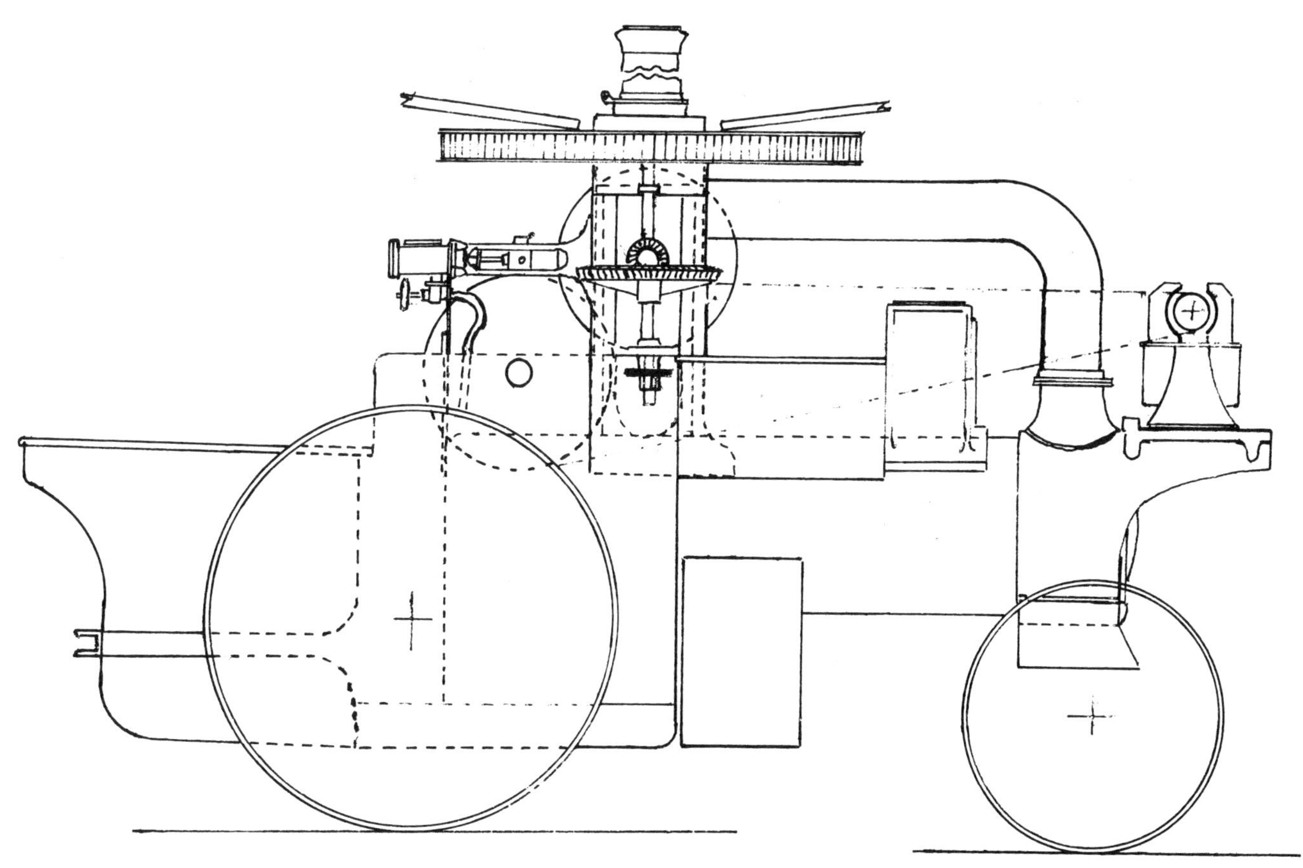

Fig 128 General arrangement of Frederick Burrell's patent No 21403 of 1895 converting a conventional engine to a traction centre engine with a separate duplex cylinder engine for driving the roundabout.

Earlier, John Fowler had specially adapted two of their class 'A' compound traction engines as traction centre engines. A structure mounted on top of the boiler formed a turret to carry the geared drive of a roundabout, thereby dispensing with the heavy centre truck and enabling the engine chimney to be diverted through the centre of the ride's canopy. The difficulty with the Fowler system was that starting and stopping the ride precluded the use of the engine for driving the constant speed electric lighting dynamo.

In November 1895, Frederick Burrell filed his patent No 21403 which provided for a small duplex cylinder engine mounted on a turret arranged to drive the ride.

Fig 129 No 1934 6 NHP SCC road locomotive after conversion to a traction centre engine by George Baker of Southampton.

This required only one-sixth of the power necessary to drive the belt-driven electric light dynamo mounted on the smokebox platform in the traditional manner. Frederick emphasised that his arrangement could be applied to any existing engine and that by locating the turret and additional engine over the firebox, the whole could easily be controlled by one man. He claimed that the ride could be more quickly put to work and that by dispensing with the heavy centre truck the traction engine could more economically haul the ride from place to place. There is no evidence that St Nicholas Works ever built such an engine, concentrating all its efforts during the next thirty years building a large number of conventional Showman's type engines. In 1898 Savage's built two fine traction centre engines, 'Empress' and 'Endurance' but neither appear to have incorporated Frederick's proposals.

The only record we have of a Burrell traction centre engine was in fact built as a standard 6 NHP single drive spring mounted SCC road locomotive, No 1934, completed in August 1896. It was converted by its owner, George Baker of Southampton, in his own workshops by simply adding a turret as an upwards extension of the hornplates to carry the top cradle wheel. We do not know if the roundabout was driven off the engine crankshaft or whether a separate engine was employed as proposed in Frederick's patent, but a smokebox mounted dynamo was retained suggesting a separate engine drove the ride. It will be noted in the attached illustration that the engine chimney could be diverted to discharge through the centre of the turret as suggested in Frederick's patent and a structure mounted on the rear end of the engine canopy carried the hinged extension chimney when lowered for travelling on the road.

Literally hundreds of engineering firms throughout the country manufactured a wide variety of stationary steam engines during the latter half of the Victorian era. It almost appeared as though a general engineering concern could not claim to have reached maturity or be worthy of a potential customer's consideration until it demonstrated that it had successfully produced a commercially viable stationary steam engine. From his earliest days Charles Burrell was no exception, but unfortunately we have very little information about the types and numbers produced. The surviving engine records list only five single cylinder horizontal engines and two vertical cylinder engines; probably others were built pre-1868.

STATIONARY ENGINES BUILT AT ST NICHOLAS WORKS

No	420	Built	1868	16 NHP	Horizontal
	457	”	1870	8 NHP	”
	521	”	1872	8 NHP	”
	670	”	1874	20 NHP	”
	1393	”	1889	10 NHP	”
	1399	”	1889	8 NHP	Vertical
	1506	”	1890	8 NHP	Compound

The first four engines were the old basic design as those illustrated in Burrells' early catalogues and almost certainly

Fig 130 The improved Burrell horizontal stationary steam engine with automatic expansion gear introduced at the 1889 Smithfield Club Show.

Fig 131 The single cylinder over-type semi-portable steam engine introduced in 1879 with a feed water heater mounted in the chimney base.

Nos 457 and 521 were sold to farmers, No 670, a 20 NHP engine was probably used in the works. No 1393 was a completely new, improved design with enlarged bearing surfaces and an extended crankshaft with the outside bearing fixed in a wallbox. It had Burrell's own design of expansion valve gear and an extremely accurate and responsive governor designed by Frederick Burrell. The engine was exhibited at the 1889 Smithfield Show and received a good reception by the technical press. No 1399 was built to drive machinery in the works turnery and was later sold to a saw mill in the town where it survived for many years. We know nothing about No 1506, a compound vertical engine built in 1890.

In 1879 Charles Burrell produced an adaptation of the portable engine which became known as the semi-portable over-type engine, intended for use in situations where the ordinary fixed engine with a separate boiler could not conveniently be applied. Most of their competitors were already offering this type of engine which found a limited market especially in mines, quarries and in developing countries overseas for belt driving machinery such as pumps, grinding mills and stone crushers. They were strongly recommended for export, offering a considerable saving in freight. They were cheap and quick to erect, not requiring expensive foundations and were compact and self contained.

We know of six of these engines being built at St Nicholas Works in the period 1879–1895 but know very little about their ultimate destinations.

OVER-TYPE SEMI-PORTABLE S.C. ENGINES

No	Built	NHP	No	Built	NHP
880	1879	6	1532	1891	12
1337	1888	10	1582	1892	10
1445	1889	12	1893	1895	12

These were followed by the semi-portable under-type engine of which 26 were built in the period 1884–1892. They differed from the over-type engine in that the cylinders and motion were mounted on a bedplate under the boiler with the cylinders forming a saddle for the smokebox end of the boiler. All except one had double crank compound cylinders. We learned in chapter 7 that Frederick Burrell used one of these engines (No 1009) for his early experiments with compounding several years before the introduction of his famous single crank compound engine. So far as can be traced nearly all these engines were exported.

8 NHP to 16 NHP engines had boilers based on then current portable engine designs pressed to 140 PSI. The large 20 NHP engines had the 'P' type boiler with an 11.0 sq ft grate and a total heating surface of 387 sq ft. The first four were pressed to 100 PSI and the last three to 140 PSI. Most had the Burrell-Kirkaldy feed water heaters, but Nos 1186 and 1227 had the feed water heater arranged in the bottom of the chimney as shown in Fig 132.

The double cranks were set at 90 degrees and Frederick Burrell's patent expansion gear actuated by his high speed governor acted on the HP cylinder. This necessitated two slide valves placed one above the other. One was driven by the link motion the other by the 'Pure centrifugal force' governor. This arrangement gave a very prompt cut-off and ensured the admission of the steam to the cylinder was regulated exactly in proportion to the duty required of the engine, making them ideal for driving the new electricity generators coming into use.

UNDER-TYPE SEMI-PORTABLE ENGINES

No	Built	No	Built
8 NHP – 5½″ × 9″ × 12″ cylinders			
No 1090	Built 1888	No 1478	Built 1890
1092	" 1884	1536	" 1891
1365	" 1888	1585	" 1892
10 NHP – 6½″ × 10″ × 12″ cylinders			
*No 1305	Built 1887	No 1447	Built 1889
1400	" 1889	1586	" 1892
12 NHP – 7″ × 12½″ × 14″ cylinders			
No 1345	Built 1888		
14 NHP – 7″ × 12½″ × 14″ cylinders			
No 1009	Built 1885	No 1326	Built 1888
16 NHP – 8″ × 13″ × 16″ cylinders			
No 1369	Built 1888	No 1413	Built 1889
1394	" 1889	1464	" 1891
1397	" 1889	1692	" 1893
20 NHP – 9″ × 14″ × 16″ cylinders			
†No 1282	Built 1887	No 1398	Built 1889
1186	" 1885	1412	" 1889
1227	" 1886	1539	" 1891
1228	" 1886		

* 10½″ × 12″ single cylinder
† 8½″ × 14″ × 16″ DCC cylinder

Fig 132 Burrell double crank compound under-type engine of 1885 fitted with the extremely sensitive automatic expansion gear which made them ideal for driving the new electric light generators then coming into use.

Fig 133 General view of machine shop – circa 1900.

Fig 134 Turning lathe section, machine shop.

About 1886 Charles II installed a small 2 HP electric light generator in his private house, 'Shrublands', on the outskirts of the town. His was the first private house in the district to have its own supply of electricity and shortly afterwards in 1888 in conjunction with Paris & Scott of Norwich an electricity generating station was established in St Nicholas Street opposite Charles Burrell's premises. Two years later a separate company was formed with the Burrell family having a controlling interest. Within a short period of time the Great Eastern Railway station which had been rebuilt in 1889, the Post Office, the Parish Church, the Anchor Hotel and the majority of the shops and private residences in the town centre were connected, the largest installation being in St Nicholas Works. The nearby streets continued to be lit by gas as did the quaint old Bell Inn.

The engine room at the generating station employed two Burrell under-type engines, probably Nos 1539 and 1586, driving Laurence, Scott & Co of Norwich dynamos. A continuous current transformer charged the fifty-eight 25 cell batteries. The engine's locomotive type boilers were fed by Worthington duplex pumps and a Maignen anti-calcaire water softening plant was installed. The plant was managed for many years by Mr R Carter, formerly a Siemens employee who is on record as saying that he was attracted to Thetford by the hunting, shooting and field sports generally available in the area.

The new machine shop at St Nicholas Works located between Minstergate Street and the river contained eighty powerful overhead arc lamps spaced at intervals of approximately 20 ft, which gave sufficient light for a man working on a lathe on a dark winter's morning. Although the cost of electricity at 6d per unit was greater than gas, the benefits and increased output far outweighed the extra cost. The lamps were connected in twos in series, each taking 6 amps across the 110 volt circuit.

The early history of passenger carrying street tramways

Fig 135 Burrell compound cylinder tram engine supplied to Birmingham Central Tramways Ltd in 1880 illustrating Frederick Burrell's patent roof condenser.

Fig 136 An early steam tram, Moseley Road, Birmingham – circa 1885.

really belongs to the United States. Once again it was the prejudice of our legislators, constantly lobbied by various vested interests which precluded development of this form of transportation in the United Kingdom.

The first passenger tramway in the modern sense was laid at Birkenhead in 1860 and the first steam powered tram to be used in England appeared in 1872. It was a combined engine and carriage consisting of an ordinary four wheeled double deck car in the centre of which on either side was a field type vertical boiler. The duplex cylinder engine was placed under the floor and drove a single axle. It was designed by John Graham; the machinery was manufactured by Merryweather, the famous fire engine builders; and the bodywork was entrusted to the Oldbury Carriage & Wagon Works near Birmingham. It underwent several unsuccessful trials in London and eventually in 1876 found its way into service on the Wantage Tramway in Oxfordshire.

After several largely abortive attempts by other engine builders, the first really practical solution was devised by the famous locomotive builders, Kitson & Co of the Airedale Foundry, Leeds in 1878. The first six engines built went to Christchurch in New Zealand and it is a testimony to their suitability and reliability that five of the six engines gave over sixty years' continuous service. In 1880 the City of Leeds adopted the Kitson engine and during the next 20 years they built over 300 engines for various public authorities. Other makers entering this field included Thomas Green & Sons of Leeds; Beyer Peacock & Co of Manchester; and the Falcon Engine Company of Loughborough.

Both John Fowler and Avelings made a few tramway engines but their interest was short lived. Charles Burrell constructed an engine in 1885 for the 7 miles long 4 ft 0 ins gauge Bradford and Shelf Tramways, similar in general design to the Falcon engine which itself was a derivative of the original Kitson design. In 1886 they built a second engine for the 17 miles long 3 ft 6 ins gauge Birmingham Central Tramways. This system formed part of a continuous network of 67 route miles operated by over 200 steam locomotives, but neither Burrell engine remained long in service.

The Board of Trade imposed very stringent regulations under the provisions of the Tramways Act 1870 which required that no visible smoke or steam should be emitted from the engine which was required also to be free from noise caused by the engine blast or the clatter of the machinery. All working parts had to be concealed from view and the engine had to be governed to a maximum speed of 10 MPH. Unlike the Falcon engines, the Burrell engines had double crank compound cylinders mounted between the frames measuring 10 ins dia × 17½ ins dia × 14 ins stroke with Joy's valve gear. The Siemen's Martin steel locomotive type boilers pressed to 160 PSI had 7.0 sq ft grates with 90 × 1½ ins dia × 4 ft 0 ins long smoke tubes. The fireboxes were copper and the tubes brass. The engines were arranged to be driven from either end; the regulator valve was mounted on top of a large steam dome and the regulator handles, reversing levers and hand brakes were duplicated at each end of the totally enclosed footplate.

The wheelbase of the engines was 4 ft 6 ins and the coupled wheels were 2 ft 6 ins dia. A countershaft belt driven from the leading axle was arranged across the frames between the two coupled axles. A centrifugal governor mounted on the countershaft controlled a sensitive steam relay valve attached to the side of the boiler through the link gear. When the vehicle attained a road speed of 10 MPH the governor actuated the relay valve admitting high pressure steam to the brake cylinders located at each end of the chassis.

In 1887 Frederick Burrell filed his patent No 14872 describing improvements to the roof mounted condenser which replaced the multi-tube transverse pattern originally fitted to the Kitson and Falcon engines. The Burrell system consisted of a bank of copper tubes placed longitudinally, usually eighteen in number, each tube containing another smaller diameter open ended tube. The exhaust steam was discharged into the annular space between the two tubes allowing air currents aided by the motion of the tram to pass through and over the tubes condensing the steam. The condensate was then returned to the water tank for reuse.

The reasons for the apparent failure of the two Burrell engines is not known. Perhaps the answer lies in comments made by David Greig, a director of John Fowler. "I have three engines standing in my shed," he said, "they run very satisfactorily making no noise or smoke, but when costed they retire from the field."

The engine of the Birmingham tramway locomotive was sold to the Iveagh Estate at nearby Elvedon as a stationary engine and it is said that the body ended its days on an allotment in Thetford. Nothing is known of the fate of the Bradford engine. In 1891 Thomas Green & Sons acquired a licence to use the condenser patent and manufactured approximately fifty engines incorporating the arrangement before they discontinued production in 1898.

For centuries the lives of the people of Thetford had been influenced in a variety of ways by the navigable Fenland waterways, especially the Little Ouse which connected the town with Kings Lynn and the open sea. The Burrell family, as we learned in chapter 1 were no exception, and it is not surprising that as St Nicholas Works grew the brothers Charles, Robert and Frederick turned their attention to the possibility of building little ships and in particular steam powered marine engines. By 1880 the Great Agricultural Depression was seriously affecting the local economy and the works had insufficient orders to keep them fully occupied. The management and technical staff were busy enough developing the recently introduced geared traction engine and other new

Fig 137 120 IHP compound marine engine exhibited at the 1882 Naval and Submarine Exhibition.

innovations such as compounding, but they were short of orders for their sheet-anchor activities.

Initially, single cylinder non-condensing tug boat engines and boilers were produced for use in vessels on fresh water rivers and canals where the boiler feed water could be drawn directly from the floatant. These were followed by a compound launch engine several of which were sold to local private owners and operators of passenger carrying vessels. Soon the firm were able to offer a range of condensing compound engines ranging from 8 NHP developing 35 IHP to 140 NHP developing 700 IHP, having 28 ins dia HP × 56 ins dia LP × 32 ins stroke cylinders. It is not known how many marine engines were built at St Nicholas Works because unfortunately the company's records give details of only seven engines built in the years 1884 to 1886. However, we do have details of a fine 120 IHP engine exhibited at the Naval and Submarine Exhibition in 1882 and a 300 IHP engine and boiler built for the SS Mona in 1884.

The cylinders of the 120 IHP engine which measured $12\frac{1}{2}$ ins dia × 22 ins dia × 18 ins stroke were mounted vertically and supported on a cast iron frame on the port side of the engine and circular columns on the starboard side. The cast iron frame also supported the condenser, oil separator and boiler feed pump and provided a fixing for the crosshead guides. The main steam valve and the reversing gear was mounted on the circular columns and were operated by large handwheels. A bypass valve was also attached to this side of the engine which enabled HP steam to be admitted to the LP cylinder if the HP piston stopped on dead centre. A cast iron bed carried the forged crankshaft in three large plain bearings. All the moving

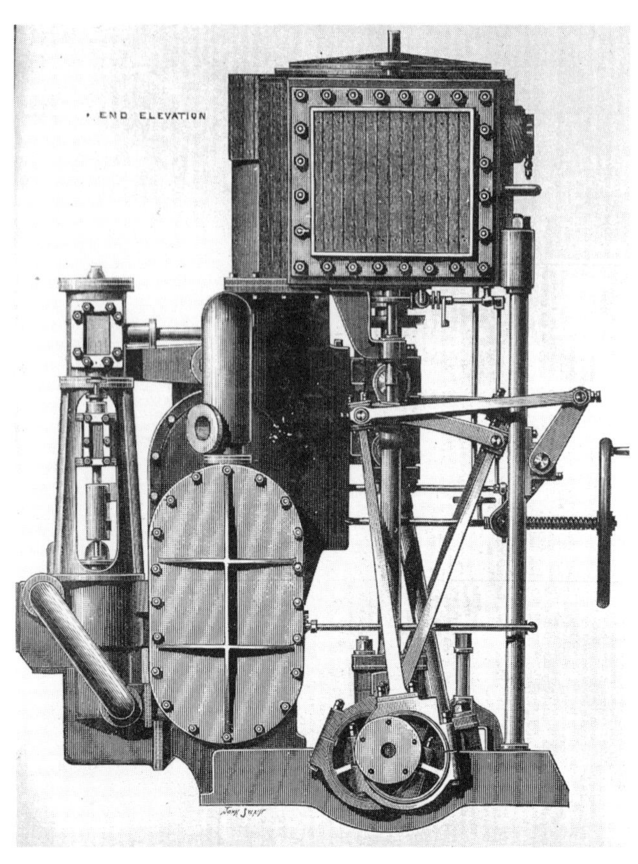

Fig 138 300 IHP compound marine engine built for the SS Mona in 1884.

parts were lubricated by centrally placed and readily accessible oil boxes and it is said that the finish and workmanship throughout were superb. The layout of the engine for the SS Mona was similar, the cylinders measuring 20 ins dia × 40 ins dia × 24 ins stroke.

The works also produced a two-furnace marine type boiler for the SS Mona which measured 11 ft 6 ins dia × 10 ft 0 ins long and weighed 25 tons. It was too large and too long to be sent to Kings Lynn by rail where the hull, which was built in Holland, was being fitted out. The works solved the problem by building a special low loading trailer weighing 14 tons. The load was hauled by a new 8 NHP road locomotive No 1029 fitted with Burrells' patent spring wheels and this epic journey of a little over 30 miles was completed in two days. After a chequered career and renamed SS Trethosa but still with her original engines, the vessel remained in service until the 1950s in the ownership of the Fowey Tug Company.

About this time St Nicholas Works also produced a number of small marine boilers to stringent Admiralty specifications for A G Mumford Ltd of Colchester for fitting into naval pinnaces. Limited production of boilers for both land and marine applications continued into the 20th century.

Concurrently with the production of marine engines and boilers the Boiler Shop built a small number of steel hulled tugs and barges and other small river craft up to 45 ft in length. Few details have survived but folklore in the town insists that the vessels were launched on skids at an acute angle to the bank due to the narrowness of the river adjacent to the works, providing entertainment for local people watching from the Town Bridge.

Frederick Burrell himself acquired a launch fitted with a compound engine of his design which he named 'Fenella'. He spent most weekends steaming on the Rivers Yare and Wensum near Norwich and became well known locally for the dubious company he kept and the wild parties he held on board.

Thomas Tank Burall was closely involved in all aspects of marine engine development and in 1884, shortly before his untimely death he started work on the design of a new breech loading gun. Frederick continued this work and received encouragement from the War Department to develop a traditional field gun in which the recoil was greatly reduced by means of cylinders charged with a mixture of water and glycerine, thereby arresting and absorbing the recoil. Eventually the Government placed an important contract with the firm for short recoil gun carriages which for a time involved every department of the works. In 1890 and 1891 Frederick unsuccessfully filed patents Nos 21065 and 552 entitled 'Pneumatic Guns.'

Between 1893 and 1895 Frederick Burrell filed several patents which had little or nothing to do with the firm's traditional activities, but they do serve to illustrate his versatility and ingenuity. At this time the works were very busy with the workforce now exceeding 300 hands and it seems unlikely that the company were actively seeking diversification. Patent No 2569 of 1893 described improvements to furniture castors in which the castor wheel was mounted on a ball race which took the end thrust as well as enhancing its ability to rotate about its vertical axis. Later in 1895 he patented a special purpose lathe to facilitate the quantity production of this castor. The lathe was fitted with a twin headstock, the two portions being controlled by clutches and both portions being able to rotate in opposite directions. The work was held in a jig on the cross saddle and the tailstock formed the other part of the invention which carried the tools for drilling the holes for the castors' centre pin. The existence of this special machine would seem to indicate that the firm had been successful in marketing this improved castor.

In 1894 he filed patent No 11778 describing a freezing machine for the manufacture of ice cream. His reasons for becoming interested in this process in the first place would be of great interest. One suspects that as Norfolk was predominently an agricultural district he was in touch with people concerned with dairy produce and knowledgeable of developments taking place. Undoubtedly, Frederick liked nothing better than a challange of this sort, but we don't know if his invention was ever put to any practical use.

In December 1894 he filed patent No 24565 describing improvements to window sash fasteners. This simple device which could be added to existing windows was designed to make the sash fastener burglar proof and the window sashes rattle proof. We do not know whether the idea was the result of a local burglary or perhaps sleepless nights caused by the sash windows rattling in the strong prevailing winds encountered in Norfolk. But a recent re-examination of the patent seems to make it as useful and relevant today as it was nearly 100 years ago when Frederick Burrell first conceived the idea.

In 1895 and 1897 Frederick and his friend Edwin Maxwell filed patents Nos 24651 and 7604 which

Fig 139 Frederick John Burrell, 1851–1927, the technical innovator in the family.

described machines for cutting rashers of bacon, slicing bread and other similar duties. Apparently these machines aroused considerable interest in the area at the time and the late Mrs Florence Owen, Robert Burrell's daughter recalled seeing them frequently used in shops in the town. Unfortunately, we have no details of where these machines were made or how many were produced. Thereafter, Frederick's health declined rapidly and only one more patent was filed in his name which described water tubes for flash steam boilers. He relinquished all responsibility in the firm about 1900 when his mother died after a long illness. The only subsequent reference to him we have is that he attended his father's funeral in Thetford in June 1906.

Another short lived activity worthy of mention had been embarked upon in 1886. Through the good offices of Ezra Lofts of Cambridge, Charles II was introduced to S D Page & Son, brush makers and an agreement was concluded whereby St Nicholas Works undertook the manufacture of their patent brush making machinery. Nothing is known of subsequent events other than that Burrell's employees engaged upon the project were required to sign a confidentiality agreement with penalties of up to £200 if they divulged any of the secrets of the patent. One can imagine how well that was received by men earning only a few shillings a week.

In July 1884, in line with most of their competitors, the company became Incorporated as a Limited Liability Company under the 1883 Companies Act. Henceforth, the firm became known as Charles Burrell & Sons Ltd having a capital of £100,000 made up of 10,000 ordinary shares of £10 each. The Articles of Association described the objective of the Incorporation, "To carry on the business of agricultural and mechanical engineers, makers of machinery and iron founders and ship and boat builders." The Board was limited to not less than three and not more than seven directors each holding a minimum qualification of not less than 100 shares.

Fig 140 St Nicholas House adjacent to the works. Robert Burrell's family home for many years largely destroyed by vandals in 1992.

The original directors and their share holding were as follows:

Charles Burrell I	– 3000 shares
Charles Burrell II	– 1640 shares
Robert George Burrell	– 760 shares
Frederick John Burrell	– 800 shares

The Company's Solicitors were B P Broomhead of Sheffield, the Accountants were J A Josolyne of London and the Merchant Bank who financed the Incorporation was Henry Vavasseur of London.

The Articles of Association required by law, had to be amended in 1897 and 1898 adding, "To carry on the business of electricians and workings and dealers in electricity, motive power and light, to produce, accumulate and supply electricity and electro-motive force or any similar or other power, force or agency to light streets, public places, public and private buildings." The following year further alterations were made describing the formal objectives of the business as follows:

1) Manufacturing as stated in the 1884 Articles
2) Electrical interests as stated in 1897 Articles
3) Purchase other companies
4) Acquire rights and subscribe to Railways, Tramways, Canals, Docks and Wharfs etc.
5) Raise Mortgages and Debentures

Apart from the retirement of Frederick Burrell in 1900 the Board remained unaltered until 1904. During this twenty year period the fortunes of the company peaked with turnover and profits reaching all time records.

Fig 141 Charles Burrell I (1817–1906) shortly before his death, with his eldest son, Charles II (1847–1929), his grand daughter Marion and his great grandson Eric Faulkner.

Three years after Incorporation in 1884 the directors took a bold step and formed a subsidiary called Burrell's Hiring Company. It had a nominal capital of £500 and was one of the first hire purchase companies in the United Kingdom formed with the object of providing finance for the purchase of the firm's products. Charles II and Frederick were appointed the new company's first directors.

The majority of Showman's engines were purchased through the Hiring Company and it became a regular feature of life in the office at St Nicholas Works to receive travelling showmen armed with bags of small denomination coin to settle their quarterly accounts, every penny of which had to be laboriously checked.

The Hiring Company purchased engines from the Parent Company at catalogue prices less 10 per cent and portable engines and agricultural machinery at less 15 per cent. They usually added a 7½ per cent management charge to the net purchase price. Repayment was normally spread over a four year period, the final payment being one shilling. All engines purchased through the Hiring Company carried a small company's ownership plate although it was well known that many of these quickly disappeared. Should an engine be re-possessed as a bad debt or taken in part exchange, the Hiring Company claimed it and sold it back to the Parent Company. A Mr Claydon managed the company for many years and later was assisted by one of Robert Burrell's daughters as cashier.

At the time of Incorporation Charles I was approaching three score years and ten and although greatly respected in the town preferred to live a quiet and private life at his home, St Mary's House on the Bury Road. He attended the works daily but was content to leave matters of day to day management to his three sons. His wife, Elizabeth, to whom he was devoted, suffered from ill health for many years and there is no evidence that he travelled far from home in later life.

All four of Charles I's sons were educated at Thetford Grammar School, although Charles II appears to have gone onto Kings College, London to complete a technical education. Robert and Frederick went straight into the works from school at the age of 14 or 15 and went through all departments of the works before being given any responsibility. Both became craftsmen on the lathe and the bench and Robert in particular made several very fine model steam engines as a young man. William became a solicitor and lived in Richmond, Surrey until his own business failed and he joined the Burrell Board in 1904. He never took any very active part in the firm's management.

Both Charles II and Robert Burrell made notable contributions to the well being of Thetford and its people throughout their adult lives. Charles served on the local council for over 55 years, was elected Town Mayor no less than seven times between 1877 and 1915 and was a Justice of the Peace. He was described, "As very dapper but somewhat stern. Always immaculately dressed with highly polished shoes, wearing a silk handkerchief soaked in lavender water." His great favourite was the comedian, Harry Lauder and in later life he enjoyed nothing more than playing his large collection of Lauder's records to his family and friends.

Fig 142 Charles Burrell II in the prime of life photographed in the 1880s.

He married twice, firstly in 1873 to Sarah Annie Thomas of York, "A plain, severe Victorian lady with a good head for money." They had three children, Herbert John born in 1875, who later succeeded his father as head of the firm; Marion, who married George Faulkner, a school teacher from Bury St Edmunds. They resided at Edge Hill in Warwickshire; and Charles William Wilberforce Burrell, who apart from distinguished service in the Royal Engineers during the First World War, was the firm's Sales Director for many years.

Charles II and Sarah were very friendly with a family named Wilberforce who lived at Scarborough. Two years after Sarah's death in 1912 he married Annie Phyllis Wilberforce who was then living at Fulford near Taunton.

Robert George Burrell also had a long record of public service to Thetford. In 1867 he joined the Volunteers, the 19th century equivalent of our present Territorial Army Reserve and attained the rank of Major, a commission he held until his death. In 1882 he was elected to the Town Council and was elevated to Aldermanic status in 1901. He served as Town Mayor for three years 1888–89 to 1890–91 and took a special interest in the work of the Town's Lighting Committee. In 1900 he became a Justice of the Peace and for many years was a Freemason. Other local activities included Presidency of the local Conservative Association and the Conservative Working Men's Club; a Governor of the local school and hospital foundation; membership of Sir Joseph Williamson's Charitable Binding Foundation and the Boys' Brigade.

He had eight children, seven girls and a boy, Robert Eden, who was tragically killed in a motor accident near Newmarket in 1921 after completing distinguished War Service in the Middle East and France. The family were all musically inclined and appear to have lived together in great harmony, firstly at a town house named 'The Paddocks', later at St Nicholas House, adjoining the works. Originally the Manager's house, Robert and his wife Ellen moved in following the death of Thomas Tank Burall in order to provide additional accommodation for their growing family.

The eldest daughter, Dorothy, born in 1883 married the Reverend Percy Johnson, of the Bengal Ecclesiastical Establishment, and spent most of her married life in India. The second daughter, Elsie, became a distinguished and popular watercolour portrait artist in early life and was given regular patronage by Queen Mary. In 1916 she married a remarkable explorer and pioneer, Major Boyd Cuninghame of the Argyll and Sutherland Highlanders. He established the first wagon route from Lobito Bay to the Lualaba River in the interior of Africa, a round trip of 2,430 miles, which remains today a record for an ox-wagon journey. On the outward journey he took machinery for the Ruwe Katanga alluvial gold fields and on the return trip brought out the first copper smelted in Katanga. In 1914 he commanded a force in Northern Rhodesia and rendered valuable military service against the Germans in the area. Although invalided out of the army in 1916, he immediately returned to Africa with his bride to farm in the Lusaka area. Sadly, after only five months of marriage, he died, but Elsie continued to manage his estate for several years. During that period, her nearest white neighbour was a Dutch woman living some forty miles distant. She became an expert lion hunter and in later life it was said that she was the best judge of cattle in Africa. In 1923 she married Sir Randolf Baker, who had commanded the Dorsetshire Yeomanry at Gallipoli and in Palestine, gaining a DSO and bar. He lived at Ranston, Blandford, which was reputed to have one of the most beautiful gardens in the country. He became a politician and represented the North Dorsetshire constituency.

Fig 143 Robert Charles Burrell (1849–1904).

DIEU ET MON DROIT

We Granville George, Earl Granville, Viscount Granville, Baron Leveson, a Peer of the United Kingdom of Great Britain and Ireland, a Member of Her Britannic Majesty's Most Honourable Privy Council, Knight of the Most Noble Order of the Garter, Lord Warden of the Cinque Ports and Constable of Dover Castle, Her Majesty's Principal Secretary of State for Foreign Affairs &c. &c. &c.

Request and require in the Name of Her Majesty, all those whom it may concern to allow Robert G. Burrell (British Subject) travelling on the Continent

to pass freely without let or hindrance, and to afford every assistance and protection of which he may stand in need.

Given at the Foreign Office, London, the 3 day of April 1883

Granville

SIX PENCE

Signature of the Bearer.

Robt. G. Burrell

Vu au Consulat-Général de Russie

Bon pour la Russie

Londres le 24 Mars / 5 Avril 1883

Le Consul-Général

Le Vice Consul

F Knapp

Taxe Perçue ... francs

Vu au Consulat Général de Roumanie

Bon pour se rendre en Roumanie

Londres, le 11 Avril 1883

Le Consul Général

No. 3185

Le Chancelier

Fig 144 Facsimile of Robert Burrell's passport issued in April 1883 with endorsements for Russia and Rumania.

Fig 145 William Burrell (1850–1927). A solicitor, appointed to the Board upon Robert Burrell's death in 1904.

Phyllis, the third child died whilst still an infant and the fourth daughter, Josephine, born in 1888 married Major George Teal, DSO, whose father was a distinguished scientist and for many years headed the Government's Geological Survey Department. Margaret, born in 1892 married Francis Molesley, the Duke of Wellington's Agent at Stratfieldsaye. Nancy, the sixth child, born in 1899 married Commander Hector Monro RN, a member of another old Dorsetshire family and himself High Sheriff of the County at one time. The youngest daughter, Florence Evelyn, married Captain John Owen, RE in June 1922. Just before the First World War, St Nicholas Works built a number of 5 ton tractors to the War Department subsidy specification and later a selected number of Royal Engineer Officers did one year of their approval course in the works. It was whilst so engaged that romance blossomed between Evelyn Burrell and the handsome young RE officer. They had two daughters, Peggy and Jennifer who as small children accompanied their parents while serving in Jamaica, Bermuda and Sierra Leone. During the Second World War, John Owen, now a Colonel, was a prisoner of war for five years. Evelyn died in 1989.

Robert's greatest pleasures in life apart from his family were travelling, model making and collecting grandfather clocks. He gave a clock to each of his children upon their marriage. For many years there was a 'secret' workshop at the rear of St Nicholas House facing Minstergate Street. Here Thomas Tank Burall developed many of his ideas and built his prototypes. Later, Robert Burrell made several very fine models of Burrell traction engines, one of which was presented to the Castle Museum in Norwich by the the family in 1955. The fine model of a Thomson Road Steamer currently on loan to the new Burrell Museum is believed to have been made by Frederick Burrell in the same workshop.

Between 1875 and the mid 1890s Robert travelled extensively all over Europe including no less than six trips to Russia. He is said to have had a good ear for languages and spoke fluent French, German and Russian. On one occasion while staying in Vienna he contracted typhoid fever and had a narrow escape with his life. On another trip during a visit to Odessa on the Black Sea while staying with John Sandalgi, he was taken seriously ill with a heart problem and his wife was sent for to help nurse him back to health.

Unfortunately the heart problem persisted and tragically at the early age of 55 he died on September 7th 1904. Happening so soon after Frederick's retirement, his death was a staggering blow to the family and the firm. As befitting the occasion the six pall bearers at his funeral were all foremen in the works; Calthrop of the Boiler Shop; Morrels of the Carpenter's Shop; Wyres, the Fitting Shop; Wellers, the Iron Foundry; Johnson of the Paint Shop and the redoubtable Spencer of the Erecting Shop. Eight hundred people attended the funeral service held in the Parish Church of St Cuthbert's. The cortege then made its way down King Street, past old Joseph Burrell's original workshop, along Bridge Street and across the river with St Nicholas Works in the background, to a moss lined grave in the London Road Cemetery where Robert was laid to rest.

The Board was reconstructed shortly after Robert's death. Charles I finally resigned the Chair and handed over the reins completely to Charles II who remained Chairman until 1920. William, Charles II's other surviving brother and his two sons Herbert John Burrell and Charles William Wilberforce Burrell joined the Board. Herbert was also appointed Company Secretary. Within less than two years, on June 26th 1906 old Charles I died peacefully at the ripe old age of 89 years thus ending an era. Things were never quite the same again at St Nicholas Works.

CHAPTER TEN

Single Cylinder and Single Crank Compound Road Locomotives

Four men dominated the scene in the 1850s when renewed attempts were made to replace the horse for the movement of heavy indivisible loads on the common road. We have considered already the part played by Charles Burrell and the Black Country Ironmaster, James Boydell. Their main competitors were William Bray, a marine engineer employed on the South Eastern Railway's ships operating out of Folkstone, and Daniel Kinnear Clark, a Scottish engineer and well known technical author. In December 1856, Bray filed patent No 3102 in which he described a road wheel having sliding blades or teeth which projected from the wheel rim as the wheel rotated. These enabled the engine to obtain a firm hold on soft ground, greatly increasing its adhesion. The first recorded demonstration of the system was held in 1857, upon a farm near Folkstone before a gathering of the Directors of the South Eastern Railway. It seems unlikely that Bray ever had any manufacturing facilities directly under his own control, although a company styled Bray's Traction Engine Company Ltd, with offices at 12 Pall Mall, London, was formed to handle the marketing of the patent and the hiring out of engines owned by the company.

Kinnear Clark was a man of many parts and after a varied career culminating in his appointment as Locomotive Superintendent of the Great North of Scotland Railway, he put up his plate as a Consulting Engineer in 1855, with rooms in London's fashionable Adelphi. Due no doubt to Clark's Scottish connections, Chaplin and Company, the Glasgow crane builders and Dübs, the celebrated railway locomotive builders at Polmadie, manufactured road engines fitted with Bray's patent wheels. Taylors of Birkenhead and F & J Hughes of New Cross, London, also built Bray engines, several of which were successfully employed in the military and naval establishments at Woolwich and Plymouth for many years. Probably the most interesting of the Clark-Bray designs was an under-type road engine named Abdul Aziz, built by Dübs in 1866 for the Ottoman Carrying Company who operated a regular service between Beirut and Damascus.

Both Boydell and Bray persevered with their ideas until their deaths, but unfortunately their successors found it impossible to sustain a profitable export market for road engines without the support of a healthy home market, and this was virtually eliminated by the Road Locomotive Act of 1861. Reference has been made already to the prejudice and penal legislation which inhibited the development and use of the road locomotive and although Parliament provided some relief in the early part of the 20th century, the harmful restrictions continued until the Salter Report on taxation, published in 1932, finally ensured the replacement of steam by the internal combustion engine for road haulage work. Only the travelling showman, who was allowed special concessions, and the road roller user, who was exempt from taxation, continued to use steam for another twenty years.

The relevant Acts of Parliament affecting the development of steam traction were the Highways Acts of 1831 and 1835; the Road Locomotive Acts of 1861, 1865, 1878 and 1898; the Locomotive on Highways Act 1896; the Heavy Motor Cars Order 1904; and the Heavy Motor Car Act 1923. Initially, the opposition to steam came from the country landowners and those with commercial interests in horses, later it was those with vested interests in our turnpike roads and the local authorities who led the opposition. The Road Locomotive Act of 1861 was the first legislation designed specifically to regulate the construction and use of road engines. Amendments made in the subsequent Acts of 1865 and 1878 offered some relief to the engine owner; indeed many of the clauses in the original Act were seemingly reasonable, but were quickly made restrictive by over zealous enforcement.

John McLaren, one of the co-founders of J & H McLaren of Leeds outlined some of the unreasonable, almost prohibitive clauses in a paper before the Institution of Civil Engineers.

> "Among the legal restrictions may be mentioned firstly, that such engines have been held to be a nuisance at common law; secondly, that in nearly every case the owner is obliged to obtain a licence from a court of Quarter Sessions, before he can travel with his engine on the Highway and that he may have to wait nearly three months before such a licence may be granted to him; that this licence, though it is evidence that his engine is constructed in accordance with the requirements of the Act of Parliament, affords the owner no protection whatever against any person or public body raising the most frivolous objections to the passage of the engine. Thirdly, that in country districts, though there may be no other traffic on the road, the speed of the engine is limited to 4 mph, and a man is required to walk in front at a distance of not less than 20 yards. Fourthly, that the road authorities have an almost arbitrary power to forbid the use of certain bridges by such engines, though the bridges themselves may be of ample strength to carry the weight without danger; and further, that although the damage done to a bridge by the passage of heavy weights drawn by horses is made

> good at the public expense, such damage must be made good by the engine owner should the same load happen to be drawn by a traction engine. Fifthly, that certain urban authorities have been allowed to embody in their local Acts clauses by which they are able to prohibit the use of road locomotives on any street or road within their jurisdiction."

Thomas Aveling was even more explicit in his condemnation of the 1861 Act.

> "If I send a boiler weighing 15 tons drawn by 15 horses over a country bridge and that boiler breaks the bridge, I have nothing to pay, but if I send the same boiler over the bridge drawn by an engine weighing 8 tons and the boiler breaks through the bridge, I have the whole expense to pay."

It became increasingly difficult to construct a road engine capable of fulfilling a useful purpose without infringing one or other of the clauses and further an owner risked a summons by the opponents of their use every time he moved his engine from one part of a district to another.

A quite unreasonable clause concerning steam blowing-off through the safety valves read, "Nor shall the steam be allowed to attain a pressure such as to exceed the limits fixed by the safety valve, so that no steam shall blow off when the locomotive is on the road." This clause was impossible to comply with so long as engines were compelled to stop to allow the passage of horse drawn conveyances.

Another clause referred to the need for an engine to consume its own smoke: "Every locomotive used on any turnpike road or highway shall be constructed on the principle of consuming its own smoke; and any person using any locomotive not as constructed, or not consuming as far as practicable, its own smoke, shall be liable to a penalty not exceeding £5." If an engine fire is properly maintained and the damper correctly manipulated, little smoke is produced when travelling on the road, due to the quick draught caused by the exhaust steam; immediately the engine is stopped black smoke will be emitted from the chimney and the fire will burn sluggishly due to the loss of artificial draught. It is on record that not infrequently summonses were taken out by persons for whose convenience the engine was stopped.

Probably the greatest harassment facing the early road locomotive operator was the restriction of the hours in which engines were allowed to travel in various districts.

> "County authorities, Town Councils of any Borough which has a separate Court of Quarter Sessions may make bye-laws regulating the use of traction engines on highways – prohibiting their use upon roads where they are satisfied such use would be attended by danger to the public and restricting the hours during which they may be used on any public road, such restriction not to exceed eight consecutive hours out of twenty-four."

This clause gave the local authorities the power to interfere with lawful trade, causing engine owners to waste valuable daylight hours and compelling them to work during the hours of darkness, thus greatly increasing the hazards of moving heavy loads. Fatal accidents in such circumstances were not unknown.

Fig 146 No 789 10 NHP single cylinder road locomotive built in 1878 and designed for continuous road work and heavy haulage duties.

Even if an engine owner escaped being fined for contravention of any of the above, sooner or later he would be called upon to pay exorbitant sums levied by the road authorities for damage alleged to be done to the highway by his engine and its train. The Acts gave, "The road authorities the power to recover expenses caused by excessive weight or extraordinary traffic." Many instances are on record where the traction engine was blatantly discriminated against.

At a meeting of the local Government Board held in 1882, it was said that the damage and inconvenience caused by road engines seriously interferred with the ordinary traffic of the district, especially where roads were less than 20 feet wide. The editor of the Engineer was quick to put the claim into its correct perspective.

> "If the roads are so narrow as this, we would think that inconvenience must also be felt when a large wagon loaded with straw, or when a horse rake or drill, most of them wider than an engine, has to be passed. These however, are not steam engines and the magistrates do not shy at them. Instead of making the traffic accommodate or reduce itself to these narrow roads, it would be much more sensible and better to seek to get the roads widened to suit the requirements of traffic."

A major step forward took place in 1893 with the emergence of the National Traction Engine Owners and Users Association, designed to provide an effective fighting force and lobby, to safeguard the interests of both engine builders and owners alike. It was supported from its inception by Aveling and Porter, Charles Burrell, Fodens of Sandbach, John Fowler, Richard Hornsby and Ransomes of Ipswich, and was especially fortunate in securing the services of Sir William Joynson-Hicks as its legal adviser.

Hicks was responsible for the establishment of the 1896 Select Committee which did much to relieve the frustrations of the traction engine owner and in due course he guided both the Locomotive Act and the Locomotives on Highways Acts through Parliament. These were followed in 1903 by the Heavy Motor Cars Order which permitted the development of the 5 ton steam tractor designed for one man operation. The 1896 Act will be best remembered as the Act which disposed of the need for a lookout man carrying a red flag walking 20 yards ahead of the engine. The Act provided also for a uniform annual licence fee of £10 for traction engines not exceeding 10 tons and £2 for every ton above that weight. Furthermore, engines were allowed to pass through counties other than that for which they were licensed upon payment of a registration fee of 2s 6d (12½p).

Although undoubtedly a step in the right direction, this clause often caused considerable inconvenience, necessitating sending a man ahead by train or bicycle to obtain the requisite permit.

With a backcloth as just described, it will perhaps come as no surprise to the reader to learn that there was a gap of fifteen years between the completion of the last Burrell-Boydell engine in 1862 and the emergence of the first conventional geared road locomotive to be built at St Nicholas Works in 1877, and that only fourteen such engines were built prior to 1890.

Essentially the road locomotive evolved from the traction engine being specially adapted for continuous haulage on the common road. The drive shafts were larger and stronger; the shaft bearings were increased in length; gear wheels were made wider, giving increased wearing surface; the wheel rims were manufactured from a heavier T-section steel; usually additional water carrying capacity was provided; and the majority had a canopy, giving the crew some protection against the weather. Other special features were motion side plates and solid disc type

Fig 147 No 826 6 NHP single cylinder unsprung road locomotive built in 1879 for Robert Payne of Methwold in Norfolk.

flywheels designed to conceal the reciprocating motion in order to minimise the risk of frightening passing horses.

Whereas the traction engine spent much of its working life belt driving stationary machinery, the road engine, by the very nature of its duty kept moving whilst working. This produced an increased supply of primary air to the fire through the ash pan, which, combined with the constant agitation of the burning coals, greatly improved an engine's steam raising capability. Generally the fire grate on a road locomotive was approximately 10 per cent smaller in area than that of a traction engine of equivalent nominal horse power. Similarly, the firebox heating surface often contributed a proportionally smaller amount to the engine's total heating surface than on a traction engine.

The first Thetford built road locomotive, an 8 NHP engine allocated works No 751 and completed in 1877 closely followed the design of the first generation 8 NHP traction engine introduced in the previous year and described in Chapter 5. The single cylinder measured 9 ins dia × 12 ins stroke and the same type 744 traction engine boiler having a 120 PSI working pressure was used. The drive to the hind wheels was through pins engaging with wheel centres attached to a strengthened hind axle, which also carried a winding drum and wire rope, but no compensating gear was fitted until 1880. Additional water was carried in belly tanks mounted under the boiler and the engine weighed 10¼ tons in working order. In 1890 the engine was rebuilt by the works including fitting a new Lowmoor Iron firebox. The Stephenson link motion was modified and the cylinder was bored out to 9⅛ ins dia and fitted with Ramsbottom piston rings.

The second road locomotive, works No 789, built in 1878 was rated 10 NHP and with the exception of the cylinder size and the boiler proportions, it conformed generally with the improved 8 NHP traction engine No 782 which was exhibited at the 1878 Smithfield Club Show. The cylinder measured 10 ins dia × 12 ins stroke, the working pressure was 120 PSI, the grate area 7.25 sq ft, and the total heating surface was 194 sq ft, of which 154 sq ft was derived from the forty-five 2¼ ins dia × 5 ft 10 ins long smoke tubes. This engine was built with compensating gear and a winding drum and the two-speed gearing had ratios of 20.9 and 13.8 to 1 driving 6 ft 6 ins dia × 18 ins wide hind wheels. The flywheel was 4 ft 6 ins dia × 7 ins wide and like its predecessor the engine had tender and belly water tanks with a total capacity of 310 gallons. Weighing 12 tons 6 cwts in working order the engine is known to have given many years excellent service in the ownership of Woods of Brandon, some six miles from Thetford. A number of modifications and renewals proved necessary during its early working life. In 1880 the hind wheel spokes worked loose in the wheel bosses, a problem encountered by many traction engine builders. Robert Burrell is credited with the solution to the problem, which remained a well-guarded secret for many years. Additives were made to the molten metal before pouring, and the spoke ends were given a coating of zinc prior to being placed in the sand mould in which the wheel boss was cast. In 1882 it became necessary to replace the transmission shafts with a stronger design and in 1886 an improved forged crankshaft was fitted.

The year 1879 saw the introduction of the first small road locomotive. Allocated works No 826, the engine was basically a second generation 6 NHP traction engine fitted with strengthened transmission shafts, a type 732 boiler having 8 NHP J type stays and a J type connecting rod. Additional water was carried in a belly tank mounted under the boiler. The engine completed its first fifteen years with Robert Payne & Sons, General Hauliers of Methwold in Norfolk and ended its days in the 1920s with a Suffolk farmer.

The fourth geared road locomotive to be completed at St Nicholas Works was built to the order of G & J Bagshaw of Norwich and was fitted with Thomas Aveling's patent hornplates, which no doubt involved the payment of a royalty to the Rochester concern. Rated 12 NHP, allocated works No 884 and completed in June 1880 the engine was not a success and had to be returned to the works after only a few weeks' service. In spite of the double riveted hornplates having cross bracing fore and aft to form a substantial box structure, the plates sprung causing difficulties with the transmission shafts and gearing. All the gearing with the exception of the single main spur wheel was housed within the box structure.

A ploughing engine cylinder measuring 10½ ins dia × 12 ins stroke was utilised and a new U type boiler having a 7.9 sq ft grate, 39 × 2¼ ins dia × 6 ft 11 ins long smoke tubes and a working pressure of 120 PSI was used giving the following ratios.

Grate area	0.658	sq ft per nominal HP
Firebox surface	3.416	"
Tube surface	11.750	"
Total heating surface	15.160	"

The smoke tube ratio – dia to length was 36.9 to 1

Four heavy duty steel transmission shafts were employed and all the gearing was produced from steel. The two speed gearing gave ratios of 14.9 to 1 and 26.1 to 1. The engine was unsprung and the compensating gear, winding drum and brake were mounted on the left hand side of the engine. The hind wheels were 6 ft 6 ins dia × 18 ins wide with eighteen 3 ins × ¾ ins spokes and the front wheels were 4 ft 1 ins dia × 12 ins wide. The spoked flywheel was 4 ft 6 ins dia × 6 ins wide and a 7 ft 0 ins long awning was supplied over the man-stand. The water carrying capacity including a belly tank under the boiler barrel was 284 gallons and the total weight of the engine

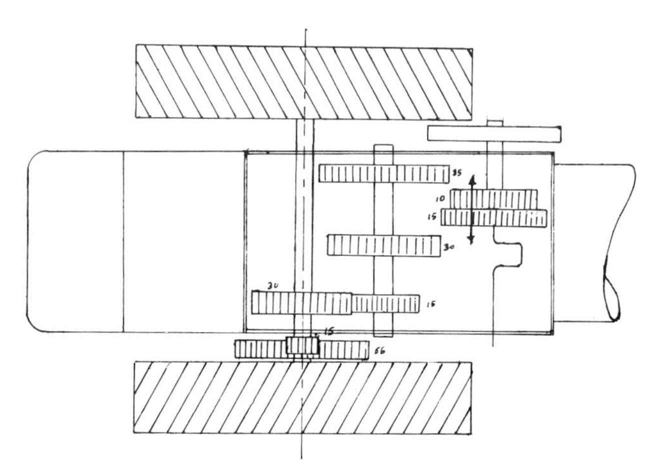

Fig 148 Diagram of road gearing employed on 12 NHP SC road locomotive No 884 built in 1880.

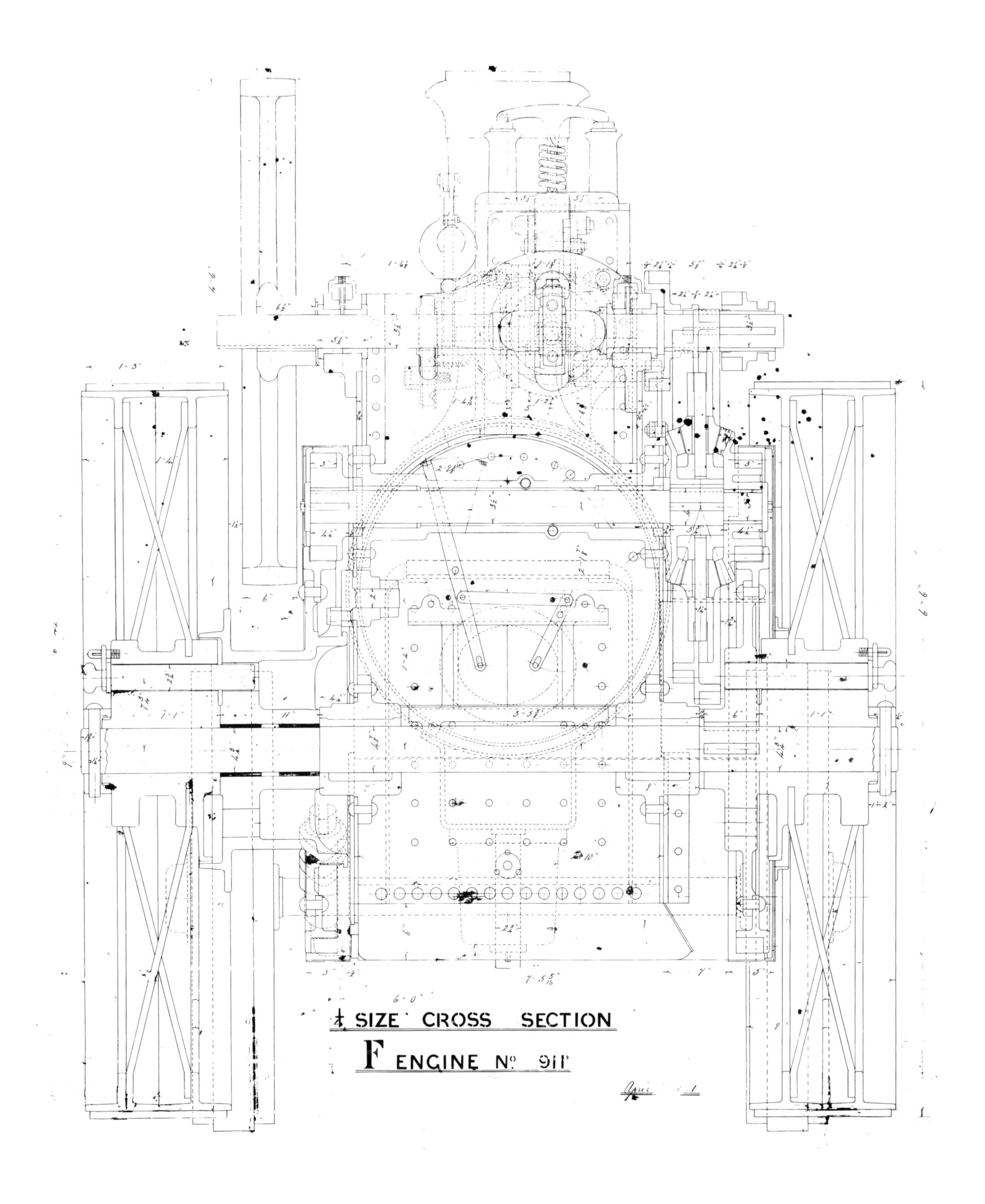

Fig 149 Cross section through the hind axle of 'F' type road locomotive No 911 built in 1882.

was 15 tons 15 cwt. The overall length of the boiler was 12 ft 4 ins and the width of the engine across the hind wheels was 7 ft 6 ins. A new design of eccentric driven feed water pump was fitted together with a Greshams' No 4 injector and a Burrell high speed governor. A spark arrester was fitted inside the smokebox. Unfortunately, we know nothing of the duties this interesting engine was called upon to perform.

In January 1882, St Nicholas Works supplied Edward Viles, a Wolverhampton haulage contractor with a unique 8 NHP road locomotive built to the new F series drawings. Undoubtedly, its most unusual feature was the use of David Joy's patent valve gear which dispensed with the two crankshft eccentrics associated with the conventional Stephenson's link motion and permitted enlarged crankshaft webs and 5½ ins long main bearings to be accommodated in the box structure formed by the fabricated extension of the outer firebox walls. Only a single example of the design, works No 911 was built. In 1885, for reasons unknown the Joy's valve gear was removed and replaced by the standard C type cylinder and Stephenson's type motion.

The original cylinder measured 9½ ins dia × 12 ins stroke and had a pair of Ramsbottom type safety valves mounted transversely on the cylinder dome. The type F3 steel boiler was pressed to 120 PSI, the grate area was 4.6 sq ft and the total heating surface was 194 sq ft, of which 157 sq ft was contributed by the smoke tubes. A new design of boiler feed pump mounted low down on the left hand side of the firebox was used, the pump eccentric pinion was carried on a stub axle attached to the firebox side and driven by the main spur wheel. No injectors were supplied.

The drive to the hind axle was double geared through a three-shaft system. The change speed wheels were mounted on the right hand side of the crankshaft, outside the main bearings, the slow speed wheel being recessed to partly cover the bearing and reduce the shaft overhang. The compensating gear was fitted on the second motion shaft on the right hand side of the engine. Both hind wheels rotated freely on the hind axle, the final drive being through pins engaging with the cast wheel centres, attached to the axle, the left hand side wheel centre being integral with the winding drum and screw-down band brake. The 6 ft 0 ins dia × 16 ins wide hind wheels were unsprung, although the forecarriage was spring mounted. A special drawbar arrangement was fitted on the tender with large india rubber washers mounted inside the water tank. The spoked flywheel was 4 ft 6 ins dia × 6 ins wide; the tender and belly tanks carried 250 gallons of water; and the engine weighed 12 tons in working order. This engine is believed to have been one of the first to be fitted with the now famous Burrell design of polished copper flared chimney top.

Six months after delivery of the F type engine, St Nicholas Works completed another 8 NHP single cylinder road engine based upon the improved C type traction engine first introduced in October 1881. A total of six of these engines were built with unsprung single drive gearing. In 1884/85 another pair of unsprung engines were built but with double geared drive to the hind axle. In 1890 a special 4-shaft single drive spring mounted engine was built for an Australian customer and in 1893 a tenth engine was completed with single drive gearing and volute type springs. Both these latter engines had wood burning colonial type fireboxes. Apart from a 7 NHP engine built in 1890 for a travelling showman and described in chapter 12, all subsequent road engines built in the 19th century had compound cylinders.

8 NHP TYPE C SINGLE CYLINDER ROAD LOCOMOTIVES

No 972	Built	1882	Single drive, unsprung	
1001	"	1882	" "	
1002	"	1882	" "	
1006	"	1883	" "	
1028	"	1884	" "	
1029	"	1884	" "	spring wheels
1068	"	1885	Double geared, unsprung	
1069	"	1885	" "	spring wheels
1498	"	1890	4-shaft, single drive, spring mounted	
1728	"	1893	3-shaft, single drive, spring mounted	

The first six single drive engines had the standard C type 9 ins dia × 12 ins stroke cylinders and the type C60 boiler pressed to 140 PSI with a grate area of 5.375 sq ft and a total heating surface of 151 sq ft. All had mechanical boiler feed pumps, but no injectors were supplied. The two double geared engines had 9¼ ins dia × 12 ins stroke cylinders and the larger type CR177 boiler with a 6.0 sq ft grate area and a total heating surface of 156.0 sq ft. The Colonial type engines had the same cylinder and the type CC124 boiler with a 4 ft 0 ins long firebox giving a grate area of 6.6 sq ft. Subsequently engine Nos 1006 and 1069 were rebuilt and fitted with single crank compound cylinders.

The single drive engines had 2-speed gear ratios of 24.0 and 13.0 to 1 and 6 ft 0 ins dia × 16 ins wide hind wheels and the double geared engines had ratios of 31.3 and 17.0 to 1 and 7 ft 0 ins dia × 18 ins wide hind wheels. All had compensating gear and winding drums; the single drive engines had screw down brakes operating on the left hand road wheel and the double geared engines had brakes operating on the compensating gear centre. Engine No 1006, which went to Finn & Company of Canterbury, was fitted with Aveling and Porter's cast iron wheels and an extra strong 5 ins dia hind axle. For a brief period both Aveling and Fowler advocated cast wheels as a means of overcoming the problem of wheel spokes wearing loose in the wheel hub, but they were heavy and costly and the option was short lived.

The search for better adhesion and improved starting performance was mentioned in Chapter 6, and in January 1884, Charles Burrell and Thomas Tank Burall filed yet another patent describing an improved spring wheel utilising tempered spring steel spokes. Two alternatives were proposed in patent No 2152 and wheels incorporating the arrangement illustrated in Fig 150 were fitted to engines No 1029 and 1069. The patentees claimed that their wheels were elastic in both a vertical and sideways direction and that the curved outer rim enabled the wheel to follow the irregularities of the road more easily, whilst at the same time permitting a lighter form of construction to be used. The curved rims were produced from a channel section, which it was claimed provided added protection for the wheel

Fig 150 Charles Burrell's improved spring wheel built in accordance with is patent 2152 of 1884, fitted to 8 NHP road locomotive No 1029 and demonstrated at the 1884 RASE Shrewsbury Show.

against curbstones and other hard projections. Be this as it may, both sets of spring wheels were replaced by conventional wheels at an early date.

At this time the Thetford drawing office was also actively concerned with developing improvements in the method of transmitting the tractive power of the engine to its load. The draw bar on the F type engine already described was spring mounted on rubber blocks attached to the inside of the tender, but this had the disadvantage of transmitting the load through the tender. The draw bar on the C type road engines was attached directly to the outer firebox side walls by means of side plates which were arranged on the outside of the tender and soon became a standard feature of all traction engine production.

The first of the C type road engines went to Robert Rintoul of North Berwick in Scotland, who a year earlier had acquired the original 7 NHP T type traction engine. The second and third in the series went to buyers in the Alton area of Hampshire; the fourth went to Kent; and the fifth and sixth went to owners in West Suffolk. It is surprising how often we find more than one engine in a batch going to different owners in the same locality; no doubt even 100 years ago the "Keeping up with the Joneses" syndrome had an important part to play in salesmanship. Another point worth noting is that at least two of the series survived as working engines for nearly seventy years. No 1068, the first of the double geared engines was exhibited at the 1883 Smithfield Club Show and then sold to Edward P Robinson & Son of Dover, who later acquired No 1216, an 8 NHP C type traction engine. No 1069 was supplied new to Tissot of Fourmies in Northern France, but six years later was returned to the works, re-conditioned and resold as No 1790 fitted with 6½ ins dia × 12 ins dia × 12 ins stroke SCC cylinders.

Number 1498 was built to the order of G Fletcher & Company, a London Confirming House upon behalf of J German, an Australian customer. This was the first Burrell engine to be shipped to Australia and incorporated a number of special features in addition to the wood burning Colonial firebox. Although the ultimate use to which the engine was put is not now known, timber haulage would seem a high probability. It was a 4-shaft engine mounted on volute type springs. The compensating gear was on the left hand side of the engine and the large winding drum was on the right hand side. A 4 ft 0 ins dia solid flywheel was fitted as well as a short awning and a spectacle plate. Several engines were built with this feature at this time including engine Nos 1451 and 1470, the first two Burrell engines supplied to travelling showmen. Spark arresters were fitted in both the smokebox and the chimney. The back of the tender was hinged so as to let down and guard rails were fitted to the top of the tender for carrying extra wood. A large hand operated force pump was fitted to the right hand side belly tank.

The final engine in the series, No 1728 was supplied to W Townsend & Sons of Ross in Herefordshire, named 'Mountain King' and used for timber haulage in the hilly wooded areas of the Wye Valley.

Engine No 1001 was the first of many Burrell road engines which were subsequently returned to the works for conversion to meet the special needs of the travelling showman. In 1894 this engine was purchased from its original owner by Charles Dack of Deopham in Norfolk and used for hauling and driving his set of Galloping Horses. It was fitted with a full length canopy with twisted brass supports, which as we learned in an earlier chapter was later transferred to No 2171 which Dack had also purchased second hand. Mention is made in this chapter and the next of all known Showman's type road engine conversions, but new engines supplied direct to showmen, although similar in all major mechanical details to standard road engines are described separately in Chapter 12.

It might be said with justification that 1890 marked a turning point in the history of Charles Burrell & Sons, for in that year the first of a long line of compound cylinder road locomotives was introduced. In March, a largely experimental 6 NHP oil-fired double crank compound road engine which we shall discuss in greater detail in the next chapter, was shipped to Germany. Two months later the first of 110 single crank compound road engines of various types was delivered to the Ash Brewery at Sandwich in Kent.

However, before considering in detail the compound road engines it is necessary to record details of six single cylinder road engines built in the early part of the 20th century for three Scottish customers residing in the fertile soft fruit growing area of the Tay Valley. The reason they chose single cylinders nearly 20 years into the compound era is not clear other than the question of initial cost.

20th CENTURY SINGLE CYLINDER ROAD LOCOMOTIVES

No	Built	NHP	Customer
2989	1908	8	John Doe
2997	1908	8	Martin & MacFarlane
3058	1908	8	Martin & MacFarlane
3161	1909	7	John Doe
3713	1916	8	R & T Chalmers
3806	1919	6	R & T Chalmers

All were double geared on the hind axle mounted on 17 leaf springs. Nos 2989 and 3713 had 3-speed gearing. All had boilers pressed to 180 PSI with 5 ft 8 ins long smoke tubes. The 8 NHP engines had 7 ft 0 ins dia hind wheels and the smaller engines 6 ft 6 ins dia wheels. All had solid type flywheels and motion side plates and the 8 NHP engines were fitted with belly tanks.

We shall learn in the next chapter that the first compound road locomotive built at St Nicholas Works was in fact a unique 6 NHP engine with double crank compound cylinders for a German customer in March 1890. Two months later the first of a batch of 17 8 NHP single crank compound road locomotives was completed. Undoubtedly the directors of the company were very encouraged by the reception given to their SCC traction engines and they were anxious to utilise the patterns and tooling already developed for these engines.

8 NHP 6¼ × 11 × 12 ins SCC SINGLE DRIVE SPRING MOUNTED ROAD LOCOMOTIVES

No	Built		No	Built	
No 1480	Built	1890	No 1654	Built	1893
1481	”	1890*	1655	”	1892*
1485	”	1890	1666	”	1893
1497	”	1890	1667	”	1893
1530	”	1891	1674	”	1893*
1542	”	1891*	1688	”	1893
1583	”	1892	1701	”	1893*
1600	”	1892	1709	”	1893*
1628	”	1892*			

* Subsequently converted to Showman's type road locomotives.

Although all were built with 11 ins dia low pressure cylinders it was found expedient after a short period of working to reduce this to 10½ ins on the majority of the batch. Subsequently, a combination of 6½ ins dia HP cylinder × 11 ins dia LP cylinder was found to give the best results.

All were fitted with the type CC20 boiler pressed to 160 PSI having a grate area of 5.375 sq ft and a total heating surface of 151 sq ft. All had mechanical boiler feed pumps and injectors, the majority of the latter being the Greshams' type, although Kortings, Madens and Penberthy types were supplied where specified by the customer. Engine No 1480 had a copper firebox and brass smoke tubes, but these appear to have had a remarkably short life for they were replaced in 1895 with a steel box and steel smoke tubes. The last three engines in the batch were built with a large manhole in the left hand side of the boiler, a feature which most other manufacturers employed but one which was only occasionally fitted by St Nicholas Works.

All except Nos 1485 and 1654 had three-shaft single drive gearing to the spring mounted hind axle and 6 ft 6 ins dia × 16 ins or 18 ins wide wheels. Some had volute type springs, others spiral springs. The two speed gearing had ratios of 29.0 and 15.8 to 1. The two exceptions mentioned above were built with four transmission shafts, having 7 ft 0 ins dia × 18 ins wide wheels and gear ratios of 30.9 and 19.6 to 1. Traction engine builders for long disagreed as to the relative merits of three-shaft versus four-shaft transmission systems. John Fowler generally opted for the latter system, but we cannot do better than to quote from Burrell's catalogue in order to understand the philosophy adopted at St Nicholas Works.

"Simplicity of construction is essential in a road engine. Road engines are constructed upon either the three or four shaft principle. The three shaft engine has one crankshaft, one countershaft, and one main axle. The advantage claimed for the four shaft engine is that by the use of the extra countershaft a portion of the gearing can be placed between the hornplates; the disadvantage being that two extra spur wheels and an extra shaft are necessary.

"Putting in extra shafts and bearings means reducing the tractive power of the engine by increased friction, and if it were necessary to demonstrate this, there would

Fig 151 No 1667 8 NHP SCC single drive spring mounted road locomotive in the ownership of Hughes & Roberts of Abergele at Llanrwst Station in 1906.

be no difficulty in putting in a sufficient number of cog wheels to take up the whole power of the engine in internal friction. The loss of power in the gearing is increased in proportion to the number of shafts.

"In all traction engines there is twice as much strain between the countershaft and the main axle as there is betweeen the crankshaft and countershaft, due to the multiplication of powers in the gearing. A good deal has been advanced upon the benefits to be derived from putting the first motion gearing between the hornplates. It is impossible to get the last motion gearing between the hornplates of any traction engine of the ordinary type and although exposed to double the working strain, it possesses no apparent disadvantages, as shafts and axles are made sufficiently strong to avoid springing and the wheels are kept as close to their bearings as possible.

"As to durability, the three-shaft engine will cost less for repairs, as the construction is simpler and has fewer bearings.

"We will construct road locomotives upon the four-shaft principle when required, but strongly recommend the three-shaft engine for all purposes, as being lighter, simpler and more powerful.

"We do not consider that any road locomotive can be so called unless it is mounted on springs, indeed springs are more important for a road locomotive, than for a railway locomotive, as they are exposed to more serious jolting and shocks when running on rough roads. However well constructed, without springs the engines are always shaking themselves to pieces."

At one stage St Nicholas Works carried out a series of tests on the Croxton road, two miles north of Thetford. They used two identical engines, excepting that one had three shafts and the other four shafts. The object of the tests was to determine the maximum load each could haul on the 1 in 18 incline at a steady 3 MPH. The results showed that with equal boiler pressure and road speeds, the three-shaft engine hauled 25 per cent more gross weight than the four-shaft contender.

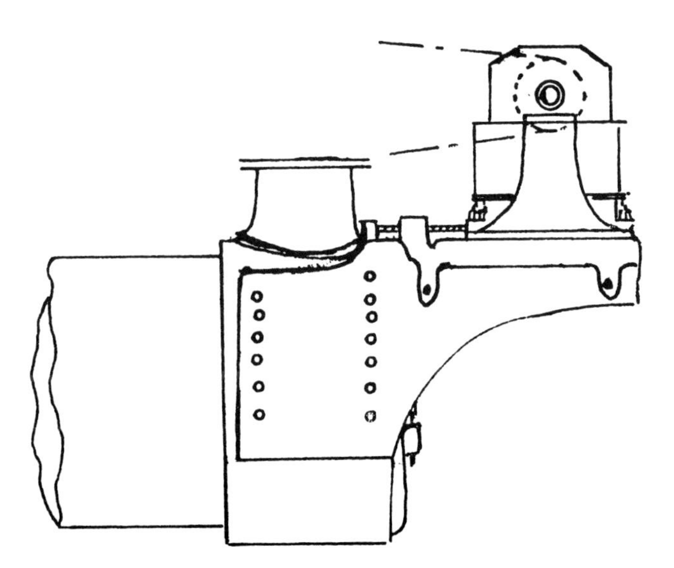

Fig 152 Sketch showing Frederick Burrell's patent No 5531 of 1894 describing the recommended method of applying a dynamo platform to existing engines.

Both four-shaft engines went to Cornish customers. No 1485 went to C H Carlyn of Kenwyn and No 1654 went to Harvey's of Hayle in Cornwall, the celebrated engineers and shipbuilders. The founder, John Harvey, a village blacksmith made many of the parts for Richard Trevithick's original steam carriage and Trevithick eventually married his daughter. In 1843 Harvey manufactured the world's largest steam pumping engine, used to reclaim land in Holland.

A variety of flywheels ranging from 4 ft 0 ins dia to 4 ft 4 ins dia were fitted to these engines; the majority were the solid 6 ins wide pattern, although the last four had spoked flywheels with the spokes covered with metal discs. The screw-down band brakes were bolted to the double spur wheel, and tender and belly water tanks having a capacity of 237 gallons were fitted as standard. All had the short pattern awning and engine No 1542 was fitted also with a spectacle plate. The total weight in working order varied between 12 tons 15 cwt and 14 tons for the crane engine variants.

Two engines in this group Nos 1497 and 1600, were built as crane engines. The 5 ton capacity forward mounted jibs were attached to the front axle and a fifth wheel clutch fitted to the crankshaft controlled a bevel wheel drive to the crane winding drum mounted ahead of the smokebox. The arrangement of working was extremely simple and the engine could lift and carry its suspended load with ease handled by one man. The jib could be removed when not required without taking off the winding drum barrel or any of the gearing. No 1497 went to Edwin Danks & Son at the Oldbury Boiler Works in Birmingham, and No 1600 went to J Wilson of Galway on the west coast of Ireland.

The seven engines in this series which were subsequently purchased by travelling showmen carried the following names.

Engine	*Showland owner*	*Engine name*
1481	George Pruett & Sons	'Pride of Bristol'
1542	Fred Gray	'Pride of Devonshire'
1628	Joseph Matthews	—
1655	William Irvin	'William the Conqueror'
1674	John Jennings	'Masterpiece'
1701	Alf Bond, Merton	'Bing Boy'
1709	J Hancock	—

They were fitted with full length awnings and dynamo platforms arranged as extensions to the smokebox top, plus varying degrees of polished brass embellishment and other decoration. The majority of the conversions were carried out by St Nicholas Works but some were dealt with by other firms nominated by the engine owners, and in order to protect the company's interests, Frederick Burrell filed his patent No 5531 in 1894, which specifically described methods of applying a smokebox dynamo platform to existing engines.

At the end of 1893 an improved updated version was introduced with 6½ ins dia × 11 ins dia × 12 ins stroke SCC cylinders. A total of 27 engines were built of which 12 were built as Showman's Road Locomotives and three were subsequently converted to Showman's type engines. All except No 1735 and 1790 were fitted with Aveling's type hornplates and Nos 1727 and 1884 had 4 ft long colonial type fireboxes with 6.6 sq ft grates. All except No 1790 had single drive gearing to the hind axle.

8 NHP 6½ × 11 × 12 ins SCC SINGLE DRIVE SPRING MOUNTED ROAD LOCOMOTIVES

No	Built	No	Built
No 1727	Built 1893	No 1902	Built 1896
1735	" 1894	1943	" 1896*
1757	" 1894	1953	" 1896
1790	" 1894	1967	" 1896
1817	" 1895	2011	" 1897*
1849	" 1896	2022	" 1897*
1884	" 1895	2038	" 1897
		2077	" 1898

* Subsequently converted to Showman's road locomotives.

With the exception of engines Nos 1727, 1735, 1790 and 1884 all had type CC123 boilers having a 5.375 sq ft grate and 41 × 2 ins dia × 5 ft 8 ins long smoke tubes giving a total heating surface of 151 sq ft. Those built after 1896 had the solid end pattern cylinder following contemporary traction engine design and most had balanced crankshafts. All had 2-speed gearing giving ratios of 29.0 to 1 and 15.8 to 1 and volute type springs were used with the single drive gearing. Most were fitted with short awnings and the average weight of the engines in working order was 13 tons 5 cwt. Nos 1902 and 2077 were supplied with 5 ton capacity forward mounted jib cranes, the former being supplied to the War Department and the latter to a South African customer, J H Chatterton in Natal.

The three engines in the series subsequently converted to Showman's type engines carried the following names.

Engine	*Showland owner*	*Engine name*
1943	Hastings & Whayman	'Surprise'
2011	Charles Hart	—
2022	Toam Harniess	'Perseverance'

The desirability of being able to provide 3-speed gearing on road locomotives soon became apparent and in August 1895 Frederick Burrell filed his patent No 23960 and in the same month the works completed an interesting 8 NHP engine for the Harrogate Gas Company who had been using Burrell engines for the delivery of coke since the days of the Thomson Road Steamer. This engine allocated works No 1870 incorporated a number of novel features.

Frederick stated that the objective of his patent was to provide an arrangement of the gearing whereby traction engines of the usual design and having 2-speed gearing could, without altering the position of the existing shafts and gear wheels or widening the distance between the road wheels, be fitted with a third speed. In order to achieve this he fitted a large internally toothed spur wheel inside the rim of the flywheel and geared into it a pinion of as large a diameter as possible in order to minimise friction. This pinion drove a countershaft running in roller bearings and having another pinion on it which could be engaged with one of the spur wheels on the countershaft of the road motion when the conventional fast and slow gears were disengaged.

In order to reduce noise Frederick proposed the use of raw hide for the large pinions driven by the flywheel internally toothed spur wheel. The proposed arrangement was equally applicable to 3-shaft or 4-shaft engines and he claimed that the third speed could be adapted to existing engines without seriously increasing the friction of the gearing and that it would actually reduce the loss of power due to the thrust upon the bearings being at the lowest possible level. In order to further reduce friction he proposed fitting all the transmission shafts with ball or roller type bearings, an idea then well ahead of its time. He claimed that by minimising friction in this manner lower piston speeds could be used for a given size of cylinder and peripheral speed of road wheels with consequent economies in fuel consumption. He claimed also that the use of ball or roller bearings would show important benefits as in their application to bicycles and would prevent the shafts from wearing out of line with each other.

Fig 153 No 1870 8 NHP 3-speed 'composite' engine mounted on rubber tyres as supplied to the Harrogate Gas Company in 1895 with its road train of coke wagons.

Fig 154 No 1870 photographed outside St Nicholas Works during acceptance trials in July 1895 clearly showing the internally toothed spur wheel on the flywheel.

In the event it appears that roller bearings were only fitted on the third speed countershaft. All the other shafts and gearing were of steel with conventional plain bearings.

The single crank compound cylinder measured 6½ ins dia × 10½ ins dia × 12 ins stroke and a short T type boiler was used, pressed to 160 PSI. The grate area was 4.9 sq ft and thirty-four 2 ins dia × 5 ft 1 ins long smoke tubes gave a total heating surface of 118.0 sq ft. The hind wheels were 5 ft 3 ins dia × 15 ins wide and were fitted with solid india rubber tyres reminiscent of its Road Steamer predecessor. The hind axle was unsprung although the front axle was carried on a sprung forecarriage. Steering was by means of a worm and rack arrangement and once again one can detect the influence of the earlier Road Steamer design. The transmission shafts were double geared to the hind axle. The compensating gear was mounted on the countershaft and the winding drum ran loose on the hind axle. The 3-speed gearing gave ratios of 25.72 to 1, 14.1 to 1 and 10.1 to 1. The engine was fitted with a short awning.

In 1925 the Harrogate Gas Company sold the engine to R Jepson, a Yorkshire showman, who ran the engine without further modification for a number of years.

At the turn of the century a further two 8 NHP road locomotives were built with the same 6¼ ins dia × 10½ ins dia × 12 ins stroke SCC cylinder. They had larger boilers than the Harrogate Gas engine having 5 ft 8 ins long smoke tubes and single drive gearing with spiral type springs on the hind axle. No 2430 was completed in November 1901 and No 2464 in March 1902, both engines spending the whole of their working lives in commercial ownership. No 2430 started life with Thomas H Edwards of Deptford for haulage work in London's Dockland and in 1904 it was acquired by Pickfords Ltd for working out of their Bermondsey depot. No 2464 was supplied new to W S Keaton of Berwick-on-Tweed and was engaged upon haulage work in the Border Country until 1916 when it was acquired by Nobel's Explosives Factory in Cornwall.

We consider next the big 7 ins dia × 11½ ins dia × 12 ins stroke SCC road locomotives. A total of 18 were built between 1891 and 1907, eight of which were built as Showman's type engines and are dealt with elsewhere and one was subsequently converted to a Showman's engine. They became known in the works as 'Contractors' type engines and those with 5.375 sq ft grates were rated 8 NHP and those with 6.5 sq ft or larger grates were rated 10 NHP. Undoubtedly they were immensely robust and powerful engines designed to compete with the big Fowler road engines and to take maximum advantage of the more enlightened attitudes then being adopted of our legislators.

8/10 NHP CONTRACTORS' TYPE SCC ROAD LOCOMOTIVES

No		Built		
No	1525	Built	1891	10 NHP
	1736	"	1894	10 NHP
	1821	"	1894	10 NHP
	1892	"	1895	10 NHP
	1935	"	1896	10 NHP
	2017	"	1897	8 NHP
	2166	"	1899	8 NHP
	2557	"	1903	10 NHP
	2661	"	1904	10 NHP
	2937	"	1907	8 NHP

No 1525 was a special 10 NHP wood burning crane engine supplied to J Wilcox & Company's London

Fig 155 No 2430 8 NHP SCC double geared spring mounted road locomotive in the ownership of Thomas Edwards of Deptford hauling a new boiler for Newgate Prison in London.

Confirming House for shipment to Jarrah Karri & Millers Forests Ltd in Western Australia, who for many years were one of the world's main sources of hard wood railway sleepers. The 160 PSI boiler had a 7.0 sq ft grate and a total heating surface of 205.0 sq ft and the lengthened smokebox was fitted with a large spark arrester. Single drive gearing to the hind axle and spiral type springs were employed; the hind wheels were 6 ft 6 ins dia × 18 ins wide and the front wheels 4 ft 7½ ins dia × 12 ins wide. Extra large water tanks with 320 gallons capacity were supplied.

Nos 1736 and 1821 were both rated 10 NHP and both had the type CL35 boiler with 6.5 sq ft grates. The former was pressed to 175 PSI with 5 ft 5 ins long smoke tubes; the latter was pressed to 160 PSI and fitted with 5 ft 8 ins long smoke tubes. Both had single drive gearing to the hind axle fitted with volute type springs and 6 ft 6 ins × 20 ins wide hind wheels giving gear ratios of 29.0 to 1 and 15.8 to 1. The spoked flywheels were 4 ft 1½ ins dia × 6 ins wide with sheet metal casing and the overall width of the engines was 8 ft 5½ ins.

No 1736 went new to Ipswich Maltsters R & W Paul. Later it was purchased by the Dorney Wood Estate at Burnham Beeches owned by Lord Courtauld Thomson, the eldest son of R W Thomson of Road Steamer fame. Subsequently this beautiful house was presented to the nation for the private use of senior members of the Government. Just after the First World War the engine was sold to T Pettigrove the well known Buckinghamshire showman. The extent to which the engine was modified and fitted with show fittings is not now known. No 1821 was the fourth of nine new Burrell engines supplied to W Arnold & Sons of East Peckham, about whom we have already made reference, who named the engine 'Conqueror'.

No 1892 was built to a special order from the Reid & Gray agency in New Zealand for hauling logs in the Kauri Forests. These splendid coniferous trees were at the time in great demand as the source of Kauri-gum resin extensively used for making varnish. Unlike the other 10 NHP 'Contractors' engines it was double geared to the hind axle and unsprung, a feature more suitable to the rugged and often muddy terrain on which the engine would normally be working. Another special feature was the large type CR194 winding drum carrying 400 yds of wire rope.

The next 'Contractors' type engine built, No 1935, was built as a speculation and exhibited at the RASE Show held in Leicester in 1896. Immediately after the show the engine was returned to the works and rebuilt with a new pattern solid end double crank compound cylinder (DCC); a balanced crankshaft with the cranks set at 90°; a 5 ton capacity forward mounted jib crane; and was renumbered No 1972. It was then exported to South Africa through the Davis & Soper agency and became one of three big Burrell crane engines and eight Burrell road locomotives to be owned by the Cape Town local authority for work in the dock area.

The final five SCC 'Contractors' type engines all went to customers in Cornwall. Nos 2017, 2166 and 2937 were rated 8 NHP and Nos 2557 and 2661, both of which went to Harveys of Hayle, were rated 10 NHP. There was a considerable amount of heavy haulage work in Cornwall at the turn of the century involving not only the movement of china clay and mineral ores from the many mines in the area, but also sea sand from the north coast which was exported as a valuable manure. There were also considerable imports of Scandinavian timber into the south coast ports. Many foreign ships preferred to use the ports at Penzance and Porthleven rather than face the hazards of entering Hayle harbour. Although Harvey's great foundry and engineering works had virtually closed down at this time, Hayle remained the hub of the Harvey empire and outposts concerned with the distribution of

Fig 156 No 1892 special 10 NHP SCC double geared unsprung road locomotive hauling kauri logs in New Zealand.

coal, timber and other building materials grew in importance.

Nos 2017 and 2166 had the solid end type cylinders and 160 PSI boilers with 5.375 sq ft grates and 5 ft 8 ins long smoke tubes. No 2937 had the same cylinder but a larger diameter boiler pressed to 180 PSI having a 6.0 sq ft grate and a total heating surface of 153.16 sq ft. In accordance with the then current fashion there was a large gap in the front box bracket for the motion rods. The drive shafts were double geared and spring mounted on 17 leaf springs and the hind wheels were 7 ft 0 ins dia × 20¼ ins wide. Unlike her predecessors the engine had neither boiler feed pump nor governors but was fitted with two injectors.

No 2557 was returned to the works within a year and the cylinder was bored out to 7¼ ins dia × 11¾ ins dia × 12 ins stroke. The 2 ft 6 ins dia boiler was pressed to 175 PSI and the grate area was 6.6 sq ft. The three shaft transmission and hind axle were spring mounted on leaf springs with 7 ft 0 ins dia × 20½ ins wide hind wheels. No 2661 was an altogether more sophisticated engine with 4-shaft transmission. The boiler was pressed 175 PSI; the grate was unusually large at 7.25 sq ft and the forty-three 2 ins dia × 5 ft 8 ins long smoke tubes gave a total heating surface of 167.0 sq ft. The hind axle was spring mounted on leaf springs and the hind wheels were 7 ft 0 ins dia × 20½ ins wide. The compensating gear was on the left hand side and the winding drum on the right hand side of the rear axle and the 2-speed gearing gave ratios of 32.1 to 1 and 20.4 to 1. A Moores steam pump replaced the mechanical feed water pump and a type BP 'H' injector and Burrell's high speed governor were fitted. The water carrying capacity was 407 gallons, a short awning was supplied and the engine weighed 15 tons 17 cwt in working order.

Although not strictly a Showman's type engine, the first small SCC compound road locomotive built at St Nicholas Works No 1657 was supplied new to S Shepherd, a South London traveller for hauling his now famous old 'Sea-on-Land' ride. This 6 NHP engine made its debut at the Smithfield Show in 1892. Later it was purchased by James Pettigrove who named her 'King of the Road'. During the First War she passed to Robert Edwards of Swindon who fitted a dynamo platform. It was followed by a batch of five 6 NHP engines, one of which No 2005 was built as a full Showman's type engine.

6 NHP 6¼ ins × 10½ ins × 12 ins SCC ROAD LOCOMOTIVES

No	Built	No	Built
1682	1893	1726	1893
1700	1893	2053	1897

All had variations of the T boiler with steel fireboxes pressed to 160 PSI. No 1682 had a woodburning firebox with a 5.7 sq ft grate; Nos 1700 and 1726 had coal burning fireboxes and 4.5 sq ft grates; and No 2053, built as a crane engine for the Geelong Gold Mining Company in Matebeleland had a large wood burning firebox with a 5.5 sq ft grate and a lengthened smokebox fitted with a spark arrester. All had thirty-four 2 ins dia × 5 ft 4 ins long smoke tubes. The smokebox doors carried a new circular nameplate inscribed, "The Burrell Compound".

An unconfirmed story persists that No 1682 was originally ordered by Wares of Truro who at the time

Fig 157 No 1657 the first 6 NHP SCC road locomotive built in 1892 seen after conversion to a Showman's type engine.

travelled an old set of steam Dobbies in Devon and Cornwall. The engine never carried any show fittings and according to the works records started its working life with T Hooper of Hartbury, passing to G F Butcher, Haulage Conractors of Gloucester by 1898. They operated 5 Burrell engines and a Fowler road locomotive in the area at the turn of the century. Similar doubts exist about engine No 1700 which was supplied new to J Beach of Tralee in County Kerry in Ireland. He is believed to have been a travelling showman and a descendant of the well known Beach family who have been travellers in West London and The Thames Valley area for many years. There is no record of this engine ever carrying any show fittings or adornments.

All except No 2053 were spring mounted on volute type springs with single drive gearing. No 2053 was double geared to the hind axle and unsprung. All had short awnings, motion side plates, solid type flywheels and were fitted with boiler feed pumps, Penberthy injectors and Burrell cross arm governors.

These were followed by a batch of nine 6 NHP road locomotives with the standard duty 6 ins dia × 10 ins dia × 10 ins stroke single cranked compound traction engine cylinders. All had single drive gearing to the sprung hind axle fitted with volute type springs. One engine, No 1741, was built as a Showman's type engine and another, No 1934, was at an early date converted to a unique traction centre engine by its owner and both are dealt with elsewhere. The remainder of the series spent all their working lives in commercial ownership.

6 NHP 6 ins × 10 ins × 12 ins SCC ROAD LOCOMOTIVES

No	Built	No	Built
No 1733	Built 1894	No 1841	Built 1895
1749	" 1894	1878	" 1895
1764	" 1894	1955	" 1896
1825	" 1855		

No 1733 went to Australia through the Howard agency in Sydney. It had an enlarged wood burning firebox and lengthened smokebox fitted with baffle plates and a spark arrester. All were fitted with Aveling's type hornplates, type T boilers and otherwise they differed little from their 6 NHP predecessors in the service of general hauliers in various parts of the United Kingdom.

Not surprisingly these engines were followed by a road locomotive version of the highly successful single crank compound 'Devonshire' traction engine, but they were totally superceded when a double crank compound cylinder version was introduced a few years later. Twenty-four SCC engines were built between 1896 and 1904, six of which were built as Showman's type engines and three were subsequently converted.

6 NHP 5½ × 9 ins × 10 ins SCC 'DEVONSHIRE' ROAD LOCOMOTIVES

No	Built	No	Built
No 1961	Built 1896	No 2293	Built 1900
2052	" 1897	2339	" 1900
2064	" 1898	2364	" 1901
2078	" 1898	2385	" 1901
2126	" 1898*	2410	" 1901
2164	" 1899	2431	" 1901
2223	" 1899*	2493	" 1902
2239	" 1899	2566	" 1903*
2283	" 1900	2675	" 1904

* Subsequently converted to Showman's type road locomotives.

Engine Nos 1961 to 2293 had the small 4.0 sq ft grate and subsequent engines had the larger 4.6 sq ft pattern. All were pressed to 160 PSI with forty 1¾ ins dia × 4 ft 9½ ins long smoke tubes. Two engines, Nos 2364 and 2410 supplied to the Cape Town Municipality in South Africa had copper fireboxes with totally enclosed motion, the remainder all had steel fireboxes. No 2675 was fitted

Fig 158 No 1961 the first 6 NHP SCC 'Devonshire' type road locomotive as new to W Arnold & Sons of Brambridge in Kent.

Fig 159 No 2364 one of a pair of identical 6 NHP SCC road locomotives supplied to the city of Cape Town with copper fireboxes and totally enclosed motion.

Fig 160 No 2126 'Island Queen' an original Devonshire type engine built in 1898 as converted to a Showman's type engine in 1923.

with a Moores steam pump whereas all the remainder had mechanical feed pumps, Holden & Brooks injectors and Burrell high speed governors and 3 ft 3 ins dia × 5 ins wide solid flywheels.

Engines up to and including No 2293 had single drive gearing with volute type springs. Those up to No 2566 were fitted with spiral springs and No 2675 had leaf springs. All had 2-speed gearing with ratios 26.3 to 1 and 15.5 to 1 and 6 ft 0 ins dia × 16 ins wide hind wheels. All except the two Cape Town and the six Showman's type engines had short awnings. The engines weighed in working order approximately 9 tons 10 cwt.

No 1961 was the first Burrell engine to actually carry the distinctive name, 'Devonshire' engine. It went new to W Arnold & Sons shortly after they had removed from South London to Brambridge in Kent. No 2052 went to the Home Brewery Company at Daybrook in Nottinghamshire and proved to be ideal for beer deliveries in rural districts prior to the introduction of the 5 ton tractor and the steam wagon. Nos 2239 and 2293 went to South Africa through the Davis & Soper Agency but shortly after the ending of the Boer War both were sold to Australian farmers. No 2293 went to J Coote in Upper Manilla, NSW, Australia and was used mainly for the transportation of wool. No 2339 went to a French customer through the Ludt agency in Paris. Four engines including the two Cape Town engines were shipped to South Africa through the Davis & Soper agency and No 2493 was shipped by G & G Brown of Liverpool upon behalf of an unknown South African customer. No 2223 was purchased by the War Office and was extensively used in the Aldershot area for carrying animal fodder. It was allocated W D No 1884.

The remaining engines in the series went to general haulage contractors in the United Kingdom; three were subsequently converted to Showman's type engines. No 2126 was acquired in 1913 by 'Professor' Arnold of Southampton who travelled the South of England and the Isle of Wight with his now famous Electric Bioscope and Theatre of Variety Show. Originally the engine was named 'Showman' but later it was changed to 'Island Queen'. It was not actually converted to a full Showman's type engine until 1923 when a full length canopy and dynamo platform were fitted for Arnold's sons. It speaks well of the breed that after 25 years' continuous service the engine was considered worthwhile overhauling and converting to a full Showman's type engine.

Following the First World War No 2223 was acquired by J Edwards of Camberwell Green in London for hauling his set of Gallopers. It is not known whether it was converted to a full Showman's type engine although a dynamo appears to have been fitted. The third engine in the series to enter showland service was No 2566. It was acquired by Gideon Roberts in 1909, converted to a full Showman's specification, named 'Perseverance' and used for hauling his set of Gallopers in the hilly districts of Glamorgan in South Wales. In 1914 the engine was requisitioned by the War Department passing to T G and H E Worboys of Stevenage in 1921.

Only five 7 NHP SCC road locomotives were built between 1892 and 1910, one of which, No 1629 was built as a full Showman's engine and is dealt with in Chapter 12. No 2279 built in 1900 had $6\frac{1}{4}$ ins dia × $10\frac{1}{2}$ ins dia × 12 ins stroke SCC cylinders and single drive gearing to the hind axle mounted on volute type springs. It spent all its working life in Hampshire and Norfolk. No 2646, built in 1904, was one of the earliest Burrell engines to be fitted with 3-speed gearing. It had 6 ins dia × 10 ins dia × 12 ins stroke SCC cylinders, 5 ft 8 ins long smoke tubes, a Moores steam pump, Pickering type governors and single drive gearing mounted on leaf type springs and spent all its working life with several haulage contractors in various parts of the country.

No 3009, built in 1908, had the same 6 ins dia × 10 ins dia × 12 ins stroke cylinders but it was fitted with a larger 175 PSI boiler with a 5.49 sq ft grate and forty-seven 1½ ins dia × 5 ft 8 ins long smoke tubes. It had 2-speed gearing and was double geared to the hind axle and mounted on leaf type springs. It started its life in the ownership of Nottingham Corporation. The final 7 NHP SCC road engine No 3210 was built in 1910. It had 6½ ins dia × 11 ins dia × 12 ins stroke cylinders, a 200 PSI boiler which was otherwise generally similar to that fitted to No 3009 and was double geared to the hind axle with leaf type springs. It started life with A J Lewis timber hauling in Herefordshire. In 1920 it was acquired by Clifford Hill of Ross-on-Wye who had it converted to a full Showman's type engine by Elias Ltd of Gloucester and renamed it 'Pride of Wye'.

This engine really marked the end of the single crank compound era. Frederick Burrell's life style had tragically finally overcame him and he spent the remainder of his life in a home at Heigham near Norwich. It is said that he worked on a drawing board in his room until the very end. Henceforth interest at St Nicholas Works was mainly focused on the splendid Burrell double crank compound system.

CHAPTER ELEVEN

The Double Crank Compound Road Locomotive

Undoubtedly, Frederick Burrell's single crank compound arrangement met a need and neatly solved the problem of applying compounding to the limited space available on a traction engine, but it created other difficulties in its wake. The large unbalanced reciprocating forces associated with the heavy crosshead assembly could not be completely balanced by the rotating parts and in operation many drivers complained about the difficulty of restarting the engine under load when the pistons stopped in the top dead centre position. Although the double crank compound arrangement with the HP and LP cylinders arranged side by side and with the two cranks set at 90 degrees to each other basically overcame the problem, this necessitated an off-set in the hornplates in order to accommodate a crankshaft having two sets of crank webs, five eccentrics and lengthened main bearings. It also necessitated the off-setting of the cylinder block on the boiler barrel in order to align the HP cylinder with the HP crank pin.

Although the first DCC road locomotive to be built at St Nicholas Works was completed in 1890 a further six years elapsed before the arrangement was developed further. No doubt its adoption was in part due to the success of the big DCC engines then being built by Fowlers, Aveling & Porter and McLaren and partly due to the anticipated easing of Government legislation affecting their usage on the common roads.

No 1415 built in March 1890 and rated 6 NHP was supplied to Gubrüder Adt of Enschüm in Germany and was a unique engine in many respects. Unfortunately, we do not know whether the specification originated in Germany or whether it was entirely the brainchild of the Thetford drawing office. It was a 4-shaft single drive spring mounted engine having DCC cylinders measuring 5½ ins dia × 10 ins dia × 12 ins stroke with a fully balanced crankshaft and a live steam starting valve admitting HP steam to the LP cylinder and was fitted with oil burning apparatus. A new boiler to drawing No RLI was designed having a 4.70 sq ft grate and a total heating surface of 128.0 sq ft. The firebox was copper and the forty-two 1¾ ins dia smoke tubes were produced from 14 SWG seamless drawn brass tubes.

The reason oil burning apparatus was fitted is unknown for there was no shortage of solid fuel in Germany and liquid fuel, unless readily available as a waste product was more expensive than coal. The system used by Frederick Burrell was based upon that developed by James Holden, then Locomotive Superintendent of the Great Eastern Railway where the availability of waste gas oil at the company's Stratford carriage works had encouraged the idea. The company had been in trouble with the local authority following serious pollution of the nearby rivers Lea and Channelsea from their carriage lighting plant and the burning of the unwanted oil residue in a locomotive firebox provided a satisfactory and economic solution to the problem.

Frederick Burrell stored the fuel oil in a 60 gallon tank mounted on the engine tender and the oil was fed by live steam to a single nozzle arranged in the bottom of the firebox. Simultaneously, steam was injected through the outer ring of the nozzle dividing the fuel into finely atomised particles which were immediately ignited by a small fire in the bottom of the firebox. The fierce flames generated were directed upwards by a contoured brick arch and mixed with the secondary air admitted through the firehole door causing complete combustion of the mixture. The system was controlled by a main burner control valve and a 3-way cock mounted on the boiler backplate regulating the live steam to both the fuel supply and the injector arranged around the burner nozzle, all of which were supplied by Taite & Carlton of London. The ashpan was arranged to hold water and was fitted with a conventional hinged damper for controlling the primary air supply to the burning fuel. One suspects that the fragility of the brick arch was a source of trouble as the engine trundled over the rough roads of the period for the experiment was not repeated. Later in 1897 Marshalls of Gainsborough made a similar oil fired engine for the Rhodesian Transport Company.

In all other respects the boiler conformed with the current German boiler regulations. Salter type spring balance safety valves were fitted on the cylinder dome and a screen type spark arrester was fitted in the smokebox. A blower ring was arranged around the blast pipe controlled by a ½ ins valve mounted on the backplate which enabled the blower to be operated without leaving the footplate. Another unique feature was built into the blast pipe, the nozzle having a tapered plug and regulating screw which enabled the blast to be varied. The exhaust steam from the LP cylinder and the flow of hot gases through the smoke tubes could be tuned to perfection by a skilled driver. In addition to the eccentric driven boiler feed pump, the engine was fitted with a Gresham's Class A type 4 injector.

At this time Gresham injectors were the most popular type fitted to British railway locomotives. James Gresham started life as an impoverished artist living in London. In 1857 upon the recommendation of his tutor, W P Frith, he joined Sharp Stewart & Company in Manchester as a

Fig 161 No. 1415 The first double crank compound road engine built at St Nicholas works in 1890 and exported to Germany.

mechanical draughtsman. After several years experience in the locomotive design department he was given special responsibility for improving the Giffard injector which Sharp Stewart manufactured under licence. In 1866 in partnership with Thomas Craven he established a company concentrating upon the manufacture of sewing machines and improved types of injector. During the next forty years Gresham prospered and was responsible for a number of important patents describing improvements to various aspects of railway machinery.

Reverting to No 1415 the engine had two road speeds having ratios of 22.3 and 35.2 to 1 driving 6 ft 6 ins dia × 16 wide hind wheels. The front wheels were 3 ft 7¼ ins dia × 9 ins wide. The four transmission shafts

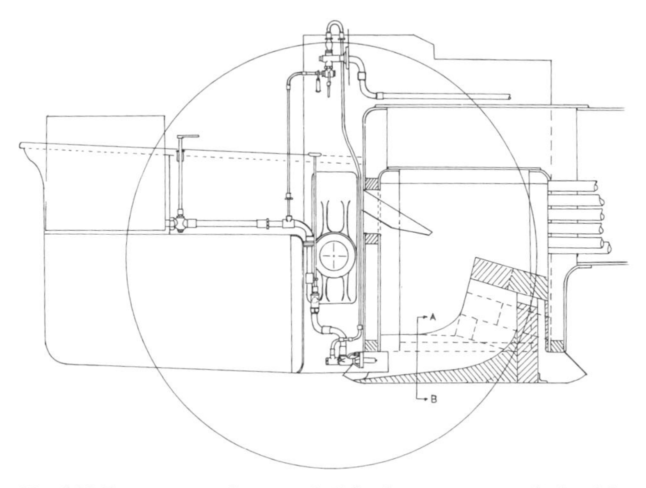

Fig 162 Diagramatic layout of oil fired apparatus applied to No. 1415 6 NHP road locomotive supplied to Germany in 1890.

incorporated the compensating gear, a winding drum and a screw-down brake operating on the second motion shaft spur wheel. The gears were produced from Jackson's cast steel machine moulded castings. The forecarriage was arranged such that the boiler could be raised or lowered hydraulically when ascending or descending hills, the boiler feed pump providing the necessary hydraulic pressure. The solid type flywheel was 3 ft 9 ins dia × 4 ins wide and the rim was grooved, which suggests that the purchaser had some specific stationary engine duty in mind. A standard cross-arm type governor mounted on the cross head slide bar bracket was arranged to control the engine speed at 175 RPM. Tender and belly water tanks were provided, the cast iron stove pipe chimney was hinged and arranged to fold forwards and the engine weighed 12 tons in working order complete with a short awning.

In July 1891 the steel straked hind wheels were replaced by Boulton's patent wheels. These were patented in 1884 in the joint names of J & H McLaren and Isaac Watt Boulton, a descendent of James Watt's partner, Matthew Boulton. The broad wheel rim was produced as an iron casting having deep square sockets cast in the face into which were fitted ironbound blocks of wood, with the end grain facing outwards and arranged in such a way that they projected beyond the wheel rim. The wood blocks bedded in the bottom of the sockets on felt or india-rubber pads and were retained by bolts and coil springs. Two parallel rows of blocks were arranged so that one row was half a space in front of the other, ensuring that at least three blocks were simultaneously in contact with the road surface, giving greatly improved adhesion. The wheels not only caused less jarring to the engine but were kinder to the roads than ordinary steel straked wheels. Some local

Fig 163 The Boulton Patent wheel as used originally on No. 1415, shown fitted to 8 NHP SCC road locomotive No. 1575 'Roving Monarch'.

authorities which formerly had prohibited the use of traction engines were persuaded to waive their restrictions.

Aveling & Porter were the first engine builder to obtain a licence to manufacture Boulton's wheels and they were followed by John Fowler, both firms agreeing to pay a royalty of £10 for each wheel produced. It can be claimed with some justification that the Boulton wheel marked the climax of the spring wheel era.

In July 1892 the engine was returned to St Nicholas Works and nothing further is known about its ultimate fate. The Boulton wheels were transferred to No 1575 an 8 NHP SCC Showman's engine illustrated in Fig 163 and referred to in greater detail in the next chapter.

The second double crank compound (DCC) road locomotive did not appear until 1896 marking the beginning of what many regard as the most exciting period in the history of St Nicholas Works. It was generally similar to the 10 NHP SCC 'Contractors' type engine with the type CL35 boiler but fitted with solid end DCC cylinders measuring 7 ins dia × 11½ ins dia × 12 ins stroke. In total 28 variants of these splendid engines were built in the nine years to 1905 designed for continuous heavy haulage duties and as heavy lift crane engines. They developed over 40 IHP and had a haulage capacity of 38 tons on the 1 in 18 Croxton Road incline. Three of these engines were built as full Showman's type engines and these are dealt with in the next chapter.

All except No 2446 were spring mounted with long travel spring gear and single drive transmission shafts, although in many other respects individual engines differed in technical detail. Nos 1947 and 2446 went to

10 NHP DCC 'CONTRACTOR'S' TYPE ROAD LOCOMOTIVES

No	Built		No	Built	
No 1947	Built	1896	No 2404	Built	1901
1972	"	1896	2446	"	1901
2030	"	1897*	2452	"	1902*
2035	"	1898*	2468	"	1902
2041	"	1897	2498	"	1902*
2055	"	1897*	2515	"	1902*
2101	"	1898	2541	"	1902
2105	"	1898	2542	"	1903*
2134	"	1898	2553	"	1903*
2187	"	1899	2640	"	1904*
2346	"	1900	2641	"	1904*
2352	"	1901	2768	"	1905
2398	"	1901			

*Fitted with forward jib mounted crane gear.

New Zealand customers through the Reid & Gray agency, No 2446 being very similar to the double geared 10 NHP SCC road engine No1892 built specially for timber haulage in 1895. No 2404 went to a sugar beet factory at Lizy-Sur-Ourcq, east of Paris. Fourteen engines went to various customers in South Africa. Nos 2041, 2101, 2346,2468 and 2541 were straight forward road engines without cranes; Nos 1972, 2030, 2452 and 2515 were fitted with 10 ton capacity cranes and Nos 2498, 2542, 2553, 2640 and 2641 had 5 ton capacity cranes. All were supplied with 60 ft of Craddock's best quality wire rope on the crane drum and 225 ft on the winding drum. No 1972 started life in 1896 as No 1935, a 10 NHP SCC road

Fig 164 No. 1947 the first DCC 10 NHP 'Contractors' type engine undergoing tests in the works yard in 1896.

Fig 165 No. 1972, formerly no. 1935, seen after conversion to a DCC 10 NHP crane engine in 1896 prior to shipment to South Africa.

Fig 166 No. 1980 10 NHP DCC 'Contractors' type engine clearly illustrating tender mounted steam brake.

engine and after being exhibited at the RASE held in Leicester was returned to the works, fitted with DCC cylinders and renumbered. It was shipped to South Africa with Nos 2030 and 2041 through the Davis & Soper agency. No 2101 went direct to Durban Corporation; No 2468 went to the De Reitfontein colliery in the Transvaal and the remaining nine engines sent to South Africa were supplied through United Engineering of Johannesburg. After brief service with Aubrey Seaman & Company of Coventry No 2055 was acquired by the War Office and allocated Army Service Corps No 3. During the First World War the engine was sold to Halifax showman, W H Church & Sons and named 'General Haigh the Mighty'. It was converted to a Showman's type engine and was used for a number of years hauling and driving their big set of Allchin & Fennell Gallopers around the hilly Yorkshire mill towns.

Seven engines in the batch went new to UK commercial owners. No 2035, a 10 ton capacity crane engine, went new to the Black Country engineers and boiler makers, Edwin Danks & Company passing eventually to Harper & Screen of Oldbury who by then were undertaking most of Danks' haulage work. Their engines were a familiar sight in the Midlands for the remainder of the steam era. No 2105 after service with F C Flower of Aconbury in Herefordshire, was acquired in 1912 by the Scottish heavy haulage contractors, William Kerr & Company of Mavisbank, Glasgow. The company was established in 1898 as machinery merchants and brokers and in 1903 they purchased No 1997, one of the three 10 NHP DCC Showmans' engines built in 1897 and both engines soon became renowned for the sevices they rendered dealing with all manner of heavy haulage tasks usually accompanied by the big 10 NHP Burrell engine, No 3419 'Clyde', which Kerr had specially built in 1912.No 2134 started life with A Wickens of Reading and after 20 years service as a haulage engine was purchased by Tom Smith of Shoreham-by-Sea in Sussex. He fitted a dynamo platform and other show fittings and named the engine 'Wanderer'. The engine remained in service with the Smith family until the late 1940's. No 2187 was purchased by the Norman Cross Brick Company near Peterborough and eventually passed to the North Wales haulage contractor, Robert Roberts of Llanwrst, who serviced the many mines and slate quarries in the area. At some stage Roberts was associated with H & W E Hughes of Llanwrst who worked in close association with Norman E Box, probably the premier heavy haulage contractor in the United Kingdom in the steam era. Nos 2352 and 2398 went new to Berkshire contractors and No 2768 went to J Brown & Sons of Belfast, where it was frequently to be seen dealing with heavy indivisible loads for Harland & Wolff's shipyard.

The three UK 'Contractor's' engines Nos 2105, 2134 and 2187 had smaller than usual boilers, having 5.375 sq ft grates and engine Nos 2640, 2641 and 2768 had greatly enlarged boilers pressed to 175 PSI with 8.5 sq ft grates, a total heating surface of 177 sq ft and 6 ft 7 ins long smoke

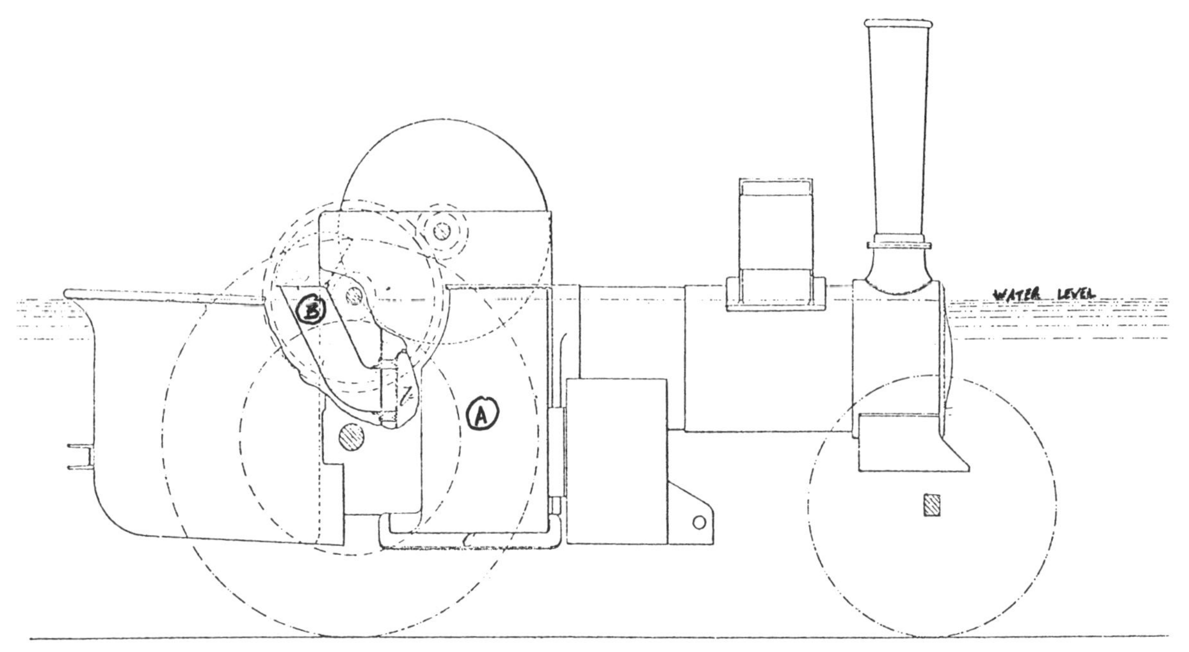

Fig 167 General arrangement of the waterproof engine proposed in Frederick Burrell's patent No. 2507 dated 1897.

tubes compared with 5 ft 8 ins long tubes on the remainder of the batch. These engines also had short 3 ft 6ins long connecting rods compared with 4 ft 3 ins rods fitted to the other engines. They were fitted with Moores steam feed pumps whereas the other engines had eccentric driven pumps and one, in some cases two, had Pemberthy injectors.

Engines built in 1897 had cross-arm governors and the remainder of the batch had Burrells' high speed governors.

Generally the hind wheels were 7 ft 0 ins dia × 20 ins wide having heavy duty 5¾ ins dia steel axles. The overall width of the engines was 8 ft 5½ ins and the overall length was 19 ft 0 ins. The solid flywheels were 4 ft 6 ins dia × 6 ins wide and were of the half cast spoke pattern. All were fitted with short awnings. The average weight of the engines in working order was 14 tons, although No cwt, the extra weight presumably being associated with the crane gear. All the batch, except Nos 2640, 2641 and 2768 were 2-speed engines with ratios of 30.5 to 1 and 17.0 to 1, the exceptions being 3-speed engines.

Engine Nos 2055 and 2101 together with the Showman's engines Nos 1971 and 1980 built in 1897 were fitted with steam brakes operating on the hind wheels. The steam brake cylinder was attached to the off-side of the tender and the arrangement will be clearly seen by reference to Fig 166. When steam was admitted to the 7 ins dia cylinder, the piston rod operated on a shaft passing through the tender and carrying long wooden brake blocks on its ends which engaged with steel brake rims fixed to the inside of the hind wheels. Poplar wood was used for the brake blocks because of its resistance to fire. The tremendous friction and heat generated when braking a heavy road train had long been a problem and it was not uncommon to see the brakeman throwing buckets of cold water over the brake blocks in an endeavour to keep them cool. The steam brake, which was a development of the tram engine brake, was not a success being too fierce in operation when used with steel straked wheels on paved and cobblestone streets.

In 1898 the works produced the largest road locomotive ever built at St Nicholas Works. It was one of a pair of engines rated 14 NHP with 7½ ins dia × 12 ins dia × 12 ins stroke DCC cylinders. No 2069 built in February 1898 had a boiler pressed to 160 PSI having a 7.25 sq ft grate, a total heating surface of 186 sq ft and forty-three 2 ins dia × 6 ft 7 ins long smoke tubes. It was fitted with 10 ton capacity crane gear and shipped to Cape Town through the Davis & Soper agency. Like the 10 NHP 'Contractor's' engines it was spring mounted with single drive gearing. The hind wheels were 7 ft 0 ins dia × 24 ins wide giving an overall width of 9 ft 1½ ins. The 2 speed gearing had ratios of 30.5 and 17.0 to 1 and the solid type flywheel was 4 ft 8 ins dia × 6 ins wide. Extra large water tanks were fitted having a total capacity of 370 gallons.

The second 14 NHP road locomotive, No 2224 was completed in September 1899. It was fitted with the smaller type CL35 boiler as fitted to the 10 NHP SCC Contractor's engines having a 6.5 sq ft grate and 5 ft 8 ins long smoke tubes indicating that it was not intended for continuous heavy haulage duties. The cylinder was of the solid end pattern, the crankshaft was fully balanced and the engine was equipped with a steam brake as just described. It was supplied to the War Office, carried WD No 1885 and was shipped to South Africa under the supervision of W K C Burrell, the deaf mute from Fornham, near Bury St Edmunds who served with great distinction as Colonel R E Templer's assistant engineer.

The War Office had for some time appreciated the potential value of road locomotives for use over terrain such as that found on the South African veldt. The main difficulty had been their limited ability to cross the many small rivers and spruits in the rainy season without

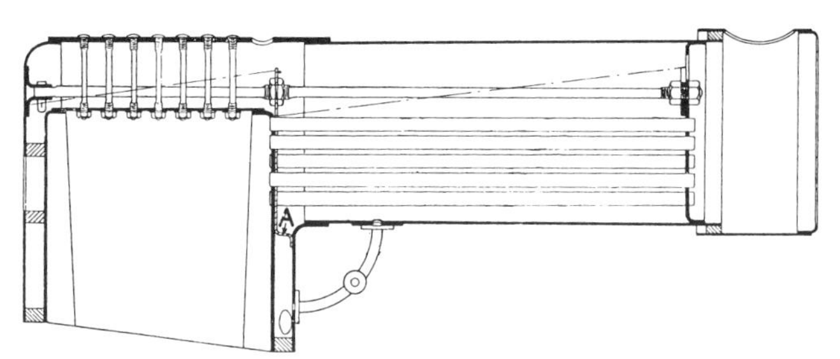

Fig 168 The arrangement of Charles II's patent No. 3649 of 1897 designed to protect the crown of the firebox.

flooding the grate and extinguishing the fire. In 1897 Frederick Burrell filed his patent No 2507 describing means whereby a road locomotive could pass through shallow rivers or watercourses without putting out the fire even though the water rose considerably above the level of the grate. He made provision for the ashpan to be made water tight and for an air pipe of sufficient size, whose inlet was above the water level, to feed primary air to the fire. He proposed a water tight hopper be mounted on the footplate to enable fuel to be fed to the fire; and thirdly he proposed that the smokebox be made water tight thereby fully protecting the heating surfaces in the boiler from any contact with the water in the river. It is not clear from the works' records whether any engines were actually built with the arrangement which is illustrated in Fig 167.

In the same year Charles II filed his patent No 3649 which described a means of protecting the crown of a locomotive type firebox as used in traction engines from becoming uncovered when the engine was descending an incline when the smokebox end of the boiler might become lower than the firebox end. He proposed fixing a plate transversely across the boiler between the inner and outer firebox (A) such that the plate acted as a bulkhead or dam preventing water passing from the firebox end of the boiler to the smokebox end or vice-versa other than through the external connecting pipe provided. The arrangement can be easily understood by reference to Fig 168.

A further two crane engines with 5 ton capacity jibs were built for South Africa in 1902. No 2524 left the works in October 1902 and No 2559 was shipped in April 1903. The boilers were made in one piece probably indicating the use of Krupps' plate and were 2 ft 9 ins dia. The grates were 7.25 sq ft, the total heating surface 167.0 sq ft and the forty-three 2 ins dia smoke tubes were 5 ft 8 ins long. Because of the size of the boilers the engines were rated 12 NHP although the cylinders were 7¼ ins dia × 11¾ ins dia × 12 ins stroke as fitted to the 10 NHP engines. The crankshafts were fully balanced and 3ft 10 ins long connecting rods were employed. Both engines were mounted on leaf springs and the now well proven 2 speed single drive gearing was employed. No 2524 had 6 ft 6 ins × 22 ins wide hind wheels but No 2559 had 7 ft 0 ins dia × 24 ins wide wheels increasing the overall width of the engine to 9 ft 2½ ins. The former had a 4 ft 6 ins dia × 6ins wide spoked flywheel whereas that fitted to No 2559 was the cast solid pattern then coming into vogue. This engine was also fitted with large belly tanks which gave a total water carrying capacity of 400 gallons.

No 2524 was supplied to Henry Pynegar Ltd of Cannon Street in London who were the Confirming House for the Geldenhuis Estate & Gold Mining Company in Johannesburg. No 2559 went to an unknown customer through the United Engineering agency also based in Johannesburg.

A decade later Burrells supplied a unique road engine to the order of William Kerr of Mavisbank. No 3419, named

Fig 169 William Kerr's special 10 NHP 'Contractors' type engine No. 3419 'Clyde' built in 1912 and for many years a legend in Scotland.

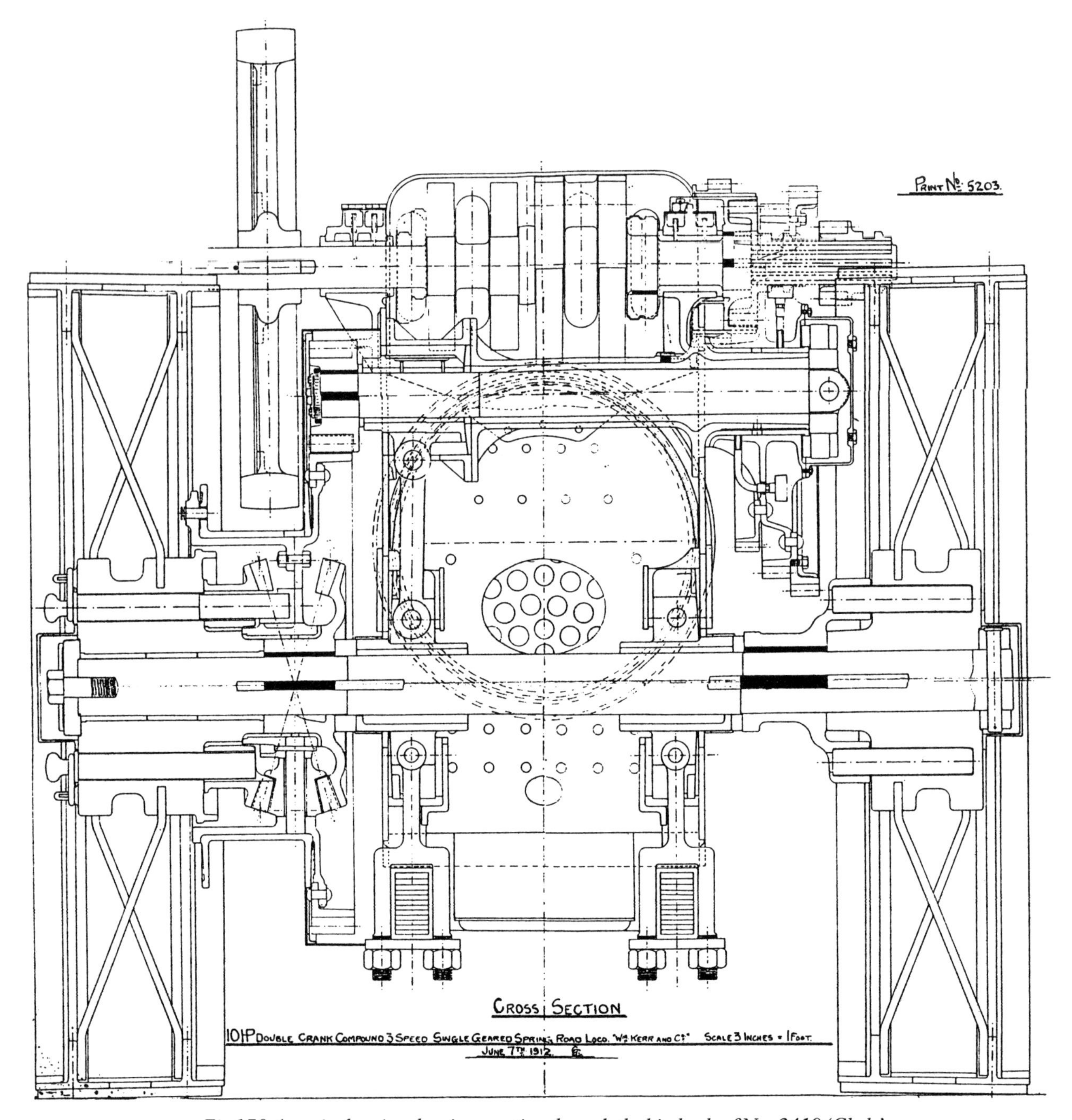

Fig 170 A works drawing showing a section through the hind axle of No. 3419 'Clyde'.

'Clyde' left the works new in October 1912 and soon became a legend in Scotland where, for over 30 years it was engaged in the movement of many and varied heavy indivisible loads. Kerrs had been well satisfied with the performance of their two Burrell engines and unreservedly placed their order for 'Clyde' with St Nicholas Works specifying that the engine must be capable of withstanding the pull of at least two other big engines in front when the load was exceptionally heavy. This necessitated special couplings on both the back and the front of the engine, modifications to the tender and smokebox and the manufacture of a special heavy duty drawbar.

The engine was rated 10 NHP in Burrells' records although its 7¼ ins dia × 11¾ ins dia × 12 ins stroke DCC cylinder and special large 200 PSI boiler no doubt accounts for the frequently quoted story that 'Clyde' was a 12 NHP engine. The grate was exceptionally large at 9.2 sq ft, the total heating surface was 174.7 sq ft and the forty-three 2 ins dia smoke tubes were 5 ft 8 ins long. Single drive gearing and long travel spring gear were employed, and the engine had three road speeds. The hind wheels were 7 ft 0 ins dia × 20 ins wide giving an overall width of 8 ft 10½ ins and the drive shafts were fitted with Burrell's differential locking gear. The winding drum carried 75 yds of Craddock's patent ⅞ ins heavy duty crucible steel wire rope. The engine was provided with a short awning, was painted Burrell Lake and weighed 17 tons 1 cwt in working order. The water tanks had a capacity of 348 gallons.

In 1932 William Kerr were merged with the Road

Steam Engine Company and became Road Engines & Kerr (Haulage) Ltd. During the war the company was requisitioned by the Admiralty because of the work of national importance they were doing in the Clydeside shipyards. There is no confirmation that No 3419 was renamed 'HMS Clyde'. Many already well documented Herculean and fascinating tasks were undertaken by 'Clyde' and its stable mates Nos 1997, 2188 and 2105 who were joined in 1942 by the famous Showman's road engines Fowler No 20223 'Supreme' and Burrell No 4092, 'Simplicity'. Shortly after the war 'Clyde' was sold, driven away from Kerr's yard by the purchasers and disappeared and is believed to have been cut-up in a Tyneside breakers yard.

Between 1905 and 1915 St Nicholas Works built eighteen 'Contractor's' type engines rated 8 NHP of which eight were built as Showman's type road locomotives and are dealt with in the next chapter. Eight of the ten commercial engines were subsequently converted to Showman's engines.

8 NHP 'CONTRACTOR'S' TYPE DCC ROAD LOCOMOTIVES

No	Built		No	Built	
No 2779	Built	1905	No 3019	Built	1908*
2812	"	1906	3352	"	1911*
2825	"	1906*	3642	"	1915*
2867	"	1906*	3648	"	1915*
2871	"	1907*	3694	"	1915*

*Subsequently converted to Showman's type road locomotives.

Fig 171 No. 2779 8 NHP DCC 'Contractors' type road locomotive built for E.J. Barnes & Sons of Swindon in 1905.

All were fitted with the large 7 ins dia × 11½ ins dia × 12 ins stroke DCC cylinders and the majority had boilers pressed to 175 PSI with 6.0 sq ft grates, 154 sq ft heating surface and forty-seven 1¾ ins dia × 5 ft 8 ins long smoke tubes. Nos 2812 and 3648 had lengthened boilers with forty 2 ins dia × 6 ft 2 ins long smoke tubes and the boilers of Nos 3352, 3642, 2648 and 3694 were pressed to 200 PSI. Five of the engines, Nos 2812, 3019, 3352, 3648 and 3694 had double drive gearing to the spring mounted hind wheels and the remainder had single drive gearing and long travel spring gear. The majority had

Fig 172 No. 2871 8 NHP DCC 'Contractors' type road locomotive photographed in the ownership of Hawkes Bros, prior to conversion to a showman's type engine.

Fig 173 No. 3648 8 NHP DCC 'Contractors' type road locomotive whilst in the ownership of the Bath & Portland Stone Firms Ltd, circa 1928.

7 ft 0 ins dia × 18 ins wide hind wheels and 2-speed gearing. All were built originally with short awnings.

No 2779 named, 'Walter Long' was supplied to E J Barnes & Sons Ltd, the Swindon timber hauliers who operated a fleet of eight Burrell engines in the southern counties, and No 2812 went to J & S F Keast in Cornwall. All the remaining engines in the series were subsequently converted to Showman's type engines.

No 2825 named, 'Dreadnought' started life with F Houghton Ltd of Durley in Hampshire timber hauling. Eventually it was purchased by Reuben Gillham of Freemantle in Hampshire and converted to a Showman's engine. No 2867 was supplied new to the Dorset Cement Company in Wareham. The engine changed hands several times and after an extensive overhaul by the Oxford Steam Plough Company just after the war was acquired by the well known London showman, Henry Gray. He had a dynamo platform and full length canopy fitted and named the engine 'Lord Lascelles'. It finished its days like many other fine engines in J W Hardwick & Sons scrap yard in West Ewell in 1947 and was replaced by a diesel engined lorry.

No 2871 went new to Henry Ryland of Royston in Hertfordshire and was eventually purchased by the South Staffordshire showman, Miles Jervis. It then passed to White Bros of Cardiff who named the engine 'Goliath'. It worked with his other Burrell engines Nos 3715 and 3858 travelling the Welsh valleys for many years. No 3019 was supplied new to Charles Openshaw Ltd of Reading who named the engine 'Conqueror'. Openshaw was a general engineer who had built up a good reputation overhauling and selling traction engines of all types. He is perhaps best remembered for his conversion of several ex-W D Fowler built engines to the Showman's specification in the 1920s. In 1926 No 3019 was acquired by Fred Gray of Hampstead who owned seven Burrell Showman's engines at various times. The big road engine with its winding drum and steel wire rope was found to be ideal for the demolition of many Blitz damaged buildings in the City of London and elsewhere. 'Conqueror' was one of several Showman's engines to render distinguished war time service in this area. Shortly after the war the engine was purchased by W Beach of Sudbury, Middlesex and spent her remaining days touring the Thames Valley fairs.

The next engine in the series to be converted to a Showman's type engine was one of no less than twenty-two Burrell engines owned by Pat Collins, the doyen of the early 20th century travelling showmen. No 3352, a double geared engine, was supplied new to Moore Bros, contractors of Bilborough in Nottinghamshire and rebuilt by Collins of Bloxwich in South Staffordshire in 1914. It is recorded that upon this occassion twisted brass canopy supports were not fitted to the new full length canopy. An Irishman by birth, Collins gave the engine an appropriate Gaelic name, 'Faugha-a-Bella'.

Ten years after taking delivery of No 2779, E J Barnes & Sons Ltd, the Swindon timber hauliers took delivery of its sister engine No 3642. They named it 'General French' after the then commander of the British army in Flanders and a popular hero. Twenty years later the engine was purchased by the renowned South Wales showman, Jacob Studt Jr of Maestag whose family had been travelling Burrell engines for over forty years. They converted the engine to a full Showman's type engine and for many years she could regularly be seen on the A40 road between Oxford and South Wales with Studt's Noah's Ark. A decade later the engine was acquired by Charles Beach of Yiewsley in Middlesex. It would be interesting to know the actual mileage covered by this engine during its thirty years working life, since it must have been very considerable.

Both No 3648 named, 'Jellicoe' and No 3694 started life in commercial ownership working in the Portland stone quarries in Dorset. No 3648 went new to F J Barnes who were later taken over by Bath & Portland Stone Firms Ltd

Fig 174 Examples of a bolster truck and traction wagon built at St Nicholas Works.

and No 3694 went direct to the Portland firm. As their name implies the firm were engaged moving large blocks of quarried stone all over the country, and they already owned three Burrell engines. In the difficult post war years they provided the works with badly needed orders for four similar double geared 'Contractor's' engines (Nos 3980, 4038, 4042 and 4091). St Nicholas Works also built several heavy duty traction wagons and short wheelbase bolster trucks with steel wheels for the Portland firm.

In 1932 No 3648 was acquired by George Baker of Southampton and converted to a full Showman's type engine. The engine then passed consecutively to Fred Gray of Hampstead, Walls Bros of Petersfield and Harry Gray of Battersea, all well known travellers in the London area, before it ended its days in Hardwick's scrap yard. No 3694 was similarly sold to William Beach Snr of Uxbridge, named 'Lord Fisher' and converted to a full Showman's engine. She performed 15 years' service in the Tobers before she too ended her days in Hardwick's yard.

Between 1897 and 1913 St Nicholas Works built eighty-nine 35 IHP road locomotives with 6½ ins dia × 11 ins dia × 12 ins stroke DCC cylinders. Forty-eight were built as full Showman's road locomotives and are dealt with in the next chapter. Of the forty-one originally supplied to commercial owners twenty-one were subsequently converted to Showman's type engines. Under test these fine engines easily proved capable of handling 32 ton loads on the 1 in 18 Croxton Road incline. In 1911 a larger version with 6¾ ins dia × 11¼ ins dia × 12 ins stroke DCC cylinders and larger 200 PSI boilers was introduced. Forty-nine of these engines were built for travelling showmen and are therefore dealt with in the next chapter.

8 NHP 6½ ins dia × 11 ins dia × 12 ins stroke
DCC ROAD LOCOMOTIVES

No	Built		No	Built	
No 2057	Built	1897*	No 2444	Built	1901*
2062	”	1898	2450	”	1902
2075	”	1898	2470	”	1902
2081	”	1898*	2472	”	1902
2083	”	1898*	2489	”	1902*
2088	”	1898	2527	”	1902
2150	”	1898*	2537	”	1902*
2160	”	1899	2547	”	1903*
2194	”	1899*	2548	”	1903
2247	”	1899*	2549	”	1903
2280	”	1900	2562	”	1903*
2281	”	1900*	2571	”	1903
2337	”	1900*	2576	”	1903*
2342	”	1900*	2584	”	1903*
2345	”	1900	2593	”	1903*
2362	”	1901	2657	”	1904
2370	”	1901*	2660	”	1904*
2387	”	1901*	2676	”	1904
2436	”	1901	2701	”	1904*
2437	”	1901	2703	”	1904
2440	”	1901			

*Subsequently converted to Showman's type engines.

Engines built prior to 1900 had the 'C' type boiler with 5.375 sq ft grates, a total heating surface of 151.0 sq ft and forty-one 2 ins dia × 5 ft 8ins long smoke tubes. Those built between 1900 and 1904 with a couple of exceptions, had their grates and heating surface reduced to 4.86 sq ft and 130.46 sq ft respectively and the 2 ins dia × 5 ft 8 ins long smoke tubes were reduced to thirty-four in number. During the next three years the grate area was again altered to 6.0 sq ft, the total heating surface to 154.15 sq ft and forty-seven 1¾ ins dia × 5 ft 8 ins long smoke tubes were employed. In 1907 the size of the boilers was again increased giving 6.6 sq ft grates, a total heating surface of 162.0 sq ft and the forty 2 ins dia smoke tubes were increased in length to 6 ft 2 ins long, which enabled the connecting rods to be lengthened by 9 ins to 4 ft 0 ins. Initially the boiler working pressure was 160 PSI, but after 1901 this was progressively increased to 200 PSI.

Fig 175 The patent wood block wheel rim as described in Frederick Burrells' patent No. 19,038 dated 1894.

The three exceptions to the above were engine No 2370 which was fitted with a short 7 NHP 'T' type boiler; No 2444 a crane engine having a large grate and special hornplates to accommodate the crane drive bracket; and No 2548 which was a special double geared unsprung engine built for the Harrogate Gas Company. It had a very short boiler with a total heating surface of 118.0 sq ft and 5 ft 1 ins long smoke tubes. Another engine in this series, No 2342 was also supplied to the Harrogate Gas Company but this appears to have been a standard single drive road engine fitted with special wooden block wheel rims which was subsequently converted to a Showman's type engine.

The majority of engines built after 1903 were fitted with the Moores steam pump and Pickering type governors, but the steam pumps were replaced at an early date. All except No 2548 were spring mounted with single drive shafts and most had 2-speed gearing having ratios of 30.5 to 1 slow speed and 17.0 to 1 fast speed with 7 ft 0 ins dia × 18 ins wide hind wheels. The engines weighed approximately 14 tons 5 cwt in working order and those supplied to commercial owners were fitted with short awnings.

No 2075 was built for the Clydesdale Collieries near Johannesburg fitted with a unique skewing crane and is illustrated in Fig 176. No 2345 was also built as a crane engine for the Black Country contractors, Harper & Screen fitted with a forward mounted jib. The other crane engine, No 2444 was built to the order of the Aruba Gold Concessions in the Dutch West Indies. It is doubtful if the

Fig 176 No. 2075 8 NHP DCC road locomotive built in 1908 for the Clydesdale Collieries, Johannesburg with a unique 10 cwt capacity skewing crane.

Fig 177 No. 2062 'Weston King' an 8 NHP DCC road locomotive built for Wansbrough Sons & Cross of Weston-super-Mare in 1898.

Fig 178 Two of W.E. Chivers & Sons of Devizes Fleet of Burrell Road Locomotives engaged upon war work on Salisbury Plain during the first world war.

engine was ever delivered and was rebuilt by the works as a full Showman's type engine in 1902.

Four of the series, Nos 2083, 2436, 2549 and 2562 were supplied new to Jonathan Lano of Portland who eventually became part of the Bath & Portland Stone Firms Ltd engaged hauling quarried stone. No 2088 went new to the War Office and in 1899 was sold to William Kerr of Mavisbank in Glasgow and named 'Charlie'. No 2160 and 2676 went to French customers through the Ludt agency and No 2703 went to Benn & Sons in Bahia, Brazil. The remaining engines in commercial ownership went to widely scattered users throughout the United Kingdom and space allows mention only of those subsequently converted for use in the fairground.

No 2057 was converted to a full Showman's type road locomotive by St Nicholas Works in 1905 and spent thirteen years in the service of John Beach of Hammersmith. After spending twenty years in the ownership of various commercial operators No 2081 was acquired by Pat Collins in 1918. Two years later the engine was purchased by J Smith, a Jarrow-on-Tyne showman and fitted with a dynamo platform. Similarly, shortly after the First World War No 2083, originally one of J Lano's stone haulage engines, was purchased by Mrs E Miller & Sons, showmen operating in the Bristol area and named 'Marshall Foch'. Later the engine passed to Jennings Bros of Devizes in Wiltshire, owners of six fine Burrell engines at various times.

No 2150 was supplied to Burrell's very successful and popular West Country agent Mr S Ford. For reasons unknown the engine was left on his hands, probably due to a cancellation or its re-possession as the result of a bad debt. In 1907 the engine was acquired by J Wright of Coventry, who named her 'King of the Midlands'. No 2194 was purchased by W & C Bibby, an Essex Traveller, after twenty-two years service in commercial ownership with H Ashley of Mansfield. It seems doubtful if the engine was ever fitted with showland fittings and adornments. No 2247 started its life with a London haulage contractor. In 1901 it was purchased by the well known Petersfield showman, Wall Bros, and was returned to St Nicholas Works for overhaul and conversion to a full Showman's type engine and named 'Emperor'. She finished her working life in the ownership of J Day of Horsham.

No 2281 was purchased by W J Chipperfield of Redditch in Worcestershire in 1908 from Smith Bros, haulage contractors of Walsall in Staffordshire. The Chipperfield family had not yet entered the Circus business and 'W J' used the engine for lighting and hauling his Bioscope Show. Later he sold the engine to Henry Chipperfield of Fleet in Hampshire who travelled her with his Switchback ride. At this time the circus scene was dominated by the American Barnham & Bailey Circus and by Buffalo Bill's Wild West Show, which last travelled the United Kingdom about the time No 2281 was purchased.

No 2337, named 'Queen of the West' also appears to have started its life with Mr S Ford, Burrells' West Country agent. In 1907 she was acquired by the old established showland family, G & J Bartlett of Fordingbridge in Hampshire and re-named 'Pride of the South' which was formerly carried by their 7 NHP single cylinder road locomotive No 1470. The engine finished her working days in the ownership of James Cole of Bristol. As already stated No 2342 was supplied new to the Harrogate Gas Company who had remained loyal Burrell customers since they purchased second hand the road steamer No 513 in 1875. In 1910 she was acquired by H Crowther of Old Radford in Nottinghamshire and then passed to Miles Jervis of Chasetown in Staffordshire who named her 'Vanguard'. He travelled an unusual 'Jack-and-Jill' ride which was an enlarged version of the Mountain Glide. When operating on a semi-permanent site in an amusement park, the riders were lifted to the top of the ride on seats attached to an endless chain driven by the engine. Later the engine passed to John Evans of Brecon, then to James Edwards of Croydon and finally in 1945 to J Body of Maidstone. Fortunately, the engine survives today in preservation.

No 2370 built as an 8 NHP engine with a 7 NHP boiler went new to David Kane of Ballymena in County Antrim. In 1910 she returned to Suffolk and was purchased shortly after the First World War by the Ipswich showman, Sidney Stocks and fitted with a dynamo platform and brass adornments. In 1924 she passed to Charles Dack of Deopham in Norfolk for a short period and then went to James Crighton who had yards in Birkenhead and Norwich. In 1929 the engine was loaned to J Ryder of Birkenhead with whom she finished her working life.

No 2387 had a chequered career in the ownership of various West Country commercial operators. During the First World War she became part of Chivers of Devizes fleet of engines engaged upon war work on Salisbury Plain. After the war she was acquired by Jennings Bros, showmen of Devizes and named 'Majestic', ending her days in the ownership of Messrs J Cole of Chichester.

Less than a year after being built as a crane engine, No 2444 was converted by the works to a full Showman's type engine. It went firstly to H Crecraft of Neath in South Wales who named her 'Patience'. After the First World War she was acquired by Arthur Bates of Rhode Heath in Cheshire and finished her useful life in the ownership of J White & Sons of Glasgow who renamed the engine 'Prince of Wales'.

No 2489 started its life in Cornwall passing to H Burden & Company, haulage contractors of Poole in Dorset in 1904. After the First World War it was acquired by C E Jackson, a Sheffield showman but it is not known if the engine was converted to a Showman's type engine. No 2537 spent most of its life in showland, firstly with T Wright of Kenilworth who named her 'Lord Nelson'; then in 1912 she was acquired by the well known Norwich travellers, Abbott & Barker and renamed 'Teutonic'. During the War she saw service with the Lancashire road rolling contractors, Isaac Ball of Wharles and returned to showland in the ownership of Connelly Bros of Blackpool in 1920.

Fig 179 No. 2547 'Endurance' an 8 NHP DCC road locomotive converted to a showmans' type engine by Wallis & Steevens of Basingstoke in the 1920's.

No 2547, which survives today in preservation, started its working life at J K Cooper's brickworks at Maidenhead in Berkshire. After the First World War it was acquired by Maurice Stokes of Basingstoke and converted to a Showman's type engine. The conversion was carried out by the local traction engine builders, Wallis & Steevens, who painted the engine green with red wheels, smartly lined out in black, red and yellow. Named 'Endurance' the engine gave many years' service hauling and driving Stokes three-abreast Gallopers throughout the Southern counties.

After ten years' service with Jonathan Lano in the Portland Stone Firms' western quarry, No 2562 was acquired by R Townsend of Weymouth and converted to a Showman's type engine for use with his Savage built three-abreast Gallopers. In 1916 the engine was purchased by William Nichols of Forest Gate in London, ending its days on an Essex farm in the 1930s. It is believed the engine was not converted to a full Showman's type engine until 1922 retaining the name, 'Empress of the South'.

Little appears to be known about No 2576. After a period in commercial ownership she was sold by Thurlows of Stowmarket, who handled many second hand Burrell engines throughout the steam era, to A Traylen of Earlsfield in London. They travelled three Burrell Showman's type engines until the 1940s and No 2576 which was named 'Marina' ended her days in Hardwick's scrap yard in West Ewell. No 2584, a 3-speed engine spent her first twenty-five years in the ownership of Rose & Andrews of Totton near Southampton engaged in general haulage work. In 1928 she was acquired by Abraham Connelly who named her 'Daisy'. Finally in 1942 she was purchased by J Sanders of Lambeth in London and is believed to have finished her days in Hardwick's yard.

No 2593 named 'Pride of Portsmouth' worked in the Portsmouth area for sixteen years before entering showland in the ownership of Wall Bros of Petersfield shortly after the First World War. She worked in the fairground for a further thirty years and like the two previous engines finished her days in Hardwick's yard. No 2660 started its life with a contractor in Liverpool and was a familiar sight in the dock area for many years. Eventually after the First World War she was acquired by W Nash of North Fleet in Kent who rebuilt her as a Showman's type engine with a dynamo platform and traditional brass canopy supports.

The last engine in this series to be converted to a full Showman's type engine was No 2701, 'Black Prince'. She spent the greater part of her life as a heavy haulage engine in the ownership of J Hickey & Sons of Richmond in Surrey. This well known firm of engineers, boilermakers and heavy haulage contractors had specialised in the removal of large indivisible loads in the London area since the 1880s and owned a fleet of four Burrell engines. In 1935 the engine was sold to the Hampstead showman, Fred Gray and is still remembered by many Londoners who attended the 'Great Holidays at Home' fairs on Hampstead Heath during the War. She also contributed greatly to clearing up the Blitz damaged buildings in the City working with No 3019. Hickey's engines were amongst the first to be fitted with the then new Mackintosh endless solid rubber tyres.

Fig 180 An unidentified 6 NHP spring mounted single drive DCC road locomotive – circa 1904 – as illustrated in Burrell's general catalogue.

After a long spell in Hardwick's yard in the 1950s, 'Black Prince' was acquired for preservation by Mr Alan Bloom of Bressingham in Norfolk and beautifully restored. The late Billy Greenwood, at one time the Chief Draughtsman at St Nicholas Works made an especially fine working model of the engine which fortunately also survives.

Reverting to the smaller types of DCC road locomotive, St Nicholas Works built sixteen very attractive Devonshire type road engines between 1909 and 1914. Nine were supplied to commercial owners, three of which subsequently saw service in showland and seven were built as full Showman's type engines and are dealt with in the next chapter. A further twenty-four of these splendid little 30 IHP engines with a hauling power in excess of 25 tons were built after the war when the ownership of the company passed to the AGE combine and these are dealt with in Chapter 18.

5 NHP DCC DEVONSHIRE ROAD LOCOMOTIVES

No		Built	No		Built
No 3202	Built	1910	No 3480	Built	1913*
3283	"	1911	3605	"	1914*
3380	"	1912	3614	"	1914
3418	"	1912	3621	"	1914*
3473	"	1913			

*Engines subsequently sold to Travelling Showmen.

Unlike the contemporary DCC Devonshire traction engines these engines were rated 5 NHP. After the War the traction engines were also rated 5 NHP and after 1919 the now world famous name, 'Devonshire' engine was dropped. This batch of engines enjoyed a remarkable degree of standardisation. All had boilers pressed to 200 PSI with 4.6 sq ft grates, a total heating surface of 100 sq ft and thirty 2 ins dia × 4 ft 9½ ins long smoke tubes. All were double geared and mounted on leaf springs. The hind wheels were 6 ft 0 ins dia × 16 ins wide and the 3-speed gearing gave ratios of 22.1 to 1, 15.3 to 1 and 9.0 to1 making them fast engines on the road. Most had 4 ft 4 ins dia × 6 ins wide solid flywheels, differential locking gear, hind wheel brakes and awnings. The water carrying capacity was 232 gallons and most relied upon two BP 'F' type injectors. The engines weighed approximately 10 tons 10 cwt in working order.

Six of the nine engines went to customers in Devonshire. No 3473 went to the Ledbury RDC in Herefordshire; No 3480 appropriately named 'Helpmate' went to Robert Wynn & Sons Ltd., the famous heavy haulage firm of Newport in South Wales; and No 3621 went to a Sussex contractor. Those with subsequent service in showland, Nos 3480, 3605 and 3621 were purchased by the following. No 3480 went to Alfred Smith of Bristol who renamed the engine 'Lord Lascelles'. In 1932 it was acquired by Reuben Gillham of Freemantle in Hampshire and was eventually cut up in Forfar's yard in Southampton. No 3605, 'Empress of Britain' was purchased in the 1920s by George Rodgers of Chipping Sodbury who owned four Burrell engines at various times. During the Second World War she returned to commercial ownership. No 3621 was purchased in 1933 by G & J Bartlett of Fordingbridge for use with their ex-Billy

Fig 181 A smart little 6 NHP DCC road locomotive, No. 3395, originally 'City of Exeter', now 'The Dalesman'.

Smith Gallopers which was a popular ride in Southern England until the war years.

We consider next the thirty 6 NHP DCC road engines supplied to commercial owners in the period 1904-1914. Eleven of these engines were subsequently rebuilt and owned by travelling showmen and a further eleven were built new as full Showman's type road locomotives and are dealt with in chapter 12.

6 NHP DCC (6 ins × 10 ins × 10 ins)
ROAD LOCOMOTIVES

No		Built	No		Built
No 2690	Built	1904*	No 3306	Built	1911
2705	"	1904	3343	"	1911*
2712	"	1904	3350	"	1912
2736	"	1905	3390	"	1912
2746	"	1906*	3392	"	1912
2827	"	1906	3395	"	1912
2907	"	1907*	3434	"	1913
2986	"	1908*	3455	"	1913
3098	"	1909	3489	"	1913*
3103	"	1909*	3530	"	1913
3166	"	1909	3542	"	1914*
3211	"	1911*	3585	"	1914
3212	"	1910*	3593	"	1914
3222	"	1910	3604	"	1914
3295	"	1911*	3632	"	1914

*Subsequently converted to Showman's type engines.

Again all the engines of this type incorporated a remarkable degree of standardisation compared with earlier Burrell production. Engines built between 1904 and 1906 had spring mounted single drive gearing, thereafter all had the spring mounted double geared drive. Initially the boilers were pressed to 175 PSI, had 4.6 sq ft grates and a total heating surface of 114.5 sq ft. After 1909 all the boilers were pressed to 200 PSI and the heating surface was increased to 118.5 sq ft. The earlier engines had thirty-four 1 3.4 ins dia smoke tubes and after 1909 thirty 2 ins dia smoke tubes were employed. Both sizes of smoke tube were 5 ft 8 ins long. The earlier engines were fitted with a single Penberty injector and a Moores steam pump mounted on the belly tanks. After 1909 all were fitted with two BP 'G' type injectors. The majority had 3-speed gearing and 6 ft 6 ins dia × 16 ins wide hind wheels. Solid type 4 ft 0 ins × 6 ins wide flywheels and Pickering type governors were employed throughout. The water carrying capacity was 235 gallons and the engines weighed approximately 12 tons 15 cwt in working order.

Nos 3166 and 3530 were built as crane engines, the former joining E J Barnes' of Swindon fleet and named 'Joe Chamberlain'. Nos 2705 and 3390 were exported to New Zealand through the Reid & Gray agency and No 2712 was supplied to the London Confirming House, Pita Ltd for an unknown destination. Fifty per cent of the engines went to customers in the West Country of which Nos 2986, 3103, 3212 and 3295 joined the fleet of eleven Burrell engines owned by William Elworthy of Tiverton in Devon. No 3392 went to Exeter Corporation Highways Department and No 3395 went to the Exeter brick and tile manufacturers, J Hancock & Son and was named 'City of Exeter'. This engine was beautifully and professionally restored by the late John Crowther in the 1960s and eventually renamed 'The Dalesman'.

Fig 182 No. 3489 the ex-Hickey 6 NHP DCC road locomotive 'City of London' as restored by Mr Jack Wharton of Minster Lovell and named 'King George VI'.

No 2690, the first of the ten engines in the series to be converted to Showman's type engines, was acquired by the celebrated West Country showmen, Anderton & Rowland in 1923, partially converted and named 'John Bull'. For a time she worked with their Gondola Switchback ride still with a half length canopy. Later, a full length canopy was fitted and in 1932 when the ride was sold she reverted to private ownership as a threshing engine in Cornwall.

No 2746 went new to the Northern Ireland traveller, William Sharples of Belfast. She was built as an ordinary road locomotive and was not fitted with a dynamo platform or full length canopy until 1909. Nothing is known of her subsequent fate. No 2907 was acquired by the Stirling showmen, William Bastable & Sons shortly after the First World War. A locally made dynamo platform of unusual shape was fitted, but she never carried the traditional twisted brass canopy supports or other adornments. Eventually the engine passed to Joseph White & Sons of Glasgow and ended her working life with W Testo of Sunderland. No 2986 also went north of the border. Firsty she was acquired and converted by J Stewart of Edinburgh and then in 1925 she was purchased by R Patterson of Berwick-on-Tweed. Five years later the engine passed to James Slater of Carlisle, ending her days back in commercial ownership.

No 3103 started life with the Tiverton quarry owners, William Elworthy and was converted to a Showman's type engine by the Tiverton based traveller William Jones in 1924. Twenty years later she went to Bert Ayers and then to W Beach Jr both based in the Uxbridge area of London. Nos 3211 saw over 20 years service in commercial ownership in the Hampshire area before being acquired by Wall Bros of Petersfield and converted to a Showman's type engine. She was named 'Dreadnought' and travelled extensively in the south east before being cut up in Hardwick's yard. No 3212 another Elworthy engine was purchased by the Cornish showman W Jones & Son of St Blazey in 1932. He rebuilt the engine as a Showman's type and named her 'Princess Victoria'. No 3295, yet another Elworthy engine was acquired and converted to a Showman's engine by Fred Adlam of Freemantle in Hampshire in 1921. The engine named 'Princess Royal' fortunately survives today in preservation.

No 3343 went new to a general contractor in Roxburghshire and is said to have been repossessed by the Burrell Hiring Company as a bad debt in 1913. The works converted her to oil firing and used her in the works to belt drive the main dynamo in the machine shop throughout the war years. After the war, during the period of greatest demand for Showman's engines, she was converted to a Showman's type engine and sold to Herbert Stocks of Ipswich and named 'Princess Mary'. After the Second World War she was purchased by Mr A Phoenix of Thetford, a former Burrell employee, for preservation.

Starting life in Devonshire, No 3489 was the first engine to be subsequently acquired by the redoubtable firm of engineers and boilermakers, J Hickey & Sons of Richmond, to whom we have already referred. They named her 'City of London'; she was easily recognisable on the streets of London with her large brass nameplate on top of the smokebox, broad brass band around the chimney shaft and a capuchon on the polished copper chimney top. She was fitted also with an acetylene generator and three big brass headlamps.

In 1935 Hickey sold the engine to Swales Bolesworth, the well known Dagenham showman. Three years later she

Fig 183 No. 3197 7 NHP DCC crane locomotive as built for Screen Brothers of Oldbury, Birmingham in 1910.

was re-sold to E Andrews Jr of Tunbridge Wells who named her 'King George VI' to mark the new King's Coronation year. After the Second World War she was acquired by Mr S J Wharton of Minster Lovell in Oxfordshire, the long serving and greatly respected President of the National Traction Engine Club. Today the engine is preserved in her Showland guise and has the distinction of being the first Showman's type engine to appear at a traction engine rally.

No 3542 started her working life in Cornwall and in 1929 was acquired by Charles Openshaw of Reading. After a thorough overhaul and rebuilding as a Showman's type engine she was purchased by the Worthing showman, James Matthews who named her 'Sunny South'. Finally when over thirty years old whe was purchased by J Beach of Sunbury and completed a further ten years strenuous service in the Thames Valley before being scrapped.

Finally we must consider the eighteen 7 NHP DCC road locomotives built at St Nicholas Works between 1904 and 1914. A further fourteen were built as full Showman's type engines and are dealt with in the next chapter. Six of the conventional road locomotives were converted subsequently to Showman's type engines and owned by travelling showmen.

All were 3-speed engines and all except Nos 2643 and 2783 were spring mounted double geared engines, the two exceptions having single drive transmission shafts. The first four engines had 6 ins dia × 10 ins dia × 12 ins stroke cylinders; No 3197 which was built as a crane engine had the same 6¼ ins dia × 11 ins dia × 12 ins stroke cylinders as the thirteen 7 NHP Showman's engines built before the war; and the thirteen conventional road locomotives had the same cylinders as the standard 8 NHP road engines measuring 6½ ins dia × 11 ins dia × 12 ins stroke. The boilers however were somewhat smaller. The majority were pressed to 200 PSI, had 5.44 sq ft grates, a total heating surface of 134.5 sq ft and 5 ft 8 ins long smoke tubes. As with the 6 NHP engines, those built prior to 1909 were fitted with Moores steam pumps, thereafter two injectors were fitted. Most had 6 ft 6 ins dia × 20 ins wide hind wheels, their water carrying capacity was 320 gallons and they weighed approximately 13 tons 15 cwt in working order.

7 NHP DCC ROAD LOCOMOTIVES

No		Built	No		Built
No 2643	Built	1904*	No 3118	Built	1909*
2647	”	1904	3129	”	1909
2704	”	1904	3180	”	1910
2783	”	1906*	3197	”	1910
2824	”	1906	3274	”	1911
2841	”	1906	3393	”	1912*
2865	”	1906	3423	”	1912*
2960	”	1907	3619	”	1914*
3057	”	1908	3633	”	1914

*Subsequently converted to Showman's type engines.

No 2647, one of the two double geared engines, was built to Australian requirements and sold through the

Fig 184 No. 3633 7 NHP DCC road locomotive supplied to W.E. Chivers of Devizes in 1914 and named 'Lord Kitchener'.

Coulson agency. It had a large colonial firebox with a 6.1 sq ft grate for burning inferior fuels, a spark arrester in the smokebox and extended racking on the fuel bunker. The hind wheels were 7 ft 0 ins dia. No 3197 was built for the Black Country heavy haulage contractors Screen Bros, the successors of Harper & Screen of Oldbury who operated four Burrell engines at various times. The engine is illustrated in Fig 183 showing the rather unusual swanneck jib and the position of the crane drum. Fortunately, the engine survives today.

No 2643 started its life as a road engine with a contractor in Clevedon in North Somerset and carried the name 'Clevedonia' throughout its working life. In 1919 it was acquired by a Plymouth traveller, A Jones, and was rebuilt as a Showman's type engine. In 1936 the engine passed to the Birmingham traveller, E Steele, who used her with his Noah's Ark until the outbreak of the Second War. No 2783 'Cock o' the North' was rebuilt as a Showman's engine in 1923 and finished her working life in the ownership of William Thomson of Dundee. No 3118 had several commercial owners before she was acquired by C W Abbott of Norwich, rebuilt as a Showman's type engine in 1920 and named 'Dreadnought'.

No 3393 started her working life with John Curtis & Sons of the Botley Brick Works near Oxford. For many years she was a regular sight in the area hauling bricks and timber with her train of three Marshall built traction waggons. In 1924 the engine was acquired by Charles Openshaw of Reading and converted to a Showman's type engine for Phil Case. In 1927 she went to J Purchase of Surbiton in Surrey who named her 'Gorgon' and used her with his fine set of Savage built Gallopers. Finally in 1932 the engine was sold to John E Whiting of Orlerton near Sheffield for his five hill Orton & Spooner built Noah's Ark. The engine was cut up in 1935.

The next engine in the series to be converted to a Showman's type engine had a similar career. No 3423 started its working life with T C Greensmith & Sons Ltd of Burton-on-Trent in 1912, passed to the Hereford Brick & Tile Company and after the First War was acquired by Charles Openshaw. He converted her to a Showman's type engine for the well known Buckinghamshire showman, Thomas Pettigrove who named her 'Star'. After lying derelict in his yard for many years the engine was eventually cut up.

No 3619, the final pre-war built 7 NHP road engine to see service in showland spent all her working life in Scotland. Delivered new in 1914 to William Middlemiss of Grunlow in Berwickshire, she was employed for many years hauling stone and belt driving a stone crusher. She was named 'Black Adder' after the nearby stream. In 1933 she was acquired by William Thomson of Dundee and converted to a Showman's type engine exactly as No 2783 and for the rest of her working life travelled extensively throughout the East Coast of Scotland.

So ends our review of both the SCC and DCC Burrell road locomotives built in the heyday of steam. So much more could be and hopefully will be said about these magnificent engines and the splendid men who devoted their lives to driving them. One thing is certain, the arguments about the merits of the Burrell versus the Fowler engines and the 3-shaft versus the 4-shaft system will long continue amongst enginemen wherever they meet. We now turn our attention to engines built at St Nicholas Works specifically to meet the needs of the travelling showman.

CHAPTER TWELVE

Showman's Road Locomotives

Following a visit to St Nicholas Works in the 1890s the Editor of the 'Engineer' commented, "Charles Burrell devote a large amount of attention to supplying traction engines to the owners of Shows and Merry-go-rounds and do a very large business with this class of men, who are much larger Capitalists than some people might imagine. The Showman finds it to his advantage to adopt the Road Locomotive for working his Steam Circus and lighting up the Show by electricity and also as a means of drawing his entire paraphernalia from town to town. . . . It is well known that the Showman often has to cover a good many miles of road during the night and early morning in order to fulfill his printed engagements. The Road Locomotives travel well at high rates *irrespective of Acts of Parliament* (author's italics) and do more work than horses could possibly achieve."

Indeed such was the importance of this trade to Charles Burrell that in the forty years 1890 to 1930 it seems probable that as much as a quarter of their turnover was derived from business emanating from the travelling showman. They built more Showman's type engines than any other engine builder and undoubtedly were greatly assisted in building up this business through the activities of their subsidiary the Burrell Hiring Company. It is said that John Fowler lost many opportunities with Northern showmen simply by refusing to accept regular part payments in small denomination coinage.

The first showman to use steam is believed to be the American born circus proprietor, James Washington Myers, who concluded a contract in 1859 with the long since defunct Bray's Traction Engine Company for the hire of one of their 12 NHP duplex cylinder engines. Myers required the engine to be suitable for hauling his six brightly decorated vans on a tour of the United Kingdom. The fascinating story of this ill-fated tour and the ensuing litigation is recorded in detail in Ronald Clark's classical work, 'The Development of the English Traction Engine'. The mediaeval street performer, the tinker and the gipsy coming from Central Europe were the first travelling showmen and from early times established the tradition of using extravagantly decorated and brightly coloured vans and equipment. We learn that James Myers had his Bray engine and train painted in many bright colours and decorated with a huge golden dragon creating a precedent for future engine owners.

Twenty years later Myers purchased a second engine from the then recently established engine builders, J & H McLaren of Leeds. We know very little about this engine other than that it carried the maker's No 85 and was named 'Sir Robert le Diable'. By this time other established showmen were beginning to show interest in the potentialities of steam power. We have already noted in chapter 6 that in 1880 Charles Burrell supplied an early 10 NHP geared traction engine No 725 second-hand to Frederic Savage, the pioneer fairground ride manufacturer in King's Lynn. This was later sold to William Marshall of Sheffield for his Savage built set of Gallopers. However, it was not until 1889 that St Nicholas Works built a traction engine to the direct order of a travelling showman. The engine No 1451, an 8 NHP single cylinder engine is described and illustrated in chapter 6.

In the following year the works supplied a Road Locomotive direct to a travelling showman. No 1470, a smart little 7 NHP single cylinder engine was supplied to G & J Bartlett of Fordingbridge in Hampshire in March 1890 and appropriately named 'Pride of the South'. The cylinder measured 8½ ins dia × 12 ins stroke and the T type boiler was pressed to 140 PSI having a grate area of 4.9 sq ft and a total heating surface of 143 sq ft. The firebox was copper, the smoke tubes were brass and the only visible embellishments were the polished copper chimney top, brass tops on the safety valves and burnished brass balls on the cross-arm type governor. The engine had 3-shaft single drive transmission shafts mounted on volute type springs with 2-speed gearing in accordance with Frederick Burrell's 1887 patent. Some of the gearing components were produced from cast steel. The hind wheels were 6 ft 6 ins dia × 16 ins wide with polished brass axle caps. It is believed to be one of the first Burrell engines to be fitted with a spring forecarriage.

A vertical screen called a Spectacle Plate was fitted just ahead of the crankshaft, together with a half length canopy, giving the footplate some protection from the elements. The motion was concealed by motion side plates and a solid 4 ft 6 ins dia flywheel was fitted, features which it was claimed were necessary 'to prevent frightening sensitive horses'. According to the engine register the tender was fitted with an extended coal rack, but this feature is not shown in the accompanying photograph. Belly tanks were fitted under the boiler giving the engine a range of 12 to 15 miles without re-watering. A mechanical feed pump and a Gresham's type injector were fitted.

The paintwork was given a Show finish by the Paint Shop and the only other special feature recorded in the engine register was the addition of a Smith's patent 4 ins signal whistle, treble toned. The engine remained in Bartlett's ownership for thirty years and in 1922 was acquired by Richard Chipperfield.

The comparatively small number of traction engines supplied direct to showmen in the early days of steam in the fairground have been identified in chapters 6 and 7. In chapters 9 and 10 we have dealt with road locomotives subsequently converted to Showman's type engines and in this chapter we shall deal only with those engines specifically built as Showman's road locomotives. Whereas in the earlier chapters we have dealt with engines produced up to and including 1914, in order to achieve better continuity we shall describe the total production of Burrell Showman's road locomotives built between 1890 and 1930 in this chapter. All 5 ton tractors and steam wagons with service in Showland which in any event were 20th century products, are dealt with in chapters 16 and 17 respectively.

The first two big 8 NHP engines supplied direct to showmen were Nos 1546 and 1575 built in July 1891 and February 1892 respectively. They were based on the 8 NHP 6¼ ins × 11 ins × 12 ins SCC single drive spring mounted road engines introduced in 1890 and described in chapter 10. Both had spectacle plates and short awnings as shown in Fig 186. No 1456 was supplied to the famous Bristol based showmen, Willian, Charles and Sophie Hancock whose names were a byword in the West Country for many years. Named 'Pride of the West' the engine initially travelled with their menagerie and later with their Bioscope picture show which was the first show to bring moving pictures to the area in the 1890s. Later the engine was acquired by Joseph Smith of Shirley in Hampshire, ending its days in commercial ownership in Sutton Scotney. No 1575, 'Roving Monarch' went to the Worksop showman, Tom Harniess and is shown in Fig 163 fitted with Isaac Boulton's patent wheels taken from No 1415.

These were followed by twelve similar engines but having 6½ ins × 11 ins × 12 ins SCC cylinders built between 1894 and 1897.

8 NHP SCC SHOWMAN'S ENGINES
6½ ins × 11 ins × 12 ins CYLINDERS

No		Built	Name
No 1729	Built	1894	—
1743	"	1894	Old Sal
1796	"	1894	Lady Combamere
1810	"	1895	Clarence
1819	"	1894	Rambler
1820	"	1895	Victoria
1905	"	1896	—
1907	"	1896	Excelsior
1909	"	1896	Majestic
1910	"	1896	—
1915	"	1896	Excelsior
1985	"	1897	Mona I

Basically, Nos 1729, 1743, 1796 and 1810 were as the standard road locomotives described in chapter 10 but it was during this period that the Showman's engine as we know it today began to take shape. A smokebox mounted dynamo platform was fitted on No 1819 and the long awning followed on No 1907. These features were fitted to most engines built subsequently together with twisted brass canopy supports and brass stars and rings on the motion side plates. When new Nos 1819, 1820 and 1905 were fitted with short awnings and spectacle plates. No 1819 was fitted also with special wooden block wheel

Fig 185 No 1470 'Pride of the South', a 7 NHP SC road locomotive supplied to G & J Bartlett in 1890. This was the second Thetford built engine supplied to the direct order of a travelling showman.

rims, the precursor of solid rubber tyres and the subject of Frederick Burrell's patent No 19038 dated 1894.

No 1729 went new to Francis Bailey of Battersea in London and in 1902 passed to Mrs Mathilda Hill of East Dulwich. Both used the engine with their four-abreast Gallopers. No 1743, 'Old Sal' went to the Birmingham showmen, J B & W Shepherd passing to H C Humphries of Great Bridge about 1904. No 1796 was supplied to the Chester showman, Charles Farrell who had slightly smaller 6¼ ins × 10½ ins × 12 ins cylinders fitted after a few years' service. In 1909 the engine passed into commercial ownership in East Anglia. No 1810, 'Clarence' spent most of its working life with Charles Warren of Lincoln, together with Burrell engines Nos 1985, 'Mona I' and No 3132, 'Mona'.

No 1819, 'Rambler' was the first of four Burrell Showman's engines purchased by John Collins of Chester. Of Irish extraction, John was the elder brother of Pat Collins of Bloxwich, the celebrated Midlands showman and later Member of Parliament. John was born in the fairground at Denbigh in North Wales in 1853, the eldest of five children all of whom made their mark in the tobers. In 1883 he married Selina Davies, daughter of the well known Potteries showman, William Davies. John moved to Liverpool at the beginning of the 20th century and was one of the largest owners of riding machines in the country. He had several sets of Steam Yachts, Steam Junks, three and four-abreast Gallopers, Venetian Gondolas and two magnificent sets of Scenic Railways. At one time he was the largest tenant at the famous Nottingham Goose Fair and was a founder member of the Showman's Guild and the Van Dwellers Association. After his death in 1929 the business was carried on by his sons, John Jr, Michael Albert and James Patrick Collins. In their heyday they owned eleven fine engines of various makes.

No 1820, 'Victoria' saw over 30 years' continuous service in the fairground, firstly with Thomas Cook of Kidderminster in Worcestershire and then from 1911 with Colonel J Print of Leytonstone finishing her days in the 1920s with the well-known London traveller, Charles Presland of Tilbury. Fig 188 illustrates the engine at Stratford-upon-Avon adjacent to Cook's Switchback with

Fig 186 No 1546 'Pride of the West' 8 NHP SCC road locomotive supplied to the renowned West Country showmen W C & S Hancock in 1891.

the famous Mop Fair ox roast in the foreground. No 1905 went new to Charles Whiting, whose yard was in the shadow of Chesterfield's crooked church spire and in 1901 it passed to William Hall, the father of the well known showman, Harry Hall who lived in Derby for many years. No 1907 went also to the Midlands, to Mrs Luke Weir of Burton-on-Trent who named her 'Excelsior'. In 1909 the engine was acquired by Clifford Hill of Ross-on-Wye in Herefordshire.

No 1909, 'Majestic' was the second of eighteen Burrell engines to be purchased by various members of the Studt family who operated over a wide area between London and South Wales. She started her working life with Jacob Studt Snr whom it will be remembered was the first travelling showman to place an order direct with St Nicholas Works. In 1901 she was acquired by G & J Bartlett for their unique set of New Forest Hunters. In the 1920s the engine passed to R & W Gritt of Romsey in Hampshire who at various times owned two 8 NHP Burrell road locomotives and two 5 ton tractors.

No 1910 was the second of these engines to be purchased by J B & W Shepherd of Stetchford in Birmingham. In 1902 the engine, which was never named, was acquired by the Chatham contractor Charles Tassell who operated a fleet of six Burrell engines. Immediately after the First World War, during a period of acute shortage of Showman's engines she returned to the fairground in the ownership of T Bolesworth of Dagenham. No 1915, 'Excelsior' was purchased new by Alfred Payne of Hull. During the First World War the engine was acquired by George Collins, later trading as Collins & Ingham of Castleford in Yorkshire. He was no relation of the well known Collins family and later the engine passed to S Waddington & Sons of Bradford.

The twelfth and final engine in the series, No 1985, 'Mona I' went new to Charles Warren of Lincoln. The engine remained in his ownership until 1930 when she was acquired by Mrs E Smith, also of Lincoln, who travelled a set of Gallopers and then finished her working life with several Lincolnshire farmers as a threshing engine.

Concurrently with the preceding 8 NHP SCC engines St Nicholas Works built eight big 'Contractor's type Showman's road locomotives having 7 ins dia × 11½ ins dia × 12 ins stroke cylinders.

10 NHP SCC 'CONTRACTORS' TYPE SHOWMAN'S ROAD LOCOMOTIVES

No		Built		Name
No	1740	Built	1894	Cornishman
	1777	"	1894	Emperor
	1845	"	1895	The Dutchman
	1876	"	1895	Emperor
	1887	"	1895	Empress of India
	1888	"	1896	Empress
	1908	"	1896	Excelsior
	1993	"	1897	Diamond Queen

Fig 187 No 1810 'Clarence' 8 NHP showman's road locomotive with Charles Warren's loads circa 1895.

Fig 188 No 1820 'Victoria' 8 NHP SCC Showman's type engine with Thomas Cook's Switchback at Stratford-upon-Avon Mop Fair.

Until the advent of the 8 NHP double crank compound 'Contractors' engine in August 1896 these were universally acknowledged as the finest engines yet produced by St Nicholas Works. The first seven engines were rated 10 NHP having the big type CL35 boiler with a 6.0 sq ft grate and a total heating surface of 164.5 sq ft. The eighth engine had the smaller type CC123 boiler with a 5.375 sq ft grate and a total heating surface of 151.0 sq ft and was rated 8 NHP. All except No 1845 were fitted new with smokebox dynamo platforms but Nos 1740, 1777, 1845 and 1876 were built with spectacle plates and short awnings. The remaining engines all had long awnings. No 1740 was the first engine to leave the works with twisted brass canopy supports, motion side plates with brass stars and rings and a cased flywheel with a brass ring around its mid-circumference. The first cast solid flywheel was fitted to Nos 1887 and 1888, and No 1908 was fitted with wood block rims on the hind wheels as described in Frederick Burrell's patent 19038 of 1894. Most of the hind wheels were 6 ft 6 ins dia × 18 ins wide. The water carrying capacity was 300 gallons, the engines were 8 ft 5½ ins wide overall and they weighed approximately 14 ton 10 cwt in working order.

No 1740, 'Cornishman' was the second new Burrell engine to be purchased by the Hancock concern. She spent the whole of her working life with a very old set of Savage four-abreast Gallopers, said to be the second set ever made. The Hancock family have been traced back to Perthshire in the 1830s. They moved to the West Country in the 1850s and William, Charles and Sophie soon became leading showland personalities in the region enjoying nothing more than entertaining the famous, even Royalty in their van. Perhaps Sophie is best remembered for she always seemed to be in trouble with the English authorities but every fine imposed upon her was always promptly settled together with a generous contribution to the Poor Box. It was said that she could swear better than any man and that she could and frequently did indulge in a stream of abuse lasting half an hour without once repeating herself.

In 1910 the engine with loads was involved in a spectacular run-away accident near Teignmouth in Devon and we are told that upon this occasion, 'Not even the primaeval ire and wrath' of little Sophie could right the engine. In 1913 whilst in Plymouth the engine and ride were seriously damaged by a fire started by suffragettes. The equipment was not insured and a public subscription fund was set up to help them and no less a person than Queen Alexandra sent a donation.

After William and Charles' death the four-abreast Gallopers and 'Cornishman' became Sophie's sole property. The Gallopers were cut down to a three-abreast ride and both engine and ride were set up on a permanent site in North London. The great pride and joy of Sophie's life was that her beloved Gallopers were awarded the unique privilege of displaying the Royal Coat of Arms by Royal Appointment over the brightly polished Savage centre engine. Upon her death in 1926 both engine and ride were sold to Ernest Manning who set up the tackle in his fair at Alexandra Palace. In 1934 they were advertised

Fig 189 No 1740 'Cornishman' 10 NHP SCC Contractor's type engine with W C & S Hancock's loads entering Brixham, Devon 1910.

Fig 190 No 1777 'Emperor', the first Burrell engine supplied to the great Midland showman, Pat Collins of Bloxwich in July 1894.

Fig 191 William Symonds' 10 NHP SCC Contractor's type engine No 1845 'The Dutchman' after fitting a dynamo platform and full length canopy, circa 1903.

for sale and failing to find a buyer both were broken up in Manning's yard.

No 1777 was the first Burrell engine supplied to the famous Midland showman, Patrick Collins. Born in Chester in 1859 both he and his elder brother John already referred to frequently assisted their father when young boys by turning the handle of his manually operated roundabout. Originally this ride was drawn from fair to fair by a team of dogs which the family had brought over from Ireland. In later life Pat Collins often recalled that in 1884 he accompanied his father to Savages works in King's Lynn when he purchased his first set of steam driven three-abreast Gallopers thus founding what soon became the largest travelling fairground business ever seen in the United Kingdom. He acquired a second set in 1886 and in 1890 he purchased one of Savage's first 'Sea-on-Land' rides which became very popular. He was always ready to pioneer new and improved riding machines and he quickly established a great reputation. In addition to owning more steam engines, roundabouts and other mechanical rides than any other travelling showman of his generation he owned several cinemas, theatres and skating rinks. Boxing and its promotion was his lifelong hobby.

When permanent amusement parks became popular he established his famous Crystal Palace of Amusements at Sutton Coldfield, near Birmingham. Between the Wars tens of thousands of Midland workers spent their Bank Holidays enjoying the pleasures of this fairground.

However, he always concerned himself primarily with the travelling fair and its paraphernalia and nobody knew better than him how to lay out a ground, called a Tober in fairground parlance. The largest annual fair of which he had control was the Aston Onion Fair in Birmingham and it was not uncommon to see over twenty Showman's engines on the fairground. Prior to the First World War, and for many years after, the Pat Collins firm was holding as many as six fairs a week.

For many years Collins had at least twenty-five engines licensed for use on the road at any one time and he was one of the first showmen to extensively use electric lighting in the fairground. Between 1894 and 1920 he purchased new seven Burrell Showman's road locomotives and between 1915 and 1946 he purchased fifteen second hand. His fleet also included engines built by John Fowler, J & H McLaren, William Foster, Brown & May of Devizes and Savage of King's Lynn. Additionally he had eight steam wagons and four horse drawn steam generating sets by Thomas Green & Sons of Leeds – a total of fifty four engines.

Pat Collins had two sons by his first wife Flora who died in 1933. Patrick Ross, known as 'Young Pat' was the eldest and John, known as 'Walsall John' the younger. Patrick Ross had two sons, Patrick (Boy Pat) and John (Goggles John) and two daughters, Margaret, who became Mrs Elias Harris and Flora, who became Mrs Eddie Monte. Walsall John married Miss Claire Hall, the sister of Harry Hall of Derby who also had two sons and two daughters. Old Pat Collins Snr always found time to interest himself in religious, political and charitable affairs. In 1900 he was elected President of the Showman's Guild. In 1922 he was elected Liberal Member of Parliament for Walsall, a distinction never before accorded to a member of his profession. He served on Walsall Town Council for over thirty years and in 1938 had the honour of being elected its Mayor. Throughout his life he did an enormous amount of good work for the local hospitals and his name is still greatly revered in the area.

No 1845 was supplied new to William Symonds of Gloucester. The fascinating story of this popular West Country showman is told in the book, 'From Boy to Prince of Showmen'. Born in 1859, the son of a labourer, he tackled a variety of odd jobs before investing his savings in a set of Swing Boats. After many years of struggle, often opposed by a 'ring' of local showmen, and the stress of a broken partnership he finally established himself about 1890. Initially he had two Switchback rides which he moved by special train comprising some twenty wagon loads. He purchased No 1845 in 1895, had a dynamo platform fitted in 1896 and in 1903 he fitted a full length awning and named the engine, 'The Dutchman'.

Symonds was dubbed 'Prince of Showmen' by a County Court Judge hearing a compensation case. In 1910 he acquired a fine big Bioscope show with a magnificent Marenghi organ built into the show front and was responsible for the introduction of moving pictures to towns and villages in the Cotswolds and Severn Valley. The show was disbanded in 1916 and the engine finished her days in commercial ownership. No 1876, the second big 10 NHP SCC Showman's engine to carry the name 'Emperor' went new to George Twigdon of Leicester. The three brothers, George, Albert and William were well known travellers in the East Midlands owning several big riding machines, three Savage portable electric light engines and later three Burrell Showman's type engines. The engine proved to be too heavy for the many canal bridges on Twigdon's circuit and was returned to the works where it was converted to a crane engine. It spent many years as the works' crane engine and finished its working life in the ownership of the East Anglian drainage contractors, Mornement & Ray. It survives today in preservation beautifully restored as a crane engine.

The engine as originally built with Twigdons' Switchback loads is illustrated in Fig 192. The manoeuvrability of such long trains, the avoidance of 'wandering' on corners and the prevention of forecarriage swivel pins becoming overloaded was achieved by the use of rods attached to and running centrally the length of each wagon, the ends being forged to accommodate the draw pins. The vee-bars attached to the wagon forecarriage were arranged to slip over the straight towing bars which took all the 'pull' when inserted in the train between each wagon and at the same time steering the forecarriage without strain. When it became necessary to break the train in order to negotiate steep hills, the engine took one or two wagons at a time up the hill. Re-alignment was achieved by the use of wire ropes, sometimes with the aid of a slipper pulley block so that the driver did not have to back the train to pick up the other wagons. Life in the 1890s moved at a much more leisurely pace. A couple of hours spent negotiating a steep hill or slipping a heavy load round a sharp corner on steel plates was of little consequence. Labour was cheap and plentiful and the drivers working largely on their own initiative developed a quiet unruffled philosophy of their own. By the time long and heavy trailers and box wagons were introduced the law intervened and in most parts of the country road trains

Fig 192 No 1876 10 NHP SCC 'Contractors' type Showman's road locomotive as built in 1895 with George Twigdon's Switchback loads at Longton, Stoke-on-Trent.

were limited to three wagons and a Water Dandy.

No 1887, Empress of India was exhibited at the 1895 Smithfield Show before delivery to Mrs Henrietta Wilson of Belper in Derbyshire. Later the engine went to her son, William, of Peckham in London for their famous richly carved and gilded spinning-top Switchback ride. It started with early motor cars but later a succession of birds, dragons and other animals took their place. Eventually these were replaced by more modern motor cars having models of famous film stars riding in the back of each car. Known as the Rodeo ride it was a regular visitor to the Islington Agricultural Hall Fair. Later the engine and ride passed to R Bailey of Gravesend in Kent who electrified the ride and mounted a crane on the engine tender as shown in Fig 194 to assist with the build-up of the ride.

No 1888, 'Empress' spent all its life with Pat Collins. It is interesting to note that Nos 1777 and 1876 were originally listed in the works registers as being named 'Empress' but for reasons which now remain obscure the names were quickly changed to 'Emperor'. Similarly No 1888 was originally named 'Emperor' and this was changed to 'Empress' when the engine was returned to the works to have its special 20 ins wide wooden rim hind wheels transferred to No 1777. All these alterations were initialled by either Charles or Frederick Burrell and probably took place when Twigdon's engine was returned to the works for conversion to a crane engine.

Fig 193 No 1876 10 NHP SCC Showman's road locomotive 'Emperor' as converted to the works' crane engine in 1905.

No 1908, 'Excelsior' was supplied new to Harry J Wallis a Lancashire showman. It was reputed to have been one of the heaviest engines ever built and the Lancashire County Council forced him to sell the engine when they introduced a 14 ton weight restriction. This engine was also fitted with Burrells' patent wooden block wheel rims.

The last of the SCC Contractors engines No 1993, 'Diamond Queen' was rated 8 NHP because of her smaller boiler. She went new to John Whittington of Sheffield in 1897 passed to John E Whiting of nearby Owlerton and then spent 25 years with W North & Sons of Denaby.

The single crank compound was never really popular with the showmen and their drivers because of the problems associated with restarting under load when the engine stopped on top centre. In 1897 three fine big 10 NHP DCC Contractors type Showman's road locomotives were completed in St Nicholas Works. Within the next five years the demand for Showman's engines more than doubled, although the smaller 8 NHP engine developing 54 IHP and having a hauling power of 40 tons soon became more popular than the larger more powerful Contractors type. The mechanical details of all these engines is given in chapter 10.

The first two of the trio, No 1971, 'Britannia' and No 1980, 'Her Majesty' went new to W C & S Hancock. No doubt it was felt that the hilly country in Devon and Cornwall necessitated a 10 NHP engine to cope with the eight loads which made up their famous Spinning Top Gondolas. Both engines were fitted with steam operated brakes mounted on the tender as illustrated in Fig 166. Upon the death of the Hancock brothers shortly after the First World War, No 1971 went to Fred Gray of Hampstead who had started his career with the firm. No 1980 ended her working life with Freeman & McLeod Ltd Granite Merchants of Penryn near Falmouth and was stabled in Carnsew Quarry for may years after a runaway accident at Hillbead near Penryn on a steep winding hill which dropped over 300 ft in less than half a mile. In 1940, during a wartime salvage drive, the engine was cut up.

Fig 194 No 1887 'Empress of India' 10 NHP 'Contractors' type SCC Showman's engine fitted with an improvised rear jib crane for lifting William Wilson's Rodeo Scenic Railway cars.

No 1997, 'Pride of North Wales' was supplied new to Arthur Wildman of Caernarvon. Within a couple of years she was repossessed by the Burrell Hiring Company and passed to Mr S Ford, Burrells' West Country agent. Eventually in 1902 she was purchased by William Kerr of Mavisbank near Glasgow. They removed the dynamo and platform and renamed the engine 'Lord Roberts'. Although the engine had a short undistinguished career in showland service, as the first of Willam Kerr's fleet of engines she performed many prodigious feats of heavy haulage in Scotland.

Several Showman's road locomotives were built based upon the 8 NHP DCC 'Contractors' type engine, but these fall into three distinct groups. No 2010 completed in August 1897 was similar to the 8 NHP SCC 'Contractors' engines and was built for a Belgian showman. Eight more were built with long boilers in the period 1905/06. The third group were built in 1924/25 after the company had been absorbed in the AGE Group in the days of the big Scenic Railway rides and these are dealt with later in this chapter. All had 7 ins dia × 11½ ins dia × 12 stroke DCC cylinders.

Fig 195 No 1908 'Excelsior' 10 NHP SCC 'Contractors' type engine with Burrells' patent wood block hind wheels.

No 2010 was built to the order of M F Speckstadt of Liege in Belgium but nothing appears to be known about the engine's fate. It had the same CC123 type boiler with a 5.375.sq ft grate and total heating surface of 151 sq ft as the SCC engines but it was built with a dynamo platform, long awning and full set of brass show fittings. A tender mounted steam brake was fitted and another unusual feature was the 3-speed cross-arm type governor. The hind wheels were 6 ft 6 ins dia × 16 ins wide and the spring forecarriage was uniquely mounted on india rubber pads.

The eight engines in the 1905/06 batch were:

8 NHP DCC 'CONTRACTORS' TYPE SHOWMAN'S ROAD LOCOMOTIVES

No 2780	Built	1905	King Edward VII
2788	"	1906	Alfred the Great
2789	"	1905	The President
2793	"	1906	The Leader
2796	"	1906	John Bull
2801	"	1906	The Major
2804	"	1906	The White Rose of York
2818	"	1906	Albert

The boilers were pressed to 175 PSI. Nos 2780, 2788, 2801, 2804 and 2818 had 6.0 sq ft grates and a total heating surface of 154.16 sq ft. Nos 2789, 2793 and 2796 had 6.6 sq ft grates and a total heating surface of 162.0 sq ft. All except the three large grate engines had forty-seven 1¾ ins dia smoke tubes whilst the latter had forty 2 ins dia × 6 ft 2 ins long tubes. In addition to an injector all were fitted with a Moores Steam pump and Nos 2789 and 2818 were unusually fitted with two, but these were quite quickly replaced. Three speed gearing having ratios

Fig 196 No 1993 'Diamond Queen' 10 NHP SCC 'Contractors' type Showman's road locomotive at a West Yorkshire fair in 1911.

of 30.5, 17.0 and 10.4 to 1 were employed and the hind wheels measured 7 ft 0 ins dia × 18 ins wide making them fast engines on the road with a haulage capacity well within the requirements of the largest rides. Flywheel brakes operated by the steersman were fitted and all had dynamo platforms, long awnings and a full set of brass show fittings.

No 2780, 'King Edward VII' was supplied new to Charles Thurston, the well known Norwich showman. This branch of the family owned seven Burrell Showman's engines at various times and operated several big rides throughout East Anglia. Originally the engine was used with Thurston's splendid Bioscope Show and the extra long extension chimney designed to throw the engine smoke well clear of the elaborately decorated front of the show will be noted in Fig 198. In 1919 the engine returned to St Nicholas Works for an overhaul and fitting an auxiliary dynamo platform between the cylinder block and the chimney which necessitated extending the smokebox.

In 1910 the Doncaster showman, Enoch Farrar had exhibited the first Savage built Electric Scenic Railway ride at King's Lynn Mart Fair. This was the first fairground machine to employ electric traction with direct conduction through its circular undulating track thus obviating the need for a centre engine and a spinning top frame. Eight motor cars were installed on the ride, each provided with a 4 HP electric motor and each weighing approximately 30 cwt. The starting load of the 110 volt series wound electric motors was in excess of 200 amps often causing the engine driven belt drive to break or be thrown off the flywheel. In 1911 Hackett & Whatham patented their idea of providing for the excitation of the main dynamo by a separate auxiliary machine. Initially it was the practice to provide the excitation current from another engine and dynamo but Hackett & Whatham proposed that both electrical machines should be carried on the same engine with the auxiliary dynamo belt driven from an extended shaft on the main dynamo. Some Fowler and Foster engines carried the auxiliary dynamo mounted on the gear side belly tank. This proved unsatisfactory because it denied the driver access to the motion for oiling when the engine was generating and the long narrow belt was often troublesome.

In 1912 Hackett & Whatham joined forces with William Foster and their first Scenic type engine No 12901 'Medina' emerged from the Wellington Foundry a few months later with the auxiliary dynamo mounted on a raised platform arranged as a backwards extension of the main dynamo platform behind the chimney. This development would have had a more immediate effect upon the fairground scene were it not for the intervention of the First World War.

Fig 197 Mr Walter Hancock passing No 1980 'Her Majesty' and loads in his pony and trap on the Bideford to Barnstable road, circa 1905.

Fig 198 No 2780 'King Edward VII' 8 NHP 'Contractors' type engine as originally built with Charles Thurston's Bioscope Show on tour in 1907.

Fig 199 No 2780 'King Edward VII' outside Burrell's paint shop after having an auxiliary dynamo platform fitted.

Fig 200 No 2789 'Lord Kitchener' originally an 8 NHP 'Contractors' type Showman's road locomotive built in 1905 minus its canopy and dynamo platform. The Moore's boiler feed pump mounted on the belly tank will be noted.

Charles Burrell were quick to appreciate the advantages of this arrangement. They found that by utilising their standard length of boiler with 5 ft 8 ins long smoke tubes and a 3 ft 6 ins long connecting rod they could incorporate a raised platform between the chimney and the cylinder block of sufficient size to accommodate an auxiliary dynamo. The first engine No 3372 so fitted was an 8 NHP DCC engine with $6\frac{3}{4}$ ins dia × $11\frac{1}{4}$ ins dia × 12 ins stroke cylinders supplied new to G T Tuby of Doncaster in 1912. In order to maintain continuity of type the story of these engines and the development of the tender mounted crane for lifting the Scenic cars belongs elsewhere in this chapter.

The rebuilt No 2780 illustrated in Fig 199 first appeared at Lynn Mart in 1920 together with a new Orton & Spooner built Golden Dragon Scenic ride. The opening ceremony was attended by the Princess Victoria who took the first ride on the Golden Dragons. After Charles

Fig 201 G T Tuby's Burrell No 2793 'The Leader' leaving Retford Market Place, October 6th 1910 with three Coliseum wagons, two living vans and a water dandy.

Fig 202 No 2804 'The White Rose of York', better known today as 'The Griffin'. 8 NHP DCC 'Contractors' type Showman's engine photographed at Taunton in 1929 in the ownership of Charles Heal of Glastonbury.

Thurston's death in 1930 the firm acquired a set of Orton & Spooner Dodgems which were attended by 'King Edward'. During World War II the engine was acquired by Charles Presland, a London traveller and today it survives in Mr G J Cushing's famous collection at Fakenham in Norfolk greatly adding to the pleasure of the thousands who congregate annually to hear his organ recitals.

No 2788, 'Alfred the Great' started life with Alfred Ball of Leytonstone with his Bioscope Show. In 1914 the engine was acquired by Pat Collins. By 1920 this famous showman was reputed to own no less than a dozen Scenic Railway rides and in 1922 he returned the engine to St Nicholas Works for conversion to a full Scenic specification. The smokebox was extended, a new dynamo platform and auxiliary dynamo were fitted and a rear jib scenic car lifting crane were added to the tender.

No 2789, 'Lord Kitchener' went new to 'President' G H Kemp of Leicester for his very popular Dreamland Bioscope show but after only two years was replaced by a smaller 7 NHP engine and 'Lord Kitchener' passed into commercial ownership.

No 2793, 'The Leader' was the second of seven Burrell engines owned by the famous Yorkshire showman and Civic Leader, George Thomas Tuby. He was successively a Councillor, Leader of the Council, Mayor, Alderman and Ex-Mayor of Doncaster and named his engines accordingly. In 1911 he sold the engine to John Evans of Edinburgh who renamed her 'King George'. In 1930 it passed to William Murphy, the leading Tyneside showman, and then in 1933 it went to John Powell of Jarrow. The engine's final owners were Palm Beach Amusements Ltd, also of Jarrow.

No 2796, 'John Bull' went new to John Proctor of Belper in Derbyshire for his Royal Bioscope show, a large two wagon fronted show. It is believed that this was the last large Biscope show to travel. In the early 1920s Proctor purchased two big Scenic rides and the engine was returned to the works for fitting an extended smokebox and auxiliary dynamo platform. When the engine was rebuilt in the 1920s the canopy was fitted with a sliding shutter to facilitate removal of the dynamo. After rebuiling all the bright parts of the engine, including the motion and decorative stars and rings and axle caps were nickel plated. The engine was painted crimson, the wheels were yellow and the underside of the canopy was green.

No 2801, 'The Major' was supplied new to Mrs Luke Weir of Burton-on-Trent. Eventually the engine was acquired by Pat Collins with whom it remained until replaced by a Scammell diesel Showtrac in 1946 which still carries the original Burrell engine nameplate. No 2804, 'The White Rose of York' another well known Pat Collins engine survives today in the ownership of Mr Bill Hunt of the Griffin Foundry, Oldbury, near Birmingham renamed 'The Griffin'. Originally the engine was supplied new to Alf Payne of York; it then passed successively to Anderton & Rowlands and Charles Heal & Sons in the West Country and R Wilson of Sunbury in Middlesex before being acquired by Pat Collins during the last days of steam in the fairground. Collins had the engine completely overhauled and the motion and other parts from No 2788 were fitted to her. Illustrated in Fig 202, the reader will note the large Mather & Platt dynamo with a double ended shaft and pulleys. They had an output of 270 amps and weighed 17 cwt.

No 2818 'Albert' spent all her life with the John Collins family of Liverpool and Manchester. Whereas the eight 8 NHP DCC 'Contractors' engines just described had spring mounted single drive gearing, this engine was spring mounted and double geared.

We now consider the forty-nine 8 NHP DCC

Showman's road locomotives built with 6½ ins dia × 11 ins dia × 12 ins stroke cylinders developing 50 IHP and having a hauling power of 35 tons on a 1 in 18 incline.

These and the slightly larger engines introduced in 1911 with 6¾ ins × 11¼ ins × 12 ins DCC cylinders soon became omnipotent in the British fairground and largely dominated the scene for the remainder of the steam era.

8 NHP DCC SHOWMAN'S ROAD LOCOMOTIVES WITH 6½ ins dia × 11 ins dia × 12 ins STROKE CYLINDERS

Engine No	Date Built	Engine Name	Original Owner
1999	May 1897	Victoria	Isaac Neal
2067	Feb 1898	City of Norwich	John Barker
2068	Feb 1898	King Edward VII	Hy Studt
2072	Mar 1898	The Masterpiece	John Cole
2076	Apr 1898	The Pride of Essex	W H Davies
2116	Jul 1898	Conqueror	Wm Beach
2170	Feb 1899	Empress	A Twigdon
2222	Sep 1899	Queen of the South	Marshall Hill
2268	Mar 1900	The Councillor	G T Tuby
2350	Feb 1901	Pride of Wales	Wm Ford
2351	Feb 1901	Ephraim	J Cox, Condor
2355	Mar 1901	Lord Roberts	W C & S Hancock
2369	Mar 1901	Queen Alexandra	Jn Murphy
*2379	May 1901	Ich Dien	E Danter
2456	Feb 1902	King Edward VII	James Crighton
2463	Mar 1902	Shamrock II	Harry Caris
2497	Aug 1902	Excelsior	Wm Taylor
2631	Nov 1903	King Edward VII/Willing	H J Scard
2650	Feb 1904	Independent/Mark Twain	Ralph & Pedley
2651	Mar 1904	Challenger	Mrs A Holland
2668	Jun 1904	Britannia	Wm Thurston
2709	Oct 1904	Mabon	James Dooner & Sons
2713	Dec 1904	His Majesty	Pat Collins
2716	Dec 1904	The Showmen	Anderton & Rowland
2721	Feb 1905	Edinburgh Castle	John Evans
2722	Mar 1905	Pride of the Road	Sam Crow
2723	Mar 1905	Doris/Bristol City	James Leo
2724	Mar 1905	Greyhound	E Danter
2733	May 1905	Lily of the Valley	Harris Bros
2740	Jun 1905	Enoch Clifford	Enoch Farrar
2744	Nov 1905	Jumbo/Beresford/Unique	Anderton & Rowland
2759	Aug 1905	Sir Colin Campbell	J Hibbert
2877	Feb 1907	His Majesty	Charles Heal & Sons
2894	Mar 1907	Pride of Worcester	H Strickland & Sons
2898	Apr 1907	Victoria/King Cole	Sm Taylor
2917	Aug 1907	The Ideal	W Testo
2979	Mar 1908	Reliance (Re-numbered 3038)	Ralph & Pedley
2983	Mar 1908	Lady Violet	James Crighton
*2988	Apr 1908	The Mascot	John Proctor
3015	Jul 1908	Perseverance/Leith	A H Faulkner
3038	Nov 1909	The Prince – (Formerly 2979)	Ruben Holdsworth
3072	Feb 1909	Shakespeare/Daisy	Wadbrook & Scard
3075	Feb 1909	Alexandra	Charles Thurston
*3093	Apr 1909	Dreadnought	Arthur Holland
*3163	Feb 1910	Doncaster	G T Tuby
3200	May 1910	Unity	Charles Thurston
*3285	Mar 1911	King George V	Abbot & Barker
*3443	Feb 1913	Lord Nelson	Anderton & Rowland
*3967	Oct 1923	Morning Star	Jacob Studt Jr

* Subsequently converted to Scenic type engines with crane horns.

Fig 203 No 2072 'The Masterpiece' 8 NHP DCC Showman's type engine built in 1898 with single drive gearing for John Cole of Staple Hill, Gloucester.

These engines were similar in all mechanical detail to the contemporary DCC road locomotives having $6\frac{1}{2}$ ins dia × 11 ins dia × 12 ins stroke cylinders. The first seven had boilers with 5.375 sq ft grates, a total heating surface of 151.0 sq ft and forty-one 2 ins dia × 5 ft 8 ins long smoke tubes. No 2222 and the next thirteen engines had smaller 4.86 sq ft grates, a heating surface of 134.6 sq ft and thirty-four 2 ins dia × 5 ft 8 ins long smoke tubes. No 2709 and the next twelve engines had enlarged 6.0 sq ft grates and a total heating surface of 154.15 sq ft with forty-seven $1\frac{3}{4}$ ins dia × 5 ft 8 ins long smoke tubes. No 2894 and the eleven succeeding engines in the series had long boilers with 6.6 sq ft grates, a total heating surface of 162.0 sq ft and forty 2 ins dia × 6 ft 2 ins long smoke tubes. These enabled 4 ft 0 ins long connecting rods to be employed. The final two engines, No 3443, 'Lord Nelson' and No 3967, 'Morning Star' retained the large grate area but the smoke tubes were reduced in length to 5 ft 8 ins giving a total heating surface of 151.7 sq ft. Until 1901 boiler pressures were 160 PSI and thereafter progressively increased to 200 PSI in 1909.

Most engines were fitted new with Moore's steam pumps mounted on the belly tank, but these were soon replaced by mechanical feed pumps. All had injectors of a variety of types specified by the customer. Engines built in 1897/98 had cross arm type governors. Between 1899 and 1904 Burrells' High Speed governors were fitted and thereafter Pickering governors became standard.

All were spring mounted and engines up to and including No 2759 had single drive gearing. Thereafter double gearing and short travel spring gear was employed. Engine No 2170, 'Empress' and 2268, 'The Councillor' were originally fitted with tender mounted steam brakes but these were soon abandoned. It was on this class of engine that the flywheel brake operated by the steersman became more or less standard equipment. Wheel sizes varied but most were 7 ft 0 ins dia × 18 ins wide. All had full length awnings, twisted brass canopy supports and decorative brasswork, individual customers often specifying their exact requirements. The engines weighed approximately 15 tons in working order and carried sufficient water for travelling 12 miles with loads without re-watering.

No 1999, 'Victoria' went new to Isaac Neal of Market Bosworth whose famous set of Gallopers, 'Neal's Newmarket Jumpers' were a well known and popular ride throughout the Midland shires. In 1915 the engine was sold to Pat Collins and Neal's son, Bob became one of the Collins' best known drivers. In later years when travelling with loads from the Aston Onion Fair in Birmingham to the annual Nottingham Goose Fair, Bob always stopped and gave the small boy who sixty years later is writing this story a ride. Dear Bob will be long remembered. In 1923 the engine was purchased by Alf Ball of Leytonstone and she finished her working life in 1952 in the ownership of George Beach of Sunbury-on-Thames.

No 2067 started its life with John Barker & Sons of Norwich and when the Barker & Thurston partnership was formed in 1915 they named her 'City of Norwich'. For many years she was painted a brilliant mid-green with bright yellow wheels and travelled extensively throughout East Anglia. No 2068 was despatched concurrently with No 2067 and went to Henry Studt of Swansea, the elder brother of Jacob Studt. Henry and his three sons owned three Burrell and three Fowler Sowman's engines and travelled extensively throughout South Wales. No 2068 which was named 'King Edward VII' in 1902 to commemorate the King's coronation usually accompanied their splendid zoological four-abreast Gallopers.

No 2072, 'The Masterpiece' is believed to be the oldest surviving Burrell Showman's road locomotive still with its original showland fittings. The earlier surviving engine

No 1876 was, as we have already seen, re-purchased by Charles Burrell and converted to the works' crane engine. No 2072 was supplied new to John Cole of Staple Hill, Gloucester. He eventually merged his interests with his brother James and trading as Cole Brothers of Yate owned five Burrell Showman's engines at various times. 'The Masterpiece' finished her working life in the ownership of Hardiman & Strong of Bristol.

William H Davies of Forest Gate, London purchased No 2076 in April 1898 for hauling his Gallopers. Due to its fierceness in operation the tender mounted steam brake soon caused all sorts of problems on London's paved streets, especially on the tramway routes. The engine was sold to John Carter of Hailsham in Sussex who also travelled a set of Gallopers. Later, the Chelmsford showman, Jack Hedges acquired the engine. During World War I it was sold to a Suffolk agricultural contractor and it finished its days as a threshing engine in Lincolnshire.

family. Marshall, the son of a typical Victorian traveller branched out on his own while still in his twenties, eventually forming a partnership with William Symonds of Gloucester. Unfortunately the wives proved to be incompatible and the partnership did not last long whereupon Marshall purchased a new Savage Switchback ride and 'Queen of the South'. He often paired up with Anderton & Rowlands' and Chipperfields' fairs and was a regular visitor to the Wanstead Flats Easter Fair. He always insisted that his employees were clean, correctly dressed and were courteous to the patrons and was often described as the 'Perfect Gentleman'.

In 1911, after covering many thousands of miles in Hill's ownership the engine was acquired by J Searle of Croydon. It then passed to Smart & Rowles of Warminster and Tom Rowels of Burford and in the 1920s was purchased by Richard Wall of Petersfield. During the next thirty years the Wall Bros owned eleven Burrell engines at various times.

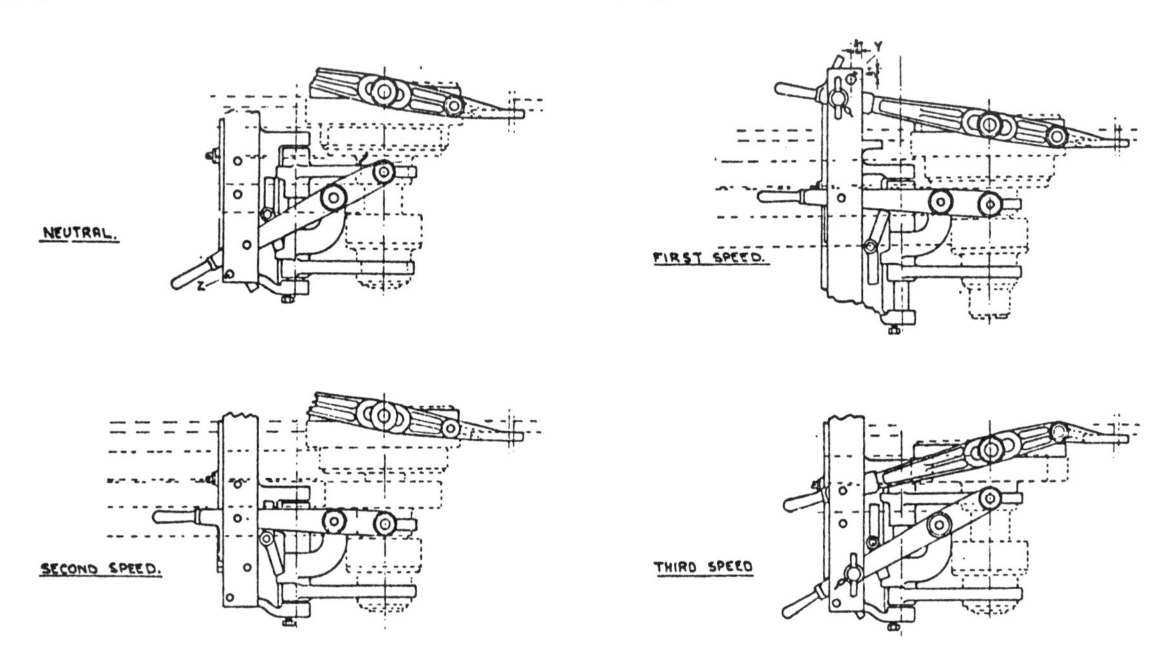

Fig 204 Burrells' very successful 2-lever, 3-speed gear change mechanism fitted to most Showman's type engines built after 1904.

William Beach was the first of three brothers to come over from Ireland and established the Beach family dynasty in the Thames Valley. In 1898 he purchased No 2116, the first of seven road locomotives and four 5 ton tractors he and his children owned at various times. In 1948, ten years after William's death his daughter Sally re-possessed No 2116.

No 2170 went originally to Albert Twigdon of Leicester and in 1910 was acquired by Pat Collins. Shortly after World War I the engine passed to Noah Judd, a Buckinghamshire timber haulier. Named 'Empress' the engine was originally built with a special awning which could be raised or lowered to enable the engine to negotiate low bridges.

No 2222 'Queen of the South' had a long and distinguished career in showland. Supplied new in September 1899 to Marshall Hill, it was the first of eight Burrell engines owned by this famous West Country

In March 1900 the well known Doncaster showman and town councillor, George Thomas Tuby took delivery of his first Showman's road locomotive. No 2268 which he appropriately named 'The Councillor' was originally fitted with a tender mounted steam brake and the canopy was arranged for raising or lowering when passing under low bridges. Although originally painted crimson with yellow wheels it was soon repainted the old Great Eastern Railway royal blue with yellow wheels, a feature which became a characteristic of all Tuby's engines.

In the early 1930s the engine was severely damaged in a runaway accident near Sheffield and was sold to Sheffield showman, John North. Fig 206 shows the rebuilt engine fitted with solid rubber tyres with North's loads on Hollins Hill, Erholt in 1935. The driver was Frank Cheffins who in later life became the President of the Road Locomotive Society.

The next eleven engines, Nos 2350–2651 built in the

Fig 205 No 2222 'Queen of the South' 8 NHP DCC Showman's engine with Marshall Hills' Motor Switchback loads in Bristol, circa 1906.

Fig 206 The ex-Tuby 8 NHP DCC Showman's engine No 2268 'Councillor' with John North's loads on Hollins Hill, Erholt, near Sheffield in 1933.

Fig 207 No 2350 'Duchess of Worcester' an 8 NHP DCC Showman's engine, formerly 'Pride of Wales' photographed in the ownership of A Peters of Worcester in 1908.

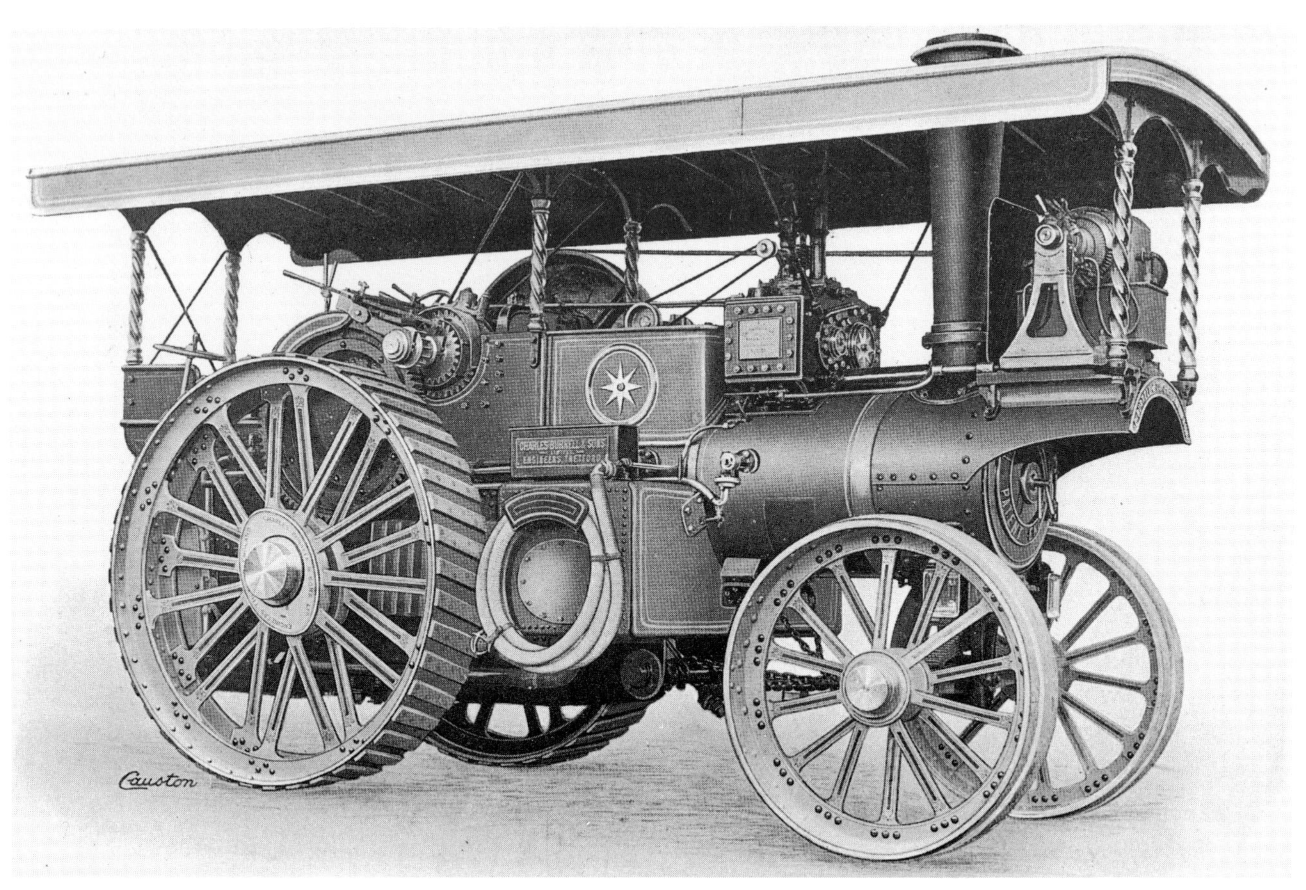

Fig 208 No 2733 'Lily of the Valley' 8 NHP DCC Showman's type engine built in 1905 for Harris Bros of Lewes, Sussex.

years 1901–1904 were similar in all technical detail having 4.86 sq ft grates and 5 ft 8 ins long smoke tubes, although the last six had the boiler pressure increased to 175 PSI. No 2350 spent all its working life in South Wales and the Severn Valley. No 2351, 'Ephraim' similarly spent all its working life in Nottinghamshire and Derbyshire. No 2355, 'Lord Roberts' went new to W C & S Hancock for hauling and lighting their two wagon front Bioscope show and eventually passed to their former employee Fred Gray who renamed her 'Mons Star'. During the Second World War she was one of several Burrell engines engaged in demolishing Blitz damaged buildings in Central London and ended her days in Hardwick's yard.

No 2369 was the first of seven Burrell engines owned by the Murphy family of Newcastle-upon-Tyne. She was believed to be the first Burrell Showman's road locomotive to be fitted with 3-speed road gearing as illustrated in Fig 204. Thereafter the majority of Showman's engines were fitted with this highly successful 2-lever system. No 2379, 'Ich Dien' started its life with Edward Danter of Newport, Monmouthshire with his Venetian Gondolas and passed to various showland and commercial owners before being scrapped in the late 1940s. Similarly, No 2456 had a varied career. She was the third of seven Burrell engines to carry the name 'King Edward VII' starting life with the Norwich showman James Crighton and ending her days in commercial ownership in Birkenhead docks. No 2463 spent all her working life in the North East of England. She went new to Harry Caris of Stockton-on-Tees, then passed to H Powell a relation of the Murphy family of Newcastle and was a regular sight at the famous Town Moor fairs for many years. Later, she went successively to Raymond Stott, the Great Carmo of Shirley in Surrey; in 1932 she was acquired by Pat Collins, who restored her original name, 'Shamrock II'; and finally she passed to James W White & Sons of Glasgow.

No 2497, 'Excelsior' was supplied new to William Taylor of Ilkeston in Derbyshire for his famous Coliseum Bioscope show. Later, Taylor renamed the engine 'Alexandra' after his daughter who was one of the attractive Paraders on the show front. Eventually the engine was acquired by Albert Twigdon of Leicester. No 2631, another 'King Edward VII' went new to the Wadbrook & Scard partnership for their well known Bioscope show. For many years the engine was magnificently decorated with gold leaf scroll work which covered every inch of the boiler and tender. In 1914 she was acquired by Henry O'Brien of Gateshead who renamed her 'Willing'. No 2650 was supplied to Relph & Pedley of Northampton. In 1907 she was acquired by Pat Collins and renamed 'Mark Twain'. Following a runaway accident in 1924 Collins sold the engine to an Irish showman, John McGurk of Tramore, where she finished her working life.

No 2651, 'Challenger' was supplied new to Mrs Annie Holland, the widow of a West Country traveller in March 1904. Although later the family's headquarters were stated as Mile End, London, they quartered at Swadlincote, a mining town in South Derbyshire and travelled extensively throughout the Midland counties. Mrs Holland had six sons, all of whom became proprietors of popular attractions and they owned four Burrell and three Foster Showman's engines at various times. 'Challenger' was

Fig 209 No 2894 'Pride of Worcester' 8 NHP DCC Showman's type engine with double gearing to the hind axle. Supplied originally to H Strickland of Worcester in 1907.

used to haul and light their fine big double fronted Bioscope show known as 'Holland's Palace of Light'.

The next engine in the series, No 2668, 'Britannia', like 'Challenger' survives today in preservation. She was supplied new to William Thurston of Cambridge and initially worked with his Bioscope show. Later she hauled and provided electricity for his ex-Pat Collins Venetian Gondola switchback. She ended her working life with J H Manning of Stevenage in the 1940s. No 2709 went new to James Dooner, W C & S Hancocks' former Manager and later brother-in-law. He named the engine 'Mabon' after the famous Welsh miners' leader and travelled the Welsh mining valleys with an ornate long fronted Bioscope show assisted by a very talented and long remembered troupe of Paraders. In 1916 the engine was sold to Pat Collins who travelled her until she was finally scrapped. No 2713, 'Her Majesty' was supplied new to Pat Collins and for many years it hauled his wife, Flora's beautiful living van and her personal paraphernalia.

No 2716, 'The Showman' was the first Showman's type road locomotive acquired by the still renowned West Country firm, Anderton & Rowland. The partnership between 'Professor' Anderton, a menagerie proprietor and 'Captain' Arthur Rowland, a lion trainer was founded in 1899 and quickly prospered. About the time No 2716 was acquired the lions were sold and for a time they travelled a Bioscope show. In 1908 their manager, George De Vey later Anderton's son-in-law persuaded his employers to invest in their first big riding machine. They purchased a Savage built Venetian Gondola Switchback, built originally for John Studt of Cardiff and the firm thereafter went from strength to strength.

John Evans, a well known Edinburgh showman purchased No 2721 in February 1905 and named her 'Edinburgh Castle'. In 1940 after thirty-five years continuous service the rear axle failed and the engine was cut up for scrap on the roadside. No 2722 similarly spent all her working life with the Crow family of Middlesborough who named her 'Pride of the Road' and No 2723 went to James Leo of Preston. The story is told that the Burrell Hiring Company had difficulty in securing payment for the engine. When their representatives called to repossess the engine she could not be found. Eventually she was traced well hidden buried in a haystack. In 1908 the engine was resold to Marshall Hill and renamed 'Bristol City'. She remained in his service for thirty-four years.

Another of the great names in showland in South Wales was that of Edward Danter of Newport in Monmouthshire. He acquired No 2724, 'Greyhound' in 1905 for their new Bioscope show working in partnership with No 2379, 'Ich Dien'. In 1919 'Greyhound' was sold to the famous local heavy haulage contractors, Robert Wynn & Sons Ltd but in 1923 she returned to showland in the ownership of Tom Drakeley & Sons of Stechford, Birmingham and was renamed 'King of the Road'.

The next engine in the series, No 2733, 'Lily of the Valley' was illustrated in several editions of Burrell's General Catalogue. The reader will note the 3-speed gearing and the Pickering type governor which had now

Fig 210 No 3093 'Dreadnought' 8 NHP DCC Showman's type engine built for Hollands of Swadlincote in 1909 with large grate and long boiler. Crane tower fitted in 1920.

become more or less standard equipment. The rack mounted on the hornplates carrying the 'spuds' will also be noted in Fig 208. These were supplied on all traction engines and road locomotives with iron wheels and steel strakes. They comprised T-section shoes designed to slip over the hind wheel rims and were secured by bolts through holes drilled in the wheel periphery. On soft ground several 'spuds' were attached to each wheel and the compensating gear or differential was locked enabling the engine to move over otherwise impossible terrain. Often they were used also for slipping a road train round sharp bends or when pulling into narrow gateways without uncoupling the train. In icy conditions some operators fixed steel spikes into the 'spud' bolt holes often with disasterous consequences to the road surface.

No 2733 was supplied new to Harris Brothers of Cuckfield in Sussex. Their father John was originally a timber merchant and he entered showland in the 1880s with a set of steam Switchbacks. He and his brother Fred at one time owned the first of the diminutive 'R' type 4 NHP traction engines, No 1082, but it seems unlikely this engine ever worked in showland. In 1907 the engine was sold to Smith Brothers of Walsall and in 1930 it was acquired by Pat Collins with whom she spent the remainder of her working life.

The Doncaster showman, Enoch Farrar took delivery of No 2740 'Enoch Clifford', named after his son, in June 1905 for their No 1 Bioscope show. In 1911 the engine was sold to John Hobson of Barnsley with whom she remained for thirty years. No 2759 'Sir Colin Campbell' went new to J Hibbert of Stockport, but within twelve months it was repossessed by Burrells. After thirty years in commercial ownership the engine returned to showland in 1936 in the ownership of H Jones & Sons of St Blazey in Cornwall who later named her 'King George VI'. In 1942 the engine was sold to Mrs J Beach & Sons of Maidenhead and eventually about 1950 she ended her days in Hardwick's scrap yard.

No further engines of this type were built until February 1907 when No 2877 'His Majesty' was delivered to the West Country showman, Charles Heal & Sons. She had double gearing to the hind axle with short travel spring gear as did all the remaining engines in this series. She was fitted with extra deep belly tanks and carried a large double ended Scenic type dynamo, the dynamo bracket being adorned by an elaborate cast brass nameplate. No 2894 went to H Strickland & Sons of Worcester in March 1907 and was named 'Pride of Worcester' travelling with their Bioscope show. In 1935 she was sold to Arnold Brothers of Southampton and later renamed 'Edward VIII'. In 1942 she went to Elias Harris of Hook in Surrey. Harris was young Pat Collins' son-in-law and he travelled the engine until 1948. After a spell in Hardwick's yard the engine was saved from the breaker's torch and purchased by Miss Sally Beach who renamed her 'Lord Fisher', the name previously carried by her Burrell No 3694. Fortunately, the engine survives today in preservation.

No 2898 went new to William Taylor of Ilkestone in Derbyshire who is probably best remembered for his magnificent 'Coliseum' Bioscope show. At this time

Fig 211 Alderman G T Tuby's 8 NHP DCC Showman's engine No 3163 'Doncaster' shortly after being fitted with an auxiliary dynamo at St Nicholas Works.

trumpet barrel organs were being replaced by bigger more spectacular types of paper organ and the huge Gavioli and Marenghi instruments becme very popular attractions in themselves. In 1915 the engine was sold to John Cole of Bristol and passed to John Evans of Edinburgh in 1920 who renamed her 'King Cole'. In 1926 she went to Frank McConville of West Hartlepool and was renamed 'King Carnival' and in 1941 she passed to her final showland owner, C Culine of Durham. In August 1907 Enoch Farrar took delivery of No 2917 for his No 2 Bioscope show. In 1911 the engine was sold to Goldthorpe Marshall of Keighley in Yorkshire who renamed her 'The Ideal'. Four years later she was again sold to Harry Dawson of Dundee but returned to Yorkshire in 1922 in the ownership of Sam Crow of Middlesborough.

No 2979, 'Reliance' was delivered to Relph & Pedley of Northampton in March 1908 for their new and then unique set of Flying Pigs. When only three months old the engine towing two living vans and a wagon ran down a rocky embankment into Thirlemere Lake in the Lake District killing the driver. Miraculously, the towing bar between the engine and living van snapped, otherwise the loss of life would undoubtedly have been greater. The engine finished upside down in the water and had to be completely dismantled on the lakeside before it could be returned to Thetford for repairs. It re-emerged in November 1909 re-numbered No 3038 and named 'The Prince' in the ownership of Ruben Holdsworth who was associated with Relph & Pedley and travelled with the Flying Pigs ride until they were laid up in 1934.

No 2983 'Lady Violet' was one of the few engines which spent the whole of her working life with one owner. In 1908 she was supplied to James Crighton who operated from both Norwich and Birkenhead and was used initially with his beautifully decorated Bioscope show.

No 2988, 'The Mascot' was supplied new to John Proctor of Belper in Derbyshire for his Bioscope show. It had the long boiler with 6 ft 2 ins long smoke tubes and 4 ft 0 ins long connecting rods. When the show went off the road the engine was sold to Pat Collins who had her converted locally to the Scenic specification. The auxiliary dynamo guide rails were mounted directly on top of the long boiler dispensing with the usual raised platform and a crane post was added to the rear of the tender. This was of the 'Feast' type and was made up from a Savage hand operated crane. In 1918 the engine was sold to Harniess Brothers of Worksop for their Velvet Coaster Scenic. Later the ride was transferred to their manager, William Starr and the engine finished her working days in his ownership.

No 3015, 'Perseverance' went new to A H Faulkner of Leigh in Lancashire for his Bioscope show and ended her days with the Glasgow traveller, George Wilmot. No 3072, 'Shakespeare' like so many of this class of engine was supplied originally for lighting and hauling their big double fronted Bisocope show. She went new to the Wadbrook & Scard partnership in London. Henry Scard was Wadbrook's son-in-law and he had spent his early life as a groom with Bostock & Wombwell's famous Menagerie. The partnership purchased the second Bioscope Show to reach this country and the climax of its very successful career was being invited to Balmoral Castle to demonstrate the projector to Queen Victoria.

Unfortunately in 1917 the show was destroyed by fire and the engine was sold to J Hoadley of Newcastle-upon-Tyne. In 1923 she was sold to John Evans of Edinburgh but reverted to Hoadley's ownership in 1928. During the Second World War she went to J G Gray of Gateshead for his Noah's Ark, finally ending her days with F B Manders whose winter quarters were also in Gateshead.

Fig 212 No 3285 'King George V' built in 1911 and converted to a Special Scenic type engine in 1920 photographed in preservation in the 1960s.

No 3075, 'Alexandra' and No 3200, 'Unity' were both supplied new to Charles Thurston of Norwich. Unlike the majority of their contemporaries they were 2-speed engines and they spent all their working lives together in East Anglia. When Thurstons' two very ornate Bioscope shows were replaced by the permanent cinema during the First World War the engines were employed with their famous steam driven Gondola Switchback ride built by Tidman's of Norwich and then owned by John Thurston based in Colchester.

We are now approaching the age of the big Scenic Railway rides,which one might say with every justification revolutionised the fairground scene. The last five engines in this series all had 6.6 sq ft grates and long boilers and were eminently suitable for adapting to what became known as the Scenic type engine. No 3093, 'Dreadnought' spent all her working life with Hollands of Swadlincote until acquired for preservation in 1952. Initially, she provided lights for the ex-Twigdon 'Wonderland' Bioscope show, then she assisted with their first big Scenic ride purchased in 1913. In 1920 the engine was returned to St Nicholas Works for overhaul and fitted with tender mounted crane horns. There is no evidence that she ever carried an auxiliary dynamo platform and therefore remained what one might term a half Scenic.

Fig 213 No 3443 'Lord Nelson'. Built originally for Anderton & Rowland in 1913, tender mounted crane horns fitted 1921. The engine today forms part of the National Motor Museum collection at Beaulieu in Hampshire.

In February 1910 Alderman George Thomas Tuby took delivery of No 3163 which he named 'Doncaster' after his much loved native town. Originally the engine was employed with his Switchback ride known as 'Tuby's 60 HP Panhard Motors' but in 1912 he acquired one of Savage's early Scenic Railways. 'Doncaster' was returned to Thetford for fitting an auxiliary dynamo platform and an exciter dynamo. In 1921 it was again returned to the works for fitting a tender mounted jib crane.

Abbott & Barker of Norwich took delivery of No 3285 in March 1911 and named her 'King George V' to mark the accession of the new King. In order to minimise the weight of the engine the flywheel was a spoked pattern covered with a sheet metal disc and the belly tanks were reduced in size, holding only 138 gallons. The engine weighed only 12 tons 18 cwt in working order.

When Abbott & Barker's Motor Switchback was sold to Anderton & Rowland after the First World War No 3285 was returned to the works for fitting an auxiliary dynamo platform and crane horns. This coincided with the rebuilding of their old Switchback to an all electric Scenic ride. Formerly the Switchback had been driven by the famous Savage traction centre engine 'Empress' and thereafter King George V accompanied the rebuilt ride until it was broken up in 1930. The engine was then sold to Swales Forrest a London traveller for his ex-Jacob Studt standing top Gondola Switchback. This ride was destroyed by fire in 1937 but fortunately the engine survives today in preservation.

No 3443, the penultimate engine in this series and the last built before the 1914–18 War went new to Anderton & Rowland. The story is told that at this time they were having a difficult time financially and they decided to christen the engine 'Lord Nelson' on the basis that Nelson once saved England and it was hoped that this new engine carrying the same name would change the fortunes of the firm. In 1921 the works converted the engine to a half scenic and fitted tender mounted crane horns. The dynamo platform was also lengthened to 4 ft 0 ins to accommodate a big Mawdsley dynamo. Today the engine occupies a central position in the National Motor Museum at Beaulieu.

Finally we must consider No 3967, which strictly speaking was built as a road haulage engine for H J Warner Ltd of Twyford in Berkshire in 1923. They named her 'Morning Star' and within a comparatively short space of time the engine was acquired by Charles Openshaw of Reading who converted her to a full Showman's type engine complete with tender mounted crane horns. In 1927 the engine was purchased by Jacob Studt Jr then based at Witney in Oxfordshire as a replacement for his big Fowler engine 'Excelsior' which had come to grief in a runaway accident on Birdlip Hill in Gloucestershire. Studt owned 'Morning Star' for sixteen years and travelled extensively between the London area and South Wales. The engine then went sucessively to William Barker of Hayes in Middlesex and J Manning of Enfield, sadly ending her days in Hardwick's yard.

In February 1911 the first of fifty 8 NHP Showman's road locomotives with 6¾ ins dia × 11¼ ins dia × 12 ins stroke double crank compound cylinders left St Nicholas

Works. They undoubtedly represented the very pinnacle of the firm's many achievements during the 75 years since Charles Burrell took over the business. After 1920 most were built as 'special scenic' type engines and the majority of those built prior to that date were subsequently converted to the Scenic specification. Any showman owning a Scenic Railway ride and a Burrell Scenic type engine was regarded as being at the peak of his profession.

8 NHP DCC SHOWMAN'S ROAD LOCOMOTIVE WITH 6¾ ins × 11¼ ins × 12 ins STROKE CYLINDERS

Engine No	Date Built	Engine Name	Original Owner
3272	1911	King George V	T Clarke
3273	1911	Queen Mary	T Clarke
3277	1911	King George V	Hill Bros
*3279	1911	Prince Albert	Jacob Studt
3284	1911	St Leger/Alderman	G T Tuby
*3291	1911	Emperor	Pat Collins
3302	1911	John Bull	Charles Thurston
3334	1911	The Baillie	George Green
*3371	1912	Lord George	Jacob Studt
3372	1912	Norah	G T Tuby
3404	1912	Kathleen Mary	Aspland & Howden
*3441	1913	William IV	Wm Murphy
3444	1913	His Lordship	Green Bros
3447	1913	The Jack Whyatt	Pat Collins
3450	1913	Always Ready	John Murphy
3470	1912	The Hope	O & E Gamble
*3483	1913	Perseverance II	Harniess Bros
**3547	1914	Amy	Escors, Wm Murphy
3561	1914	Fearnought	E Danter
3579	1914	Monarch	Jacob Studt
3590	1914	Kitchener	John Collins
*3599	1914	Earl Kitchener	H Studt
3610	1914	William V	Wm Murphy
*3659	1915	Lord Kitchener	O'Brien Bros
3715	1916	City of Cardiff	White Bros
3724	1916	Victory	Holland Bros
3787	1918	Thomas William	Goldthorpe Marshall
**3827	1920	Victory	Charles Thurston
3833	1920	Queen Mary	Alf Payne
**3840	1920	Queen Elizabeth	John Wilmot
**3865	1920	No 1	Pat Collins
**3866	1920	Vanguard	Marshall Hill
**3872	1921	Hero	John Caris & Sons
**3879	1921	Jack	John Proctor
**3884	1921	I Wonder	Fred Gray
3885	1921	The Alderman/The Mayor	G T Tuby
**3886	1921	Lord Lascelles	H Gray
**3887	1922	The Prince of Wales	Hy Jennings
**3888	1921	General Gough	Swales Bolesworth
**3896	1921	Earl Beatty	Anderton & Rowland
**3909	1922	Pride of the Road	A Holland
**3912	1921	Dragon	Anderton & Rowland
3932	1922	Mona	F Warren
**3936	1922	Renown	E Danter
**3938	1922	Quo Vadis	Wm Wilson
**3948	1923	John Bull	H Studt
3949	1923	Princess Mary	Wm Nichols
**4021	1925	The Dolphin/The Whale/Lord Curzon	Harry Hall
4039	1926	[A Crane Road Loco – See Chapter 18]	
4092	1930	Simplicity	A Deakin & Sons

* Subsequently converted to Scenic type engines with car lifting crane.

** Built new as Scenic type engines.

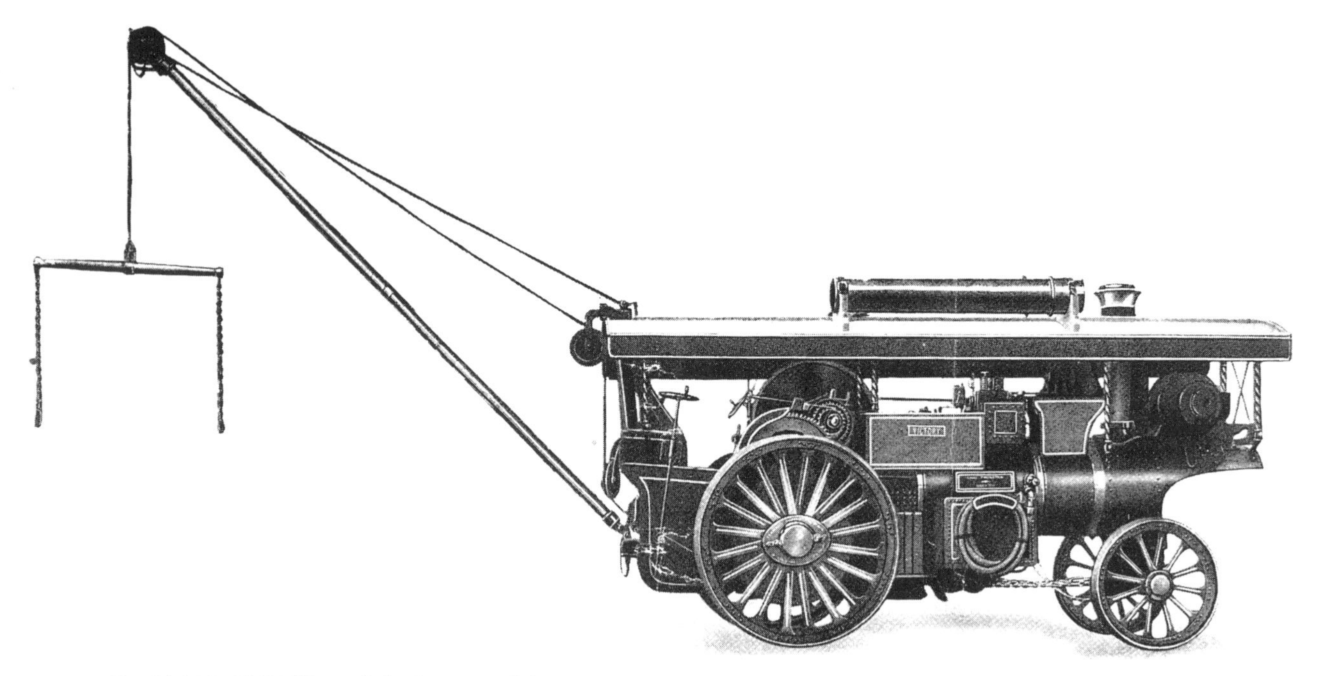

Fig 214 No 3827 'Victory' the first Burrell Special Scenic engine showing the car lifting crane in position, the tender mounted crane horns and the boiler mounted auxiliary dynamo platform. Built in 1920.

These splendid engines all had 2 ft 6 ins dia boilers pressed to 200 PSI and hydraulically tested to 400 PSI with 6.6 sq ft grates. All except five had the long pattern boilers with 6 ft 2 ins long smoke tubes enabling 4 ft 0 ins long connecting rods to be used. The exceptions were Nos 3334, 3372, 3470, 3833 and 3949 which had 5 ft 8 ins long smoke tubes and 3 ft 6 ins long connecting rods. Forty 2 ins dia smoke tubes were fitted to all except Nos 3341 and 3547 which had thirty-five 2 ins dia tubes and additional longitudinal stay tubes. The long boilers had a total heating surface of 162.0 sq ft of which 37.7 sq ft was derived from the firebox and the short boilers had a total heating surface of 151.7 sq ft. Engine Nos 3334, 3441, 3444, 3450, 3547, 3715 and 3787 had extended smokeboxes fitted with liners and the German pattern spark arrester, but one suspects these were short-lived. The engines had a reputation for steaming extremely well and had a hauling capacity of 40 tons on a 1 in 18 incline. The indicated horse power was given as 54 IHP.

Most had hind wheels 6 ft 6 ins dia × 22 ins wide with 3-speed gearing through the robust spring mounted double geared transmission shafting. The two-lever three-speed gear change mechanism gave ratios of 24.4 to 1 slow speed; 13.6 to 1 intermediate speed; and 8.3 to 1 fast speed. By 1911 all gears fitted to Burrell engines were of cast steel, but after 1922 special machine cut gears were used on these engines. Most were fitted with the patent differential locking gear operated from the footplate and the winding drums carried 75 yds of best quality steel wire rope. The solid pattern flywheels were 4 ft 6 ins dia × 8 ins wide it being generally reckoned that 6 HP could be transmitted to the dynamo by each inch width of the driving belt used. Screw-down brakes were fitted to both the hind wheels and thc flywheel rims. The overall length of the long boiler engines was 22 ft 3 ins and the overall width of the engines with 22 ins wide wheels was 8 ft 8½ ins. Their overall weight in working order was 15 tons. The tender bunker carried 8 cwt of coal and the water carrying capacity was 345 gallons, sufficient for travelling 12–16 miles with loads without rewatering.

Most engines had mechanical feed pumps and one or two injectors. A new type of geared feed pump was fitted to No 3279 and in 1921 this feature became standard equipment. All had Pickering type governors which were usually set to operate at 155 RPM when working on the belt. All had long full length awnings with twisted brass canopy supports and unless otherwise specified by the customer they were painted Lake with yellow wheels.

In February 1914 No 3547 was built complete with an auxiliary dynamo platform mounted behind the chimney and a Savage tender mounted post crane suitable for lifting the Scenic Railway cars. However, six years elapsed before No 3827, 'Victory' emerged from St Nicholas Works with an auxiliary dynamo platform and a new Burrell designed tender mounted crane. It comprised an upwards extension of the coal bunker to form the crane horns on top of which was mounted a cast bracket approximately at canopy level. This bracket incorporated a swivel from which the 21 ft long crane jib and the top pulley for the lifting rope was suspended. When erected the jib was at 45 degrees to the vertical giving a working radius of 16 ft and movement through an arc of 180 degrees. with a load up to 35 cwt. The arrangement which could, of course, only be used when the engine was stationary is clearly illustrated in Fig 214. Thereafter, engines incorporating both an auxiliary dynamo platform and crane horns became known as 'special scenic engines'. Several engines built prior to 'Victory' were subsequently converted and most of the large Showman's cngine built after 1920 incorporated these features.

The majority of Scenic engines were supplied with Mather & Platt main and auxiliary exciter dynamos. The

Fig 215 No 3272 'King George V' one of a fine pair of 8 NHP Showman's engines with 6¾" × 11¼" × 12" stroke DCC cylinders supplied to Tom Clarke of Kidderminster in 1911.

main dynamo, type P8C was a 29.7 KW compound-wound 4-pole/4 interpole externally excited machine and the auxilary dynamo, type P3C was an 8.8 KW compound-wound machine belt driven from the commutator end of the main dynamo. The general specification of the electrical machines was as follows:

	Main P8C	Auxiliary P3C
Voltage	110	110
Output (amperes)	270	80
Speed (RPM)	750	1350
Driving pulley dia (ins)	12	7
Approx weight (cwts)	17	5

The system of control used on the big Scenic rides in 1920 was known as the Ward-Leonard system. This enabled the power output from the main generator to be varied from zero when the ride was stationary to full load when it was starting up and accelerating, by reducing or increasing the current creating the magnetic field in the main generator with current supplied from an auxiliary machine passing through a potentiometer type regulator. The control gear also enabled the Scenic Cars to 'creep' at very slow speed, giving the passengers the opportunity and added thrill of boarding or leaving the cars without bringing them to a complete standstill. A further device gave automatic control from slow to full speed at a predetermined rate. The excitation load on the auxiliary dynamo was of the order of 1 KW and could be used also to supply current for lights and organ.

Both No 3272, 'King George V' and No 3273 'Queen Mary' went new to Tom Clarke of Kidderminster spending all their working lives with his Scenic Motors. In 1931 following Charles' death, both the engines and the ride went to his step-son, Frank Wilson. It is reputed that the engines cost £1750 each when new. No 3272 is illustrated in Fig 215. It will be noted that the belly tank mounted water lift with 40 ft of lifting hose incorporated a branch connection which was very useful when filling the 'Water Dandy' or other external vessels.

No 3277 also named 'King George V' was supplied new to Hill Brothers of Bedminster, Bristol for their early Savage built Scenic Railway. Originally the engine was fitted with a soda water starter, an early device for coping with the heavy electrical load when starting the ride from rest, which had the reputation of making the flywheel belt jump violently. Before delivery to Hill Brothers the engine was displayed at the 1920 Lynn Mart Fair. It had become customary for Burrells to send an example of their latest production to this great fair each year just as agricultural engines were exhibited at Smithfield and the great RASE Shows. In 1941 the engine was purchased by Jennings Brothers of Devizes, ending its working life with J Stokes of Southampton. After some years in Hardwick's yard at West Ewell it is believed that the engine was sold abroad to an unknown destination.

In February 1911 Jacob Studt took delivery of the third Scenic Railway ride manufactured by Savage and Burrell engine No 3279 'Prince Albert'. They made their first public appearance at Lynn Mart Fair together with Enoch Farrar's 1910 Scenic Railway and Pat Collins converted Scenic ride referred to earlier, providing the people of Kings Lynn with a never to be forgotten spectacle. In 1920 the engine was returned to the works and fitted with an auxiliary dynamo platform and tender crane horns.

Three of the engines in the series, Nos 3284, 'St Leger', 3372, 'Norah' and 3885, 'The Mayor' were supplied new to the indefatigable Doncaster showman, George Thomas Tuby. No 3284 was renamed 'The Alderman' in 1925 when Tuby was elevated to aldermanic rank. No 3372 was named after his daughter Norah and was said to be his favourite engine. Originally it was ordered by Pat Collins but he refused to wait for delivery when Burrells decided

Fig 216 No 3291 'Emperor' built for Pat Collins in 1911 and experimentally fitted with a Hans Reynolds chain drive from the flywheel to the dynamo photographed in St Nicholas Works yard.

to exhibit the engine at the 1912 RASE Show. Tuby had the engine repainted Great Eastern Railway royal blue with yellow wheels to match his other engines and later had an auxiliary dynamo fitted. The engine was driven by George Power for most of its working life.

No 3291 'Emperor' delivered new to Pat Collins in May 1911 was fitted experimentally with a Hans Reynold chain drive from the flywheel to the special Boothroyd dynamo as illustrated in Fig 216. It was fitted at Savage's suggestion in an attempt to overcome increasing problems with the

Fig 217 No 3334 'The Baille' built for George Green of Glasgow in 1911 and passing eventually to Silcock Bros of Warrington photographed in preservation.

Fig 218 The ex-William Murphy 8 NHP DCC Showman's engine No 3441 'William IV' photographed in the 1930s when in the ownership of Anderton & Rowlands.

Fig 219 No 3610 'William V' 8 NHP DCC Showman's engine originally supplied to William Murphy of Newcastle-upon-Tyne photographed at a traction engine rally in the 1960s.

conventional leather belt as electrical starting loads increased with the new Switchback and Scenic rides. The experiment was not a success and the chain drive was abondoned after a few months. 'Emperor' was the second engine to be fitted with a geared boiler feed pump and additionally it had two White's type injectors.

Eventually Collins converted the engine to the Scenic specification and fitted an auxiliary dynamo platform and a 'Feast' post-type car lifting crane. In 1925 it was sold to the John Collins concern in Liverpool passing in 1932 to Michael Albert Collins based in Manchester, eventually ending her days in commercial ownership in Lancashire.

No 3302 'John Bull' was the fifth new Showman's type engine supplied to Charles Thurston of Norwich. She was never converted to the Scenic specification but after a period in the ownership of John Parker of Ipswich she was acquired by Savages of Kings Lynn. They used her in the works yard for testing new rides built at the St Nicholas Iron Works until the outbreak of war in 1939. No 3334 'The Baille' and No 3444 'His Lordship' started their working lives in Scotland with George Green of Glasgow. When Green gave up travelling at the beginning of the First World War, 'The Baille' and his 7 NHP Burrell Showman's engine went to H Bradley, also of Glasgow. At the same time No 3444 'His Lordship' and his other 7 NHP Burrell, No 3089 'His Majesty' went to his brother John, the father of the popular Green Brothers of Preston in Lancashire. Both the 8 NHP engines were eventually acquired by Silcock Brothers of Warrington. Neither engine was ever converted to the Scenic specification and both engines were fitted with Simkin, Wilkinson & Gibson dynamos. No 3334 survives today in preservation in Lincolnshire and No 3444 ended her days in the ownership of Tom Alberts of Bolton.

No 3371 'Lord George' delivered new to Jacob Studt in March 1912 was one of the first long boilered engines to be converted to the Scenic specification in 1915 and remained with the Studt family and their Scenic ride until 1940. After a period with S Mayne of Earlsfield in London she was sold to an Irish buyer and all trace of her has been lost. In later life when solid rubber tyres became mandatory 'Lord George' was fitted with pneumatic tyres on the front axle giving her an unusual and distinctive appearance.

Both No 3441 'William IV' and No 3610 'William V' went new to William Murphy of Newcastle-upon-Tyne and spent many years providing power and lights for his Scenic Motors. Both engines were built with auxiliary dynamo platforms, but these were never used, nor were car lifting cranes ever fitted. In 1934 'William IV' was sold to Anderton & Rowland and attended Captain Rowland's Dodgems for many years. During the 1946 Redruth Fair the engine seized up and was left in J & F Pool's yard in Hayle; some months later she was cut up on the spot. In 1933 'William V' was sold to Sam Ingham of Hyde, near Manchester. Following a short period with another Manchester traveller, H Royle, she passed into commercial ownership. The engine survives today in preservation.

No 3447 was the last Burrell engine acquired by the Pat Collins firm before the First World War for their No 2 Switchback and they named the engine 'The Jack Whyatt' after the manager of the show. It was fitted with an auxiliary dynamo platform at the works but it never carried a car lifting crane. After the war the engine was sold firstly to George Wilkie of New Brighton and then to John Evans of Edinburgh who renamed it 'Stirling Castle'.

No 3450 'Always Ready' spent all its working life in the North East firstly with John Murphy of Newcastle-upon-Tyne and then, in 1925, with A Newsome of Darlington. She too was fitted with an auxilary dynamo platform and was specially prepared to take a 'Feast' type crane post for handling Murphy's Steam Motors. No 3470 'The Hope' had the short type boiler with 5 ft 8 ins smoke tubes and never carried any Scenic additions. She was supplied new to O & F Gamble of Glasgow and then in 1915 went south to the O'Brien Brothers of Winchester for the remainder of her working life.

Harniess Brothers, the South Yorkshire travellers took delivery of their fourth Burrell engine, No 3483 'Perseverance the Second' in June 1913 for their Savage built 'Little Wonder Scenic'. The Burrell and a Fowler

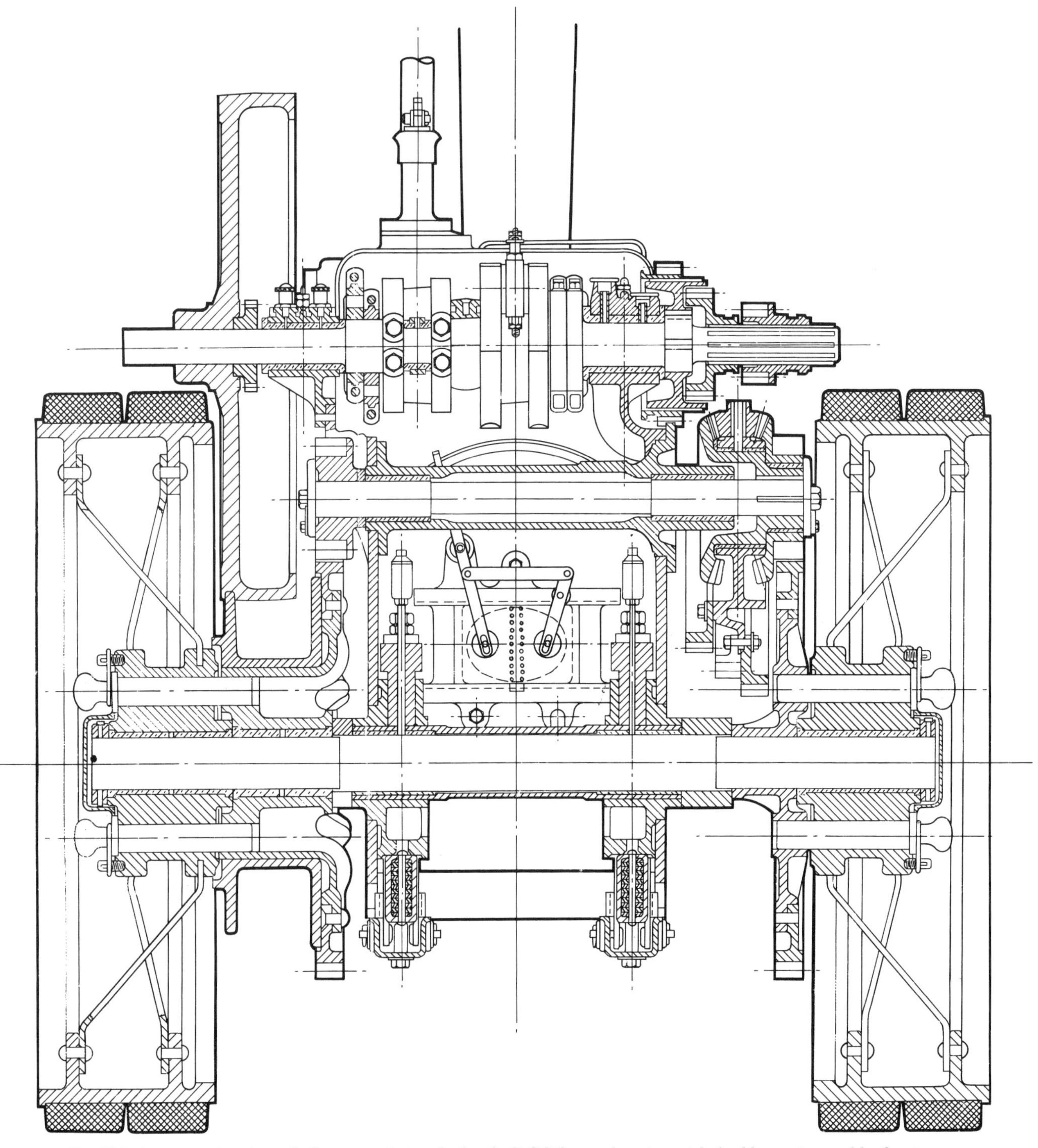

Fig 220 A cross section through the transmission shafts of a DCC 3-speed engine with double gearing and leaf spring gear on the hind axle and the compensating gear on the intermediate motion shaft.

engine 'Enterprise' attended the ride for many years, 'Perseverance' providing the electrical power for the Scenic cars and the organ; 'Enterprise' providing the lighting. As built 'Perseverance' had an auxiliary dynamo platform and was prepared for but never fitted with a post type crane. In the 1920s Burrell built crane horns were added to the tender. Eventually the engine was sold to Mrs John Cole of Chichester for her Savage built spinning top steam Switchback. The engine survives today in preservation.

No 3547, 'Amy', renamed 'Tucker' in 1925 was the first engine built at St Nicholas Works complete with an auxiliary dynamo platform and a Savage patent post-type car lifting crane. In the 1920s this was replaced by Burrell crane horns. She was one of several engines fitted with a 5 ft 5 ins long dynamo platform to carry the Baxendale P4A and P9A dynamos and had a large hinged door in the canopy roof to facilitate lifting the dynamo. Like most of the engines of this class built subsequently she had the long boiler and 3 ft 6 ins long connecting rods and was

Fig 221 No 3827 'Victory', the first Burrell built new as a Special Scenic engine in 1920. Photographed after restoration in Mr George Cushing's splendid collection.

fitted additionally with a lengthened smokebox and the German type spark arrester. Originally she was registered in the names of the Escors of Walter Murphy, passing to J W Murphy and then to Mrs W Murphy. The engine always attended their Scenic ride which was a converted steam Switchback with jungle scenery, a waterfall and a fine large 110-key Marenghi organ. Finally the engine went to John Powell of Jarrow, a relative of the Murphy family. The canopy sideboards continued to carry the inscription, 'Walter Murphy's New Jungle Railway'.

No 3561, 'Fearnought' spent all its working life with Edward Danter's Scenic Motors. In 1923 the Motor Cars were replaced by Peacocks and the ride continued to travel the South Wales, Gloucestershire and Herefordshire fairs until the late 1930s. She carried an auxilairy dynamo platform and Baxendale dynamos but never had a car lifting crane. No 3579 went new to Jacob Studt Junior in July 1914 and retained the name 'Monarch' used on their original 1889 engine. Concurrently, Studt acquired a new Savage built Scenic ride and the engine and ride travelled together until the Second World War. The engine was then sold to Reuben Gillham of Southampton then trading as Gillham & Adlam, with whom she ended her working days. She was one of the few big Showman's engines having a spoked flywheel with a disc cover. The steam chest covers were lagged and fitted with large engraved brass plates and she was one of the few Showman's engines to use a Westinghouse dynamo. No 3590 'Kitchener' was a similar engine and went new to John Collins of Liverpool for his Orton & Spooner built Scenic Motors. When the ride was packed away in the 1930s the engine was sold to Edward Danter. Neither No 3579 nor 3590 ever carried car lifting cranes.

The Swansea branch of the Studt family purchased No 3599 in June 1914 for their Scenic ride. After Henry Studt's death the engine passed to his son-in-law, Vic Tuson. During the First World War it was named 'Earl Kitchener' after the famous wartime army commander. It incorporated several special features including a forward roping pulley mounted on the side of the smokebox just below the chimney base. The steam chest covers were lagged and covered with brass cleading on which was embossed the Welsh Dragon. The hind wheels were 6 ft 9 ins dia × 20 ins wide and the forecarriage was of the fabricated plate type. In 1921 it was converted to a full Scenic type engine with an auxiliary dynamo platform and crane horns.

No 3659 purchased by the O'Brien Brothers of Winchester in 1915 had a similar career. She too was named 'Lord Kitchener' and spent all her twenty-four

Fig 222 No 3865 'No 1', the last big 8 NHP Special Scenic engine supplied to the redoubtable Pat Collins concern in 1920.

years working life with this family, firstly with their Gondola Switchback and later with their ex-Dagnall's Dragon Scenic ride purchased shortly after the war. She was converted to a full Scenic engine and fitted with an auxiliary dynamo platform and crane horns at this time. In the late 1930s she was scrapped in Hardwick's yard. The next engine in the series, No 3715, 'City of Cardiff' was purchased by the White Brothers in 1916. The three brothers, William, George and Tom, sons of a well known Victorian showman, Sidney White were renowned in South Wales for the superb condition of their rides, organs and transport. They owned one of the earliest Dragon Scenic rides which appeared at Olympia for several seasons and was always accorded pride of placed at the Stratford-upon-Avon Mop fairs. On one occassion it was taken over to Paris where it was enthusiastically received. The engine was fitted with Mather & Platt type P9A and type P4A dynamos but it was never fitted with a car lifting crane.

The second Showman's engine to be completed at the height of the Great War was No 3724 and appropriately named 'Victory'. It spent all its working life with Hollands of Swadlincote with their Scenic Motor Car ride. In common with contemporary fashion in the fairground the Motor Cars were eventually replaced by Whale cars. After the Second World War both Holland's Scenic rides were purchased by Butlins and permanently erected at their seaside holiday camps.

No 3787 went new to Goldthrope Marshall of Keighley in Yorkshire for his Scenic Motor Cars. Originally the ride was a Gondola Switchback; in 1906 the Gondola cars were replaced by Motor cars; and in 1912 the ride was converted to an electric Scenic ride. Finally in 1923 Peacocks replaced the Motor Cars. The engine was named 'Thomas William' after William Marshall who managed the ride until it was sold in 1930. The engine was simultaneously sold to Walter Shaw & Sons of Sheffield, who renamed it 'Her Majesty'. Shortly before the Second War the engine was again sold to Wall Brothers of Petersfield and then after a short period with Dan Baker of Hook in Hampshire in the 1940s it was retired to Hardwick's yard. 'Thomas William' carried an auxiliary dynamo, but never carried a car lifting crane.

The next engine in the series, No 3827, 'Victory' completed in May 1920 marked a milestone in the history of St Nicholas Works for as already mentioned it was the first 'Special Scenic Engine' built new with both an auxiliary dynamo platform and tender mounted crane horns. Supplied new to Charles Thurston of Norwich for his new Orton & Spooner built Golden Dragon Scenic ride it remained with this celebrated traveller until he replaced steam by diesel traction in the late 1930s. Today the engine is beautifully restored in Mr George Cushing's Norfolk collection.

The works engine register, Book No 25, page 162, lists the following distinctive features of this splendid engine.

"Long awning on 8 twisted brass supports (DWGS 4993/5001/5067); Plate coal rack 12 ins deep; plain brass extension tubes from safety valves; brass segmental nameplate on front of main dynamo platform; platform for main dynamo (DWG 4976);

Fig 223 No 3912 'Dragon' 8 NHP Special Scenic engine supplied new to Anderton & Rowland in 1921.

platform for auxiliary dynamo (DWG 5009); Mather & Platt type P8C and P3C dynamos supplied by Davenport & Hackett; sheet iron guard between chimney and main dynamo; brass band round boiler next to smokebox; clutch gear to lock compensating gear (DWG 3437); Wrought iron exhaust pipe in two parts to facilitate removal; rear jib crane and crane horns for lifting Scenic Railway cars (DWG 5026–9); ring on smokebox door 'The Burrell Road Locomotive'; type 282 lubricators for large ends of connecting rods; and AGE monograms on belly tanks, on axle caps, on centre of smokebox door and on steam chest covers."

No 3833, 'Queen Mary' also completed in May 1920 was similar in all respects to 'Victory' except that she never carried any Scenic specification additions and carried only a big Mather & Platt type P7C dynamo. She went new to Alf Payne of York for his splendid four-abreast Gallopers. In 1923, the engine together with Payne's big DCC 'Contractors' type Showman's engine No 2804 'White Rose of York' and the ride were sold to Anderton & Rowlands. It is said that the two engines complete with loads made the mammoth journey to Babbacombe within a week. In 1943 'Queen Mary' was sold to Mrs Symonds of Gloucester and fortunately survives today in preservation.

In August 1920 the controlling interest in Charles Burrell & Sons Ltd was acquired by Agricultural & General Engineers Ltd. A fuller account of this ill-fated takeover is given in Chapter 18, but No 3840 was the second engine despatched from St Nicholas Works carrying the AGE monogram. She was built new with crane horns but an auxiliary dynamo platform was not fitted until 1921. The engine sold through the Burrell Hiring Company went new to Mrs John Wilmot of Glasgow, the widow of 'The father of Scottish Showland' for their Switchback ride, but within six months it was sold to J Green & Sons of Preston for their Golden Dragon Scenic. Green's named the engine 'Queen Elizabeth' and returned her to Thetford for conversion to a 'Special Scenic Engine'. After nearly thirty years continuous hard work she was finally cut up in the late 1940s.

No 3865, 'No 1' was purchased in November 1920 by Pat Collins for his Scenic Whales which were managed by Miss Clara Mullett who eventually became his second wife. Like its predecessor 'Queen Elizabeth' it was built with crane horns but was not given an auxiliary dynamo platform until Collins acquired No 4021, 'Lord Curzon' from Harry Hall in the 1930s. 'No 1' was always prominent at the famous Aston Onion fairs and at the Nottingham Goose Fair and participated at the great Battersea Park fun-fair during the Festival of Britain celebrations in 1951. She was said to have been the last 'Special Scenic' type engine seen working the fairground and remained in Collins' ownership until the 1970s.

No 3066 'Vanguard' was built as a 'Special Scenic' engine for Marshall Hill in December 1920 for his Savage built Scenic Railway. This ride was the second Scenic built by Savages in 1910 and had the distinction of being the first ever to be seen in the London area. Marshall died in 1927 and the engine and ride were travelled by his widow until 1930. His sons then had the ride rebuilt by Orton & Spooner who fitted a new front with tropical roundings and

Fig 224 Anderton & Rowlands' No 3896 'Earl Beatty' at work lifting the heavy Scenic Railway cars onto the ride's undulating track during erection.

Dolphin cars. The engine finished its working life in the ownership of Marshall Hill's grandson in 1952 and was cut up. No 3872 'Hero' was also built new as a special scenic engine for John Caris & Sons of Newcastle-upon-Tyne for their Gondola Switchback, although the works never supplied a crane jib with the engine. In 1931 she was acquired by Sam Crow of Middlesborough and spent the rest of her useful life in his ownership.

In 1921 Charles Burrell demonstrated special Scenic engine No 3879 'Jack' at the February Lynn Mart fair prior to delivery to John Proctor of Belper. He ordered the engine for his No 2 Scenic ride, a magnificent set of Peacocks, which thereafter always held pride of place at the Nottingham Goose Fair until withdrawn in the mid 1930s. An identical special Scenic engine No 3884 with the cryptic name, 'I Wonder' went new to Fred Gray of Hampstead a month later for his new Scenic Motors. Subsequently the engine was renamed 'Gladiator' and it extensively travelled the London fairs until the 1950s.

No 3886 'Lord Lascelles' went new to Harry Gray of Battersea and she too spent all her showland life in the London area, mostly with his large four-abreast Gallopers. Gray never owned a Scenic ride and the engine was ordered without crane horns, although an auxiliary dynamo platform was supplied. In 1951 after a spell in Hardwick's yard the engine was purchased by the heavy haulage contractors, J Hickey & Son of Richmond who renamed the engine 'Tulyar'.

Although the next two engines in the series had consecutive numbers they were actually delivered twelve months apart. No 3887, 'Prince of Wales' was the sixth Burrell engine purchased by Jennings Brothers of Devizes and travelled extensively throughout the Southern Counties between London and Bristol until 1938. It is generally believed that this engine was the first Showman's

Fig 225 No 3909 'Pride of the Road' built for Hollands in 1922 as seen after very professional restoration by the late F P Middleton of Hartlebury, Worcs. and renamed 'Winston Churchill'.

Fig 226 No 3938 'Quo Vadis' another very professional restoration completed by the late Edward Hines of Shaftesbury. A regular sight at traction engine rallies in the 1960s.

type engine to be purchased privately for preservation. Shortly after the Second World War it was acquired by Mr R Uvedale Corbett of Alresford in Hampshre. No 3888, 'General Gough' was delivered to Swales Bolesworth of Dagenham in June 1921 for his ex-White Brothers Motor Switchback. Fortunately this engine also survives in preservation.

No 3896 'Earl Beatty' and No 3912, 'Dragon' were identical twins supplied to Anderton & Rowland and were probably the best known Showman's engines in the South West between the two Great Wars. 'Earl Beatty' was despatched from St Nicholas Works on 13th May 1921 and travelled under her own steam to Burton-on-Trent to collect Anderton & Rowland's new 'Super Scenic Railway' from Orton & Spooner's works. The ride was erected and tested in the works yard with the engine providing the power before undertaking the long journey to Devonshire complete with loads six weeks later.

The late Cecil Quick wrote a series of articles about the Anderton & Rowland concern in which he vividly described this magnificent machine. "What a lovely machine this Scenic was," he wrote. "In fact it was just typical of the era which presented the fairgrounds, from the riding machine aspect, at their grandest – good organ music, with delightful carved work and colourful painting. I doubt very much whether we shall ever see the like of it again. Those carved Dragon cars, with the green and red lamps inside the heads, the cascade of water over the rocks and steps of the waterfall with the coloured lights sparkling through the spray were a sight to behold. I recall the grand picture which was presented by this machine, with the inimitable Solly Maddern inviting one and all to ride, with his pleasant smile and graceful wave of his baton towards the cars.

This great character was in the habit of varying his attire according to the vagaries of the English weather – "When he appears in cream flannels and straw hat the weather is certain to continue warm and fine; evening dress and silk hat denotes very fair; while the bowler hat and morning suit signifies unsettled weather. If he dons brown trilby and mackintosh, look out for anything." The famous 'Goodwin Midgets' also appeared on the front of the ride with Solly, but Mr Quick went on to say, "The most outstanding personality of all was the late Mr George de Vey Senior who was usually to be found at the controls of the machine and who kept an ever watchful eye on the erecting and dismantling operations.

Both 'Earl Beatty' and 'Dragon' were sent to Fowlers in the early 1930s for major repairs under Sydney Harrison's supervision. New fireboxes and press-on type 'Endless traction' rubber tyres were fitted. The addition of solid rubber tyres had been made mandatory on all road locomotives a few years earlier. The leading supplier of these was Charles Macintosh & Co Ltd of Manchester who supplied them in either endless form or in sectional pad form. In the 1920's John Fowler & Company enjoyed the sole selling rights for Macintosh tyres.

No 3909 was originally ordered by Charles Warren of Lincoln as an ordinary 8 NHP Showman's type engine. For reasons which are now unknown the order was cancelled and Burrells put the engine into stock. By mid-1921 the post-war boom was showing signs of ending and Lloyd George's 'Land fit for heros' moved into recession as our major manufacturing industries felt the

Fig 227 No 3949 'Princess Mary' with William Nichols' loads, a regular sight at fairs in the London area during the 1930s and 1940s.

loss of many of their traditional overseas markets. In March 1922 Hollands of Swadlincote purchased the engine for their Peacock and Dragon Scenic which necesitated hurriedly fitting an auxiliary dynamo platform and crane horns. Almost simultaneously Warren reinstated his order and the works supplied No 3932, which he named 'Mona'. Originally Hollands named No 3909 'Prince Albert' but when the engine was acquired for preservation after the Second World War it was renamed 'Winston Churchill'. Warren continued to use 'Mona' until 1942 when she was sold to John Barlow & Sons who renamed her 'Bill Barony'.

No 3936, built as a Special Scenic type engine spent the whole of her working life with Edward Danter of Newport for his rebuilt Scenic Peacock ride. Initially named 'Renown' in later life she carried the name 'Ich Dien' from Danter's older Burrell No 2379. Forward roping pulleys were attached to the belly tank and smokebox and the front wheels were fitted with widening rings. The works' engine register included a note to the effect that the engine was to be supplied with twenty 'spuds' for attachment to the hind wheels and that, "Mr Danter to accept full responsibility," all of which suggests that he expected the engine and loads to become frequently bogged down on soft ground.

In August 1922 William Wilson of Peckham, London took delivery of No 3938, another Special Scenic type engine for his steam driven Rodeo Switchback. This richly carved and gilded spinning top machine had a succession of novelty cars depicting animals and birds and finally motor cars were substituted with full-sized figures of famous film stars in the back seats of each car. For many years No 3938 which Wilson named 'Quo Vadis' ('Whither Goest Thou') was accompanied by the big old SCC engine No 1887, 'Empress of India' until the ride was finally laid up in 1940. 'Quo Vadis' was sold to Wall Brothers of Petersfield, who in 1948 sold her to Hardwick's where she remained until acquired for preservation by a Dorset enthusiast.

Charles Burrell exhibited No 3948, 'John Bull' at the Smithfield Show prior to delivery to Henry Studt as an additional engine for his Scenic Dragons. The engine is perhaps best remembered by many for the valiant services it rendered with its wire rope demolishing bomb damaged buildings in Swansea during the Nazi Blitz. A special feature of this engine was that all the steel gears were machine cut. No 3949 'Princess Mary' was an ordinary 8 NHP Showman's engine and is believed to have had the distinction of being one of the last Burrell Showman's engines to appear in a British fairground in the ownership of a professional showman, travelling as late as 1958. Originally owned by William Nichols of Forest Gate it was

Fig 228 No 4092 'Simplicity' – the last of the breed, built at Richard Garrett's works in Leiston in 1930 for Mrs Alfred Deakin of Brynmawr. The engine achieved great fame both in the fairground and with Road Engines & Kerr of Glasgow engaged upon heavy haulage work during the war.

a regular sight at the great London area fairs for over thirty years latterley in the ownership of Charles Presland of Tilbury. In 1958 the engine was acquired for preservation. Unlike her contemporaries she had the short boiler with 5 ft 8 ins long smoke tubes. Illustrated in Fig 227, the reader will note the lower than usual and rounded top canopy, which was presumably specified to enable the engine to negotiate low bridges.

Production of the penultimate engine in the series was put in hand in 1923 and allocated works No 3958. When almost complete the purchaser, Harry Hall of Derby, decided that he wanted the larger cylinder 'Contractor's' type engine and his order was transferred to engine No 3968 which was delivered to him in February 1924. However, one year later, Burrells persuaded Hall to take the original engine off their hands and they re-numbered the engine No 4021. Hall named the engine 'Lord Curzon' after the distinguished Statesman who lived at nearby Kedleston Hall and both engines attended his Scenic Whales for many years. Eventually as already mentioned 'Lord Curzon' was purchased by his brother-in-law, John Collins of the Bloxwich concern, where she ended her working days.

No 4092, 'Simplicity' the final engine in the series and the last Showman's engine built to carry the Burrell name was completed at Richard Garrett's works at Leiston in Suffolk in October 1930. Both Burrells and Garretts had been taken over by the Agricultural & General Engineers Ltd conglomerate and events leading up to this finale are described in greater detail in Chapter 18. The engine was built as an ordinary long boilered 8 NHP Showman's engine and fitted with an auxiliary dynamo platform for the widow of Alfred Deakin of Brynmawr in South Wales. Originally the Deakin family had travelled the North East in association with John Murphy and after moving South in 1923 soon established a reputation as leading Amusement Caterers in South Wales. They travelled a Cakewalk ride and a set of chairs and owned two smaller Burrell engines. 'Simplicity' was delivered direct to them at the Stratford-upon-Avon Mop Fair in October 1930 for their new set of Dodgems. Three years later they acquired the last Fowler built Showman's engine, No 20233, 'Supreme'.

In the early 1920s Fowler's Works Manager, Harold Livesey left the company following a dispute with Mr Charles Fowler and joined Charles Burrell as General Manager. A close relationship developed between Livesey and Sydney Harrison, a second generation loyal and valued employee at St Nicholas Works. His father had been managing clerk and buyer under Thomas Tank Burall. Both Livesey and Harrison became increasingly frustrated by the AGE management and Livesey returned to the Steam Plough Works. Sydney Harrison joined him in 1928, his knowledge of the Burrell product and his popularity with the Showmen proving of great assistance to Fowlers. Modifications were carried out to their now famous B6 road locomotive and four 'Super Lion' Showman's engines – No 19782, 'Lion', No 19783, 'King Carnival II', No 19989, 'Onward' and No 20223, 'Supreme' – were built in the years 1932–1934. They were often referred to as Burrell-Fowler engines and undoubtedly they represented the ultimate in the development of the Showmen's type road locomotive.

It will be recalled that in 1923 Harry Hall had insisted upon having a 'Contractor's' type engine with 7 ins dia × 11½ ins dia × 12 ins stroke cylinders. Whether this was responsible for Burrell's renewed interest in these big engines or whether the credit for their re-introduction lies with the drawing office we do not know. We have already seen that St Nicholas Works built a batch of three of these engines for use in the Portland Stone quarries in 1915 and that thereafter production was concentrated upon the 54 IHP engines with 6¾ ins dia × 11¼ ins dia × 12 ins stroke cylinders, all of which went to Travelling Showmen. Between 1924 and 1930 they built nine 'Contractor's' type road locomotives of which five were built as Showman's type engines and four were built originally for the Portland Stone Firms, although all four were subsequently converted to Showman's type engines.

FINAL BATCH 8 NHP 'CONTRACTOR'S' TYPE ROAD LOCOMOTIVES

Engine No	Date Built	Engine Name	Original Owner
3968	1924	The Whale	Harry Hall
3969	1924	Majestic	Enoch Farrar
*3980	1924	Her Majesty	Charles Heal
3995	1924	Wandering Willie	Wm Bastable
4000	1925	Ex-Mayor	G T Tuby
4030	1925	The Dolphin	W S Davies
*4038	1926	England's Glory	Charles Heal
*4042	1926	Robin Hood	Ernest Robinson
*4091	1930	Royal Manor	Mrs Codona

* Originally Bath & Portland Stone Firms Ltd engines.

All had long boilers with forty 2 ins dia × 6 ft 2 ins long smoke tubes, 6.6 sq ft grates and a total heating surface of 162 sq ft. All were double geared to the hind axle except Nos 3995 and No 4000 which had single drive gearing and long travel spring gear. The four engines supplied to the Portland Stone Firms were 2-speed engines and the five Showman's engines had 3-speed gearing. Nos 3968, 3969 and 4030 had 6 ft 6 ins dia × 22 ins wide hind wheels and the remaining six engines all had 7 ft 0 ins dia × 18 ins wide wheels. Only No 3995, 'Wandering Willie', was fitted new with Mackintosh twin rubber tyres. The five Showman's engines had 8 ins wide solid flywheels and those fitted to the Portland Stone engines were only 6 ins wide. The Showman's engines were also fitted with geared boiler feed pumps and one type BP 'G' injector but the Portland Stone engines carried two injectors. Only No 4030, 'The Dolphin' was fitted with differential locking gear. All nine engines carried 120 yds of 2¼ ins best quality steel wire rope.

No 3968, 'The Whale' as mentioned already went new to Harry Hall of Derby for his Scenic Whales in February 1924. Eventually in the twilight years of steam in the fairground she passed to Fred Cox of Condor. No 3969 'Majestic' went to the well-known Doncaster showman, Enoch Farrar for his Golden Dragon Scenic. Although built as a Special Scenic type engine she carried neither an auxiliary dynamo nor twisted brass canopy supports or other brass adornments and was used mainly for hauling Farrer's loads on the road and generating for lights.

No 3980 was originally one of the Bath & Portland

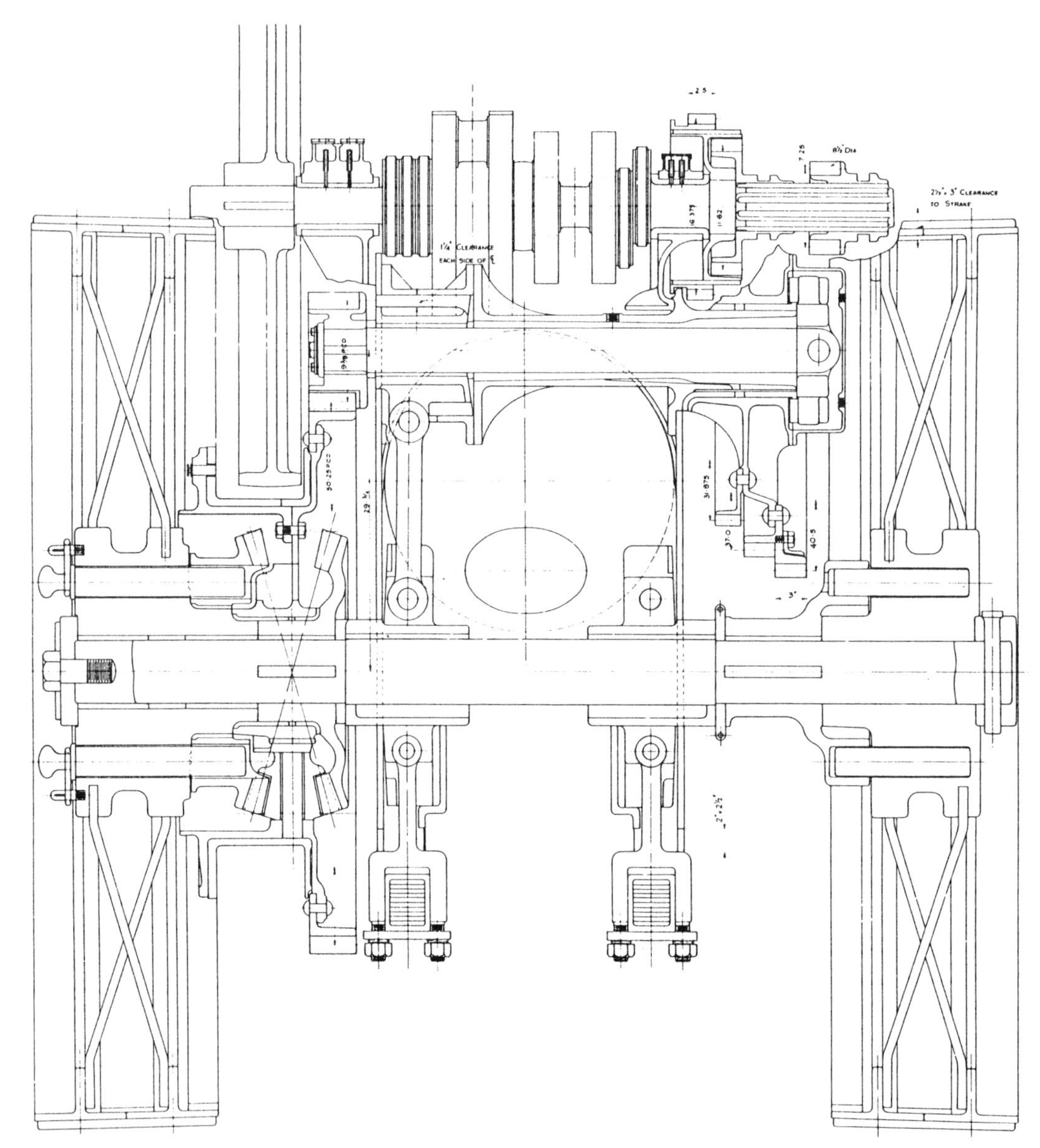

Fig 229 Cross section through the hind axle assembly of 8 NHP DCC 'Contractors' type engine with 3-speed gearing single drive transmission shafting and long travel road springs.

Stone Firms engines. In 1932 she was purchased by Charles Heal of Glastonbury to replace his old Fowler engine No 9383. Heal converted her to an ordinary 8 NHP Showman's type engine carrying a large Mather & Platt dynamo and named her 'Her Majesty'. In 1941 the engine was sold to Mrs Amy Lock of Taunton for hauling and lighting her ex-Deakin Noah's Ark.

During the difficult days of World War II the engine and ride were laid up. It is said the engine changed hands for the riduculous sum of 7s 6d (37½ p) in 1942.

No 3995, 'Wandering Willie' was the third Burrell Showman's type engine purchased by William Bastable & Sons of Stirling. She had single drive gearing with long travel spring gear and was fitted when new with Mackintosh's 7 ft 3 ins × 9 ins wide twin rubber tyres on the hind wheels. Another unique feature was the complete lack of traditional brass adornments and the use of straight brass tubes on the canopy supports. She carried neither an auxiliary dynamo platform nor tender mounted crane horns. No doubt the specification was intended to cheapen the engine as much as possible, because Scotland in particular was still feeling the serious effects of the post-war recession. Such was the state of trade generally that St Nicholas Works too was reduced to a four-day working week at this time.

The six big Burrell Showman's engines operated by the redoubtable Yorkshire showman Alderman George Thomas Tuby were undoubtedly the finest fleet of engines to be seen in the northern fairground in 1924. All were purchased new from St Nicholas Works between 1900 and 1921 and were smartly turned out in the distinctive Great Eastern Railway Royal Blue with bright yellow wheels. The story is told that when Alderman Tuby was discussing the purchase of his seventh engine with members of his family, his sons expressed preference for the Fowler built engine with its narrower overall width, single drive gearing and long travel spring gear. The old gentleman is reputed to have replied that they could have whatever sort of engine they wanted so long as Charles Burrell built it.

The outcome was the splendid Special Scenic engine

Fig 230 No 3995 'Wandering Willie'. William Bastable's of Stirling big 8 NHP DCC 'Contractors' type single drive gearing Showman's engine built in 1924.

No 4000 'Ex-Mayor' delivered new at the Kings Lynn Mart fair in February 1925. It had the big type 708 boiler pressed to 200 PSI with a 6.6 sq ft grate and 6 ft 2 ins long smoke tubes and is said to have developed in excess of 70 BHP. The arrangement of the single drive gearing, the long travel spring gear and the 3-speed pinions mounted on the end of the crankshaft can be clearly seen in Fig 229. The combined compensating gear and winding drum mounted on the hind axle will also be noted. This system permitted the compensating gear to be locked, giving a rigid drive for negotiating soft ground by the insertion of a long driving pin through the compensating gear centre. Removal of the pins freed the drive to the hind wheels allowing the winding drum and the wire rope to be brought into action. Originally the engine was supplied with steel straked wheel rims but at an early date Tuby had solid rubber tyres fitted to comply with the new regulations. At the time the order was placed with St Nicholas Works Tuby intended that the engine should attend his Scenic ride, but the story is told that shortly before the engine was delivered the Alderman was collecting fares on the ride when a fault developed in the waterfall and he received a thorough soaking. There and then he sold the ride to the Pat Collins concern, which is the reason 'Ex-Mayor' never carried an auxiliary dynamo.

A few years later when the Noah's Ark ride was introduced 'Ex-Mayor' took over the ride and Fig 231 illustrates the engine and ride en-route to Lincoln Fair in 1932 shortly after it had been fitted with a new firebox by Marshalls of Gainsborough. She remained with the ride for the whole of her working life, mostly in the charge of driver Franklin Cheffins. In 1946 when the Tuby concern replaced its Burrell engines with diesel engined vehicles, Cheffins could not bear to see 'Ex-Mayor' fall victim to the breaker's torch. With his meagre life savings he purchased the engine which then spent some years in retirement on his Lincolnshire smallholding before being purchased for restoration.

During the period 1959–1960 extensive rebuilding was undertaken by Mr John Salem who had already rebuilt the famous Fowler engine No 14862, 'Excelsior' and a Burrell 5 ton tractor No 3846, 'Pouss-Nouk-Nouk'. 'Ex-Mayor' was sent to a commercial firm in Crewe and had a new smokebox and chimney fitted. The motion and all external fittings were stripped down and all bruises and blemishes plus years of dirt were removed. All bearings were replaced and many small components were remachined and refitted; new piston rings were fitted and the slide valve faces remachined; all glands were replaced which resulted in smooth running and steam tightness at least equal to the day she left St Nicholas Works in 1925. The old Tuby blue livery was stripped off and all painted surfaces were rubbed down and given several coats of primer and undercoat before the more conventional Burrell lake with yellow wheels was applied and the whole beautifully lined out.

Unfortunately the original dynamo supplied with the engine was no longer available and a more modern ex-Royal Navy McClure & Whitfield machine was acquired. The 110 volt continuous rating compound wound DC generator produced 220 amps at 1000 RPM, which necessitated a smaller than usual 7¾ ins dia driven pulley in order to suit the 166 RPM governed speed of the engine crankshaft. The theoretical electrical diagram of the circuit employed is shown in Fig 232.

The author purchased the engine in 1964. Fig 233 illustrates the engine upon completion of the first stage of restoration. During 1965 the engine appeared at various traction engine rallies including the great Steam Fair held

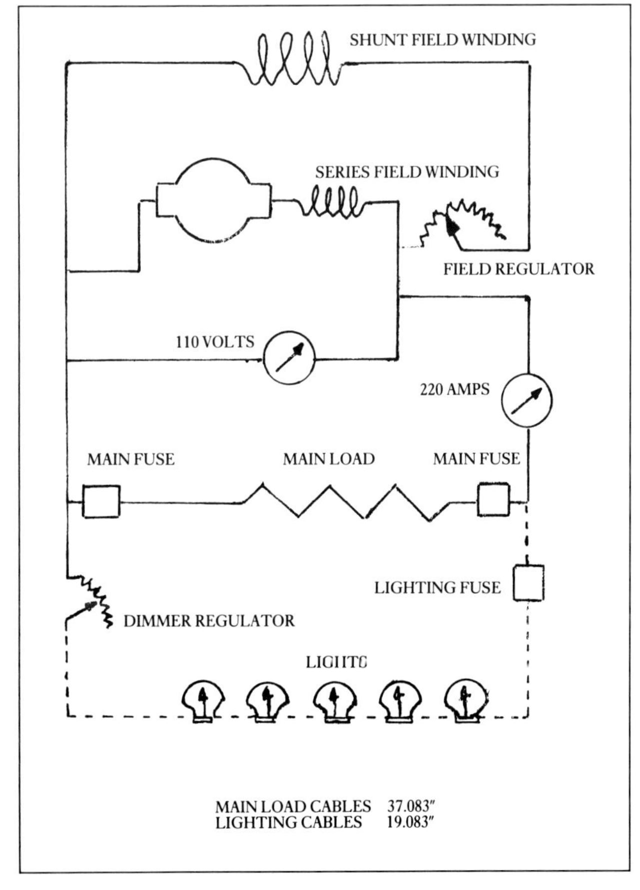

Fig 231 No 4000 'Ex-Mayor' with Alderman G T Tuby's Noahs Ark loads en route to Lincoln Fair in 1932.

at Castle Howard. The second stage of restoration was undertaken during the winter of 1965–66. She was sent to an old established commercial firm near Burton-on-Trent who for many years had carried out Holland Bros engine overhauls and boiler work.

Due to ash having been habitually left on the grate when the engine was cold, some wastage had taken place around the heads of the bottom row of stays. The old stays were removed, the firebox wrapper plate was built up by electric welding and new stays were fitted. Some building up was done immediately below the firehole door, a difficult place for other than the most fastidious driver to keep free from ash and clinker. Another precaution taken was to build up and re-tap the hole in the firebox crown for the fusible plug. The smoke tubes were renewed, the smokebox was lined and the mud-lids were built up where wastage had taken place and carefully refitted.

The four wheels were removed and sent away for vulcanising new solid rubber tyres which necessitated turning the inner edge of the tyre in-situ on the flywheel side of the engine due to the small clearance with the flywheel hub and new wheel brasses were fitted. The hind axle springs were also sent away for re-setting and tempering thereby restoring the full 1½ ins travel to the

Fig 232 Diagram showing electrical wiring on No 4000 'Ex-Mayor'.

Fig 233 No 4000 'Ex-Mayor' as acquired by the author in the 1960s prior to raising the canopy and fitting solid rubber tyres.

spring gear. The compensating gear and winding drum mechanism was stripped down and re-fitted with new bearings and where necessary the gear teeth were built-up. All water pipes and the internal surfaces of the water tanks were cleaned and treated to prevent corrosion. Absolutely nothing was left to chance.

Finally, the lowered canopy was restored to its correct height, the top of the roof was recovered with canvas and new twisted brass canopy supports were fitted. The canopy sideboards were re-written in gold leaf, 'The Burrell Showman's Road Locomotive No 4000' and the wheel spokes were relined by one of Orton & Spooner's most skilled painters. A new 8 ft long extension chimney was provided.

In 1968 the engine was acquired by the Hon Sir William Mc Alpine and for a number of years formed the centre piece of his wonderful collection of engines at Fawley, near Henley-on-Thames. In 1981 she passed to the Saunders family at Stotfold near Hitchin, Herts who completed the third stage of restoration. They rebuilt the boiler and firebox, fitted a new dynamo and re-painted the engine its correct Great Eastern Railway Royal Blue. Throughout the 1980s the engine appeared at a great many events all over the country and quite apart from the pleasure it has given by its sheer beauty and majesty it has been instrumental in raising large sums of money for charity. It was entirely appropriate that the engine should have been present at the formal opening of the Burrell Museum in Minstergate, Thetford on March 25th, 1991.

No 4030, delivered in September 1925 was the last Showman's type engine to be built at St Nicholas Works before all manufacturing activity was transferred to their sister company, Richard Garrett & Sons Ltd in Leiston. Unlike the two preceeding engines she had the double geared drive to the hind axle and was fitted with Burrell's patent differential locking gear. The hind wheels were 6 ft 6 ins dia × 22 ins wide and the 3-speed gear ratios were therefore reduced from 30.5, 17.6 and 10.4 to 1 to 24.4, 13.6 and 8.3 to 1. In all other mechanical detail the engine was basically as No 4000, 'Ex-Mayor'. She was supplied new to the Potteries Showman, William Davies for his Scenic ride and named 'Dolphin'. Two years later she was acquired by John Shaw of Sheffield and re-named 'The Guv'nor'. Whilst in Shaw's ownership the canopy was lowered by 6 ins giving the engine a slightly odd appearance. Shaw also fitted two large mechanical lubricators, one supplying the cylinder, the other the crosshead guide bars, valve spindle guides and the intermediate drive shaft to the Pickering governor. Later the engine passed to H J Wallis Jr of Seaforth near Liverpool, who again renamed her 'The Commando'. Finally in 1959 she was acquired for preservation and

Fig 234 Mrs F Codona's ex-Bath & Portland Stone Firms engine No 4091 'Royal Manor' built at Richard Garrett's Leiston works in 1930.

today forms part of the magnificent collection of Showman's engines owned by Mr Frank Lythgoe of Lymm in Cheshire.

The last three big engines we have to deal with which saw service in the fairground, Nos 4038,4042, 4091 were all built by Richard Garrett & sons Ltd in the period 1926–1930 and supplied originally as road locomotives to the Bath & Portland Stone Firms Ltd. Although built over a four year period,they seemed to many to represent the last gulps of a drowning man. The days of the reciprocating steam engine in the fairground were clearly numbered. Only No 4092, 'Simplicity' built to the special order of Mrs A Deakin, which we have already described, remained to surface in a world fast becoming dominated by the internal combustion engine. The meagre concessions obtained by the Showman's Guild following the publication of the Government's Salter Report simply delayed the phasing out of existing steam in the fairground but all manufacture ceased in the United Kingdom after 1934.

The Bath & Portland Stone Firms abandoned steam in 1932 and all their engines were sold. No 4038 was purchased by Charles Heal of Glastonbury. They named the engine 'England's Glory' and fitted a full length canopy with twisted brass supports and a dynamo platform. No 4042 was acquired by Ernest Robinson of Barnsley, named 'Robin Hood' and similarly rebuilt. No 4091 was purchased by Mrs Codona of Glasgow and named 'Royal Manor'. They fitted a full length canopy and dynamo platform, but the engine never carried twisted brasses or other showland adornments.

In concluding our examination of the compound type Showman's road locomotives built at St Nicholas Works we must now consider the sixty-three smaller type engines (5, 6, & 7 NHP) built between 1892 and 1924. The fairground proprietors were slow to adopt engines smaller than 8 NHP and only five, all with single crank compound cylinders were built in the 19th century. After 1902 all had double crank compound cylinders and the engines conformed very closely in mechanical detail with the contempory sizes of road locomotive already considered in chapter 11.

The first smaller compound engine to be ordered direct by a Showman was No 1629, a 7 NHP engine with 6 ins dia × 10 ins dia × 12 ins stroke SCC cylinders. Apart from its compound cylinders it was almost identical to the 7 NHP SC engine No 1470 'Pride of the South' supplied to G & J Bartlett in 1890. The copper firebox and brass smoke tubes were retained. The engine was built in 1892 for Charles Heal of Glastonbury and named 'Pride of Somerset'. He fitted a dynamo platform in 1899. In 1908 the engine was sold to William Davies of Stoke-on-Trent, which is somewhat ironic when one considers that two of the last batch of Showman's engines to carry the Burrell name, Nos 4030 and 4038 were acquired by the same two showmen. Finally just after the First World War the engine was purchased by W Piper, an Irish showman with whom she ended her working days.

No 1741 also went to an Irish showman, J Tofts of Belfast in 1894. Basically it was a standard 6 NHP SCC road locomotive with 6 ins dia × 10 ins dia × 12 ins cyldiners, a steel firebox, single drive gearing, volute type springs a disc type flywheel and motion side plates. It is not known if a dynamo platform was ever fitted to the engine. No 2005 was a larger 6 NHP with 6¼ ins dia × 10½ ins dia × 12 ins stroke SCC cylinders built in 1897 with a dynamo platform, twisted brasses and brass stars and rings. It was supplied new to Hastings and Whayman of Llanelly but soon passed to Samuel Jones of Battersea.

Inevitably it was not long before a showman acquired

Fig 235 No 2195 'Pride of Kent', an early 6 NHP SCC 'Devonshire' engine having an enlarged and strengthened dynamo platform with Thomas Andrews loads in Tunbridge Wells 1923.

one of the successful 6 NHP 'Devonshire' engines. Between 1899 and 1902 six SCC road locomotives were supplied direct to showmen.

6 NHP SCC 'DEVONSHIRE' TYPE SHOWMAN'S ROAD LOCOMOTIVES

Engine No	Date Built	Engine Name	Original Owner
2173	1899	The Empress	Smith & Whittle
2195	1899	Pride of Kent	Thomas Andrews
2354	1901	Lord Roberts	Henry Thurston
2438	1901	—	A Stocks
2455	1902	Edward VII	James Pettigrove
2471	1902	John Bull	John Proctor

All conformed exactly with the SCC 'Devonshire' type road locomotive specification given in chapter 10. For some reason No 2195 was delivered five months ahead of No 2173, but neither engine was fitted with show fittings when new. In 1914 James Biddall of Fife acquired No 2173 and he rebuilt the engine fitting a dynamo platform. No 2354 and 2438 were built with full show fittings but unusually they both left the works new in 1901 painted khaki, which suggests that both were originally intended for the military authorities. No 2455 was supplied new to James Pettigrove, but like his earlier 6 NHP road engine she never carried a dynamo platform or other show fittings. The last engine in the series, No 2471 'John Bull' went new to John Proctor of Belper complete with a dynamo platform and a full set of brass adornments although the engine was not lined-out in the customary manner. Four years later Proctor took delivery of a big 'Contractor's' type engine which he also named 'John Bull' selling the smaller engine to Anderton & Rowlands. The 6 NHP engine is illustrated in Fig 236 outside Burrell's works prior to delivery to Proctor.

The first of the smaller DCC type Showman's engines was completed in February 1904. No 2625, 'Lady Pride of England' was a 7 NHP engine with 6 ins dia × 10 ins dia × 12 ins stroke cylinders built for W Buckland of Coventry. She had a standard 7 NHP boiler pressed to 175 PSI with the boiler shell made in one piece. She was fitted with 3-speed road gearing, carried a Moore's steam pump, a Pickering governor and a full set of standard show fittings. She was painted green with vermillion wheels. Later she was acquired by George Billings of Leicester and is illustrated in Fig 237 with Billings' Gallopers en route to Northampton fair. Fortunately this unique engine survives today in preservation.

Thereafter St Nicholas Works produced fourteen 'Devonshire' type DCC showmen's road engines with 5½ ins dia × 9 ins dia × 10 ins stroke cylinders which were now rated 5 NHP; eighteen 6 NHP engines with 6 ins dia × 10 ins dia × 10 ins stroke cylinders; and twenty-two 7 NHP engines with 6¼ ins dia × 10½ ins dia × 12 ins stroke cylinders. Nine of these 7 NHP engines were built in the post-First World War years with 200 PSI boilers and other refinements which made them as powerful as the early 8 NHP DCC engines built at the turn of the century.

5 NHP DCC 'DEVONSHIRE' TYPE SHOWMAN'S ROAD LOCOMOTIVES

Engine No	Date Built	Engine Name	Original Owner
3090	1909	Fernoy	Pool & Bosco
3167	1910	Queen of the Road	John Manders
3278	1911	Shamrock	O'Brien Bros
3311	1911	St Patrick	J North, Neath
3365	1912	Shamrock	T Harrison
3509	1913	Rajah	Bostock & Wombwell
3555	1914	The Busy Bee	Taylor Bros
3641	1915	Venture	A Traylen
3669	1915	Nero	Bostock & Wombwell
3837	1920	Perseverance	J H Norman
3898	1921	Little Joe	J Fletcher
3906	1921	Earl Beatty	Mrs J Smith
3926	1922	Margaret	Henry Thurston
3927	1921	Queen of the Borders	Taylor Bros

The boilers and principal mechanical details were as described in chapter 11. However, the wheel sizes of the Showman's engines varied in accordance with customer requirements, some were 6 ft 6 ins dia, others were as small as 5 ft 7½ ins dia. All had the 2-lever, 3-speed gearing, the majority having Burrell's patents differential locking gear. Full length canopies and dynamo platforms were fitted to all the Showman's engines. The name 'Devonshire' engine was dropped in 1920 and all subsequent engines carried the AGE monogram.

Special mention must be made of the two Bostock & Wombwell engines No 3509 'Rajah' and No 3669, 'Nero'. They were named after two of Bostock's famous lions and it is claimed that they travelled a greater mileage than any other Showman's engines. Bostock & Wombwells famous circus travelled the length and breadth of the British Isles until 1931, each engine usually hauling two heavy beast wagons and a living van. The final performance of the show was given in the Scotswood Sheep Market in Newcastle-upon-Tyne on November 30th 1931 when the engines were then auctioned. 'Rajah' fetched £180 and 'Nero' £200. Both engines were purchased by the Staffordshire threshing contractor, John Henton of

Fig 236 No 2471 'John Bull' 6 NHP SCC 'Devonshire' type Showman's engine, spring mounted with single drive gearing awaiting delivery to John Proctor of Belper, Derbys.

Fig 237 No 2625 'Lady Pride of England', the first 7 NHP DCC Showman's engine with George Billings' Galloper loads en route to Northampton fair.

Fig 238 No 3509 'Rajah' one of a pair of 5 NHP DCC Showman's engines extensively travelled throughout the UK by Bostock & Wombwell's famous circus 1913–1931.

Hopwas near Tamworth and completed another twenty years useful work before being acquired for preservation.

6 NHP DCC SHOWMAN'S ROAD LOCOMOTIVE WITH 6 ins × 10 ins × 10 ins CYLINDERS

Engine No	Date Built	Engine Name	Original Owner
2652	1904	A Tryer	John Cottrill
2677	1904	The Border Queen	Thomas Day
2714	1904	Edinburgh Castle	John Evans
2806	1906	Sir Colin Campbell	J Hibbert
2868	1906	Lusitania	Walter Payne
2874	1906	Prince of Wales	J M Lock
3063	1909	Houpla	J H Herbert
3281	1911	Baby the Flower of Belshill	H Harris
3413	1912	The Philadelphia	J Smith, Shirley
3466	1913	Mac	Mrs MacIntosh
3471	1913	The Rover	A Newsome
3660	1915	Victor	James Jennings
3675	1915	Pride of Erin	Wm Sharples
3822	1920	The Snip	R Sedgewick
3830	1920	Try Again	J Corrigan
3874	1921	Chaser	Thos Taylor
3878	1921	Excelsior/Island Chief	Robert Payne
3889	1921	City of Exeter	Smith Bros

These engines developed 36 IHP and were capable of hauling with ease 30 ton loads on a 1 in 18 incline. The first four engines had the standard 6 NHP road locomotive boiler pressed to 175 PSI and were fitted with Moore's steam pump; the remainder had boilers pressed to 200 PSI, some had 1¾ ins dia smoke tubes, others had 2 ins dia tubes; most had two injectors and no feed pump. The first five engines had single drive gearing with leaf springs, the remainder were spring mounted and double geared. All had the 2-lever, 3-speed gearing with ratios of 30.2, 16.8 and 10.3 to 1 and 6 ft 6 ins dia hind wheels. Engines built after 1910 were fitted with Burrell's patent differential locking gear. The solid flywheels were 4 ft 0 ins dia × 6 ins wide and the Pickering governors were set for 175 RPM running on the belt. The works records listed the following standard features for the Showman's version of the 6 NHP road locomotive – long awning with six twisted brass canopy supports; plated coal rack 12 ins deep; plain brass tubes through awning for safety valves; engraved brass plates on the steam chests; brass stars and rings on the motion side plates; brass stars on the cylinder end covers; brass ring on the flywheel, segmented plate on the dynamo platform; sheet iron guard between chimney and dynamo; and wrought iron chaffing plates on the sides of the boiler. The last three engines built in 1921 carried the AGE monogram. Most were painted Burrell lake colour with red or yellow wheels.

Generally these engines as will be noted in the above list of original owners were acquired by the smaller firms of Amusement Caterers. They tended to operate the smaller types of ride and consequently had less paraphernalia and lighter loads to move. The engines and rides also changed hands more frequently than those owned by the larger firms. Perhaps of special interest is No 3878 purchased by Arnold Bros of Cowes in the Isle of Wight in 1931 and renamed 'Island Chief'. It was not uncommon to see her in tug-hauled barges crossing the Solent from Cowes to Southampton complete with her loads.

7 NHP DCC SHOWMAN'S ROAD LOCOMOTIVES WITH 6¼ ins × 10½ ins × 12 ins CYLINDERS

Engine No	Date Built	Engine Name	Original Owner
2879	1907	Lord Nelson	Henry Thurston
2984	1908	Premier	'President' Kemp
3007	1908	Prince of Wales	James Dooner
3078	1909	Sir Henry Irving	J Hibbert
3081	1909	Rob Roy	George Green
3088	1909	A Tryer	John Cottrell
3089	1909	His Majesty	John Green
3159	1909	The Gladiator	Anderton & Rowland
3178	1910	Dreadnought	Hill Bros
3183	1910	Help Mate	Pat Collins
3288	1911	Nancy	James Manders
3512	1913	Nonesuch	J J Graham
3526	1913	Lightening II	Emerson & Hazard
3714	1916	Violet Lily	H Shuttleworth
3817	1919	Perseverance	Arthur Bates
3871	1921	Teresa	Sidney Stocks
3890	1922	Majestic	J H Herbert
3910	1921	Wait & See	Crowther & Johnson
3933	1922	Princess Mary	John Anderton
3945	1922	Prince of Wales	H Coneley
3952	1923	Modesty	A Deakin
3978	1924	Duchess of York	J H Royle

No 2879, 'Lord Nelson' was a one-off built in 1907 for Henry Thurston of Stanstead in Essex for illuminating his Savage built Scenic ride. She had a small boiler pressed to 175 PSI with a 4.86 sq ft grate,a total heating surface of 130 sq ft and spring mounted single drive gearing. After the First War the engine passed to Thurston's son and was fitted with a tender mounted crane tower. In 1933 she was acquired by F Harris & Sons of Ashington in Sussex and for a time carried the name 'Sweet Nothing' but this was shortly changed to 'Princess Royal', the name she carries today in preservation.

No 2984 was the first of thirteen 7 NHP Showman's engines with large 6.11 sq ft grates and thirty-five 2 ins dia × 5 ft 8 ins long smoke tubes. These engines had a steam raising capacity at least equal to the standard 8 NHP road engines. No 2984 was pressed to 180 PSI, the rest had 200 PSI boilers. The remaining eight engines, (Nos 3817–3978) all built after the First War had similar boilers but the grate area was reduced to 5.49 sq ft. Engines built up to 1910 were fitted with Moore's steam pumps, thereafter some carried two type BP 'G' injectors and the postwar engines were fitted with geared mechanical feed pumps. All had 4 ft 0 ins long connecting rods and all were double geared to the hind axle, most having 3-speed gearing and 6 ft 6 ins hind wheels. The engines were governed at 165 RPM on the belt, they had an overall width of 8 ft 0 ins and weighed approximately 14 tons.

No 2984 went new to the self-styled 'President' G H Kemp of Leicester in 1908 for his very popular Theatre Unique Show which was for many years a centre-piece at

Fig 239 No 3890 'Majestic' 7 NHP DCC Showman's engine with J H Herbert's of Southampton Galloper loads near Dorchester in the 1920s.

the Nottingham Goose fair. She was fitted with Burrell's patent wood-block wheel rims on the hind wheels and was painted crimson with bright yellow wheels. In 1926 the engine was acquired by J H Chipperfield then based at Castle Douglas in Dumfries.

It will be noted from the above original owners list that many of these engines went to the larger well known Amusement Caterers. No 3007, 'Prince of Wales' went to James Dooner who had married into the famous W C & S Hancock family. Nos 3081 and 3089 went to the Green family and No 3088 supplied originally to John Cottrell subsequently spent many years with the Murphy family on Tyneside. No 3159 'The Gladiator' was purchased new by Anderton & Rowland in 1909 for their Bioscope Show and passed later to the Cornish section of the firm under Captain Arthur Rowland. In 1932 it was acquired by T Whiteley of Plymouth and is today owned by the Gladiator Preservation Society in Redruth. No 3178 'Dreadnought' started its life with Hill Bros of Bedminster and in 1927 was acquired by W Nash who for many years travelled under the Anderton & Rowland banner and No 3183 'Helpmate' went to Pat Collins Jr of Chester.

The next engine in the series, No 3288, 'Nancy' had a less illustrious career than her predecessors. She was supplied new to John Manders of Mile End in East London and was named after his sister who was partner in the firm. Within two years the engine was repossessed by Burrells and eventually found its way into the Naval Dockyard at Devonport where it was used for generating electricity. Later in 1917 it passed to the Dartmoor China Clay Company who were engaged upon war work in the area. After the war the engine was acquired by Joe Brewer of Liskeard who travelled a set of Gallopers and renamed her 'Queen Mary'. In 1928 she was laid up at nearby Indian Queens where she lay derelict for forty years. In 1968 the engine was purchased for preservation and at the time of writing is undergoing a complete rebuild.

No 3512 which carried the cryptic name, 'Nonesuch' spent all her working life in the Kingdom of Fife on the east coast of Scotland with J T Graham. No 3526 'Lightening II' painted green with yellow wheels spent all her working days in Northern England with Emerson & Hazard of Whitehaven. Eventually she was purchased for preservation by Richard Preston, a haulage contractor of Potto. During the 1956 Suez crisis, when all motor fuels were rationed 'Lightening II' was brought back into use hauling wagon loads of bricks in North Yorkshire.
No 3714 'Violet Lily', the last 7 NHP Showman's engine built before the AGE take-over spent all her working life in Lancashire.

Eight more of these excellent engines were built between 1919 and 1922 but all had the smaller 5.49 sq ft boiler. No 3817, 'Perseverance' went to the Cheshire Amusement Caterer, Arthur Bates. No 3871, 'Teresa' started life with Ipswich showman Sidney Stocks and was sold to Hardiman & Strong of Bristol in 1930. Eventually she passed to John Cole of Bristol who renamed her 'Western Pioneer'. The engine survives in preservation. The next two engines survive in the Hunt collection at Oldbury near Birmingham. No 3890, 'Majestic' spent all her working life with J H Herbert in Southampton.
No 3910 'Wait & See' spent two years with Crowther & Johnson of Leeds and was then acquired by Pat Collins. She was uniquely painted light yellow, lined lake, light green and black with white wheels lined in red and blue. The front cross-member of the canopy was inscribed in gilded letters, 'Members of the Showman's Guild'.
No 3933, 'Princess Mary' was the last Burrell engine purchased by the Anderton & Rowland concern. She was actually delivered to John Anderton of Exeter, a relative

and subsequently re-possessed by Burrells. After remaining in stock at the works for some time she was sold to G A Whittle of Woking with whom she remained until being acquired for preservation.

The final three engines were all built during the post-war depression when orders were extremely difficult to obtain and they were said to have been sold at bargain prices. They incorporated the most up to date design features and their workmanship and finish was of the highest order; all had machine cut gears, differential locking gear and geared boiler feed pumps. No 3945 'Prince of Wales' was exhibited at Smithfield and then went to H Coneley of Bristol for his Helter Skelter ride. In 1933 she passed to the old established Amusement Caterers William Marshall of Bradford. No 3952 'Modesty' which was fitted with a novel design of rear jib crane spent her brief life in showland with Alfred Deakin & Sons of Brynmawr. The engine was taken off the road in 1937 and during the war she was acquired by Jack Johnson of Banks near Southport and ended her days as a threshing engine. No 3978, 'Duchess of York' spent all her working life in the ownership of J H Royle of Gorton in Manchester. Nothing appears to be known of her ultimate fate.

It is perhaps appropriate that the final engine to be mentioned in our review of the Burrell Showman's engines should carry the name at one time accorded to our beloved Queen Mother. Few machines have given longer service and more pleasure in any way comparable with this great lady's life of devoted service to the nation.

CHAPTER THIRTEEN

The Double Crank Compound Traction Engine

It was quite clear by the turn of the century that sooner or later St Nicholas Works would apply the double crank compound arrangement to their GP traction engines. As we have seen, the arrangement had been almost instantly successful when applied to road locomotives in 1896, although it must be said that it never succeeded entirely in replacing the now well proven single crank compound system. The final engine of this type left the works as late as October 1928. Price, coupled with the fact that over 50 per cent of the DCC traction engines built were rated 6 NHP or smaller would seem to be the main explanation for the apparent anomaly.

A total of 137 GP traction engines with DCC cylinders of various sizes were built or 20 per cent of the number of SCC GP traction engines sold. They were completed at an average rate of four per annum before the First War, increasing to six per annum in the ten years to the closure of St Nicholas Works in 1928. Both before and after the War the agriculturist was faced with a bewildering array of engines, with over a score of British manufacturers vying for orders at the great agricultural shows. The larger firms such as John Fowler and Marshalls indulged in a great deal of aggressive selling, but the market was small and right until the very end Charles Burrell enjoyed a high degree of customer loyalty.

The first Thetford built DCC GP traction engine, No 2192 was completed in June 1899. Its boiler and other mechanical details were as the contemporary 8 NHP SC and SCC engines but with 6½ ins dia × 11 ins dia × 12 ins stroke DCC cylinders. It had spring mounted single drive gearing and was sent new to Charles Pitt, a Sussex farmer. In 1901 the engine was acquired by the War Department. On August 18th that year a test run was held from Thetford to Mundford via Northwold and return. It is recorded that the distance covered was 25 miles, the gross load was 43.5 tons, the time on the road was 9 hours 50 minutes and an average travelling speed of 3.125 MPH was maintained. Three years later three 8 NHP DCC engines, Nos 2636, 2638 and 2639 were exported to the Reid & Gray agency in New Zealand. They had the special Stevens boiler with an arched roof firebox, a one piece boiler barrel and five solid stay tubes as fitted to several earlier engines supplied to New Zealand. The DCC cylinders measured 6¼ ins dia × 10½ ins dia × 12 ins stroke and the engines were double geared and spring mounted on the hind axle. Only one more engine of this size was built, No 3239, completed in September 1910 had a nominally 7 NHP boiler pressed to 200 PSI and was actually sold to a Kent farmer as a 7 NHP engine. Concurrently with the three engines sent to New Zealand in 1903 the works built a single drive spring mounted 7 NHP engine, No 2633, with 6 ins dia × 10 ins dia × 12 ins stroke DCC cylinders. It spent its first ten years in the West Country with a series of haulage contractors and eventually in 1924 was acquired by A Traylen, a showman from Earlsfield in London. He had it converted to a full Showman's type engine and renamed it 'Shamrock'.

The first two of the thirty standard duty 7 NHP double geared spring mounted engines with 6 ins dia × 10 ins dia × 12 ins stroke cylinders Nos 2618 and 2619 were built in 1903 for the Reid & Gray agency in New Zealand. No more were built until 1907.

7 NHP 6 ins × 10 ins × 12 ins DCC COMPOUND GP TRACTION ENGINES

No 2618	Built 1903	No 3445	Built 1913
2619	" 1903	3505	" 1913
2919	" 1907	3514	" 1913
2920	" 1907	3544	" 1914
2924	" 1907	3636	" 1915
2936	" 1907	3686	" 1915
2949	" 1907	3687	" 1915
2966	" 1907	3704	" 1916
2987	" 1908	3747	" 1917
3045	" 1908	3779	" 1918
3074	" 1909	3789	" 1918
3168	" 1910	3811	" 1919
3169	" 1910	3825	" 1920
3257	" 1911	3923	" 1922
3406	" 1912	3940	" 1922

Four engines in the series went to New Zealand. In addition to Nos 2618 and 2619 these included Nos 2924 and 3045. The former had short boilers with 5 ft 0 ins long smoke tubes giving a total heating surface of 116.0 sq ft, the latter had the 5 ft 8 ins long tubes. No 3045 was of special interest as it was fitted with a Richardson's of Patricroft type 653 totally enclosed horizontal steam feed water pump. Five of the engines, Nos 2920, 2949, 3074,3168 and 3169 went to Australia through the Coulson agency. These had 6.11 sq ft grates suitable for burning inferior fuel; extended smokeboxes with spark arresters; enlarged fuel racks on the tender; 3-speed gearing; and 4 ft 0 ins long connecting rods.

Four similar engines in the series, Nos 3704, 3779, 3789 and 3811 subsequently sold to UK customers had

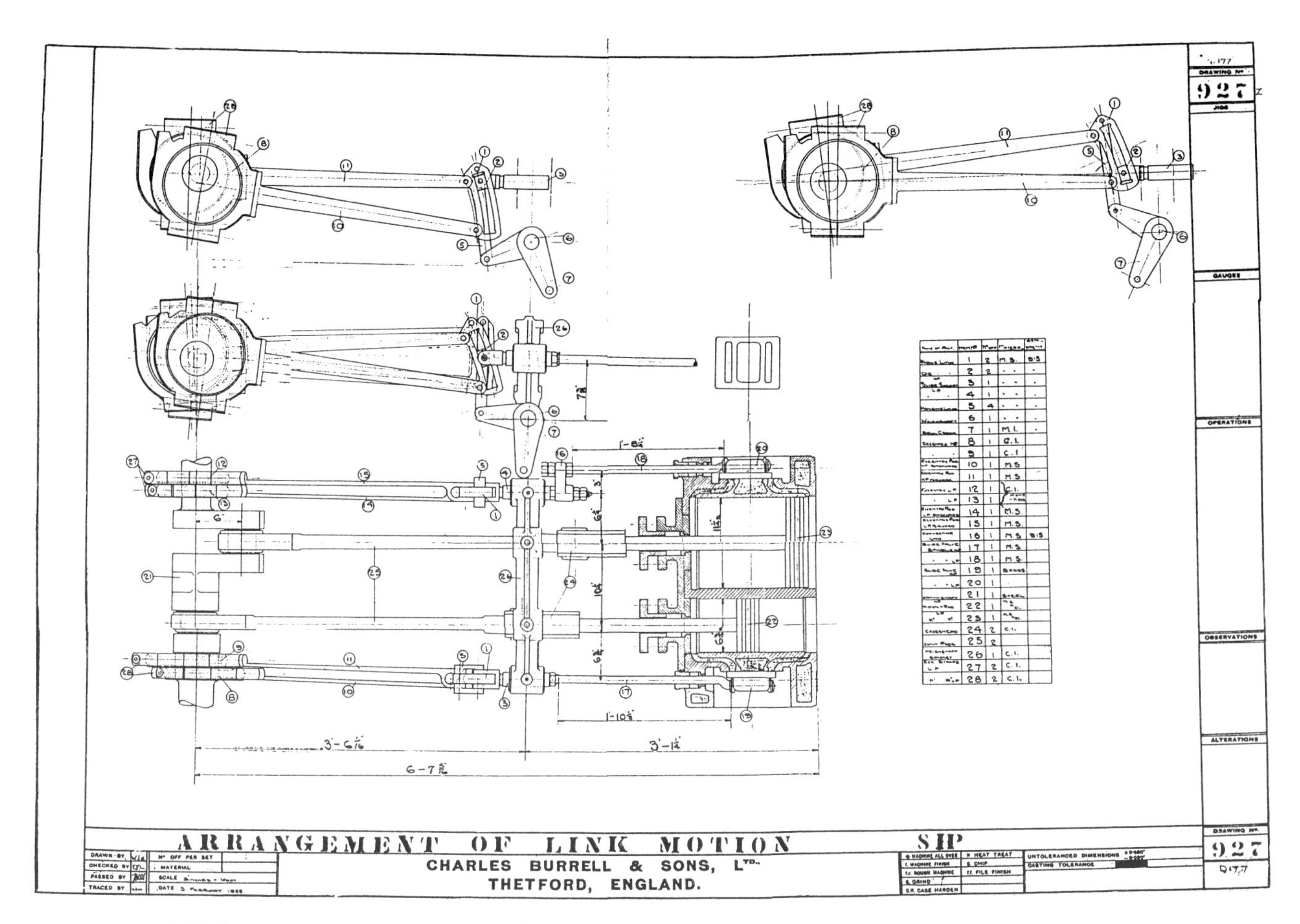

Fig 240 General arrangement drawing of Stephenson's link motion as applied to the 8 NHP DCC traction engine.

the same enlarged boilers indicating that they were either built against cancelled Australian orders or that they had been put in hand in anticipation of orders which never materialised. It was at this time that the Australian government imposed punitive import duties upon traction engines and No 3169 was the last Burrell supplied to this market. No 2966 was one of six engines supplied to Moore Bros, contractors of Bilborough in Nottinghamshire and for some reason this had a special boiler with a 5.49 sq ft grate and forty-seven 1½ ins dia smoke tubes. No 3257, after nine years service with the Wingham Engineering Company in Kent was acquired by Mornement & Ray Ltd, the well known East Anglian drainage contractors of East Harling near Thetford. They owned no less than twenty-two Burrell engines at various times including the famous ex-Edward Box chain driven road locomotive, 'Oregon', a pair of 10 NHP Universal drum ploughing engines and the first road roller built at St Nicholas Works in 1891. No 3257 was the only DCC engine they ever owned; this was fitted with a special roping pulley attached to a strap around the boiler barrel as described in works drawing No 4115. In total fourteen of these engines went to English customers, five went to Scotland and one went to Ireland. In addition to the above spring mounted engines, No 2936 was built in 1907 to the same general specification but was unsprung on the hind axle. After thirty years' service in Berkshire the engine finished its working life with R J & H Wilder, the well known Wallingford Agricultural Engineers.

Almost concurrently twenty-seven similar 8 NHP GP traction engines were built with 6½ ins dia × 11 ins dia × 12 ins stroke DCC cylinders. No less than twenty-five of these went to New Zealand customers through the Reid & Gray agency.

8 NHP 6 ins × 11 ins × 12 ins DCC DOUBLE GEARED SPRUNG TRACTION ENGINES

No	Built		No	Built	
No 2696	Built	1904	No 3165	Built	1909
2698	"	1904	3227	"	1910
2764	"	1905	3228	"	1910
2778	"	1905	3229	"	1910
2852	"	1906	3348	"	1911
2878	"	1907	3519	"	1913
2886	"	1907	3529	"	1913
2939	"	1907	3568	"	1914
2940	"	1907	3640	"	1915
2941	"	1907	3679	"	1915
2957	"	1907	3875	"	1921
3033	"	1908	3974	"	1924
3131	"	1909	3975	"	1924
3142	"	1909			

Sixteen of the earlier engines had long boilers with forty 2 ins dia × 6 ft 2 ins long smoke tubes. Most of the later engines had 5 ft 8 ins long tubes with six iron stay tubes. All had 6.6 sq ft grates and engines built after 1908 had 200 PSI boilers. Six of the earlier engines were fitted with

Fig 241 No. 3519 8 NHP DCC traction engine engaged upon an unusual task of moving house in New Zealand.

Moore's steam pumps and Nos 2852 and 2886 had the Richardson feed pump. Eleven of the engines were fitted with the American International injector.

All twenty-seven engines were double geared with seventeen leaf springs. Some had the patent differential locking gear and some carried 150 yards of wire rope on their winding drums. Unless otherwise specified it was usual to fit 75 yards of rope on all GP engines. All had 3-speed gearing with ratios of 24.4, 13.6 and 8.3 to 1 and the hind wheels were 6 ft 6 ins dia × 18 ins wide although Nos 3227, 3228 and 3229 were fitted with 20 ins wide wheels and belly tanks having a total water carrying capacity of 335 gallons. It is believed that these engines were used for direct traction ploughing with 2 and 3 furrow ploughs as well as their normal duty as threshing engines. All the New Zealand engines were fitted with a large rectangular headlamp on top of the smokebox.

No 3640 went new to Henry Johnson of Banks near Southport and No 3679 went to a County Wicklow farmer in Ireland. Eleven years later Johnson took delivery of a similar but unsprung double geared threshing engine, No 4050. This engine was originally built as No 3893 in 1921 and for reasons now unknown was apparently left on Burrell's hands renumbered as No 4050 and sold to Johnson in 1926 no doubt at a suitably discounted price. It had the short boiler with 5 ft 8 ins long smoke tubes, a 6.0 sq ft grate and was unusually painted green with brown wheels.

The 6 NHP version of the DCC standard duty GP traction engine was delayed for three years after the introduction of the 7 NHP engines, probably due to lack of sales of the latter. A total of thirty 6 NHP engines with 6 ins dia × 10 ins dia × 10 ins stroke DCC cylinders were produced between 1906 and 1924.

6 NHP 6 ins × 10 ins × 10 ins DCC COMPOUND GP TRACTION ENGINES

No		Built	No		Built
No 2850	Built	1906	No 3739	Built	1916*
2854	"	1906	3746	"	1917
3008	"	1908	3772	"	1917*
3020	"	1908	3782	"	1918
3030	"	1908	3794	"	1919
3040	"	1908	3798	"	1919
3060	"	1908	3813	"	1919
3238	"	1910	3836	"	1920
3252	"	1910	3838	"	1920*
3322	"	1911*	3895	"	1921
3335	"	1911	3916	"	1921
3416	"	1912*	3921	"	1921
3463	"	1913	3925	"	1922
3523	"	1913	3965	"	1923
3612	"	1914	3983	"	1920
3655	"	1915			

*Engines were unsprung on the hind axle.

All except one of these engines had the standard 6 NHP short boiler with a 4.5 sq ft grate, a total heating surface of 117.5 sq ft and thirty-five 2 ins dia × 5 ft 1 ins long smoke tubes. The boilers of engines built after 1910 were pressed to 200 PSI. The exception, No 3322, was built for a New Zealand customer having a 185 PSI boiler fitted with thirty 2 ins dia × 4 ft 9½ ins long smoke tubes. Nos 2850 and 2854 were fitted with Moore's steam pumps and No 3030 had a Worthington steam pump; all three, together with Nos 3030, 3238 and 3335 went to New Zealand.

All the series were double geared to the hind axle, but Nos 3322, 3416, 3739 3772 and 3838 were supplied unsprung. A third of the engines had 3-speed gearing and

Fig 242 No. 3836 6 NHP DCC 3-speed traction engine 'Starlight' photographed in 1932 with Edwards' of Swindon loads.

most had 6 ft 6 ins dia × 18 ins wide hind wheels. Nos 3836 and 3838 both built in July 1920 carried the AGE monograms and were fitted with a full set of machine cut gears. Two of the engines, Nos 3655 and 3836 started life with Noah Judd, a Buckinghamshire timber haulier who operated three Burrell engines for a number of years. In 1922 No 3836 was converted to a Showman's type engine and saw service with S Drake & Sons of Worcester and Charles Butler of Brockley in Gloucestershire before being acquired by R Edwards & Sons of Swindon in 1932. Edwards owned ten Burrell engines at various times in connection with their business as agricultural contractors, road hauliers and travelling showmen. Fig 242 illustrates the engine minus its dynamo platform and show fittings with Edwards' loads at Charlbury in Oxfordshire in the 1930s.

In total seven of the thirty engines in this series went to West Country customers, six went to New Zealand, six went to Scotland and three went to Ireland. No 3925 went to the Suffolk maltsters R H & R Paul and the remaining seven engines went to Northern farmers and haulage contractors.

In 1909 the only DCC 'Aberdeenshire' type engine built, No 3073, was supplied to Stapleton & Sons of Torrington in Devon. It was a 3-speed engine conforming in all respects with the specification given in Chapter 7 for the SCC version. Although generically a traction engine it was much more akin to a light spring mounted double geared road locomotive with a short awning, solid flywheel, motion side plates and belly tanks.

6 NHP DCC 'DEVONSHIRE'
GP TRACTION ENGINES

No	Built	No	Built
No 3061	Built 1908	No 3768	Built 1917
3232	» 1910	3784	» 1918
3297	» 1911	3790	» 1918
3325	» 1911	3812	» 1919
3368	» 1912	3816	» 1919
3421	» 1912	3834	» 1920
3493	» 1913	3835	» 1920
3758	» 1917	3894	» 1921

All except two engines, Nos 3297 and 3816, had the type 3222 boiler pressed to 200 PSI with 4.6 sq ft grates, a total heating surface of 100 sq ft and thirty 2 ins dia × 4 ft 9½ ins long smoke tubes. No 3297 had forty 1¾ ins dia × 4 ft 9½ ins long tubes which had the effect of increasing the total heating surface to 113.0 sq ft and No 3816 had a lengthened boiler with 5 ft 10½ ins long smoke tubes increasing the total heating surface to 116.0 sq ft. Nos 3812, 3834 and 3835 had their smokeboxes lengthened to 1 ft 10½ ins and the firebox roof stays were fitted with nuts instead of being riveted over.

It must remain a matter of frustration to the historian that the circumstances which dictated these special features remain a mystery. Probably they were due to nothing more than a whim of the buyer in a period when competition was severe and orders were difficult to obtain.Generally but not all had 3-speed gearing, 5 ft 7½ ins dia × 16 ins wide wheels, 4 ft 4 ins dia × 5½ ins wide solid flywheels, belly tanks and three-quarter length awnings. Nos 3758 and 3834 were sprung on the hind axle only with solid unsprung forecarriages. Nine of the engines went to agriculturists in the West Country. Three went to the Dumfries and Galoway district in Scotland, two of which, Nos 3061 and 3493 joined J Carswell's fleet of nine Burrell engines. No 3297 went to Charles Burrell's friend Isaac Ball of Wharles in Lancashire, who owned nineteen Burrell traction engines and rollers at various times; No 3812 went to Major George Benson at Much Wenlock in Shropshire and No 3894 went to J B Dugdale a Warwickshire landowner, uniquely painted black. Whilst in preservation the engine has been converted to a Showman's type engine and named 'Saint Brannock'. The works records list No 3834 and 3894 built shortly after the AGE take-over in May 1920 as 5 NHP engines. No mention is made of the name 'Devonshire' engine although they were identical in every detail with No 3812 built prior to the take-over and described in the works' records as 6 NHP 'Devonshire' engine (Batch No drawings 23/321). Both the 1920 engines carried a full set of AGE monograms.

During the First World War No 3696, a light 5 NHP 'Irish' type traction engine was built for the Durham

Fig 243 No. 3816 special long boilered 'Devonshire' type DCC traction engine built in 1919 for Parsons Bros of St Columb Major in Cornwall.

County Council Highways Department. It was as the SCC engines already described in chapter 7 but with 5 ins dia × 8½ ins dia × 9 ins stroke DCC cylinders. The boiler was pressed to 200 PSI, had a 3.7 sq ft grate, a total heating surface of 77.4 sq ft and thirty 1¾ ins dia × 4 ft 2 ins long smoke tubes. The hind wheels were 5 ft 0 ins dia × 14 ins wide, the overall width of the engine was 6 ft 5 ins and it weighed less than 8 tons in working order.

Finally we must consider a miscellany of twenty eight DCC GP traction engines built after the AGE merger during the ten years 1919-1929. The fact that the number built averages less than three engines per annum indicates just how severely trade was depressed. The most numerous were fourteen of the former 'Devonshire' type engines now rated 5 NHP due no doubt to the improved continuous performance figures recently published by some of their competitors for contemporary products due to the higher boiler pressures being used.

5 NHP DCC 5½ ins × 9 ins × 10 ins CYLINDER GP TRACTION ENGINES

No	Built	No	Built
No 3828	Built 1920	No 4014	Built 1928
3902	" 1921	4019	" 1925
3903	" 1921	4020	" 1925
3908	" 1922	4037	" 1926*
3913	" 1923*	4045	" 1926*
3917	" 1921	4055	" 1927
3971	" 1924*	4080	" 1929

*Engines were unsprung on the hind axle.

The engines were basically as the SCC 'Devonshire' engines built between 1907 and 1925 but with DCC cylinders, although a greater proportion had 3-speed gearing with the smaller 5 ft 7½ ins dia × 16 ins wide wheels instead of the more usual 6 ft 0 ins dia wheels. All were double geared on the hind axle, but Nos 3919, 3971, 4037 and 4045 were unsprung and Nos 4014 and 4019 were sprung on the hind axle only. The works specially prepared No 4019 for the 1925 RASE Show held at Chester where it was exhibited painted dark olive green with brown wheels. Latterly this colour was becoming more popular than the traditional Burrell Lake with red wheels. The engine also had a geared feed pump and a special Pemberthy auto-positive injector. No 4080 was unique in that both the crankshaft and the intermediate motion shaft were fitted with Timken taper roller bearings. This undoubtedly represented an important technical development, but unfortunately it came too late in the day.

All fourteen engines went to agriculturists, six in the Eastern Counties, five in the West Country, one in Scotland and one in Ireland. No 3828 went to an organisation calling itself the Llandowgor & Laugharne District Threshing Committee in Cornwall, and No 4020 went to the Wishaw District Dairy Farmers Association Ltd in Scotland illustrating a renewed post war activity in co-operative farming. No 3971 went to the Earl Cadogan of Culford, near Bury St Edmunds as a replacement for his 1891 8 NHP SC engine.

In 1924 the works built a very smart little 5 NHP Showman's type engine, No 3982, with 5½ ins dia × 9 ins

Fig 244 Two views of St Nicholas works erecting shop in the 1920's.

Fig 245 No. 3989 6/7 NHP DCC traction engine, one of four identical engines supplied to Limerick CC Highways Department in the 1920's.

dia × 10 ins stroke DCC cylinders with the intention of exhibiting it at the 1924 RASE Show being held in Leicester. The works records indicate the engine was given a special Class 'A' finish and the intention was to exhibit it with a 5 ton wagon and a 7 NHP SC traction engine to herald a major new AGE sales drive. However, it is by no means certain the engine ever appeared at Leicester, for we next learn that the HP cylinder had been fitted with a liner reducing the bore to 5¼ ins dia. In March 1925 the engine was re-numbered No 4011 and was sold to W S Dewing of Norwich as a 4 NHP GP traction engine. It was a 3-speed engine with 6 ft 0 ins dia × 16 ins wide wheels and was in all other respects as the final 5 NHP DCC engines built in the post war years.

In the same period five engines were sold as 6 NHP engines although fitted with 7 NHP DCC cylinders and three apparently similar engines were sold as 7 NHP engines. It is believed that this anomaly was a last vain attempt to meet competition from Fowlers and Fosters of Lincoln who were getting a lions share of the very limited business then available for GP traction engines. Both these firms were outside the AGE combine which in any event the agricultural fraternity never warmly accepted and loyal Burrell customers were beginning to place orders elsewhere.

FINAL TYPES 6/7 NHP
DCC GP TRACTION ENGINES

No	*Built*	*Rated*
3928	1921	7 NHP
3935	1922	7 NHP
3989	1924	6 NHP
3997	1924	6 NHP
3998	1924	6 NHP
4031	1925	6 NHP (formerly No. 4007)
4049	1926	6 NHP
4053	1926	7 NHP

All had 6 ins dia × 10 ins dia × 12 ins stroke DCC cylinders and all were double geared and unsprung except No 4049 which was sprung on the hind axle only. No 3928 had the standard 7 NHP boiler with 5 ft 8 ins long smoke tubes and a 4.9 sq ft grate. No 3935 had a 7 NHP road locomotive boiler with a 5.49 sq ft grate and 5 ft 8 ins long tubes. Nos 3989, 3997, 3998 and 4053 were fitted with standard 6 NHP boilers with 4.5 sq ft grates, a total heating surface of 117.5 sq ft and thirty-five 2 ins dia × 5 ft 1 ins long smoke tubes. The final three engines, Nos 4031, 4049 and 4053 had the enlarged 4.9 sq ft grates and 5 ft 8 ins long smoke tubes which increased the total heating surface to 130.0 sq ft.

Smithy

Foundry

Fitting Shop

Boiler Shop

Drawing Office

Paint Shop

Fig 246 Typical scenes at St Nicholas works photographed by Lieut. John Owen RASC during his period of training in the works – circa 1923.

Fig 247 A late 8 NHP DCC traction engine, widely acclaimed as the Rolls Royce of traction engines.

All were 2-speed engines with 6 ft 0 ins dia × 18 ins wide hind wheels. They were painted Quaker Green with maroon wheels except No 3928 which was painted chocolate with red wheels. Nos 3928 and 4053 were supplied to Thomas Robey of Melling near Liverpool with 4 ft 0 ins long extension chimneys suggesting they were used mainly for stationary engine duties. No 3935 was fitted with special sensitive governors for working a large saw bench.

No 4049 was used mainly for timber haulage and was fitted with a special wire rope guide on the front axle. It is known that at this time St Nicholas Works produced a number of four and six wheel all-steel timber drags for customers engaged in forestry work. Nos 3989, 3997 and 3998 went to Limerick CC Highways Department for hauling road stone and similar duties increasing to ten their fleet of Burrell engines. The remaining three engines went to contractors in Essex and the Home Counties.

One last DCC traction engine, No 4090, remains for our consideration. In August 1929 Richard Garrett supplied Aveling & Porter Ltd, a member of the AGE concern, with a 8 NHP DCC Burrell traction engine for export to Australia. It had 6¾ ins dia × 11¼ ins dia × 12 ins stroke cylinders, a large boiler with a 6.6 sq ft grate, a total heating surface of 162.0 sq ft and thirty-four 2 ins dia × 6 ft 2 ins long smoke tubes. The engine was double geared and spring mounted with 2-speed gearing and 6ft 6 ins dia × 18 ins wide hind wheels. Unfortunately nothing is known about its ultimate destination or the duties it performed. One thing is certain however, this engine and the preceding double crank compound traction engines were referred to in the heyday of steam as the Rolls Royce of traction engines with every justification.

It is interesting to speculate what further developments we might have seen in the General Purpose traction engine had not the power of the oil lobby and the introduction of the American built Ford tractor during the First World War not spelt the inevitable end of steam in agriculture in the 1920s. Your author feels that primarily the concentration would have been on the greater use of standardisation; the use of taper roller bearings and machine cut gears on the drive shafts thereby reducing friction losses; and improvements in the water circulation and thermal efficiency of the boilers.

CHAPTER FOURTEEN

Colonial Engines

By the time the Burrell geared traction engine became established immediately prior to the world wide agricultural depression (1880–1885) the United Kingdom's external trade exceeded that of Germany, France and Italy together and was four times that of the United States. Sadly this prosperity did not last and British supremacy in manufactured goods was never wholly regained as other European countries established their own industries and the vast cereal growing lands of Central Europe and the North America prairies came under cultivation.

Although Charles Burrell had established a European presence as early as 1863, it was the larger firms like John Fowler, Marshalls of Gainsborough and Clayton & Shuttleworth who made big investments in securing their overseas markets, the fruits of which they enjoyed until the outbreak of war in 1914 changed the face of the world. Essentially, Burrell remained a country agricultural machinery manufacturer until the 1890s, supplying mainly the needs of East Anglia. The limited export business they obtained resulted largely from their regular participation in the now internationally recognised annual Smithfield and RASE Shows.

As we have seen, Robert Burrell began to venture further afield in the mid 1880s, making regular visits to France, Germany, Eastern Europe and Russia. Undoubtedly, he built up goodwill wherever he went and achieved considerable success, but the value of exports as a proportion of total sales remained small until the New Zealand market for G P traction engines was established in the late 1880s.

During this period the only design concessions made by St Nicholas Works to the special needs of overseas markets were modifications to engine boilers thereby making them suitable for burning wood, straw, and other kinds of inferior fuels. It was relatively easy to adopt portable engines for burning straw where 3½ times the weight of straw was required to achieve the same heat output as coal, but it proved much more difficult to apply straw burning to self-moving engines. Not only were there problems associated with the transportation and feeding large quantities of straw into the firebox, but it became necessary to increase the grate area of the firebox and develop water filled ashpans in order to increase the thermal efficiency of the boiler and ensure an acceptable firebox life, whilst minimising the increased fire risks. Rocking grates became necessary to facilitate removal of the greater quantity of ash generated and firebox arches and baffle plates became necessary in order to reduce the formation of clinker and ensure complete combustion of the fuel before it reached the smoke tubes. Similarly, improved smokebox spark arresters proved essential to prevent igniting the stockpile of straw awaiting to be fed into the firebox. As has already been noted in chapter 8, special straw feeding apparatus was frequently incorporated in portable engines supplied overseas, such as the patent Head & Schemioth system and the R & T Elworthy and Ruston systems.

Similarly, wood fuel necessitated a larger grate area, increased provisions for storing the bulky fuel on the engine tender and improved spark arresting facilities in the smokebox.

Burrell traction engines built for overseas customers where the only significant difference from those sold in the United Kingdom was the enlarged grate, have already been dealt with in Chapters 6 and 7. A typical example is illustrated in Fig 90 showing No 3071, a 7 NHP G P traction engine built for the Australian market in 1909. It had an enlarged grate, a lengthened boiler and smokebox fitted with a spark arrester and a special tender for carrying the bulky wood fuel.

The score of Burrell engines built uniquely for export between 1894 and 1914 may conveniently be divided into three categories. Firstly, those built primarily for the difficult Australian market where there were vast undeveloped areas having virtually no roads, where skilled labour was scarce, American competition was severe, and the Australian Government imposed penal import restrictions. These engines basically retained their British character whilst every effort was made to lighten and cheapen them and they became known as the 'Colonist' type engine.

Secondly, there were the South American straw burning engines. Only two were built at St Nicholas Works and both must be regarded as experimental designs. They were intended for the lucrative Argentinian market which had been built up by Marshalls and to a lesser extent by Fowlers during the previous two decades, both firms having achieved their market share in direct competition with American manufacturers. Between 1894 and the introduction of their Gainsborough Light Traction Engine in 1906 Marshalls built over 130 10 NHP and 12 NHP self-propelled traction engines for the Argentine. Fundamentally they were little different from portable engines made self-moving and generally they were lighter than their conventional traction engine counterparts. They were very basic engines without any frills other than exhaust steam water heaters. Later a friction clutch incorporated in the flywheel became a feature of these

Fig 248 The first big 8 NHP wood burning road locomotive supplied to an Australian customer in 1890.

engines which were used mainly for threshing on the vast Argentinian Pampus. Generally they had single speed gearing and were unsuitable for continuous haulage duties. After 1906 variants of the Gainsborough Light Traction Engine became very popular with overseas buyers and they found their way to the four corners of the world. Many of these engines were used for direct traction ploughing and by 1914 several other UK manufacturers such as Clayton & Shuttleworth, Ransomes, Richard Garrett, William Foster, J & H McLaren, Ruston & Proctor and Robey's of Lincoln had entered the field with varying degrees of success.

The third category of Burrell engine built uniquely for export was the Italian direct traction ploughing engine. Although a number of Italian firms had produced portable engines based on British designs since the 1850s it was once again Marshalls of Gainsborough who opened the market to the English traction engine. They were fortunate in having an excellent agent, Alberto Riva of Milan, and from 1880 he produced a steady flow of orders for 7 NHP and 8 NHP G P traction engines which were used mainly for threshing and direct traction ploughing in the enormously fertile valley of the River Po centred around the towns of Piacenza and Parma. Marshalls' success undoubtedly encouraged Robert Burrell to explore the market potential himself and he appointed a small Milanese portable engine manufacturer with English principles, Bale and Edwards, as agents. They produced their first tangible results in 1900 with an order for a large 10 NHP SCC double geared unsprung traction engine, No 2285, which was specially prepared for direct traction ploughing. There the matter rested for thirteen years. In retrospect one suspects that the 2-speed gear ratios selected for this engine proved unsuitable, for these were substantially altered when interest was renewed in 1913. Ten engines of differing sizes were built in the period 1913 to 1915 but the market appears to have become a war casualty and after the war the Italians relied mainly upon local production. The ten Burrell engines went to a new agent, Societa Italiana Macchine of Piacenza and nothing further was heard of Bale and Edwards.

The first two of these engines, Nos 3477 and 3492 were delivered in the early summer of 1913. They were 8 NHP DCC engines with 6½ ins dia × 11 ins dia × 12 ins stroke cylinders and had unsprung double gearing to the hind axle. The boilers, pressed to 200 PSI had 8.5 sq ft grates, a total heating surface of 196.5 sq ft and thirty-five 2 ins dia × 7 ft 6 ins long smoke tubes. The exceptionally long boiler enabled 4 ft 6 ins long connecting rods to be used and still left sufficient space for a McLaren exhaust steam feed water heater to be mounted between the cylinder and the chimney. In accordance with local boiler regulations the boilers were fitted with Salter type spring safety valves. The engines were fitted with 2-speed gearing having ratios of 37.5 and 21.5 to 1 and had 6 ft 6 ins dia × 24 ins wide hind wheels which permitted ploughing speeds in excess of 2.5 MPH. The spoked flywheels were 4ft 6 ins dia and a special 2-speed Pickering governor was fitted operating at 192 and 220 RPM. Belly tanks were fitted and the engines had a water carrying capacity of 324 gallons. The overall width of the engines was 9 ft 4½ ins and they weighed 15 tons 15 cwt.

A further two 8 NHP engines, Nos 3564 and 3567 were supplied in May 1914 and December 1915 respectively, but these had the cylinders increased to 7 ins × 11½ ins × 12 ins stroke. In all other respects they were as the 1913 engines except that 3-speed Pickering governors were fitted operating at 220, 250 and 280 RPM.

Almost concurrently a similar 10 NHP engine No 3559 with 7¼ ins dia × 11¾ ins dia × 12 ins stroke cylinders

Fig 249 No 3477 8 NHP DCC double geared unsprung direct traction ploughing engine seen at work in the Po Valley in Northern Italy.

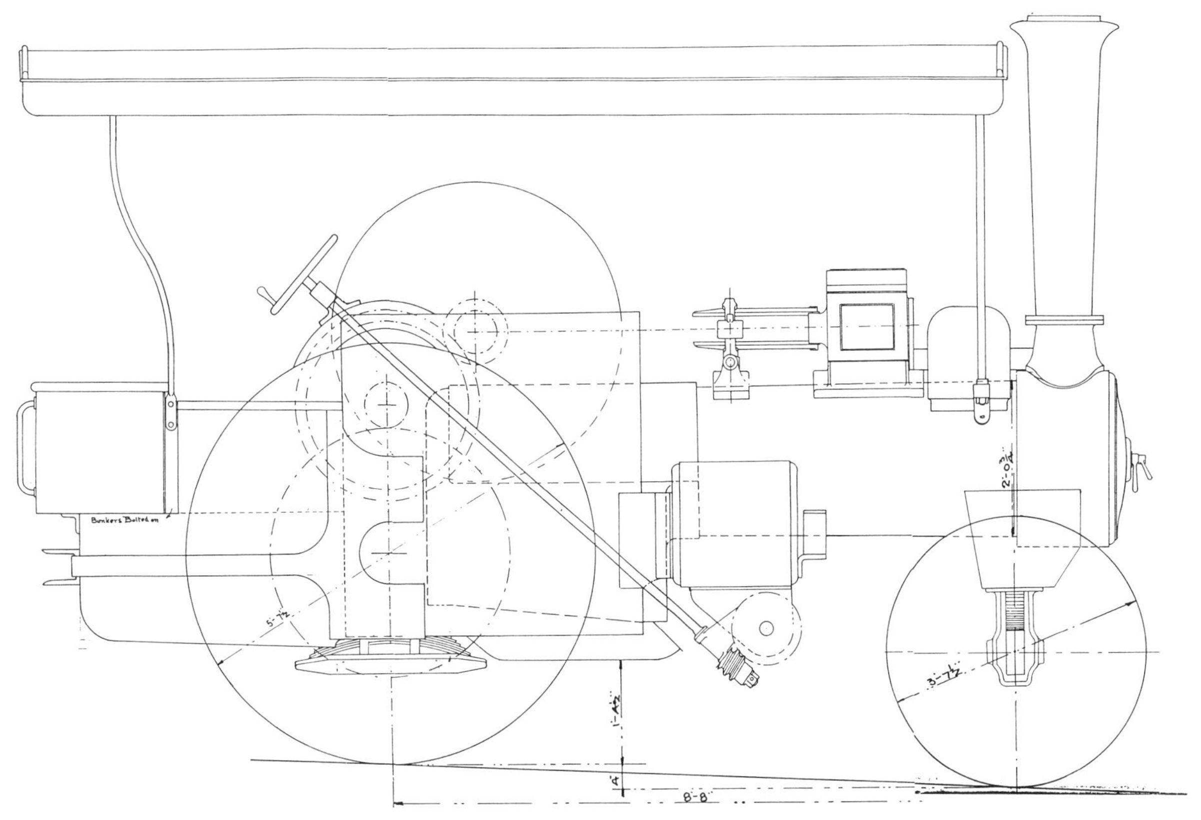

Fig 250 Works' General Assembly drawing of No 3573 6 NHP 'Italian' type direct traction ploughing engine built in 1914.

Fig 251 No 3130 10 NHP DCC direct traction ploughing engine with extra large belly tanks supplied to New Zealand in 1909.

was supplied having an even larger boiler. Pressed to 200 PSI the grate area was 9.2 sq ft, the total heating surface 234.3 sq ft and the thirty-eight 2 ins dia smoke tubes were 8ft 6 ins long. The gearing, wheel sizes and 3-speed governor were as the 8 NHP engines but the all-up weight was increased to nearly 17 tons.

The remaining five engines were rated 6 NHP. No 3573 delivered in May 1914 had 5 ins dia × 8½ ins dia × 9 ins stroke SCC cylinders and was similar to the 'Irish' type engines previously described, but with a larger 200 PSI boiler having a 4.2 sq ft grate and 5 ft 1 ins long smoke tubes which increased the total heating surface to 91 sq ft. The engine was double geared and unsprung on the hind axle having 2-speed gearing with ratios 45.2 and 24.2 to 1. The hind wheels were 5 ft 7½ ins dia × 20 ins wide. The spoked flywheel was 4 ft 0 ins dia and the Pickering governor was set to operate at 300 RPM. The tender comprised two circular bunkers with central entry to the footplate and like all the other Italian engines the steering was on the right hand side of the engine. Although it was fitted with a long awning, belly tanks and 20 ins wide wheels giving an overall width of 8 ft 1 ins the engine weighed only 9 tons 12 cwt.

The other four Italian engines had 6 ins dia × 10 ins dia × 10 ins stroke DCC cylinders and 200 PSI boilers with 5.76 sq ft grates and 5 ft 8 ins long smoke tubes. All were fitted with the McLaren exhaust steam feed water heaters. Nos 3563, 3569 and 3570 were double geared and unsprung with 2-speed gearing having ratios of 48.5 and 26.2 to 1 and 6 ft 0ins dia × 20¼ ins wide hind wheels. No 3577 was double geared and spring mounted, the 2-speed gear ratios were 23.7 and 13.9 to 1 and the hind wheels were 5ft 7½ ins × 16 ins wide. Like all the Italian direct traction ploughing engines, they were provided with special draw bar arrangements for the attachment of gang ploughs which included two vertical and two horizontal guide rollers on the back of the tender. As might be expected all were fitted with differential locking gear. No 3577 carried no belly tanks and was only 7 ft 0 ins wide compared with the 8 ft 3 ins of the unsprung engines; it was 2 tons lighter and is presumed to have been intended mainly for vine cultivation.

Before considering the Australian Colonial engines mention must be made of two big direct traction ploughing engines produced by St Nicholas Works in the early part of the 20th century. No 2596, a 10 NHP engine with 7 ins dia × 11½ ins dia × 12 ins stroke DCC cylinders and spring mounted double gearing to the hind axle was ordered by the London Confirming House of Henry Pynegar for a South African customer in 1903. Unfortunately we do not know the ultimate destination of this unique engine, but immediately after the conclusion of the Boer War there was considerable new investment in agricultural machinery in both Natal and the Transvaal. It was during this period that John Fowler acquired their 22,000 acre experimental farm at Vereeniging in the district of Heidelberg and appointed William McLaren, the third of the McLaren brothers of Leeds as their Resident Engineer. The situation on the Veldt was not unlike that on the Canadian Prairies where it was often said that the length of a furrow was equal to the distance an engine could travel in a working day.

Fig 252 No 3168 7 NHP DCC traction engine with large wood burning grate supplied to Australia in 1910.

The boiler was pressed to 175 PSI with an 8.5 sq ft wood burning grate, a total heating surface of 177.0 sq ft and the forty 2 ins dia smoke tubes were 6 ft 7 ins long. It is believed that this was the first Burrell traction engine to be fitted with a rocking grate to drawing No 1974. Uniquely, this exceptionally long 2 ft 6 ins dia boiler barrel was rolled from a single $\frac{7}{16}$ ins thick plate which almost certainly was originally rolled by Krupps of Essen.

The special 20 leaf spring gear was supplied by J & H McLaren of Leeds. The double geared transmission shafts were fitted with a screw down brake mounted on the left hand main spur wheel, and the winding drum carried 100 yards of $2\frac{1}{4}$ ins circumference steel plough rope. The 2-speed gearing had ratios of 24.4 and 13.6 to 1 and the hind wheels were 6 ft 6 ins dia × 36 ins wide, giving an extraordinary overall width of 10 ft 11 ins. Exceptionally large belly tanks were fitted giving a total water carrying capacity of 445 gallons. The engine was fitted with a special draw bar for the attachment of gang ploughs; a short awning; and a 12ins plate rack for carrying the wood fuel. The overall weight was 17 tons $1\frac{1}{2}$ cwt.

Nine years later in 1909 St Nicholas Works built a similar 10 NHP DCC Direct Traction Ploughing engine for New Zealand. No 3130, shipped through Gardiner & Co of London for the Reid & Gray agency in Dunedin, the engine had the same cylinder and boiler as the 1903 South African engine. The detailed variations were that the boiler was pressed to 200 PSI and a Richardson steam pump and an International injector were supplied to deal with the boiler feed water. The engine was spring mounted and double geared to the hind axle, but on this occassion Burrells used their own design of 17 leaf spring gear. It had 3-speed gearing with ratios of 24.4, 13.6 and 8.3 to 1 driving 6 ft 6 ins dia × 20 ins wide hind wheels. Although the water carrying capacity was increased to 465 gallons the overall width of the engine was reduced to 8 ft $6\frac{1}{2}$ ins and the total weight was nearly 3 tons lighter than the earlier engine. Hopefully at some time in the future somebody somewhere will be able to tell us more about the life and usage of these two special engines.

Charles Burrell were obviously dissatisfied with the level of sales achieved in Australia and in 1904 they terminated the Howard agency and appointed E Coulson of Melbourne to look after their interests. Several other British manufacturers had been more successful and the growing competition from the Americans, especially the Buffalo-Pitts Company was a matter for concern. In 1907 the first of four specially designed 'Colonist' type engines was completed at St Nicholas Works in a last attempt to secure a larger share of this difficult market. All were basically 5 NHP engines although each differed considerably in detail and it is clear the Drawing Office had very much in mind the need to cheapen the product as much as possible, consistent with performance and

Fig 253 No 2902 'The Colonist' light SCC traction engine specially designed for the Australian market in 1907.

reliablity. No 2902 built in May 1907 had 5 ins dia × 8½ ins dia × 9 ins stroke SCC cylinders. It was double geared and spring mounted on the hind axle. No 2945 built in October 1907 had the compound cylinders replaced by a single cylinder measuring 7 ins dia × 9 ins stroke. No 2981 built in March 1908 had a larger single cylinder measuring 7½ ins dia × 10 ins stroke. It was unsprung and had single drive gearing to the hind axle, and finally, No 2990 built in May 1908 reverted to the 7 ins dia × 9 ins stroke single cylinder and double gearing to the hind axle but was unsprung. One suspects that each option was offered slightly cheaper than its predecessor.

Nos 2902, 2945 and 2990 had boilers with 4.7 sq ft grates, a total heating surface of 80.6 sq ft and thirty 1¾ ins dia smoke tubes, 4 ft 2 ins long. No 2981 had a larger boiler with a 5.76 sq ft grate, a total heating surface of 104.16 sq ft and thirty-four 1¾ ins dia × 4 ft 9½ ins long smoke tubes. All had 2-speed gearing with ratios 28.9 and 17.6 to 1 driving 6 ft 0 ins dia hind wheels. None were fitted with belly tanks and weighed between 9 tons 3 cwt and 7 tons 18 cwt each. All had spark arresters in the longer than usual smokeboxes and a ring on the smokebox door was inscribed 'Burrells' Colonist'. The tenders were fitted with 18 ins high racks extended backwards by 14 ins. All were fitted with the novel 'Tick-a-tock' eccentric driven lubricators mounted on the boiler backplate. Sadly, no repeat orders were forthcoming.

Burrells' two attempts to gain a footing in the South American special straw burning engine market were widely spaced and unfortunately in neither instance do the surviving works' records tell us the precise destination of the engines. No 1794 was built in September 1894 and was supplied to the English Manufacturing Export Company of London. Probably their only interest was that of a Confirming House. The second engine, No 3053, built in November 1908 was supplied to Veithardt & Hall of Eastcheap, London acting upon behalf of the Argentinian firm A G Pruden & Co who were probably agents.

No 1794 had a single cylinder measuring 9 ins dia × 12 ins stroke and 4-shaft transmission double geared to the unsprung hind axle. The boiler, pressed to 140 PSI had a 6.8 sq ft grate, a total heating surface of 143.78 sq ft and twently-six 2½ ins dia × 6 ft 2 ins long smoke tubes. The firebox contained a large fixed baffle plate and a smaller hinged plate. The smokebox was of the extended pattern fitted with a spark arrester and the ashpan was arranged to hold water. The straw was mechanically fed to the firebox by a chain drive from an intermediate shaft mounted behind the boiler backplate which was belt driven from the crankshaft. The layout of the footplate and the Head & Schemioth patent straw feed arrangements can be clearly seen by reference to Fig 255. The supply of boiler feed water relied upon a single eccentric driven feed pump.

The 4-shaft drive drove the hind wheels through large cast internally toothed spur wheels attached to the inside of the wheel rims thereby relieving the spokes of any strain. The chill cast iron wheel rims had integral strakes and the

Fig 254 No 1794, an experimental 8 NHP 4-shaft South American type straw burning engine built in 1894.

spokes were round in accordance with then current American practice. It appears that the second transmission shaft gearing was mounted on a stub axle attached to the side of the firebox, which was undoubtedly a retrograde design feature.

The third transmission shaft was arranged across the engine below the boiler in front of the firebox. The 2-speed gearing had ratios of 19.69 and 12.8 to 1 driving the 5 ft 9 ins dia × 20 ins wide hind wheels. Usually the American built engines had only a single speed geared drive. Compensating gear was provided on the third transmission shaft but the engine was without a winding drum, a differential locking device or brakes of any description. It will be noted that no hornplates were used and the regulator lever and reversing lever were mounted on cast brackets attached to the round top firebox. A standard 4ft 6 ins dia × 6 ins wide flywheel was mounted on the left hand side of the engine. It was not uncommon to find a smaller flywheel on the right hand side of American built straw burners because whereas British threshing machines always had the drive pulleys on the left hand side of the machine, the Americans fitted them on the right hand side. Another practice common on the American continent was the use of exceptionally long belts to drive the threshing machine. Often these were in excess of 100 feet long and were intended to minimise the engine's exposure to dust and the inherent fire risks when handling large volumes of straw. Burrells' standard cross arm governors were fitted and a large water tank was mounted under the boiler barrel. The engine was 7 ft 8 ins overall width and weighed 9 tons 17 cwt.

No 3053 was a larger and altogether more modern design rated 12 NHP. The single cylinder measured 10 ins dia × 12 ins stroke and the 160 PSI boiler had exceptionally long smoke tubes. The grate area was 9.1 sq ft, the total heating surface 206.4 sq ft and the thirty-three 2½ ins dia smoke tubes were 7 ft 8 ins long making it fully comparable in performance with the 100 HP American engines then dominating the South American market. The firebox was fitted with a brick arch, the ashpan was arranged to hold water, improved mechanical straw feeding arrangements were provided and the latest type of spark arresting gear was fitted to the smokebox and on the 5 ft 0 ins long wrought iron hinged chimney top.

Fig 255 No 1794 photographed in the Works' yard clearly showing the patent Head & Schemioth straw feeding apparatus.

Fig 256 No 3053 12 NHP SC South American type straw burning engine built in 1908 illustrating the clutch gear on the end of the crankshaft.

The layout of the footplate and the straw feeding arrangements can be seen by reference to Fig 257.

The 4-shaft double geared transmission system was retained, but all the shafts ran the full width of the engine in bearings carried in the hornplates. The compensating gear was on the gear side of the third motion shaft, but no springs, winding drum, differential locking gear or brakes were provided. A friction clutch was fitted on the gear side end of the crankshaft in accordance with the latest American practice. This was incorporated in a smaller flywheel. The object of the friction clutch was to enable the engine to set back without stopping when the long driving belt stretched in the heat. It was claimed also that it made the engine easier to handle when starting under load and when manoeuvring on soft ground. The engine was really only suitable for driving a threshing machine and was considered quite unsuitable for continuous haulage duties. Two-speed gearing was provided having ratios of 24.0 and 13.4 to 1 driving 6 ft 0 ins dia × 30 ins wide hind wheels which had cast strakes riveted onto the outer rims.

The main spoked flywheel was 3 ft 6 ins dia × 12 ins wide making it suitable for use with a long driving belt and the Pickering governor was set to control the engine speed at 200 RPM. It carried only 64 gallons of water in a tender mounted water tank confirming the engines' use primarily as being for stationary duties.

The engine had an overall width of 9 ft 9 ins and weighed 12 ton 11 cwt. It was given a Show finish by the Paint Shop indicating that it was probably shipped to the Argentine in order to participate initially in an exhibition or agricultural show. It was painted Burrells' standard lake finish with broad gilt lining on the motion shaft splashers and flat wheel spokes.

1908 marked a peak year in the fortunes of Charles Burrell & Sons Ltd. The number of employees exceeded the 400 mark and sales reached new heights. Charles I and Robert Burrell were dead and Frederick was incarcerated in a home at Heigham near Norwich. The Board comprised Charles II as Chairman and Managing Director holding the majority of the shares and his son, Herbert John born in 1875. After spending some time in Paris, Herbert was educated at Oundle School and Cambridge and then worked in the City training to be a Stockbroker.

Fig 257 A footplate view of No 3053 showing the manual straw feed arrangement and the 30 ins wide hind wheels.

Fig 258 No 2293 6 NHP SCC road locomotive seen undergoing repairs in the Australian Out-back illustrating the primitive conditions in which engines often had to be erected and repaired in overseas territories.

No doubt pressure from his father brought him back to Thetford, but he was generally regarded by the workforce as an unsympathetic sort of man. It was felt that he was never really interested in the welfare of the firm or its continuity although it undoubtedly enabled him to live the pleasant life of a country gentleman. In 1902 he had married Maud Salmon of Blandford in Dorset, the niece of the then Town Clerk of Thetford and they resided at Nunthorpe in Thetford. In due course he was appointed to the Town Council and became a Justice of the Peace. For many years he was Vice President of the local Conservative Association and throughout his life cricket remained his great love.

Charles II's wife, Sarah died in 1910 and two years later he remarried an old family friend, Annie Phillis Wilberforce, a widow of Fulford in Somerset. In 1914 the Board was increased to five members and Charles II's son, Charles William Wilberforce (1879–1962) was appointed to the Board as Director responsible for Sales, together with Ellen Elizabeth Burrell, Charles II's spinster sister and Mrs Ellen Burrell, Robert's widow. Within a few months Wilberforce joined the army and served in the Royal Engineers with great distinction. By the end of 1914 Thetford held the record of having sent the largest percentage of men to the Colours in relationship to its population. Wilberforce served in Gallipoli and was mentioned in despatches several times. He was eventually awarded the OBE and retired in 1918 with the rank of Lieut. Colonel. Tragically his only son, Brian was killed in a motorcycle accident and he finally retired from business when the company went into liquidation, devoting the remainder of his life to the affairs of Thetford Town Council of which he became an Alderman.

Following the outbreak of world war in August 1914 it is said that the Directors made absolutely no effort to secure Government Contracts for the company's traditional products, nor did they seek contracts for any of the multitude of manufactured goods needed for the war effort. In 1915 the Ministry of Munitions stepped in and compulsorily made the company undertake the manufacture of 18 pound shrapnel shell bodies and fuse parts. A number of women were recruited and trained for work in the machine shops and during the next three years St Nicholas Works produced:

37,000	– 18 pound high explosive shells
22,000	– High explosive shrapnel shells
1,796,000	– Fuse adaptors
180,000	– 13 pound & 18 pound explosive base plates
70,000	– Shrapnel discs

In 1918 the firm and the local Bench were greatly embarrassed by a prosecution brought against the company by Woolwich Arsenal for trying to disguise faulty shell production. The fault had been recognised by the shop floor management and crude attempts had been made to rectify the matter without consultation with the Ministry's inspectors. This would have meant that had the shells been fired in anger they would have been too thin to resist the ignition of the propellant charge, with disastrous consequences. Before passing judgement the Mayor as Chairman of the Bench made a statement saying, "I should like to express on behalf of the Magistrates our regret that our greatly respected neighbours, Messrs Charles Burrell & Sons are placed in the present position of affairs." Imposing a fine of £100 on both Campbell Wilson, the Works Manager and Samuel Wyres, the Machine Shop Foreman he added, "We are in a painful position but we have to carry out our duties."

This was probably the only black mark in the long and distinguished history of the Burrell concern. After the cessation of hostilities events moved slowly but nevertheless inexorably towards the merger with the Agricultural & General Engineers conglomerate. We shall deal with these events in Chapter 18 after considering the company's activities in the fields of steam road rollers, one man operation steam tractors and steam lorries.

CHAPTER FIFTEEN

Steam Road Rollers

The credit for building the first steam powered road roller goes to a French construction engineer, Louis Lemoine, an employee of the Bordeaux Municipality. He filed his patent in 1859 just ninety years after his compatriot, Nicholas Cugnot, a military engineer, tested a steam road engine in the streets of Paris. Lemoine demonstrated his roller in the Bois de Boulogne in August 1860. Concurrently, another French engineer, Amedée Ballaison working independently of Lemoine patented an entirely different version of the steam road roller. This was commercially developed by another Parisian company, Gallerat et Cie who succeeded in hiring several rollers to the Paris Municipality. In due course they concluded a licencing agreement with the Leeds locomotive builders, Manning Wardle & Company who are known to have built at least one Gallerat engine, but they soon abandoned the project. At this time the worldwide demand for railway locomotives was at an unprecedently high level and it seems probable that Manning Wardle were aware that promising developments were taking place elsewhere and they decided to step down.

In 1862 William Fothergill Batho, formerly a draughtsman at Sharp Brothers in Manchester and later Manager of Nettlefold's screw factory in Birmingham put up his plate as a Consulting Engineer. He became engineering advisor and agent to the Calcutta Municipality and Port Trust and the Oude & Rohilkund Railway. Working with William Clark, the superintendent of New Works in Calcutta, he completed drawings of a steam road roller which Clark had proposed. Not having any manufacturing facilities of his own, Batho commissioned the well known Birmingham railway engineers, Worsdell & Evans to build his prototype engine which was shipped to Calcutta in 1863. The engine appears to have been successful but Worsdell declined to undertake further production. A younger son of Quaker Thomas Clarke Worsdell who built the tender for Stephenson's 'Rocket' and the first carriages for the Liverpool and Manchester Railway in 1829, Worsdell was steeped in the railway tradition and saw no future for road engines of any description.

Batho next turned his attention to work that had been done in London's Hyde Park in 1866 by Thomas Aveling of Rochester in conjunction with Easton, Amos & Anderson, well known mechanical engineers and consultants to the Royal Agricultural Society of England. It appears that Batho and Aveling established a rapport whilst attending meetings of the Institution of Mechanical Engineers. Both men had been elected members of this august body and both attended the paper given by Gellerat in 1869 in which he described the construction and performance of his Paris engines.

At this time Aveling had already secured several orders as a result of the Hyde Park trials and he was quick to appreciate the benefits of Batho's design which provided him with a greatly improved three-point roller whose wheels effectively covered the full width of the engine thereby eliminating the problem of unequal compaction which characterised his original design. Aveling's first engine to embrace these features was a 30 ton monster supplied to Liverpool Corporation. In 1870 the two men jointly presented an interesting paper before the Institution of Mechanical Engineers describing their work. Later in the same year Aveling introduced his celebrated hornplate design which was soon found to be equally applicable to both traction engines and road rollers. The Batho design was not readily adaptable to this important innovation and Aveling also appreciated the need to reduce the weight of the Batho type engines. Henceforth, the two men went their separate ways and for the next decade Aveling concentrated upon improving the design of the roller forecarriage.

By 1890 the Aveling concern had sold nearly 500 road rollers and virtually held a complete monopoly in the United Kingdom. The only competition came from Thomas Green & Sons Ltd of Leeds who entered the market in 1874 with a light steam powered roller primarily intended for use on large estates. Following Aveling's untimely death in 1882, John Fowler & Co produced their first roller in 1884, but production remained small and was mainly exported until the 1890s. There had always been a tacit agreement between Aveling and his friend David Grieg, a partner in Fowlers', that the latter would refrain from the manufacture of road rollers so long as Aveling left the field clear for Fowler to concentrate upon their steam ploughing engines.

The situation radically changed with the passing of the Local Government Act of 1888 which created the County Councils substantially in their present form, thereby removing the responsibility for the maintenance of our roads from the Turnpike Trusts. The position was further consolidated by the Act of 1894 which established the present Urban and Rural District Councils. Within a few years eight more British traction engine builders had entered the field and by the end of the steam road roller era in the middle of the present century over 6000 rollers had been supplied to UK Local Authorities and road rolling contractors, many more were exported.

Fig 259 No 1535 the first Thetford built road roller with 4-shaft drive and 5" × 9" × 9" SCC cylinders. Built in December 1891.

Thomas Aitken in his contemporary treaties on Road Making and Maintenance summed up the advantages of road rolling as follows:

1 A saving of metalling materials as the stones are interlocked by the process of consolidation and present only one surface subject to wear compared with the abrasion inseparable from the system of patching and consolidation by normal wheeled traffic.
2 A harder and more regular surface is obtained, the road generally has a better appearance, ease of traction is promoted, injury and suffering to animals are avoided and the damage to wheels of vehicles is reduced.
3 The crust of the road contains only a small amount of binding or soluble matter, consequently there is a reduction of mud in wet and dust in dry weather; and the surface of the road does not require the constant attention which is necessary with metalling during the long process of consolidation by vehicular traffic.
4 Scraping and cleaning are reduced to a minimum by reason of the road being practically impervious to the effects of weather and traffic; the surface wears longer and the absence of loose stones in dry weather secures greater efficiency and diminishes maintenance costs.

Generally, 12 ton rollers were used for country roads, although most makers produced 15 ton models and even a few 20 ton were made. Ten ton rollers were for the most part employed in the towns and cities due to the danger of fracturing gas and water mains and other service pipes.

The selection of a roller also depended to a great extent upon the local metalling material available, the optimum weight being that which would fully consolidate the coating without crushing the stones of which it was composed. A 15 ton roller with 18 ins wide wheels would be equivalent to a weight of 5.42 cwt per inch width of the driving wheels, which would crush and render useless stones of the less tough or brittle variety. By contrast a 12 ton roller with 17 ins wide driving wheels would be equivalent to a weight of 4.59 cwt per ins and a 10 ton roller with 16 ins wide wheels, 3.94 cwt per ins of width. With the advent of tarmacadam in the early years of the 20th century, roller weights were further reduced and 6 and 8 ton machines were added to most manufacturers' range.

A 15 ton roller working continously for a nine hour period would consolidate between 60 and 70 tons of material, equivalent to 60 cubic yards a day depending upon the type of material used, the thickness of the coating applied and the type of binding. The amount of work done by a 10 or 12 ton roller under similar conditions and time would be 40 to 50 tons. At the time of the passing of the 1888 & 1894 Acts most authorities based their costs on a figure of 10d per ton for working expenses including depreciation and repairs.

Most County Authorities worked on the principle of one road roller for every 100–120 miles of road used primarily for local traffic and agricultural needs, and one roller for every 60–80 miles where there was a significant volume of industrial traffic. In provincial towns and cities one roller was regarded as sufficient for every 40–50 miles of road. At the turn of the century 100 steam rollers were in daily use in London maintaining over 2000 miles of road.

Charles Burrell built their first road roller in 1891 but it is by no means certain that events at home were primarily responsible for their decision to enter this market. The company were by then reaping the benefits of Robert Burrell's hard work in Europe where a large potential was known to exist. The majority of road rollers built by St Nicholas Works before the First World War were exported. Out of a total of 405 road rollers and convertible engines built between 1891 and 1929 no less than 237 were exported. 108 went to Germany, 49 to France and 17 to Sweden. During the same period only 40 Burrell rollers went to UK Local Authorities and 125 went to UK contractors. Most of the latter were built in the post war period after the company had lost many of its established export markets and was struggling for orders.

Before considering the different types of roller produced at St Nicholas Works in detail, it is of interest to note that of the 405 engines built, 295 had single crank compound

Fig 260 No 1836 a second generation road roller with 3-shaft drive and 5″ × 9″ × 9″ SCC cylinders built for a Hungarian customer in 1895.

cylinders, 60 had single cylinders and 50 had double crank compound cylinders. All were 3-shaft engines except the first ten and three built in 1911 for the French rolling contractor, Jean Bonhoure of Toulouse, which had the 4-shaft transmission system. The reasons for initially employing the 4-shaft principle are obscure. However, it made possible the use of larger and longer bearings and most of Burrells' competitors employed this arrangement on their rollers which may have been sufficient justification in itself when entering a new field. Similarly, the great preponderance of the SCC arrangement is of interest. The company's early literature placed great stress on the fuel and water savings associated with compounding and upon the engines quietness in operation thereby avoiding, "the objectionable snorting of the single cylinder engine which frightens horses upon the highways and in the towns." Although the exhaust of the single crank compounds certainly had a softer note, the starting characteristics were similar to the single cylinder engine and the heavy crosshead assembly mitigated against quick reversing of the engine.

5 ins × 9 ins × 9 ins SCC 4-SHAFT ROAD ROLLER

No 1535	Built 1891	No 1673	Built 1893
1598	" 1892	1681	" 1893
1608	" 1892	1713	" 1893
1613	" 1892	1737	" 1894
1653	" 1892	1753	" 1894

The same steam jacketed 5 ins dia × 9 ins dia × 9 ins stroke SCC cylinders and motion were employed as used on the 6 NHP light compound GP traction engines introduced in 1890 including the patent starting valve admitting live steam directly into the LP cylinder when required. The 160 PSI boiler was also similar to that used on the traction engine although the proportions were somewhat smaller. The steel firebox had a grate area of 3.6 sq ft, the total heating surface was 76.4 sq ft and thirty 1¾ ins dia × 4 ft 2 ins long smoke tubes were employed. All ten engines were fitted with eccentric driven boiler feed pumps and either Gresham's, Madan's or the Schutte injector.

The 4-shaft transmission provided 2-speed gearing having ratios of 22.3 and 14.3 to 1. Neither compensating gear nor a winding drum were fitted, the wheels being driven through pins engaging with the axle mounted draw box. Both sets of rolls were produced from a special cast iron mix with mild steel plate added to improve the hardness. No 1535 had 5 ft 0 ins dia × 18 ins wide hind rolls but the remaining nine engines had 5 ft 6 ins wide hind rolls and all had two 3 ft 7½ ins dia × 25½ ins wide front rolls. The front end was very similar to the contemporary Aveling rollers with the cast forecarriage bolted directly to the smokebox forming an integral part of the chimney base. The forecarriage fork was arranged to swivel both horizontally and vertically and the steering arrangement allowed the engine to turn in its own length. No 1535 had a solid 3 ft 4 ins dia × 4 ins wide flywheel, the remaining engines in the series had 4 ft 0 ins dia × 5 ins wide solid flywheels which permitted belt driving stationary machinery such as stone breakers in either a backwards or forwards position. All were fitted with motion side plates and carried water sufficient for two hours working.

No 1535 went new to Mornement & Ray at nearby Harling in Norfolk which no doubt enabled the works to carefully monitor its performance and suitability. Three engines, Nos 1598, 1653 and 1713 went to Local Authorities and Nos 1608 and 1613 went to UK road rolling contractors. The remaining four engines, Nos 1673, 1681, 1737 and 1753 went to Germany fitted with boilers built in accordance with then current German boiler regulations and had spark arresters and a baffle plate designed to protect the front tube plate mounted in the smokebox. All four engines were supplied through the newly established Franz Schulte agency in Magdeburg, but No 1681 is of special interest because it was shipped direct to Theodor Ohl, a road rolling contractor of Diez near Limburg, east of Koblenz. During the next twenty years this firm took delivery of no less than seventy-four Burrell road rollers of all types. Although No 1681 was supplied as a complete engine, the great majority, as we shall see, were supplied less rolls and forecarriages. Later the flywheels also were manufactured locally and fitted by Ohl. In some instances the firebars were also obtained locally. It made good sense not to ship unnecessarily large lumps of cast iron which could adequately be produced locally giving worthwhile savings in duties, taxes and transportation costs.

The second generation of Burrell road rollers appeared in March 1895. They had the same 5 ins dia × 9 ins dia × 9 ins stroke SCC cylinders as the 1891 engines with slightly enlarged boilers and the 4-shaft transmission was abandoned in favour of the well proven 3-shaft system.

5 ins × 9 ins × 9 ins SCC 3-SHAFT ROAD ROLLER

No		Built	No		Built
No 1836	Built	1895	No 1904	Built	1896
1868	"	1895	1926	"	1896
1877	"	1895	1932	"	1896
1880	"	1895	1948	"	1896
1894	"	1895	1958	"	1896
1895	"	1895	1965	"	1896
1896	"	1896	1969	"	1896
1897	"	1896	1974	"	1896
1901	"	1896	1982	"	1897

The enlarged boilers had 4.6 sq ft grates, a total heating surface of 101.0 sq ft and forty 1¾ ins dia × 4 ft 2 ins long smoke tubes. On No 1982 the boiler was lengthened to accommodate 4 ft 9½ ins long tubes. All were fitted with spark arresters and baffle plates in the smokebox and had Madan's type injectors.

The principle alterations incorporated in these engines were the improvements to the front rolls and forecarriage assembly which were described in Frederick Burrell's patents 8017 of 1893 and 3035 of 1895. The front roller forks were provided with a central pivot carrying a die-block having curved cheeks. The die-block was housed in a redesigned saddle having matching curved cheeks, the saddle being attached to and forming the front support of the engine. The arrangement permitted the fork to rotate for steering whilst allowing the front rolls to follow the irregularities in the surface of the road. Great attention was given to the distribution of the weight of the engine on the rolls so as to roll with as near as possible equal pressure. The smokebox was enlarged to the diameter of the lagging and riveted to an extension of the boiler barrel plate through a 2½ ins × 1¼ ins ring which enabled the smokebox to be removed without disturbing the front tube plate. The forecarriage saddle casting was bolted to an extension of the smokebox and replaced the heavy saddle casting previously used in which the chimney base formed an integral part.

The hind rolls were 5 ft 6 ins dia × 16 ins wide and the two front rolls were each 3 ft 7½ ins dia × 25½ ins wide. The front rolls overlapped the hind rolls by 4 ins on each side so as to avoid missing portions of the road when rolling curves. The overall width of the engine across the hind rolls was 6 ft 3 ins. In order to ensure the hardness and soundness of the roll castings they were cast 8 ins longer than the finished width and turned off to size in the machine shop.

The 2-speed gearing ratios were altered to 25.6 and 15.1 to 1 and with the exception of No 1932 were without compensating gear and winding drums. No 1932 which was supplied to Cromer UDC carried a winding drum and 100 yards of wire rope. No 1880 which went to Flyde RDC in Lancashire was the only engine to be fitted with governors. Earlier engines in the series had 4 ft 1 ins dia × 5 ins wide cased flywheels, later models built in 1896 had similar size solid flywheels. All carried 110 gallons of water sufficient for 2 hours continuous working.

Six engines in this series went to Budapest, the second city in the Austro-Hungarian Empire. Nos 1836 and 1904 went to H Reinisch & Miller and Nos 1894, 1895, 1896 and 1897 were sold through Granz & Company, Burrells' agents in the Budapest area. The latter were supplied less rolls, forecarriage and flywheel. Three engines went to Germany; No 1868 was sold through the Franz Schulte agency; No 1926 through the Meissner & Dietlein agency; and No 1948 went to Theodor Ohl less rolls and forecarriage. Two engines went to French customers; No 1901 was supplied through the Ludt agency in Paris; and No 1958 was supplied direct to Louis Mathieu, a road rolling contractor in Toulon in the South of France. Mention has already been made of Nos 1880 and 1932 which went to UK District Councils. No 1877 went to St Mary's Vestry in Battersea. Before the advent of the London Boroughs the general administration of the parishes was vested in committees called Vestries. St Mary's Battersea owned a fleet of three Burrell engines by the turn of the century. In 1896 the works received a prestigious order for two rollers, Nos 1965 and 1969, from Eddison & De Mathos of Dorchester, for many years the largest road rolling contractors in the country. Numbered 31 and 32 in their fleet they gave many years satisfactory service and subsequently Eddisons owned eleven Burrell rollers at various times. They enjoyed a special relationship with Avelings and Fowlers and the bulk of Eddison's business went to these firms for many years. The final engine in the series, No 1982 was a special shipped to Cape Town, South Africa through the Davis & Soper agency in 1897.

In 1897 the Class 'B' roller was introduced based upon the highly successful 'Devonshire' type GP traction engine and 131 variants were produced in the twenty-four years to 1921. Ninety-six were exported and over 40 per cent of these went to Theodor Ohl in Germany. Nominally the engines were rated 10 tons but some weighted up to 14½. injectors were fitted to the first fifteen engines, thereafter the majority had the Holden & Brookes type. Some of the later engines dispensed with the mechanical boiler feed pump and were fitted with two BP 'F' injectors. The same 2-speed gearing as used on the second generation rollers without compensating gear or winding drums. Similarly

CLASS 'B' 5½ ins × 9 ins × 10 ins SCC 3-SHAFT ROAD ROLLER

No 1979 Built 1897	No 2235 Built 1899*	No 2551 Built 1903	No 3080 Built 1909*
1981 ” 1897*	2237 ” 1899	2555 ” 1903*	3083 ” 1909
1984 ” 1897	2238 ” 1900*	2556 ” 1903*	3091 ” 1909
1996 ” 1897	2242 ” 1899	2564 ” 1903*	3096 ” 1909*
2000 ” 1897	2259 ” 1900	2565 ” 1903*	3097 ” 1909*
2020 ” 1897*	2269 ” 1900	2570 ” 1903*	3104 ” 1909
2023 ” 1897*	2273 ” 1900	2588 ” 1904	3115 ” 1909
2037 ” 1897	2274 ” 1900	2589 ” 1903	3127 ” 1909
2049 ” 1897	2291 ” 1900	2595 ” 1903*	3173 ” 1909*
2058 ” 1897	2315 ” 1900	2642 ” 1904	3174 ” 1909*
2065 ” 1898*	2325 ” 1900	2649 ” 1904	3175 ” 1910*
2080 ” 1898	2338 ” 1900	2653 ” 1904	3198 ” 1910
2085 ” 1898	2347 ” 1901	2654 ” 1904	3206 ” 1910
2090 ” 1898*	2353 ” 1901	2655 ” 1904	3207 ” 1910
2096 ” 1898	2356 ” 1901*	2658 ” 1904*	3220 ” 1910
2097 ” 1898	2357 ” 1901*	2719 ” 1905	3251 ” 1910
2110 ” 1898*	2359 ” 1901	2720 ” 1905	3261 ” 1910
2137 ” 1898	2360 ” 1901	2727 ” 1905	3298 ” 1911
2138 ” 1898	2373 ” 1901	2734 ” 1905*	3300 ” 1911
2141 ” 1898*	2384 ” 1901	2794 ” 1906*	3305 ” 1911
2151 ” 1899*	2395 ” 1901	2829 ” 1906	3320 ” 1911
2154 ” 1898	2401 ” 1901	2832 ” 1906*	3337 ” 1911
2157 ” 1899*	2428 ” 1901	2888 ” 1907	3356 ” 1912
2165 ” 1899	2447 ” 1902*	2895 ” 1907*	3366 ” 1912
2168 ” 1899	2448 ” 1902*	2928 ” 1907*	3388 ” 1912
2174 ” 1899	2457 ” 1902*	2970 ” 1908*	3408 ” 1912
2175 ” 1899	2458 ” 1902*	2973 ” 1908	3426 ” 1912
2176 ” 1899	2466 ” 1902*	2980 ” 1908	3440 ” 1913
2184 ” 1899*	2467 ” 1902	2991 ” 1908	3600 ” 1914
2193 ” 1899	2516 ” 1902	3013 ” 1908*	3733 ” 1916
2199 ” 1899*	2522 ” 1902	3070 ” 1908*	3819 ” 1918
2200 ” 1899	2526 ” 1902	3076 ” 1909*	3880 ” 1921
2230 ” 1899	2528 ” 1902	3077 ” 1909*	

* Engines supplied to Theodor Ohl of Diez in Germany. The first six engines were supplied less rollers and forecarriage. No 2141 and subsequent engines were supplied also less flywheels. For invoice purposes engines supplied to Germany had 3300 added to the works number, ie. No 2020 became 5320.

All had the 'Devonshire' engine SCC cylinder measuring 5½ ins dia × 9 ins dia × 10 ins stroke. Engines built up to and including No 2338 had the contemporary solid end cylinder casting, thereafter the more conventional casting with loose cylinder end covers were employed.

Engines built up to February 1908 had boilers pressed to 160 PSI, thereafter the majority had boilers pressed to 185 PSI. All had 4.6 sq ft grates and initially a total heating surface of 101 sq ft and forty 1¾ ins dia × 4 ft 2 ins long smoke tubes. Engines supplied to Germany had boilers built in accordance with German boiler regulations which included a Salter type spring safety valve. Some of these engines, but not all, were fitted with smokebox spark arresters and baffle plates to protect the front tube plate. Engines built after August 1908 had lengthened boilers to accommodate 4 ft 9½ ins long smoke tubes. Madan's type most had 5 ft 6 ins dia × 16 ins wide hind rolls and two 3 ft 7½ ins dia × 25½ ins wide front rolls although there were some variants on engines supplied to France and Germany. Frederick Burrell's successful patent forecarriage and front roller fork assembly was used as standard. A number of engines were fitted with novel six figure counters operated from the second motion shaft for measuring and recording the work done. The majority of flywheels were the solid type 4 ft 1 ins dia × 5 ins wide and motion side plates were fitted as standard. About half the engines were supplied with awnings, some long and some short and those supplied to Theodor Ohl were the short corrugated iron type.

In addition to the forty-two engines supplied direct to Ohl, twenty-two of these engines went to the Meissner & Dietlein agency in Magdeburg. It is known that at least six of these engines, Nos 2359, 2360, 2395, 2653, 2654 and

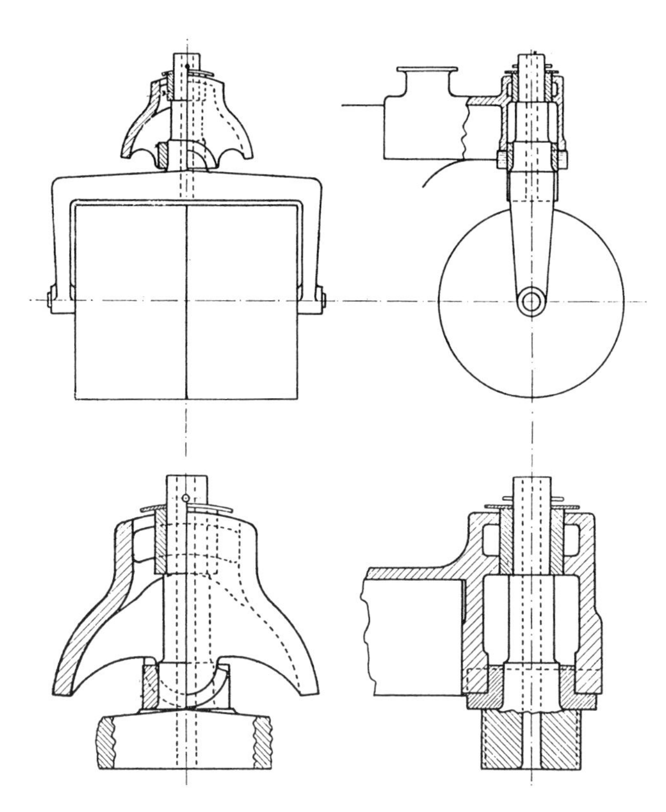

Fig 261 Frederick Burrell's patent road roller forecarriage assembly of 1895.

2727 were sold to B Ruthemeyer, the German traction engine manufacturer of Hoest. All six engines were supplied less rolls, forecarriage and flywheels. Eventually Ruthemeyer obtained a licence from Charles Burrell and manufactured himself SCC road rollers until well into the 1930s. The remaining sixteen rollers supplied as complete engines to the Meissner & Dietlein agency for unknown destinations were:

2096	2097	2174	2175	2176	2273	2291	2373
2551	2570	2888	2973	2980	3083	3104	3366

Nineteen of these engines were supplied to French customers. Nos 2080, 2168, 2200, 2230 and 2259 went to the Ludt agency in Paris who acted as distributors and we do not know their ultimate destination. The remaining fourteen engines were sold through Burnell et Cie, who appear to have acted as commission agents. Nos 1984 and 2516 went to Louis Mathieu of Toulon, Nos 2137 and 2315 went to Pineau Fortune, also of Toulon, No 2000 went to Coupet Py et Carricart at Perpignan on the Spanish border. No 2058 went to M Mader of Toulouse; No 2347 went to Jean Francois of Marseilles and No 2589 went to a M Brun of Grenoble. Six of this series, Nos 2516, 2719, 2720, 3091, 3251 and 3261 were supplied to Jean Bonhoure of Toulouse without rolls but they had special cranked forecarriages suitable for 5 ft 0 ins dia front rolls. The hind axles were prepared for 5 ft 6 ins dia rolls. Known as the Bonhoure System these engines were specifically designed to meet the needs of the

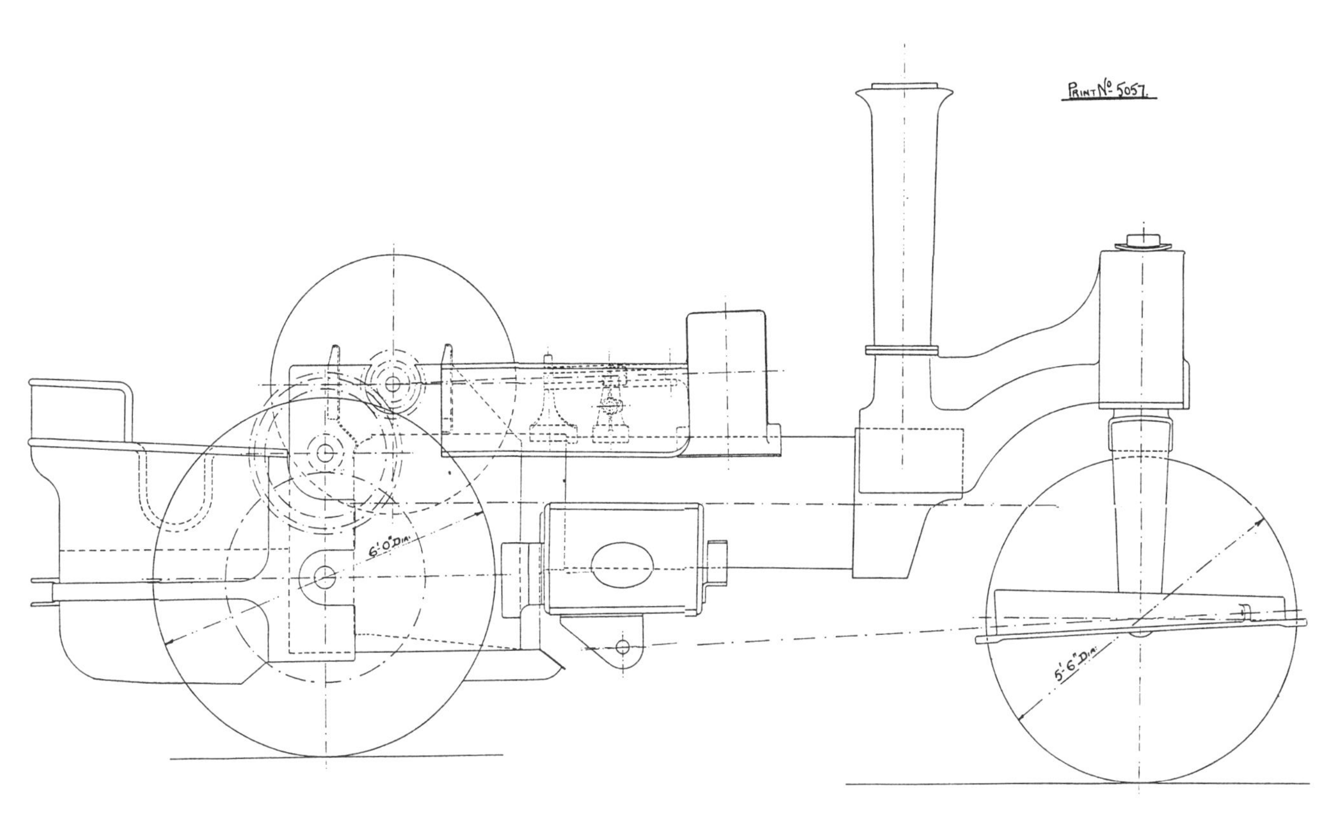

Fig 262 Works' drawing illustrating the proposed conversion of No 2798 6 NHP SCC 'Aberdeenshire' type engine to a System Bonhoure road roller – December 1911.

Fig 263 No 2274 Class 'B' SCC road roller fitted with the first Rutty scarifier built in accordance with Patent 15926 of 1896 for Leigh RDC.

French National Roads Authority. Particular attention had been paid to the need for equal compression and to the problems of wave formation created by the front rolls of conventional rollers. Eventually Bonhoure purchased a total of twenty-one Burrell engines when new plus the two 'Aberdeenshire' Showman's engines Nos 2798 and 2799 which were converted to rollers in 1911.

Examination of the surviving Burrell drawings reveals that a considerable amount of Drawing Office time was devoted to the preparation of designs and specifications for this customer between 1900 and 1912.

Individual engines in the series went to Italy (No 3206), Belgium (No 3127), Sweden (No 3115), Finland (Nos 2991 & 3300) and Greece (No 2829). For reasons now unknown the Belgian purchaser of No 3127 insisted that Burrells' name should not appear anywhere on the engine. No 2829 started its life in the works as No 2670 in 1904. Later it was altered to No 2752 and later still when the engine was finally sold it was allocated No 2829. Either the original order had been cancelled and new works numbers allocated when new orders were received, or the more likely explanation is that there had been difficulties and delays with the Letter of Credit. Five engines (Nos 2138, 2154, 2165, 2237 and 3207) went to South Africa and a further two engines (Nos 3198 & 3320) were ordered through London Confirming Houses and their ultimate destination remains unknown, although South Africa would seem to be the most likely country.

Eleven engines in the series went to UK Local Authorities scattered as far afield as South Shields in the North East and Kingsbridge in the South West. Nos 2085 and 2325 went to St Mary's Vestry, Battersea and No 2353 went to the newly formed London Borough of Hackney. No 2049 supplied to Nantwich UDC in Cheshire displayed a smart brass plate, "By Royal Letters Patent" on the forecarriage, a custom more usually associated with the nearby engine builders, Fodens of Sandbach. No 2274 went to Leigh RDC fitted with a Rutty scarifier as described in patent 15,926 of 1896. Filed jointly by Harold Rutty, a road rolling contractor of Ilford and Frederick Burrell, the patent detailed an arrangement similar to that patented by Voysey & Hosacks in 1890 and used on Burrell engines built for the Road Breaking Company of London.

The working stresses of the heavy Hosack scarifier were carried by the engine tender. The improvement claimed for the Rutty version was that most of the load was carried by the hind axle. A pair of triangular cast frames were attached to the hind axle at their centre point, one each side of the off-side hind roller, such that they were free to pivot on the axle. Tynes were attached to each of the free ends of the frames such that one set were in front of the rolls and the other behind. The tynes entered the ground by pulling when travelling either backwards or forwards instead of being alternately pulled and pushed, and by this means the roller did not pass over the newly broken road surface. The tynes could be brought into action either by a mechanically operated screw or by means of a steam or hydraulically operated cylinder mounted on the tender. The system was costly and heavy and its excessive weight adversely affected the balance of the ground pressure. Other types of scarifier concurrently developed by Jacksons of Wistaston, Wallis & Steevens, Harry Evershed, later a partner of Bamford & Evershed, Morrison and Charles Price of Altrincham soon became more popular.

Twenty-four of this series of road rollers went to UK Road Rolling Contractors. Most had their roots as either threshing or ploughing contractors and were thoroughly experienced in the use of steam. Several had small but extremely competent engineering workshops undertaking diverse but important work in predominently agricultural communities. S J Rosebotham of Bickerstaff in Lancashire is a good example. He owned eight rollers of this type, Nos 2338, 2428, 2588, 3356, 3426, 3733, 3819 and 3880 and at various times owned fifteen Burrell engines. Isaac Ball of Wharles, another Lancashire agricultural contractor and friend of the Burrell family purchased four of these rollers, Nos 3220, 3298, 3305 & 3388. In total his fleet comprised nineteen Burrell engines. Another worthy of mention is Samuel Jackson of Wistaston near Crewe. He purchased No 3440 but had a fleet of ten various types of Burrell engines. He was the patentee and manufacturer of a popular scarifier.

In 1911 St Nicholas Works produced three special engines for Jean Bonhoure of Toulouse. They were similar to the road rollers just described but with 4-shaft transmission, and were allocated Nos 3268, 3275 and 3282.

The cylinders, motion and boilers were as the Class 'B' rollers. The 4-shaft transmission had 2-speed gearing having ratios of 26.1 and 15.5 to 1 and they were without compensating gear and winding drums. No wheels were supplied but the engines were made suitable for 5 ft 6 ins dia hind rolls and the special cranked forecarriage was suitable for 5 ft 0 ins dia front rolls. The 4 ft 6 ins dia solid flywheels were only 2 ins wide and the total water carrying capacity of the engines was increased to 233 gallons.

In 1898 the works introduced an 8 ton roller based on the diminutive 'Irish' type traction engine. In 1905 they became known as the Class 'A' 10 ton road roller and a total of 75 were built of which 49 were exported.

Fig 264 No 3150 Class 'A' SCC road roller built in 1909 to the order of a London Confirming House for export to a now unknown destination abroad.

casting. Engines supplied to Germany and Sweden had boilers conforming with the then current German boiler regulations and were fitted with Salter's type spring balance safety valves. Nos 3016 & 3312 were wood burning engines ordered by the Crown Agents and fitted with enlarged grates and extended tenders for carrying the wood fuel. The final two engines built in the 1920s had 200 PSI lengthened boilers having a 4.18 sq ft grate, a total heating surface of 80.0 sqft and thirty 2 ins dia × 4ft 9½ ins long smoke tubes. All had eccentric driven boiler feed pumps and the majority had Holden & Brookes type injectors. Generally the flywheels were 4 ft 0 ins dia × 5 ins wide, the hind rolls were 5 ft 6 ins dia × 17 ins wide and the front rolls 4 ft 0 ins dia × 25½ ins wide giving a

CLASS 'A' 5 ins × 8½ ins × 9 ins SCC 3-SHAFT ROAD ROLLER

No	Built	No	Built	No	Built	No	Built
No 2028	Built 1898	No 2623	Built 1903	No 2863	Built 1906	No 3312	Built 1911
2111	" 1898	2656	" 1904	2915	" 1907	3347	" 1911
2232	" 1899	2692	" 1904	2916	" 1907	3357	" 1912
2258	" 1900	2702	" 1904	2998	" 1908	3376	" 1912
2266	" 1900	2717	" 1904	3016	" 1908	3383	" 1912
2316	" 1900	2725	" 1905	3018	" 1908	3411	" 1912
2320	" 1900	2726	" 1905	3021	" 1908	3414	" 1912
2328	" 1901	2729	" 1905	3085	" 1909	3451	" 1913
2358	" 1901	2730	" 1905	3099	" 1909	3459	" 1913
2374	" 1901	2756	" 1905	3101	" 1909	3468	" 1913
2403	" 1901	2765	" 1905	3120	" 1909	3476	" 1913
2434	" 1901	2769	" 1905	3128	" 1909	3556	" 1914
2460	" 1902	2777	" 1905	3150	" 1909	3571	" 1914
2461	" 1902	2809	" 1906	3171	" 1909	3591	" 1914
2491	" 1902	2813	" 1906	3181	" 1910	3602	" 1914
2535	" 1902	2823	" 1906	3204	" 1910	3699	" 1915
2558	" 1903	2839	" 1906	3217	" 1910	4002	" 1925
2561	" 1903	2849	" 1906	3244	" 1910	4043	" 1926
2580	" 1903	2858	" 1906	3270	" 1911		

All had 5 ins dia × 8½ ins dia × 9 ins stroke SCC cylinders, engines built prior to 1902 having the solid end type cylinder casting. The 160 PSI boilers fitted to the majority of the engines had 3.7 sq ft grates, a total heating surface of 77.4 sq ft and thirty 1¾ ins dia × 4 ft 2 ins long smoketubes. Nos 2232, 2258, 2266 2320 & 2328 were fitted with Marshall's patent throttle valves in the cylinder

rolled width of 6 ft 4 ins. The water carrying capacity was 100 gallons.

Eight of the engines went to Germany, six of which Nos 2028, 2111, 3021, 3101, 3171 and 3414 were supplied to Theodor Ohl less wheels and forecarriages. No 2358 went to the Meissner & Dietlein agency in Magdeburg and No 2726 went to the German engine

Fig 265 A Class 'C' SCC 3-shaft road roller built at the turn of the century for export to France.

builder H Ruthemeyer. Thirteen of this series – Nos 2232, 2320, 2460, 2725, 2765, 2777, 2809, 2813, 2823, 3018, 3085, 3099 & 3591, went to the Martin Saaf agency in Gothenburg, Southern Sweden. No 2374 went to Finland and No 2839 went to Denmark. The Makeef & Fadeef agency of Ekaterinburg in the Russian Urals 800 miles East of Moscow sold eight engines – Nos 2491, 3120, 3204, 3383, 3451, 3556, 3571 & 3602. No 3120 was supplied uniquely with special Van-de-Loo unpainted cleading. No 3602 although paid for remained at St Nicholas Works until 1930. Just before shipment the works learned that one of the partners had been murdered by the Bolsheviks and the remaining partner, being unable to provide proof of ownership, was denied possession. It is believed that Doran Bros, the Thetford road rolling contractors acquired the engine when St Nicholas Works finally closed.

Three engines were sold through the Burnell agency in Paris. No 2692 was the second Burrell roller supplied to M. Brun in Grenoble and Nos 2849, a double geared engine, and No 2998 went to Deniscott & Malgras of Epinal in Eastern France. No 3347 was one of four Burrell road rollers supplied to Consorzis di Pontidara in Italy. Four engines crossed the Atlantic, Nos 2561 & 2580 went to Port Arthur on the northern shore of Lake Superior in Ontario, Canada. They are believed to be the only Burrell engines to see service in North America. Nos 2729 & 2730 went to Cuba but their ultimate destiny is unknown. No 2656 went to Mossel Bay in Cape Province, 200 miles east of Cape Town and three engines went to the Antipodes. No 2858 went to Australia and Nos 3270 & 3699 went to New Zealand. Nos 2915 & 2916 were supplied to Kerr Stuart, the Glasgow railway plant dealers and probably ended up in India or South Africa. Both were fitted with Wallis & Steevens patent scarifier. Nos 3016, 3150 & 3312 were supplied to UK Confirming Houses for unknown destinations.

UK Local Authorities purchased eight of these engines. Nos 2258, 2316, 2328, 2434, 2461 & 2702 were described as standard 8 ton rollers although all weighed in excess of 10 tons according to the works records. Nos 2863 & 3476 were described as Class 'A' 10 ton rollers, but the latter weighed 11 ton 16 cwt in working order. It was supplied new to Manchester Corporation with double gearing to the hind axle and with David Wood's of Yeadon patent sprinkler equipment.

Eighteen of the engines in the series went to UK Road Rolling Contractors. Nos 2623 & 3468 went to Samuel Jackson of Wistaston. The latter, a double geared engine weighing 13 tons started life as No 3429 but due to a cancellation was left on Burrells' hands and renumbered when sold a year later. Nos 2769, 3244 & 3411 went to Fred Payne of Red Ball on the Devon Somerset border. Price's scarifiers were fitted in the 1920s. Pamplin Bros of Cherry Hinton in Cambridgeshire formerly well known ploughing contractors purchased Nos 3217 & 3459. Isaac Ball acquired No 3128 which was originally built as a double geared traction engine but soon converted to a road roller. It is described in the works' records as having special link motion, but precise details have not survived. Nos 4002 & 4043 went to J S Rosebotham, the latter being fitted with the latest type of Price's 2-type scarifier. Regretably space precludes mention of the ownership of each and every engine; in any event engines changed hands frequently, often upon the completion of a specific contract. The most exhaustive record of ownership is to be found in the excellent records compiled by the late Alan Duke upon behalf of the Road Locomotive Society.

We now come to the thirty-four class 'C' road rollers variously rated between 15 and 18½ tons. Although the boilers and the 3-shaft transmission systems were similar, two sizes of cylinder were optionally available. All except two of the engines in this series were exported, the majority going to France and Germany.

The first alternative was introduced in March 1896 based on the then current 7 NHP SCC GP traction engine with 6¼ ins dia × 10½ ins dia × 12 ins stroke cylinders. The 160 PSI 'T' type boiler had a 4.9 sq ft grate, a total

Fig 266 No 1824 the first traction engine-cum-road roller Convertible engine built for Lord Iveagh for use on his Elveden Estate near Thetford in 1895.

CLASS 'C' 6¼ ins × 10½ ins × 12 ins SCC 3-SHAFT ROAD ROLLERS

No	Built	No	Built
No 1906	Built 1896	No 2073	Built 1898
1942	" 1896	2095	" 1898
1990	" 1897	2109	" 1898
2001	" 1897	2240	" 1900
2009	" 1897	2323	" 1900
2040	" 1898		

heating surface of 118.0 sq ft and thirty-four 2 ins dia × 5 ft 1 ins long smoke tubes. The engines supplied to Germany had spark arresters and baffle plates in the smokebox. As usual with Thetford built road rollers all the gearing was on the right hand side of the engine and was without compensating gear or winding drum. The 2-speed gearing gave ratios of 25.7 and 14.1 to 1. No 2040 was fitted with the German built Hans Renold scarifier and supplied to Littleborough UDC in Lancashire.

The alternative cylinder arrangement was introduced in June 1896 having 6 ins dia × 10 ins dia × 12 ins stroke SCC cylinders.

The first nine engines had the same boilers as the larger size cylinder engines. Thereafter they were fitted with lengthened boilers pressed to 185 PSI having thirty-five 2 ins dia × 5 ft 8 ins long smoke tubes which increased the total heating surface to 130 sq ft. Transmission shafting and gearing remained as the alternative cylinder engines.

Six of the engines, Nos 1906, 1990, 2073, 2095, 2109 & 2240 were supplied to Theodor Ohl less front and hind rolls, although in these instances the works appear to have supplied the forecarriages and 4 ft 4 ins dia × 6 ins wide solid flywheels. In 1921 the War Office acquired No 1906 upon behalf of the British Army of Occupation in the Rhineland. Three more of the series, Nos 2009, 2563 & 2887 went to German customers through the Meissner & Deitlein agency. Two engines Nos 3258 & 3330 went to Consorzis Agaris di Pontidara in Italy, but the majority of the series went to French customers. Nos 1973, 2349, 2427, 2591 & 2683 were sold through the Burnell agency, Nos 1939, 1987 & 2001 went through the Jean Ludt agency and twelve engines, Nos 2323, 2954, 2958, 2967, 2968, 2971, 2972, 2974, 3084, 3338, 3339 & 3340 went to Jean Bonhoure in Toulouse.

All the Bonhoure engines had special cranked forecarriages and were supplied less wheels, the engines being suitable for 6 ft 0 ins dia hind rolls and 5 ft 6 ins dia front rolls. All except the last three engines had 4′ 6″ dia × 3 ins wide solid flywheels and Schaffers 5-figure counters were fitted to the hind axles. Nos 3338, 3339 & 3340 had 5ft 0 ins dia × 2 ins wide solid flywheels. These three rollers, the last supplied to Bonhoure, were also uniquely

CLASS 'C' 6 ins × 10 ins × 12 ins SCC 3-SHAFT ROAD ROLLER

No	Built	No	Built	No	Built	No	Built
No 1939	Built 1896	No 2563	Built 1903	No 2967	Built 1908	No 3258	Built 1910
1973	" 1896	2591	" 1903	2968	" 1908	3330	" 1911
1987	" 1897	2683	" 1904	2971	" 1908	3338	" 1911
2344	" 1900	2887	" 1907	2972	" 1908	3339	" 1911
2349	" 1901	2954	" 1907	2974	" 1908	3340	" 1911
2427	" 1901	2958	" 1907	3084	" 1909		

fitted with copper fireboxes. One engine in the series, No 2344 went to a customer in Queensland, Australia and finally, Nos 1942 & 2040 went to UK Local Authorities having 6 ft 0 ins × 20 ins wide hind rolls and 4 ft 0 ins × 27¾ ins wide front rolls giving a rolled width of 7 ft 6 ins. Before leaving the SCC Burrell road roller mention must be made of the twenty-three SCC traction engine-cum-road roller convertible engines built between 1895 and 1911. The idea was that the engine could be used as a road roller during the rolling season and then be readily converted to a conventional traction engine for hauling road stone and similar materials during the remainder of the year. The idea initially appealed to a number of Local Authorities and road rolling contractors but with the advent of water bound tarmacadam the system soon fell into disfavour. Furthermore, it was found that the gear ratios ideal for road rolling were too slow and unsuitable for road haulage work.

Basically Burrell used two types of roller forecarriage on their convertibles. The first known in the works as the R91 design involved fitting a rolled steel plate to the top of the smokebox onto which was bolted the front roller forecarriage saddle. The assembly is clearly illustrated in Fig 266. The second system introduced in 1899 and referred to as the type 1179 is illustrated in Fig 267. It will be noted that the smokebox saddle casting was integral with the chimney base. The traction engine front axle perch bracket was riveted to the underside of the smokebox.

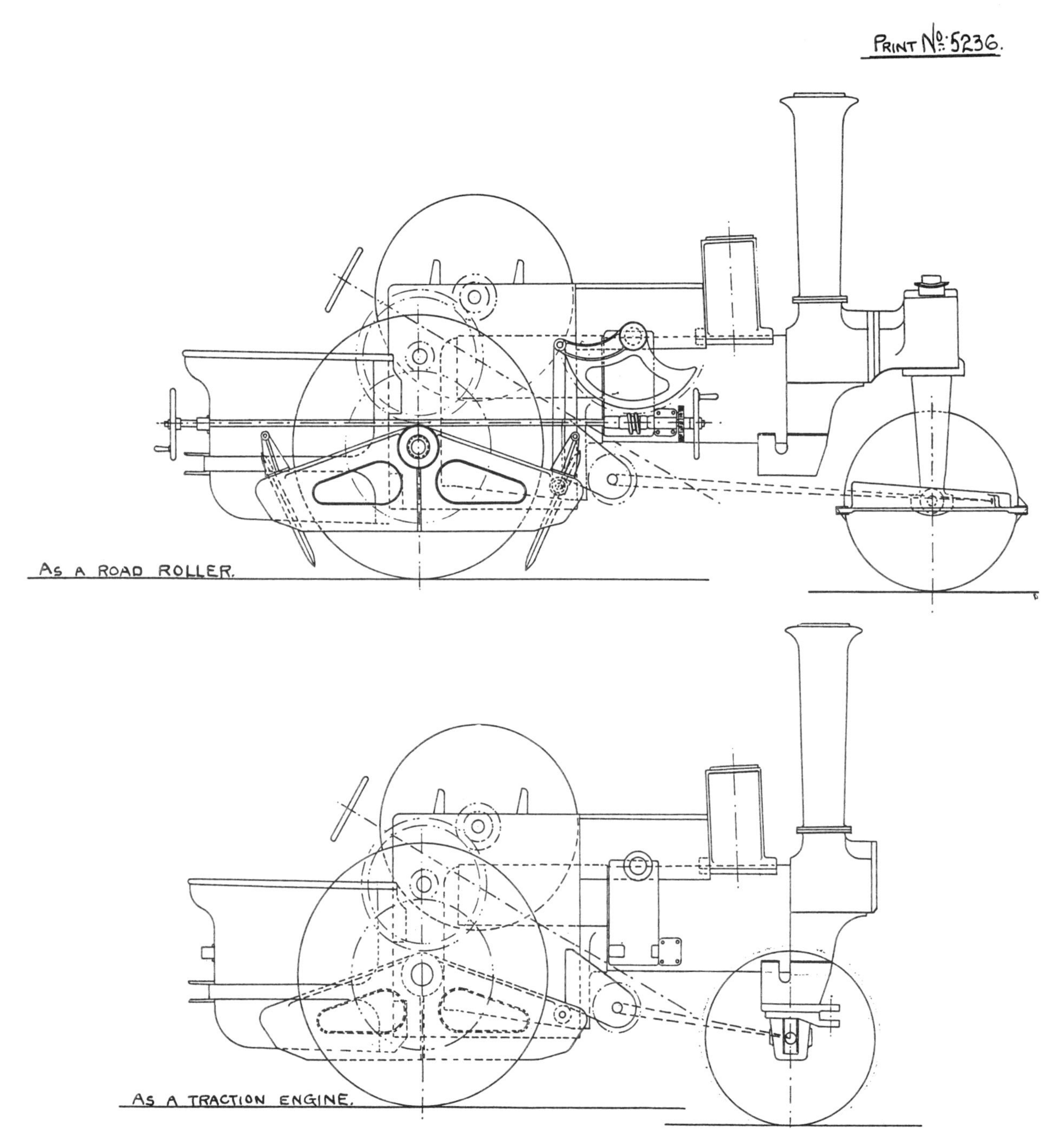

Fig 267 Works drawing of 6 NHP SCC Convertible engine illustrated as either a road roller or a traction engine. Note the cast bracket integral with the chimney base for the attachment of the roller forecarriage.

SCC TRACTION ENGINE-CUM-ROAD ROLLER CONVERTIBLES

No 1824 Built 1895 6 NHP	No 2145 Built 1898 6 NHP	No 2529 Built 1902 6 NHP	No 2900 Built 1907 6 NHP
1886 " 1895 6 NHP	2234 " 1899 6 NHP	2550 " 1903 6 NHP	3140 " 1909 5 NHP
1952 " 1896 6 NHP	2253 " 1899 6 NHP	2626 " 1903 6 NHP	3265 " 1911 5 NHP
1964 " 1896 6 NHP	2261 " 1900 6 NHP	2708 " 1904 6 NHP	1960 " 1896 6 NHP
2117 " 1898 6 NHP	2417 " 1901 6 NHP	2790 " 1905 6 NHP	3062 " 1909 6 NHP
2123 " 1898 6 NHP	2519 " 1902 6 NHP	2792 " 1906 6 NHP	

Boilers were as used on the equivalent size and type of traction engine. All were double geared to the hind axle except No 3140 which had single drive gearing Nos 3062 & 3265 were spring mounted on the hind axle. All had traction engine type transmission shafts with compensating gear and winding drums. Generally the traction engine wheels were a few inches larger in diameter than the hind and front rolls enabling the traction engine version to travel more quickly on the roads.

The first Thetford built convertible, No 1824, was supplied to Lord Iveagh for use on his nearby Elveden Estate. Four SCC engines went to UK Local Authorities. Nos 2261 & 2900 were purchased by the Mutford & Lothingland RDC in the Suffolk coastal area and No 2253 went to Thingoe RDC, the administrative area of which Bury St Edmunds is the focal point. Fifteen SCC convertibles were purchased by UK road rolling contractors and three engines were exported. No 2117 went to Rumania, No 2123 went to Deniscott & Malgras of Epinal through the Jean Ludt agency and No 2790 went to Cape Town through the Davis & Soper agency.

Only one single cylinder convertible No 2445 was built. This was based on the standard 7 NHP traction engine with 8½ ins dia × 12 ins stroke cylinder. Supplied to a Cornish road rolling contractor, it was a heavy engine weighing 17 ton 5 cwt in its roller guise and was classed as a Class 'C' roller. The hind rolls were 6 ft 0 ins × 18 ins wide and the front rolls were 4 ft 6 ins dia × 32¾ ins wide giving an overal width of 7 ft 10 ins.

Less than twenty per cent of all road rollers built at St Nicholas Works had single cylinders. Although the roller was launched in the compound era and inspite of the worthwhile savings in fuel and water consumption claimed by the makers, the demand for single cylinder engines persisted and could not be ignored. The difference in price between a compound engine and a single cylinder engine was approximately twelve per cent and of course, as with the GP traction engine initial cost was of prime importance to some buyers. The cost of maintenance of the single cylinder was also somewhat less than the compound and mitigated against the savings in fuel and water.

The recommended sizes of cylinder were as follows:

6–8 ton nominal	6½ ins dia × 8½ ins stroke
10–12 ton nominal	7½ ins dia × 9 ins stroke
13–15 ton nominal	8 ins dia × 10 ins stroke
16–18 ton nominal	8½ ins dia × 12 ins stroke

The first five engines had 175 PSI boilers, thereafter, the pressure was increased to 200 PSI. All had 3.0 sq ft grates, and all except the last three engines in the series were fitted with twenty-five 1¾ ins dia smoke tubes. Nos 3582 & 3688 and the final three engines had 4 ft 2 ins long smoke tubes, the remainder had 4 ft 4½ ins long tubes. The total heating surface varied between 60.95 sq ft and 68.75 sq ft.

8 TON 6½ ins × 8½ ins SC 3-SHAFT ROAD ROLLER

No 2962 Built 1907	No 3962 Built 1923
3301 " 1911	3973 " 1924
3456 " 1913	3985 " 1925
3582 " 1914	4046 " 1926
3688 " 1915	4058 " 1926
3946 " 1922	4065 " 1927
3956 " 1923	4083 " 1928

All had the gearing on the right had side of the engine and were without compensating gear and winding drums and the 2-speed gear ratios of 24.4 and 13.6 to 1 were maintained. All had 5 ft 0 ins dia hind rolls. Nos 2962 & 3973 had 3 ft 6 ins × 23 ins wide front rolls, the remainder had 4 ft 0 ins × 21 ins wide front rolls. No 3946 and succeeding engines with the exception of No 4065 were fitted with renewable rim rolls. In the early part of the 20th century road rolling contractors travelled considerable distances between jobs often on hard metalled roads thereby greatly increasing the wear on the rolls. Originally the whole wheel was replaced when worn, but this was costly and in due course Aveling & Porter proposed bolting the rims to the wheel spokes. Although in theory this made it possible for replacement rims to be easily fitted, in practice this often caused problems. When built, the engines were erected by hand without the use of jigs and fixtures and it was often difficult to correctly align the

Fig 268 No 3140 'Irish' type SCC convertible engine built for William H Burgoyne & Co of Kingsbridge in Devonshire.

Fig 269 No 3301 8 ton SC road roller built in 1911.

fixing holes in the replacement rims with those in the ends of the wheel spokes without a lot of filing and fitting. Unless this was done correctly the rim either ran eccentric to the axle or the fixing bolts became sloppy and eventually sheared. In due course it became more usual for worn rolls to be replated.

No 2962 went to the Hinganghat Municipal Committee at Wardha in India. The Indian roads at this time were of a remarkably high standard and India provided an extremely important market for Aveling & Porter, John Fowler and especially Marshall road rollers. Charles Burrell appeared to be unable to find a good agent for this huge territory. No 3582 went to Theodor Ohl in Germany without wheels, forecarriage or flywheel. An identical engine originally destined for Ohl was completed just after the start of the 1914–18 War. In 1915 it was requisitioned by the War Office and sent overseas. The boilers of both engines were produced from Krupps' rolled steel plate and fitted with three additional iron stay tubes. A large manhole was fitted on the right hand side of the boiler and as was usual on engines destined for Germany carried a Salters' spring safety valve. The remaining eleven rollers all went to UK customers. Nos 3956, 3973 & 3985 were fitted with machine cut steel gearing. Nos 3962 & 4083 were double geared to the hind axle and fitted with winding drums. Nos 3946, 3956 & 3985 were supplied fitted with Hosack's 2-type scarifiers, and No 4083 had Price's patented 2-type scarifier. No 4046 originally built as No 4009 and No 4065 were supplied to H Williams of Camberley were sold without rolls and forecarriage. No 4083, a late engine was completed in January 1928 shortly before St Nicholas Works finally closed and was the third Burrell road roller to be acquired by the Mutford & Lothingland RDC.

We must next consider the thirty-three Class 'A' 10 ton single cylinder road rollers manufactured between 1895 and 1927, although it is worth noting that sixty per cent were built in the third decade of the period 1917–1927.

Nos 1867 & 1900 had 160 PSI boilers exactly as the contemporary Class 'B' compound road rollers with 5½ ins dia × 9 ins dia × 10 ins stroke SCC cylinders and No 2773 to 3931 had 160 PSI boilers as the contemporary Class 'A' compound road rollers with 5 ins dia × 8½ ins dia × 9 ins stroke SCC cylinders. Nos 3942 to 4070 were virtually a new design having 200 PSI boilers as introduced on the Class 'A' compound road rollers in 1915 with a 4.18 sq ft grate and forty 1¾ ins dia × 4 ft 2 ins long smoke tubes. The boiler plates were supplied by the Steel Company of Scotland who traditionally supplied most of the steel plate used on Clydeside. The same 3-shaft drive and 2-speed gearing as used on compound engines was employed with the exception of No 4040 which was a special having double geared drive to the hind axle with compensating gear, a winding drum and differential locking gear. The standard hind rolls were 5 ft 6 ins dia × 17 ins wide. All from No 3942 had renewable rims and 4 ft 0 ins dia × 5 ins wide solid flywheels. Two-thirds of these post-war engines were fitted with flywheel rim brakes and most had Prices's 2-type scarifiers. Roll water spray equipment by Hodges & Sons of Exeter was fitted to eight engines which went to the West Country.

No 1867 went to the Franz Schulte agency in Germany and Nos 3170, 3292, 3293, 3346, 3431 & 3462 went to Theodor Ohl. The latter engines were supplied less rolls, forecarriages and flywheels and the boilers were all subject to special certification by Lloyds before shipment. No 3667 was also destined originally for Ohl but the outbreak of war in August 1914 frustrated delivery. In

Fig 270 No 3931 10 ton SC road roller with Hosacks 2-type scarifier supplied to J Haigh & Sons, of Emley, Yorkshire.

CLASS 'A' 10 TON 7½ ins × 9 ins SC 3-SHAFT ROAD ROLLER

No	Built	No	Built	No	Built	No	Built
No 1867	Built 1895	No 3462	Built 1913	No 3955	Built 1923	No 4012	Built 1925
1900	" 1896	3482	" 1913	3970	" 1924	4013	" 1925
2773	" 1905	3484	" 1913	3986	" 1924	4040	" 1926
3170	" 1909	3667	" 1915	3987	" 1924	4041	" 1926
3292	" 1911	3748	" 1917	3990	" 1924	4047	" 1926
3293	" 1911	3781	" 1918	3991	" 1924	4060	" 1927
3314	" 1911	3931	" 1921	3999	" 1924	4069	" 1929
3346	" 1911	3942	" 1923	4005	" 1925	4070	" 1927
3431	" 1912						

Fig 271 One of Doran Bros Burrell road rollers with living van and water cart about to leave their yard in Thetford in the 1920s.

1915 the engine was completed and sold to J Haigh & Sons in West Yorkshire who also purchased No 3931 six years later. Only two of the series went to UK Local Authorities, the remainder all going to UK and Irish road rolling contractors. No less than seven of these went to R Dingle & Son of Stoke Climsland in East Cornwall and four went to William Elworthy of Tiverton. Between them these two firms employed eighteen Burrell engines at various times.

The second of the original single cylinder rollers, No 1900 built in 1895 was the first of nine Burrell engines subsequently supplied to T R Doran, a Thetford road rolling contractor. One of the Doran brothers, Frederick William was for many years the Chief Draughtsman at St Nicholas Works and fortuitously his notebook containing a wealth of information is still extant. In 1910 he and Charles II jointly filed patent 29382 describing a roller, which by means of sliding pinions, could be operated as either a 3-shaft or as a 4-shaft engine. Which ever drive was brought into action the relative direction of rotation of the crankshaft and the road wheels was the same enabling the engine to use 'open' eccentric link motion.

Only one road roller was built with 7½ ins dia × 10 ins stroke cylinders. No 2161 was supplied to Walsall RDC in Staffordshire in January 1899. The cylinder casting was the solid end pattern and the boiler, pressed to 160 PSI had a 4.6 sq ft grate, a total heating surface of 101.0 sq ft and was fitted with forty 1¾ ins dia × 4 ft 2 ins long smoke tubes. The engine weighed 12½ tons and in all other respects was similar to the engines with 7½ ins dia × 9 ins stroke cylinders.

CLASS 'B' 8 ins × 10 ins SC 3-SHAFT ROAD ROLLERS

No	Built	No	Built
No 2748	Built 1905	No 3012	Built 1908
2891	" 1907	3069	" 1908
2892	" 1907	3172	" 1909
2934	" 1907	3501	" 1913
2969	" 1908	3929	" 1921

Ten Class 'B' road rollers with 8 ins dia × 10 ins stroke single cylinders were built and all these were originally intended for Theodor Ohl.

All except No 3929 were supplied less rolls, forecarriages and flywheels. Obviously the delivery of the final engine was cancelled due to the outbreak of war with Germany. The engine remained in stock part finished until the end of 1921 when it was completed, allocated works number 3929 and sold to Isaac Ball. The boiler pressure

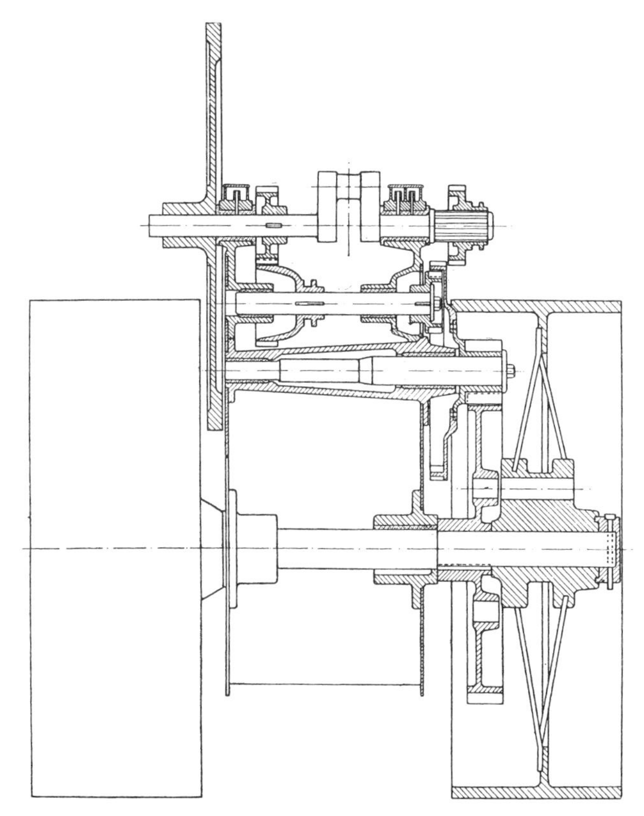

Fig 272 Charles Burrell's & Frederick Doran's 3 shaft-cum 4 shaft drive arrangement. Patent No 29382 filed in 1910.

Fig 273 No 3313 Class 'A' DCC road roller built for Doran Bros of Thetford in 1911.

Fig 274 No 4062 8 ton DCC road roller with Price's scarifier seen in W J King's of Bishop's Lydeard, Somerset livery in 1927.

Fig 275 No 3359 6 ton DCC road roller exported to Sweden in 1912.

was increased to 200 PSI by the addition of 3 iron stay tubes and 5 ft 8 ins dia hind rolls and 4 ft 0 ins dia × 25½ ins front rolls, both with renewable rims were fitted.

The engines sent to Germany had 140 PSI boilers, 4.6 sq ft grates, a total heating surface of 101.0 sq ft and forty 1¾ ins dia × 4 ft 2 ins long smoke tubes. As was usual with engines sent to this market they were fitted with Salters spring safety valves, German type Inspectors' gauge cocks and the boiler plates were certified by Lloyds.

A single Class 'C' road roller No 2844 was supplied to Ohl in August 1906. This had an 8½ ins dia × 12 ins stroke single cylinder and a 140 PSI boiler with a 4.9 sq ft gate, a total heating surface of 117.0 sq ft and thirty-eight 1¾ ins dia × 5 ft 1 ins long smoke tubes plus four iron stay tubes. The roller was supplied less rolls, forecarriage and flywheel.

Shortly after the introduction of double crank compound cylinders on the GP traction engine in the early part of the century the arrangement was applied to the Class 'A' road roller. Forty-four DCC road rollers were built which represented only 12 per cent of the number of rollers of all types built at St Nicholas Works and two thirds of these were completed in the decade following the First World War.

CLASS 'A' 5 ins × 8½ ins × 9 ins DCC 3-SHAFT ROAD ROLLERS

No	Built	No	Built
No 2896	Built 1907	No 3934	Built 1922
3047	" 1908	3943	" 1923
3182	" 1910	3947	" 1923
3313	" 1911	3957	" 1924
3364	" 1912	3959	" 1923
3400	" 1912	3961	" 1924
3448	" 1913	3964	" 1923
3535	" 1913	3966	" 1923
3584	" 1914	3993	" 1924
3608	" 1914	4077	" 1927

The first nine engines had boilers as the contemporary engines having 5 ins dia × 8½ ins dia × 9 ins stroke cylinders but the working pressure was increased to 200 PSI. Thereafter, the boilers were slightly enlarged as the last two SCC engines built, although the 4 ft 9½ ins long smoke tubes were replaced by 4 ft 2 ins long tubes.
No 3313, 3961, 3993 & 4077 had double gearing to the hind axle and Nos 3313 & 4077 were additionally fitted with Burrell's patent differential locking gear. The hind rolls were 5 ft 6 ins dia × 17 ins wide and the front rolls varied between 3 ft 6 ins dia × 23 ins wide and 4 ft 0 ins dia × 26 ins wide. The weight of the engines in working order varied between 10 ton 10 cwt and 14 ton 2 cwt.

Customers specified a variety of scarifiers including Hosack's, Morrison's and Allen's 3-tyne types. Three engines, Nos 3400, 3448 & 3934 went to Samuel Jackson of Wistaston and it is believed that all were fitted locally with their patent scarifier. No 3959 which was exported to South Africa was supplied with a special 2-tyned Thackray & Barford independently towed scarifier and 14 ft of wire rope. No 3535 which went to Leyland UDC in Lancashire was fitted with Van Putten's water spray equipment. This was found to be necessary when dealing with asphalt and bitumen surfaces. Unless the rolls were kept wet the material tended to adhere to a dry wheel damaging the new road surface. Most of these road rollers were supplied with awnings and the majority of these were the long pattern.

Nine of this series of road roller were exported.
Nos 3947 & 3966 went to Sweden; Nos 3961 & 3964 went to New Zealand and Nos 3943, 3957 & 3959 went to South Africa. Nos 3182 & 3584 were ordered for export by London Confirming Houses and it is believed that these too went to South African customers. Only two of the series went to UK Local Authorities, the remaining nine engines in this series going to UK road rolling contractors. Nos 3047, 3313 & 3993 were purchased by T R Doran of Thetford who latterly traded as Doran Bros Ltd.

One similar engine, No 3175 having a 5½ ins dia × 9 ins dia × 10 ins stroke DCC cylinder went to Theodor Ohl in November 1909. This had a 200 PSI boiler as the single cylinder Class 'B' engines supplied to Ohl between 1905 and 1908. This was supplied less rolls, forecarriage, flywheel and firebars.

The 8 ton version of the DCC road roller was introduced in 1907 having the same cylinder and boiler as used on the highly successful 5 ton tractors introduced in 1906.

It will be noted that the first three engines were built in 1907; then there was a gap of six years before another two were built; this was followed by a further gap of ten years. Between 1924 and 1929 seventeen engines of this series were completed. Your author has found no satisfactory explanation for these long gaps other than the loss of the company's export markets following the outbreak of war in 1914. All the engines built prior to 1914 were exported, but only one was exported after the war.

Nos 3506 & 3572 were built in accordance with the German boiler regulations. The former went to Theodor Ohl less wheels, forecarriage, flywheel and firebars and No 3572 went to the Meissner & Dietlein agency in Magdeburg. Both had 175 PSI boilers and the remainder of the series had 200 PSI boilers. All had 3.0 sq ft grates but the number and length of the smoke tubes varied. Some had twenty-three 1¾ ins dia tubes others had twenty five. Some were 4 ft 2 ins long others were 4 ft

8 TON 4½ ins × 7½ ins × 8½ ins DCC 3-SHAFT ROAD ROLLER

No	Built	No	Built	No	Built	No	Built
No 2922	Built 1907	No 3976	Built 1924	No 4024	Built 1925	No 4059	Built 1927
2923	" 1907	3994	" 1924	4025	" 1926	4061	" 1927
2935	" 1907	4004	" 1925	4044	" 1926	4062	" 1927
3506	" 1913	4017	" 1925	4052	" 1926	4067	" 1927
3572	" 1914	4018	" 1925	4056	" 1927	4073	" 1929
3972	" 1924	4022	" 1925				

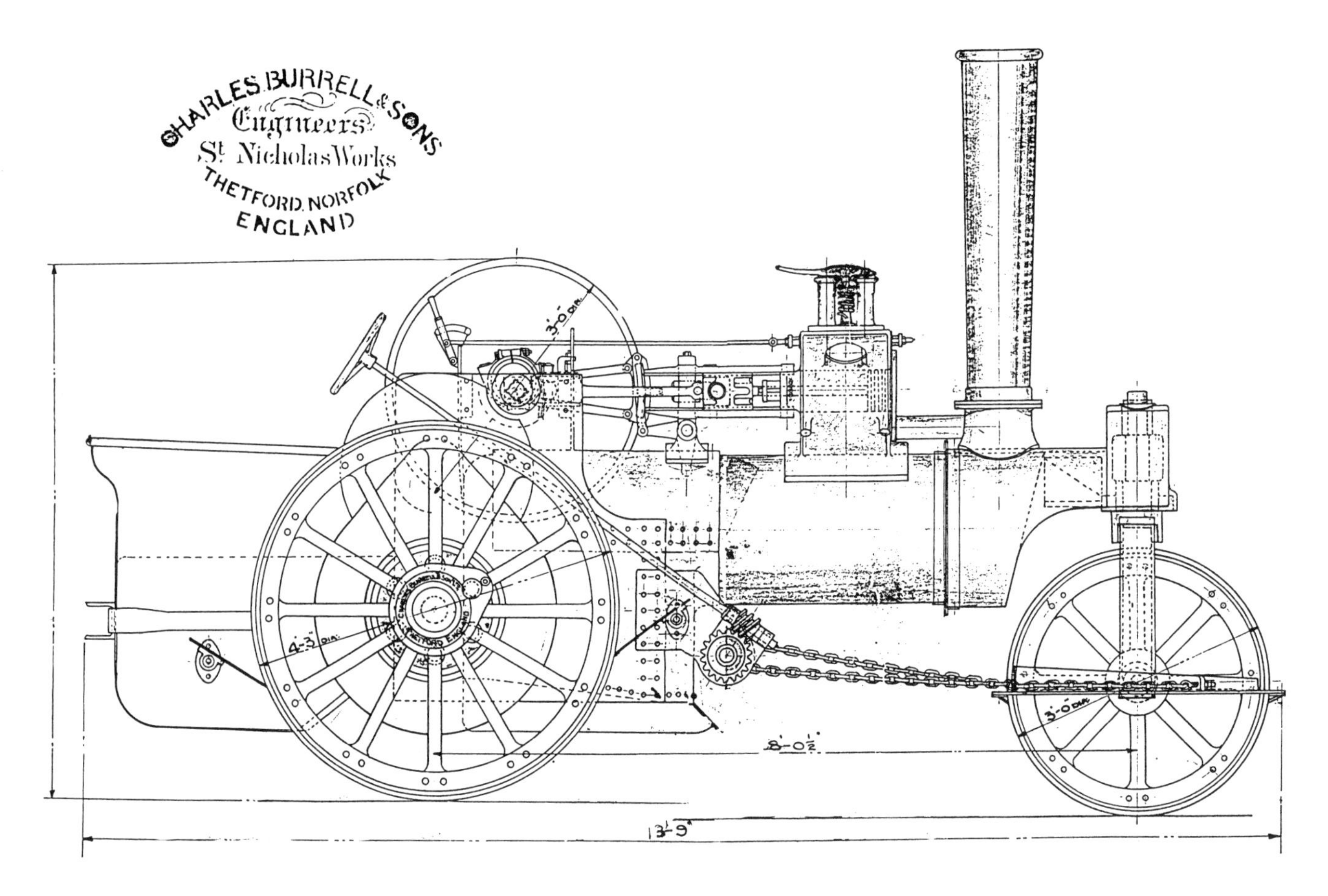

Fig 276 A 3 ton SC road roller proposed in 1924 but never built.

4¼ ins long. Generally the hind rolls were 5 ft 0 ins dia × 16 ins wide and the front rolls were 4 ft 0 ins dia × 22 ins wide giving a rolled width of 5 ft 10 ins. No 4044 and all subsequent engines had renewable rim rolls. The solid flywheels were 3 ft 6 ins dia × 4 ins wide and the engines in working order less scarifier and awning weighed approximately 8½ tons.

Nos 2922 & 2923 were supplied to Kerr Stuart the Railway Plant dealers and are believed to have been exported to India or South Africa. Both were fitted with Wallis & Steevens scarifiers. No 2935 went to Denmark and No 3976 went to Australia fitted with a Morrison scarifier.

No 4022 was built as No 3988 and this almost certainly was originally intended for Australia. In due course the engine was sold to John Hardy of Halstead in Essex who had also acquired No 3972 in 1914.

Only one of the series, No 4059 went to a UK Local Authority, the remainder all going to UK road rolling contractors. Doran's of Thetford had Nos 3994 & 4073. W J King of Bishops Lydeard in Somerset, the owner of seven Burrell engines and steam wagons at various times, acquired Nos 4004, 4044 & 4062. F Sharpe of Blandford in Dorset had Nos 4017, 4018, 4024 & 4025 and John Ball of Forton in Lancashire had Nos 4052 & 4056. All except John Ball's engines were fitted with Price's 2-tyne scarifiers. We shall see in the next chapter that a number of 5 ton tractors were subsequently converted to road rollers as this series.

Shortly after the introduction of the 5 ton tractor St Nicholas Works produced three 4¾ ton models with 4⅛ ins dia × 7 ins dia × 7½ ins stroke DCC cylinders. The same cylinder casting was used extensively on the 5 ton steam wagon introduced in 1911. In September 1912 one 6 ton road roller, No 3359 was produced for the Martin Saaf agency in Sweden using this same cylinder. The 200 PSI boiler had a small 2.78 sq ft grate, a total heating surface of 54.5 sq ft and twenty-six 1½ ins dia smoke tubes 3 ft 10¾ ins long. The same arrangement of 3-shaft 2-speed gearing was employed as on the larger engines and the renewable rim rolls, 4 ft 6 ins dia × 17 ins wide at the rear and 3 ft 3 ins dia × 21½ ins wide on the front gave a rolling width of 6 ft 0 ins. In working order the engine weighed 6 ton 15 cwt.

An extant works drawing (No 6762) drawn by Billy Greenwood when Chief Draughtsman in May 1924 reveals an interesting "might-have-been". Described as a 3 ton nominal road roller it is reproduced in Fig 276. The single cylinder measured 5½ ins dia × 8 ins stroke, the grate area appeared to be approximately 3.0 sq ft and the smoke tubes approximately 3 ft 2 ins long in a 1 ft 9 ins dia boiler shell. The hind rolls were 4 ft 3 ins dia and the front rolls 3 ft 0 ins dia × 18 ins wide giving a rolled width of 4 ft 8 ins. The solid flywheel was 3 ft 0 ins dia × 3½ ins wide. There is no evidence that such an engine was ever built.

We are left now to consider the seven DCC convertible engines built between 1910 and 1925.

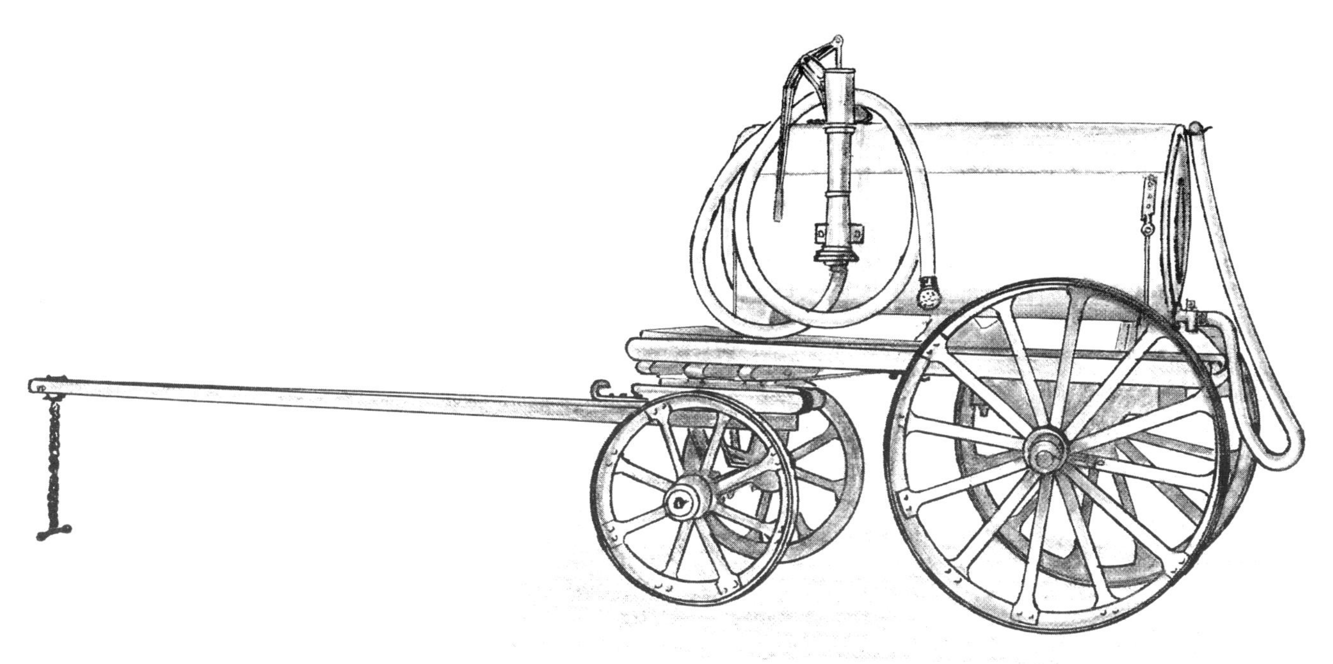

Fig 277 A typical 4-wheel horse drawn water cart having a 365 gallons capacity.

DCC TRACTION ENGINE-CUM-ROAD ROLLER CONVERTIBLES

No 3219	Built	1910	cyls.	5″ × 8½″ × 9″
3351	"	1911	"	5″ × 8½″ × 9″
3381	"	1912	"	5½″ × 9″ × 10″
3398	"	1912	"	5½″ × 9″ × 10″
3859	"	1920	"	5½″ × 9″ × 10″
3409	"	1912	"	6″ × 10″ × 10″
3864	"	1925	"	4½″ × 7½″ × 8½″

All had 200 PSI boilers similar to their contemporary GP traction engines. Nos 3219 & 3351 were spring mounted with single drive gearing and the remainder had double drive gearing to the hind axle. Nos 3381, 3398 & 3864 were spring mounted and Nos 3409 & 3859 were unsprung. All had compensating gear and winding drums and Nos 3381 & 3398 were 3-speed engines. The popularity of the convertible engine was short lived and little interest was shown in these engines after the First War. No 3351 went to Belgium; No 3409 went to New Zealand; three went to UK Local Authorities and two went to road rolling contractors.

Throughout the steam road roller era, St Nicholas Works continued to produce wooden bodied living vans with accommodation for up to four men. They produced also 2-wheel and 4-wheel water carts, the latter having a capacity up to 400 gallons of water. Both these accessories were originally developed to meet the needs of the Steam Ploughing Contractor in the 1860s but production remained small.

CHAPTER SIXTEEN

Steam Tractors

Undoubtedly by the mid-1890s there was considerable resentment amongst the operators of road locomotives caused by the restrictive legislation in force governing their use. A powerful lobby led by the distinguished lawyer and parliamentarian, Sir William Joyson-Hicks, had existed for some time and it was widely predicted that relaxations would soon be introduced. Most engine builders were closely watching the situation and the general opinion was that engines within a 3-ton unladen weight limit would qualify for the maximum relief. It was of particular concern that such engines should be allowed on the public highway operated by one man.

On September 19th 1896 W A Scott, a draughtsman at St Nicholas Works completed an outline drawing of a 3 ton DCC Road Steamer, which at first sight was reminiscent of R W Thomson's original duplex cylinder vertical boiler engines built in the 1860s. A side elevation of this unique engine is shown in Fig 278. The driver sat on a pedestal mounted seat towards the front of the engine with the direct worm drive steering column and engine controls placed conveniently around him. The vertical boiler was arranged behind the driver and behind the boiler a vertical DCC cylinder measuring 5½ ins dia × 8½ ins dia × 9 ins stroke was mounted transversely, its 3-bearing crankshaft being parallel with the motion shafts. Sliding pinions of differing sizes on the ends of the crankshaft engaged with spur wheels on the intermediate motion shaft thereby giving 2-speed gearing to the hind axle. Compensating gear was mounted on the intermediate motion shaft and pinions on the outer ends of the shaft engaged with large internally toothed annular spur rings attached to the hind wheels. The slow speed gearing was on the left hand side of the engine and the fast speed was on the right hand side. The driver had two levers, one on either side of his pedestal seat which enabled him to engage or disengage the gearing. The unsprung 6 ft 0 ins dia × 11 ins wide hind wheels were fitted with solid rubber tyres and retaining clips as described in Burrell's patent No 3105 of 1871. The water tank was slung under the engine frame between the driver's seat and the boiler. Fuel was carried in bunkers placed either side of the boiler. The engine was 9 ft 6 ins overall length and 5 ft 7 ins overall width. It is doubtful if an engine of this design was ever built because the weight distribution was all wrong, adhesion was poor and access to the boiler and firebox was difficult when travelling.

Be that as it may, this design was the precursor of the 5 ton tractor which became legalised under the Heavy Motor Car Act 1904. This Act allowed the engine to be operated on the public highway by one man. The speed was restricted to 5 MPH and the unladen weight was limited to 5 tons. Most leading engine builders were ready to take advantage of this new legislation and very quickly the steam tractor, in reality a miniatiure Road Locomotive, became a common sight on our roads. Like their big brothers they were almost invariably spring mounted compound engines with belly tanks, solid flywheels, motion side plates and canopies. In later years most were fitted with solid rubber tyres.

Completed in December 1905, the first Burrell 5 ton tractor had a 6½ ins dia × 8½ ins stroke single cylinder. Between 1906 and 1927 a further 220 tractors were built at St Nicholas Works, but only nine of these had single cylinders, the remainder all having DCC cylinders. The first engine, No 2787 underwent extensive trials both in the Thetford area and with Charles Hart of Barking before eventually being sold to Woods, Sadd & Moore, Wool Merchants of Loddon in Norfolk in March 1909 and renumbered No 2805.

6½ ins DIA × 8½ ins STROKE SC 5 TON TRACTORS

No		Built	No		Built
No 2787	Built	1905	No 3510	Built	1913
2797	"	1906	3645	"	1915
3041	"	1908	3646	"	1915
3225	"	1910	3647	"	1915
3333	"	1911			

The boilers had 3.0 sq ft grates, a total heating surface of 65.5 sq ft and twenty-five 1¾ ins dia × 4 ft 4½ ins long smoke tubes. The first four had a working pressure of 180 PSI, thereafter the boilers were pressed to 200 PSI. Nos 2787 & 2797 were fitted with Richardson's steam pumps and a Penberthy injector. The next four engines had two BP 'D' injectors and the final three engines in the series had a geared feed pump and a single injector. All were double geared and spring mounted with a winding drum on the hind axle. The 2-speed gearing gave ratios of 24.4 and 13.6 to 1. The hind wheels were 5 ft 0 ins dia, the first two engines having 9 ins wide wheels which gave an unladen weight of 4 ton 19 cwt and an overall engine width of 5 ft 2 ins. Thereafter 12 ins wide wheels were supplied which increased the weight to 5 ton 5 cwt. The solid type flywheels were 3 ft 0 ins dia × 4½ ins wide. Hind wheel and flywheel brakes were fitted and the Pickering governor controlled the engine speeds at 235 RPM when working on the belt. The tender water tank and belly tanks carried

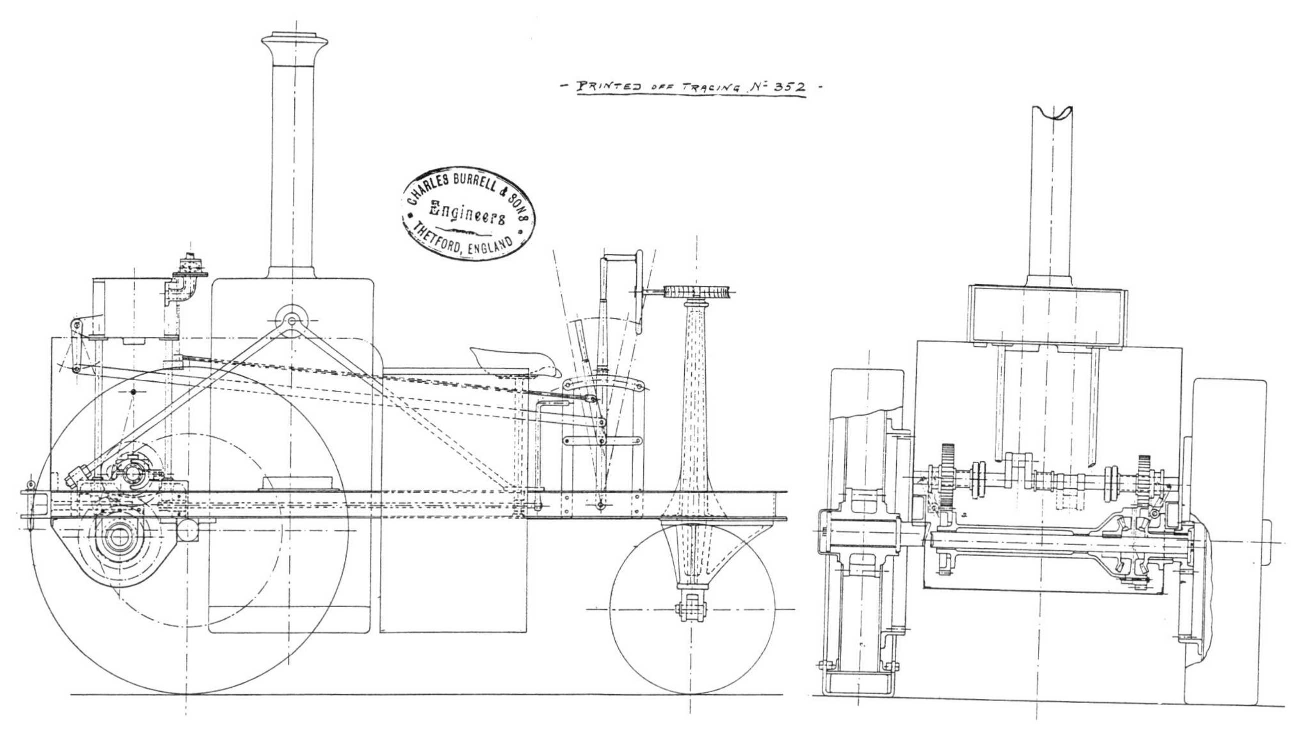

Fig 278 W A Scott's 1896 design for a 3 ton DCC tractor having a vertical boiler and solid rubber tyres on the hind wheels.

150 gallons of water sufficient for travelling 12 to 14 miles with loads without rewatering. All had short awnings. Nos 2787, 2797 and No 2808 (later renumbered No 2996) and the next eight compound engines were initially fitted with quadrant and worm drive steering. There are reports of some early failures caused by the rough rutted roads of the period breaking the gear teeth and they were all replaced with the conventional chain steerage. These engines were also originally fitted with 11 leaf hind axle springs but these too were eventually replaced by 15 leaf springs.

No 2797 was purchased by J & W Harding of Woking. Nos 3041, 3225, 3333 & 3510 were supplied to the Reid & Gray agency in New Zealand and were purchased mainly for hauling bales of wool from the homesteads to the railhead. Nos 3645, 3646 & 3647 were supplied to the War Department in 1915 and were part of a large fleet of engines used for hauling animal fodder on Salisbury Plain. After the War these engines were sold to local authorities who were increasingly acknowledging the advantages of steam haulage for road maintenance work. The advent of the one-man operation tractor was of special interest to them and most engine builders made special efforts to secure a share of this market although competition was fierce and profit margins lean. However, firms like Charles Openshaw of Reading did good business overhauling and selling surplus W.D. engines to local authorities in the 1920s.

Before considering the 203 standard DCC 5 ton tractors which first appeared in 1906 it is appropriate to refer to five special tractors with DCC cylinders built between 1906 and 1910.

4 ins × 7½ ins × 8½ ins DCC 5 TON SHOWMAN'S TRACTORS

No 2802 Built 1906	No 2803 Built 1906

These engines were built to the order of Lord John Sanger & Sons, successors to the renowned Victorian circus proprietor, Lord George Sanger, only five months after the great man had retired and disposed of all his circus equipment, horses and animals. The business was restructured and his brother John continued the great tradition. The circus survived in Sanger family hands until it was eventually wound up by a Court Order in 1962 after 177 years.

In all major respects the mechanical details of these engines were similar to No 2787 except that they had 4 ins dia × 7½ ins dia × 8½ ins stroke DCC cylinders, full length awnings with twisted brass canopy supports and smokebox dynamo platforms with Crompton dynamos. The 5 ft 0 ins hind wheels were only 7 ins wide, giving an overall engine width of 4 ft 9 ins, which must have presented problems when the engines were pulling onto soft ground. Painted crimson with red wheels the unladen weight of the engines was only 4 tons 15 cwt.

Fig 279 No 2787 the first SC 5 ton tractor originally built in 1905 as rebuilt and renumbered No 2805 in 1909.

Fig 280 No 2808 as originally built with toothed quadrandt and worm steering in 1906. Later rebuilt and renumbered No 2996.

4⅛ ins × 7 ins × 7½ ins DCC 4¾ TON TRACTORS

No 3004 Built 1908	No 3185 Built 1910
3109 " 1909	

These miniature road engines had the same 4⅛ ins dia × 7 ins dia × 7½ ins stroke DCC cylinders as subsequently used on the 5 ton steam wagons; they developed 14 BHP whilst having an unladen weight less the canopy of only 4 ton 5 cwt. They were suitable for handling 10 ton loads on a 1 in 18 incline and could travel 14 or 15 miles without rewatering. They would undoubtedly have been built in greater numbers were it not for the imminent introduction of the 5 ton steam wagon in 1911.

The small 200 PSI boilers had 2.78 sq ft grates, a total heating surface of 38.0 sq ft and twenty-six 1½ ins dia × 3 ft 11 ins long smoke tubes. The engines were spring mounted with double geared drive and axle mounted winding drums. The 2-speed gearing had ratios of 18.6 and 10.4 to 1. The hind wheels were 5 ft 0 ins dia and in the case of Nos 3004 & 3109 were only 9 ins wide giving an overall engine width of 5 ft 1 ins. The solid flywheels were 3 ft 0 ins dia × 4½ ins wide and the Pickering governors controlled the engine speed at 250 RPM when working on the belt.

Nos 3004 & 3109 went to commercial owners and No 3185 went to the Deptford Amusement Caterers, Purchase Bros for hauling their menagerie beast wagons. The hind wheels were increased in width to 12 ins, a full

Fig 281 No 2803 one of two small DCC cylinder 5 ton Showman's tractors built for Lord John Sanger's famous circus in 1906 having toothed quadrant and worm steering.

Fig 282 No 3185 4¾ ton DCC tractor built for Purchase Bros Menagerie of Deptford in 1910.

length canopy with twisted brass supports and a dynamo platform carrying a Siemens dynamo were fitted increasing the unladen weight to 5 ton 3 cwt.

The 203 5 ton tractors with 4½ ins dia × 7½ ins dia × 8½ ins stroke DCC cylinders built between 1906 and 1927 were the most numerous single type of engine built by Charles Burrell. They probably incorporated the least number of detailed variations from standard of any class of engine built at St Nicholas Works. They were supplied to general haulage contractors, quarry owners, suppliers of bricks and building materials, timber hauliers, flour millers, wharfingers, furniture removers, the military authorities and amusement caterers. Some were acquired by agriculturists and they are even known to have be used for direct traction ploughing. But essentially these engines were used mainly for the transportation of goods in urban areas usually hauling a 3 or 5 ton traction wagon. Many of these were fitted with screw-down brakes arranged such that they could be operated by the driver without leaving the footplate.

4 NHP 4½ ins × 7½ ins × 8½ ins DCC 5 TON TRACTORS

No 2808	Built	1906	No 3226	Built	1910	No 3531	Built	1913	No 3685	Built	1915
2830	”	1906	3234	”	1910	3534	”	1913	3689	”	1915
2831	”	1906	3245	”	1910	3540	”	1914	3693	”	1915
2842	”	1906	3250	”	1910	3543	”	1914	3700	”	1915
2847	”	1906	3253	”	1911	3545	”	1914	3705	”	1915
2861	”	1906	3264	”	1910	3548	”	1914	3707	”	1916
2866	”	1906	3266	”	1910	3549	”	1913	3709	”	1916
2870	”	1906	3269	”	1911	3550	”	1914	3718	”	1916
2876	”	1907	3287	”	1911	3551	”	1914	3719	”	1916
2880	”	1907	3294	”	1911	3554	”	1914	3722	”	1916
2881	”	1907	3308	”	1911	3557	”	1914	3725	”	1916
2882	”	1907	3315	”	1911	3560	”	1914	3729	”	1916
2883	”	1907	3318	”	1911	3562	”	1914	3738	”	1917
2885	”	1907	3336	”	1911	3574	”	1914	3741	”	1916
2899	”	1907	3341	”	1911	3575	”	1914	3742	”	1916
2904	”	1907	3349	”	1911	3576	”	1914	3745	”	1917
2913	”	1907	3354	”	1911	3588	”	1914	3749	”	1917
2925	”	1907	3355	”	1912	3589	”	1914	3752	”	1917
2929	”	1907	3361	”	1912	3594	”	1914	3753	”	1917
2932	”	1908	3363	”	1912	3595	”	1914	3754	”	1917
2955	”	1907	3369	”	1912	3596	”	1914	3757	”	1917
2975	”	1908	3374	”	1912	3601	”	1914	3759	”	1917
2976	”	1908	3375	”	1912	3603	”	1914	3762	”	1917
2977	”	1908	3377	”	1912	3606	”	1914	3776	”	1917
2978	”	1908	3379	”	1912	3613	”	1914	3783	”	1918
2982	”	1908	3387	”	1912	3615	”	1914	3785	”	1918
3028	”	1908	3389	”	1912	3617	”	1914	3786	”	1918
3037	”	1909	3397	”	1912	3618	”	1914	3791	”	1918
3064	”	1908	3415	”	1912	3620	”	1914	3795	”	1919
3086	”	1909	3417	”	1912	3622	”	1914	3802	”	1919
3102	”	1909	3425	”	1912	3624	”	1914	3807	”	1919
3105	”	1909	3428	”	1912	3626	”	1914	3808	”	1919
3113	”	1909	3433	”	1912	3630	”	1914	3814	”	1919
3122	”	1909	3435	”	1912	3631	”	1915	3815	”	1919
3141	”	1909	3442	”	1913	3637	”	1914	3820	”	1919
3147	”	1909	3449	”	1913	3638	”	1915	3823	”	1919
3156	”	1909	3453	”	1913	3639	”	1915	3826	”	1920
3162	”	1909	3457	”	1913	3643	”	1915	3839	”	1920
3177	”	1910	3458	”	1913	3649	”	1915	3846	”	1920
3186	”	1910	3464	”	1913	3650	”	1915	3848	”	1920
3187	”	1910	3465	”	1913	3653	”	1915	3850	”	1920
3190	”	1910	3475	”	1913	3656	”	1915	3851	”	1920
3191	”	1910	3481	”	1913	3658	”	1915	3852	”	1920
3192	”	1910	3486	”	1913	3662	”	1915	3857	”	1923
3193	”	1910	3495	”	1913	3663	”	1915	3861	”	1920
3194	”	1910	3497	”	1913	3672	”	1915	3862	”	1921
3199	”	1910	3504	”	1913	3673	”	1915	3868	”	1920
3203	”	1910	3508	”	1913	3677	”	1915	4071	”	1927
3214	”	1910	3515	”	1913	3678	”	1915	4072	”	1927
3223	”	1910	3524	”	1913	3681	”	1915	4084	”	1927

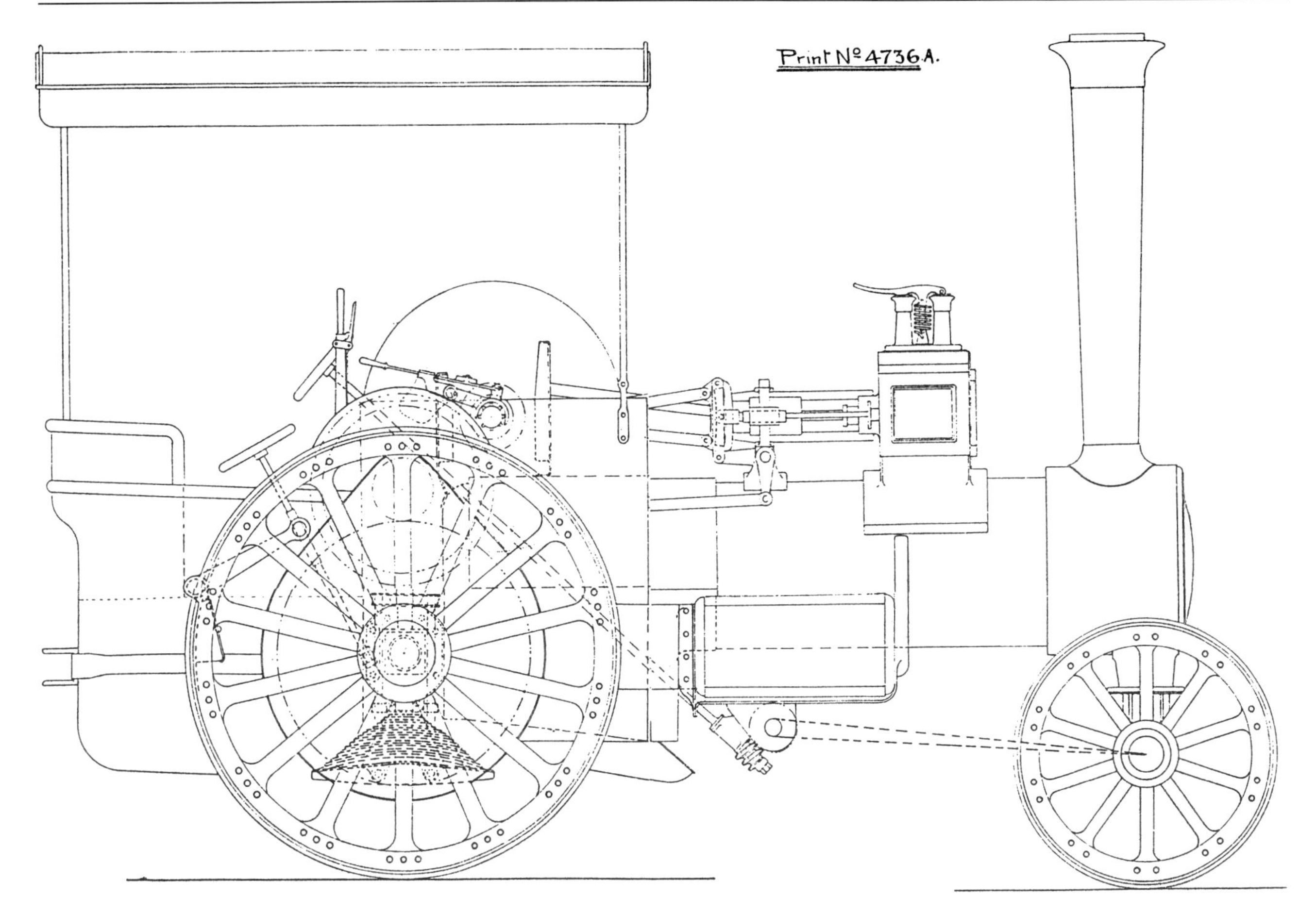

Fig 283 A Burrell General Arrangement drawing of an early double crank compound 5 ton tractor – circa 1909.

Throughout the twenty-one years the tractor was in production the 1 ft 10 ins dia boilers remained basically unaltered. The first eighteen had a working pressure of 180 PSI thereafter the working pressure was increased to 200 PSI. The grate was 3.0 sq ft, the total heating surface was 65.5 sq ft and the boilers had twenty-five 1¾ ins dia × 4 ft 4½ ins long steel smoke tubes. The firehole door was arranged slightly below the level of the footplate which initially caused unfamiliar drivers some difficulty in seeing the front of the fire when in motion. Because of the smallness of the grate and the comparatively large compound cylinders it was also necessary to use good quality steam coal for best results. The drivers soon adapted to new techniques of driving and by 1920 the ubiquitous Burrell tractor became much loved and respected. With the advent of 3-speed gearing in 1910 the ability to return home empty in fast speed was greatly appreciated.

The engines developed 16 BHP and were well able to handle 12 ton loads on a 1 in 18 incline. The first 18 were fitted with Richardson's steam pumps and a single Penberty injector, thereafter most were fitted with two BP 'D' type injectors. A handful of engines built after 1914 had geared boiler feed pumps. A quarter of those built were fitted with Pickering governors and these were set to control the engine speed at 230 RPM. Six of the engines supplied to the War Department in 1910 were fitted with Burrell's totally enclosed chain driven governors.

All were double geared to the hind axle with compensating gear and winding drums. Some had Burrell's patent differential locking gear which was particularly applicable to those engaged on timber hauling work and likely to encounter soft ground. The majority had 2-speed gearing having ratios of 24.4 and 13.6 to 1. Later 3-speed engines had an additional fast speed having a ratio of 7.6 to 1.

Generally the hind wheels were 5 ft 0 ins dia × 9 ins wide. In order to save weight some had 6 ins wide hind wheels built on a single T-ring, others including the ten engines supplied to the War Department in 1910 had 12 ins wide wheels. Earlier engines had 3 ft 0 ins dia × 4½ ins wide solid flywheels, but the majority had 3 ft 11 ins dia × 4½ ins wide flywheels. All had motion side plates and either long or short awnings. Both hind wheel and flywheel brakes were fitted to most engines and the water tanks carried 70 gallons of water. The overall width of the standard engines with 9 ins wide wheels was 5 ft 2 ins and the unladen weight of the engines varied between 5 tons and 5½ tons.

Eleven 5 ton tractors were supplied new to amusement caterers, complete with dynamo platforms, long awnings and varying degrees of traditional Showman's embellishments. A further five standard tractors were supplied direct to showmen and these may have been converted subsequently by private firms as was No 3177. Shortly after delivery Charles Openshaw Ltd of Reading

Fig 284 No 3868 George Baker & Sons smart 5 ton DCC tractor 'The Russell Baby'. Later renamed 'Island Prince' whilst in the ownership of Arnold Bros.

modified this engine for Jacob Studt of Maesteg.

Nos 2880, 2977 & 2978 were supplied to French showmen through the Burnell agency. All had dynamo platforms and long awnings but none carried twisted brass supports or stars or rings. No 2880 went to Mr Ranay, of Assiceres near Paris and the other two engines went to M D Matlus et Cie operating in the Vosges. A fourth similar engine No 2881 went to Robert Johnson a Leicester based showman. No 2982, the first tractor built with a full set of traditional showman's embellishments went to Walter Payne of Dartford. The engine, named 'Independence' received considerable notoriety during a 7,000 mile tour of Southern England with Payne's Bioscope Show. The tour was sponsored by the *News of the World* newspaper and 'Independence' hauled one of the show's wagons and generated current for ten large Arc lamps. A subsequent testimonial published in Burrell's General Catalogue claimed that during the three years the engine was on tour it never once required any attention in a workshop. After the War it was sold to the well known London traveller, W Nichols of Forest Gate and ended its working life in the ownership of R Theodore of Coventry.

The sixth 5 ton Showman's tractor No 3341, 'St Bernard' went new to Hill Brothers of Bedminster. In 1914 it was acquired secondhand by George Baker & Sons of Southampton who subsequently purchased new a further two similar engines. No 3453, 'The May' went new to W Sedgewick of Oldham in Lancashire for his menagerie and spent her working life hauling one of his beast wagons. It will be noted the engine was fitted with extra large belly tanks enabling it to travel up to 25 miles without re-watering. No 3551, 'Norah' was purchased by the Tyneside showman, Nicholas Knight and No 3725, 'Excelsior' went to Robert Payne of Beverley in Yorkshire, ending her days with A Chadwick in the Potteries.

The final two Showman's tractors, Nos 3560 and 3868 went new to George Baker & Sons, Southampton. No 3868 illustrated in Fig 284 originally named 'The Russell Baby' was an especially attractive miniature Showman's road locomotive which Burrells exhibited at the 1920 Smithfield Show and the full specification of the extras supplied as listed in the works engine records is worth quoting.

> 'Long awning on six twisted brass supports; 8 ins deep plate coal rack; All pipes of copper; AGE transfer on each belly tank; AGE plates on HP cylinder cover, on smokebox door centre and on brass axle caps; Brass tubes to convey steam from safety valves through awning; Brass stars and rings on motion side plates; Brass cylinder covers; dynamo platform to DWG 2981; Sheet iron guard between chimney and dynamo; Brass segmented name plate on dynamo platform; Gilded lettering on awning sides "George Baker & Sons Ltd, Southampton"; Engine to be painted lake lined gilt, red & black; yellow wheels lined gilt, red & black.'

The unladen weight of the engine was 5 ton 16 cwt and it was supplied new with Mackintosh's solid rubber tyres. The straight exhaust steam pipe from below the LP cylinder end cover direct into the cast chimney base will also be noted in Fig 284. On the original 1906 engines the exhaust pipe curved down from the end of the cylinder and

Fig 285 No 3190, one of six special 5 ton DCC crane engines built for the War Department in 1910. Note the additional large water tanks carried on top of the belly tanks.

entered the smokebox on the flywheel side of the engine. From 1907 until after the First War the exhaust steam was taken from below the LP valve chest through an elbow entering the smokebox on the flywheel side of the engine. Obviously the post war arrangement caused the least back pressure and enhanced the blast pipe performance. This engine was also noteworthy as one of only four 5 ton tractors having the eccentric driven boiler feed pump driven through reduction gearing.

Later the engine was acquired by Arnold Bros of Southampton and renamed 'Island Prince'. She worked with Arnold's other Burrell, No 3878 'Island Chief' until after the Second World War and regularly travelled between Southampton and the Isle of Wight in an open barge. In 1955 she was sold to Hardwick's scrap yard but fortunately was rescued for preservation.

Between 1908 and 1910 ten 5 ton tractors were supplied to the War Department. Nos 2975, 2976, 3186 & 3187 were basically standard 2-speed tractors and Nos 3190, 3191, 3192, 3193, 3194 & 3226 were special 3-speed crane engines with 2 ton capacity forward mounted swanneck jibs carrying a differential pulley block. Nos 2975 & 2976 had specially strengthened smokeboxes 2 ft 4½ ins long and three additional stay tubes were incorporated in the boiler. These two engines had long awnings whereas Nos 3186 & 3187 had short awnings covering only the footplate.

The six crane engines had enlarged winding drums carrying 100 yards of galvanised wire rope and additional water tanks were mounted on top of the standard belly tanks increasing their water carrying capacity to 320 gallons. The hind wheels were 5 ft 1 ins dia × 12 ins wide and a works photograph of one of the versatile little engines which were all painted Service Green is shown in Fig 285.

It speaks well for these engines that of the 180 5 ton compound tractors supplied new to a wide variety of commercial users, over one-third went to only twenty-four customers. At least forty-seven of the total were subsequently purchased secondhand by amusement caterers during the declining days of steam and six were converted to road rollers. Reflecting the national decline of British exports in the 20th century, only eight compound tractors were sold abroad. Seven went to French buyers through the Burnell agency and as we have already seen, three of these were Showman's type engines. Nos 2866, 2904, 3738 & 3749 went to contractors in Epinal in the Vosges and to Plambres-les-Bains. No 3435 was the sole example to be sent to New Zealand.

Probably the best known of all the Burrell 5 ton tractors was No 2932, which the firm entered in the 1908 Royal Automobile Club Trial. The engine and its 6 ton gross load travelled 686 miles in 22 days and the coal consumption achieved was a remarkable 9.2 lbs per mile. By winning this prestigious event the marque became universally known as the 'Burrell Gold Medal Tractor'. In all major respects it was a standard engine although it was fitted with special hind wheels. The naves, spokes and rims were of steel fitted with wooden blocks and the motion was totally enclosed. After the trial the engine was purchased by Clements Knowling & Co of Brentford who already owned No 2882. In 1923 it passed to Alf Bond of Merton and spent the rest of its working life with his Gallopers.

William Elworthy of Tiverton in Devon, already mentioned elsewhere and owner of eleven Burrell engines at various times had five 5 ton tractors – Nos 3294, 3374,

Fig 286 No 2932 Gold Medal winning 1908 RAC Trials engine. Note totally enclosed motion and special wood block hind wheels.

3595, 3673 & 3745. The Horsehay Steam Haulage Company, Shropshire haulage contractors had four 5-ton tractors – Nos 3379, 3389, 3417 & 3486, as did the Wingham Engineering Company of Dover – Nos 3113, 3162, 3264 & 3603. C & G Yeoman of Canterbury also owned four tractors – Nos 2847, 3245, 3630 & 3742 and several other well known haulage contractors had two or three tractors.

Richard Pool, a contractor of Fleet in Hampshire had a special hoist added to the tender of No 3638, one of three Burrell tractors he owned. C Light & Co Ltd, timber hauliers of Christchurch in Hampshire had an IRA Miller 'Handy' hoist added to the tender of their tractor and Ben Musson, a Coventry timber merchant had a 2 ton capacity forward jib crane added to his tractor No 3508. The British Cyanide Company of Oldbury, near Birmingham purchased No 3807, another tractor with a forward jib crane. Three tractors, Nos 2870, 2899 & 3475 were owned by the granite quarries in the Malvern Hills, and No 3622 was one of two Burrell engines owned by the Saffron Walden furniture remover, W C Goddard. The Poole, Dorset wharfinger, H Burden & Co Ltd owned two Burrell 5 ton tractors – Nos 2955 & 3606. Heavy haulage contractors found the Burrell tractor ideal for light duties. Robert Wynn of Newport added No 2842 to his fleet and No 3752 was acquired by the renowned Norman Box concern of Manchester.

Some Local Authorities also liked the Burrell tractor. Norfolk CC had Nos 3795, 3820 & 3861. Wigtownshire CC had Nos 3549 & 3589 and Dorking RDC had Nos 3851 & 4071. It is of interest to note that in 1932 Norfolk CC sold No 3795 to the East Anglian engine builder, John M Collins of Bacton. Collins built his first tandem compound traction engine in 1910 and he fitted similar tandem cylinders to No 3795.

Five years after the end of the Great War the law was altered again and the Heavy Motor Car Act 1923 allowed the unladen weight of one-man operation tractors to be

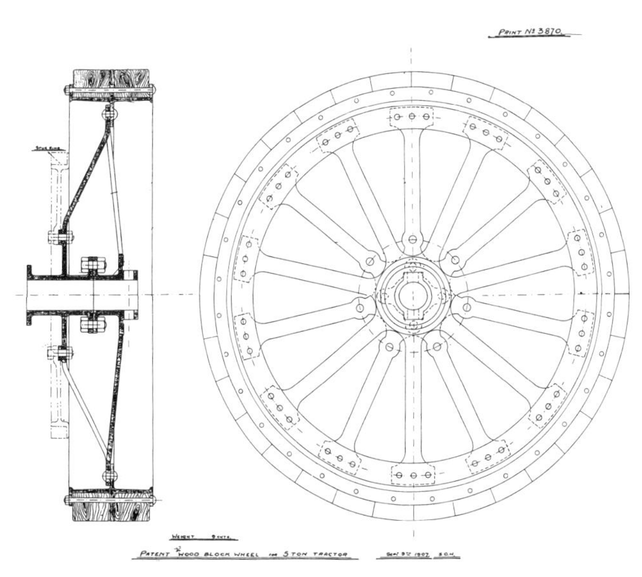

Fig 287 Special patent wood block rim hind wheels used on 1908 Trials engine.

Fig 288 No 4015 7 1/4 ton 5 NHP DCC tractor built in 1925 standing outside the Minstergate Street Paint Shop.

increased to 7¼ tons. Sadly the concession came too late to be of any real assistance to the ailing Burrell concern and only three engines were built to the revised specification.

5 NHP 5 ins × 8½ ins × 9 ins DCC 7¼ TON TRACTORS

No 4015	Built	1925	'The Baby'
4028	"	1925	(formerly No 3951)
4057	"	1926	'Jellicoe II'

Drawings for a 7¼ ton tractor were completed in the early part of 1923. The prototype, originally allocated works No 3951 was exhibited at the RASE Show held that year in Newcastle-Upon-Tyne where it aroused considerable interest in the technical press. During the show the engine was sold to F Tongue, a London area showman, subject to conversion to a full Showman's type engine. For reasons which are now unknown the engine was left on Burrells' hands for nearly two years. Eventually it was re-converted to a road locomotive, re-numbered No 4028 and sold to Sydney Jewell of Wadebridge in Cornwall. Fortunately the engine survives today.

The three 7¼ ton tractors built were more or less identical. The 5 ins dia × 8½ ins dia × 9 ins stroke cylinders and 200 PSI boilers were as used on the Class 'A' DCC road rollers. They had 4.18 sq ft grates, a total heating surface of 78.0 sq ft and were fitted with thirty 1¾ ins dia × 4 ft 2 ins long smoke tubes. Feed water was provided by two BP 'D' type injectors.

They were double geared 3-speed engines with 15 leaf spring gear, winding drums and differential locking gear. The gear ratios were 24.4, 13.64 & 7.43 to 1 and the hind wheels, which varied between 4 ft 6 ins dia and 5 ft 3 ins dia were all fitted with Mackintosh's twin rubber tyres. The flywheels were 3 ft 0 ins dia × 4½ ins wide and the engine speed was controlled by Pickering governors. The water carrying capacity was 210 gallons and the unladen weight of the engines excluding their long awnings was 7 tons 4 cwt. Although no precise figures appear to have survived they must have developed in excess of 20 BHP and been suitable for handling 20 ton loads on the Croxton 1 in 18 incline.

CHAPTER SEVENTEEN

Steam Wagons

Road legislation introduced at the end of the last century provided some alleviation to the users of steam and encouraged several British manufacturers to develop steam powered vehicles able to carry their payload on themselves. The difficulty was to devise a vehicle whose tare weight was acceptable in relation to the net load it could carry. Development of the internal combustion engine had already begun in Europe and the weight of steam boilers and the associated water to be carried by the vehicle was a severe penalty on engine designers.

In February 1901 Charles Burrell produced an under-type wagon design having a vertical cross-tube boiler mounted on the front of the frame and a horizontal totally enclosed double crank compound engine slung under the frame mid-way between the front and hind wheels. The boiler was similar to that developed for small marine craft in the 1880s. The drive to the hind axle was on either side of the wagon driven off a countershaft mounted behind and in line with the crankshaft. Two sliding pinions of differing diameters mounted on the crankshaft engaged with spur wheels on the countershaft giving two road speeds. It appears that the compensating gear was mounted on the countershaft within the spur wheel casting. Both the front and hind axles were carried on semi-elyptical springs. The hind wheels were fitted with wood block rims and a traction wagon type screw brake was provided on the outside rim of the wheels, operated by the driver from his sitting position on top of the water tank. Ackerman type steering through a fixed vertical column was employed.

There is no proof that this engine was actually built, but folklore in Thetford insists that a wagon of this type was frequently to be seen plying between St Nicholas Works and the railway station. Certainly no works number applicable to this wagon exists in the surviving engine records. It is interesting to note that the original drawing reproduced in Fig 289 refers to a 'Steam Lurry', a north country term used by early Lancashire and Yorkshire steam wagon pioneers at the turn of the century.

During the first decade of the 20th century Fodens of Sandbatch, Willam Foster of Lincoln, Wallis & Steevens of Basingstoke, Garretts of Leiston, Aveling & Porter of Rochester and William Allchin of Northampton all introduced over-type steam wagons. Designs soon crystallised and superficially their external appearances were similar, although Fodens were involved in litigation in an endeavour to protect their pioneering designs.

Obviously Charles Burrell had been considering entering this market for several years and in 1911 they produced the first of four experimental over-type steam wagons. All were built in accordance with their patents 20738 of 1909 and 7867 of 1911 filed jointly in the names of Charles II and William Campbell Wilson, the then Works Manager.

ORIGINAL EXPERIMENTAL BATCH 5 TON OVER-TYPE WAGONS

No 3276	Built 1911	No 3290	Built 1911
3289	" 1911	3303	" 1911

The DCC cylinders measured $4\frac{1}{8}$ ins dia × 7 ins dia × $7\frac{1}{2}$ ins stroke and the 200 PSI locomotive type boilers had 3.0 sq ft grates, a total heating surface of 53.0 sq ft and fifty-three $1\frac{1}{4}$ ins dia × 2 ft $4\frac{1}{2}$ ins long smoke tubes. The wagons developed 24 BHP at 400 RPM.

The novelty of these engines lay in the 3-speed transmission system shown in the works drawing reproduced in Fig 290. No 3289 left the works three months ahead of No 3276 and was fitted with a new awning as shown in Fig 291. It will be seen that sliding pinions on the end of the crankshaft could be engaged with spur wheels carried on an intermediate shaft mounted behind and below the crankshaft. On each end of this shaft which also accommodated the compensating gear, were chain pinions taking a double Morse chain drive to a second intermediate motion shaft mounted under the engine frame and adjacent to the hind axle. The chain spur wheels on each side of the engine were independently driven through the compensating gear. Both road wheels were free to rotate on the hind axle and were driven by pinions attached to the chain spur wheels carried on the second motion shaft. These driving pinions engaged with large internally toothed spur rings attached to the hind wheels. Patent 7867 of 1911 also made provision for externally toothed spur wheels to be used on the hind axle, but it remains unclear if this system was ever employed. The dead hind axle was provided with two sprung retaining arms attached to a chassis cross-member, which ensured the correct and constant mesh of the final drive gears as the axle rose and fell due to the action of the semi-elyptical road springs.

The 3-speed gearing had ratios of 18.0, 10.0 and 5.4 to 1. The hind traction engine type wheels were 4 ft 0 ins dia × 10 ins wide and the front wheels were 3 ft 0 ins dia × 6 ins wide. Both hind wheel and flywheel brakes were provided and the driver sat on the flywheel side of the engine. The flywheel was 2 ft 0 ins dia × 4 ins wide and

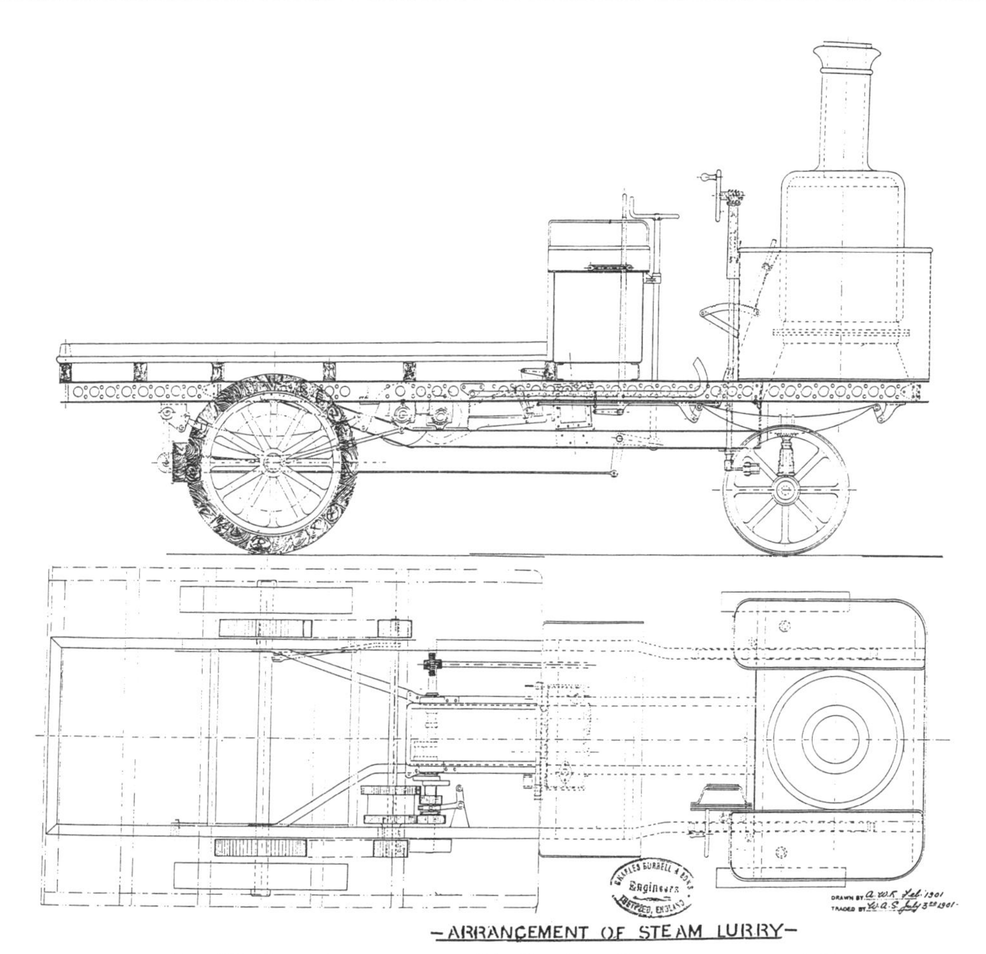

Fig 289 General arrangement of the first Burrell steam wagon – 1901.

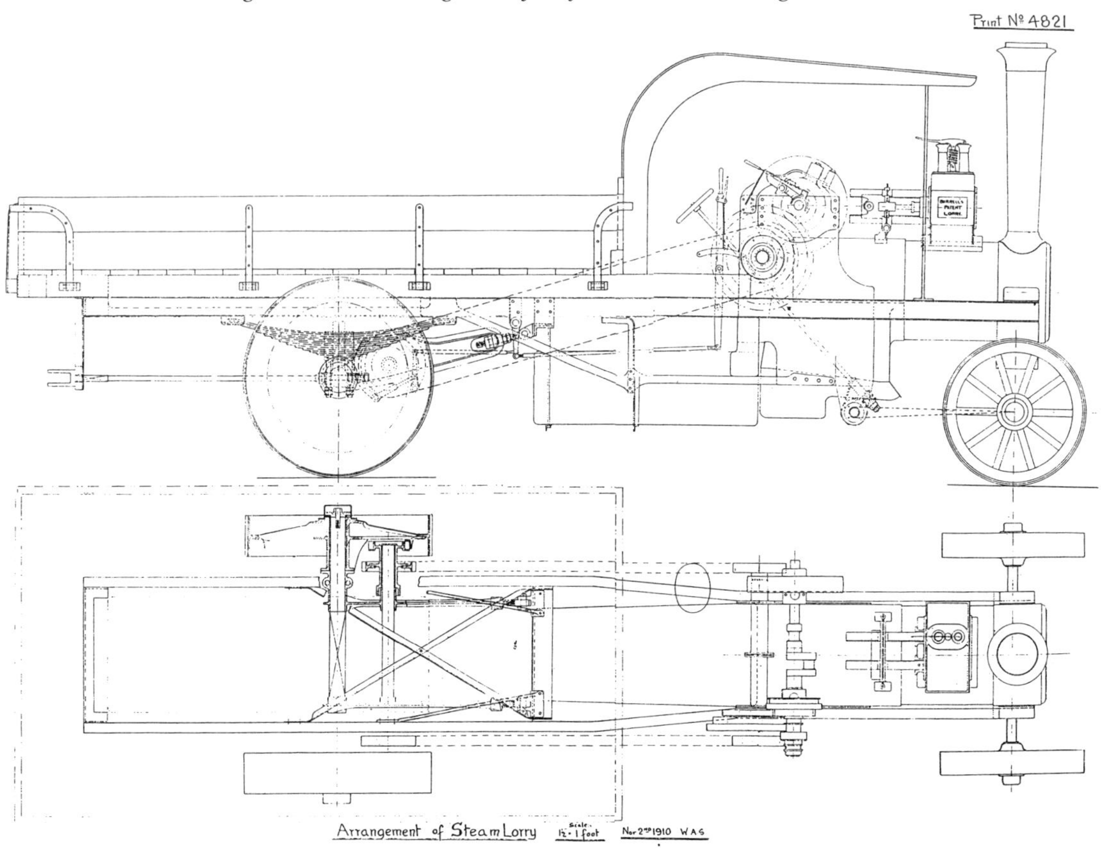

Fig 290 No 3289 5 ton experimental wagon as built in 1911 with conventional front axle and chain steering.

the tank carried 142 gallons of water. The wheelbase of the wagons was 13 ft 6 ins, the overall width was 4 ft 11 ins and the unladen weight 5 ton 17 cwt.

No 3276 was unique in that it was fitted with Ackerman type steering and both front and hind axles were mounted on 14 leaf semi-elyptical springs which added 6 cwt to the unladen weight of the wagon. The other three in the quartet had totally enclosed worm drive chain steering and conventionally sprung front axles.

During the next two years St Nicholas Works completed a batch of eleven double chain drive wagons in accordance with the 23–1 series drawings.

2nd GENERATION DOUBLE CHAIN
5 TON WAGONS

No 3319	Built	1911	No 3384	Built	1912
3358	"	1912	3386	"	1912
3360	"	1912	3401	"	1912
3362	"	1912	3412	"	1912
3370	"	1912	3436	"	1913
3373	"	1912			

The same $4\frac{1}{8}$ ins dia × 7 ins dia × $7\frac{1}{2}$ ins stroke DCC cylinders were employed but the grate area was slightly increased to 3.16 sq ft, the smoke tube size, number and length remaining as before. All had 3-speed gearing, with the compensating gear mounted on the intermediate motion shaft located just behind and below the crankshaft. The Morse double chain drive directly drove large spur wheels attached to the hind wheels carried on a dead axle. Throughout the development of the steam wagon considerable experimentation was done with various types of wheel in order to try and minimise the loss of power resulting from the tendency of the wheels to cut up the surface of the road. It was known this could absorb about 10HP in a wagon weighing 10 tons gross. Initially traction engine wheels were employed, then for a period heavy duty gun carriage wheels were used having wooden spokes and wooden felloes. These were followed by the composite wheel, which was largely developed by Henry Spurrier of the Leyland Motor Company. Next came fabricated steel plate wheels and finally the cast steel wheel often with Y-shaped spokes. The most successful was undoubtedly the Bauley wheel which St Nicholas Works used extensively after the First War. Solid rubber tyres appear to have been introduced in 1912 and tyres by Pirelli, Spencer Moulton and latterly Dunlop were fitted whenever specified, usually in combination with cast steel or Bauley wheels.

The wooden bodywork was built by St Nicholas Works and most of these wagons had long awnings extended to the chimney and flat platforms to accommodate the payload. Nos 3319 & 3401 were specially fitted out as Brewers' Drays. In 1924, No 3319 was acquired by William Bagnall, a Birmingham showman and is believed to have been fitted with a smokebox dynamo platform and other show fittings.

A school of thought soon emerged suggesting that the double chain drive could with advantage be replaced by a single drive. It was reckoned that savings could be achieved in both initial and maintenance costs and that the unladen weight of the wagon could be reduced without affecting the

Fig 291 No 3289 undergoing final tests at Thetford before delivery to Paramors Ltd of Margate in April 1911. Note new awnings.

carrying capacity. In August 1912 the first of a batch of 7 single chain engines was completed.

SINGLE CHAIN 5 TON WAGONS WITH
$4\frac{1}{8}'' \times 7'' \times 7\frac{1}{2}''$ DCC CYLINDERS

No 3394	Built	1912	No 3452	Built	1913
3424	"	1912	3454	"	1913
3437	"	1912	3485	"	1913
3439	"	1913			

The 200 PSI boilers had 3.0 sq ft grates and fifty-three $1\frac{1}{4}$ ins dia × 2 ft 6 ins long smoke tubes which combined to increase the total heating surface by 7.75 per cent to 60.34 sq ft. Like most steam wagons all employed two injectors and no boiler feed pumps.

All had 3-speed gearing. The compensating gear was mounted on the hind axle and reduction gears were incorporated in each hind wheel on all but Nos 3437 & 3439, which had direct drives to the hind wheels. A large 15 ins dia contracting brake was attached to the flywheel side of the hind axle and as was standard on all steam wagons a flywheel brake was provided. Most of these engines had artillery gun carriage type wheels. The new cranked frame on the gear side of the wagon designed to accommodate the countershaft spur gears and the neat layout of the chain casing will be noted in Fig 295. The 160 gallons capacity water tank, sufficient for at least 20 miles travelling without rewatering was attached to the underside of the frame mid way between the front and hind wheels. The wheelbase was 14 ft 4 ins. No 3424 was fitted with a special Brewer's Dray body, the remainder had flat backs.

Fig 292 No 3303 the fourth experimental 5 ton double chain wagon supplied to George Arnold of East Peckham after being exhibited at the RASE Show, Norwich 1911.

Fig 293 No 3362 5 ton double chain wagon supplied to A Adams & Son, St Albans February 1912.

But the single chain era was short lived and all remaining wagons built up to 1917 had the double chain drive. Eighteen only of the 100 5 ton wagons built at St Nicholas Works had the single chain drive. In the fifteen months April 1913 to July 1914 St Nicholas Works produced twenty-five 5 ton double chain wagons with slightly enlarged cylinders.

5 TON DOUBLE CHAIN WAGON WITH 4½ ins × 7½ ins × 8½ ins DCC CYLINDERS

No 3469	Built 1913	No 3502	Built 1913	No 3525	Built 1913	No 3539	Built 1914
3472	" 1913	3507	" 1913	3527	" 1913	3546	" 1914
3478	" 1913	3513	" 1913	3532	" 1913	3552	" 1914
3490	" 1913	3517	" 1913	3533	" 1913	3553	" 1914
3494	" 1913	3518	" 1913	3537	" 1913	3583	" 1914
3496	" 1913	3521	" 1913	3538	" 1914	3592	" 1914
3499	" 1913						

The 4½ ins dia × 7½ ins dia × 8½ ins stroke DCC cylinders with 1 ft 8½ ins long connecting rods were as used on the standard 5 ton tractors with the exhaust steam discharging from the bottom of the LP steam chest through a curved pipe into the flywheel side of the smokebox. The boilers and transmission arrangements were generally as the 1912 single chain engines and were built in accordance with the 23–121 series of drawings. The majority of these engines had 109 link roller chains having 2½ ins pitch and 8 ft 9 ins chain wheel centres supplied by Brampton Bros of Birmingham. Nos 3494, 3496, 3533 & 3592 were 2-speed engines, the remainder had 3-speed gearing. Nos 3527 & 3537 had manually operated end tipping bodies, No 3546 had a special tarpaulin covered body and Nos 3446, a small cylinder wagon, and 3592 supplied to Taylor's Eagle Brewery in Manchester had special Brewers' Dray bodies. The remainder all had flat back bodies and all had long awnings extended to behind the chimney. The majority left the works painted Burrell lake or green, although Nos 3553 & 3583 were supplied to Joseph Sterling of Benwell in Northumberland painted bright Prussian blue.

Later in 1914 the larger cylinder was abandoned and the works reverted to the smaller 4⅛ ins dia × 7 ins dia × 7½ ins stroke cylinder. It is tantalising that with the passage of time the reasons for design changes of this nature are lost for ever. Presumably it was found that the smaller cylinder provided adequate power to cope with the carrying capacity of the wagon and that the use of larger cylinders only increased steam consumption with a consequent unnecessary increase in fuel consumption.

Fig 294 No 3319 the first of two Burrell wagons supplied to Mitchell & Aldous Ltd, Kilburn Brewery – 1911.

Fig 295 No 3437 5 ton single chain wagon built 1912. Note cranked frame to clear countershaft spur gearing.

5 TON DOUBLE CHAIN WAGON WITH 4⅛ ins × 7 ins × 7½ ins DCC CYLINDERS

No	Built	No	Built	No	Built	No	Built
No 3446	Built 1913	No 3661	Built 1915	No 3698	Built 1915	No 3734	Built 1916
3616	" 1914	3664	" 1915	3701	" 1915	3743	" 1917
3623	" 1914	3666	" 1915	3706	" 1916	3760	" 1917
3627	" 1914	3671	" 1915	3710	" 1916	3764	" 1917*
3628	" 1914*	3674	" 1915	3712	" 1916	3769	" 1917
3634	" 1914	3680	" 1915	3716	" 1916	3796	" 1918
3635	" 1914*	3683	" 1915	3717	" 1916	3843	" 1920*
3644	" 1915	3684	" 1915*	3727	" 1916	3867	" 1920
3652	" 1915	3691	" 1915	3731	" 1916	3877	" 1923
3654	" 1915	3697	" 1915*	3732	" 1916	3881	" 1922

* 2-speed wagons, remainder 3-speed

In all major technical detail these wagons were similar to the larger cylinder double chain engines already described. Nos 3627, 3734 & 3769 had manually operated end tipping bodies; No 3664 was supplied to the Westerham brewers, Bushill, Watkins & Smith and had a special Brewers' Dray body; and No 3716 was supplied to W C Goddard of Saffron Walden and was fitted with a special furniture removers container. The remainder, including No 3843 which went to the Workington showmen, Taylor Bros, all had flat platform bodies. No 3635 was acquired secondhand by the Nottinghamshire showman, Tom West in 1922 and converted to the unique Showman's tractor illustrated in Fig 297. The only non-standard wagon built in the series was No 3732 for Green & Son of Sutton, Surrey. The wheelbox was increased to 15 ft 6 ins and the chain drive centres were increased to 9 ft 6 ins. A Burrell-Kirkcaldy type feed water heater and a geared type feed water pump were fitted. Rather surprisingly, so far as can be traced, none of these wagons has survived and all are believed to have been scrapped leaving a most regrettable gap in the types of engine in preservation.

In the decade before the works finally closed only eleven single chain and two double chain 5 ton wagons were built at St Nicholas Works. All the indications are that the 'magic' for long associated with Burrell designs had been surpassed by some of their many competitors in this field.

Fig 296 No 3623 5 ton 3-speed double chain wagon, built November 1914.

Fig 297 No 3635 5 ton 2-speed double chain wagon after conversion to a Showman's tractor in 1922.

Fig 298 No 3883 the only example of a full Showman's type wagon built at St Nicholas Works in February 1921 for Charles Summers of Norwich.

2nd GENERATION 5 TON SINGLE CHAIN WAGONS WITH $4\frac{1}{8}$ ins × 7 ins × $7\frac{1}{2}$ ins DCC CYLINDERS

No 3756	Built	1917	No 3883	Built	1921
3773	"	1917	3954	"	1923
3793	"	1918	4006	"	1925
3800	"	1919	4008	"	1925
3844	"	1920	4034	"	1925
3863	"	1920			

All had identical 200 PSI boilers with 2.46 sq ft grates, a total heating surface of 67.0 sq ft and fifty-six $1\frac{1}{4}$ ins dia × 3 ft 0 ins long smoke tubes. Nos 3756 to 3883 inclusive were fitted with feed water heaters and mechanical boiler feed pumps. No 4034 was built originally as No 3960, but after being left in stock for nearly two years was modified for wood burning by fitting larger smoke tubes and sold to McBeth Taylor & Co for export to India. All except Nos 4006 & 4008 had 2-speed gearing having ratios of 17.4 & 7.2 to 1. The two 3-speed engines had an

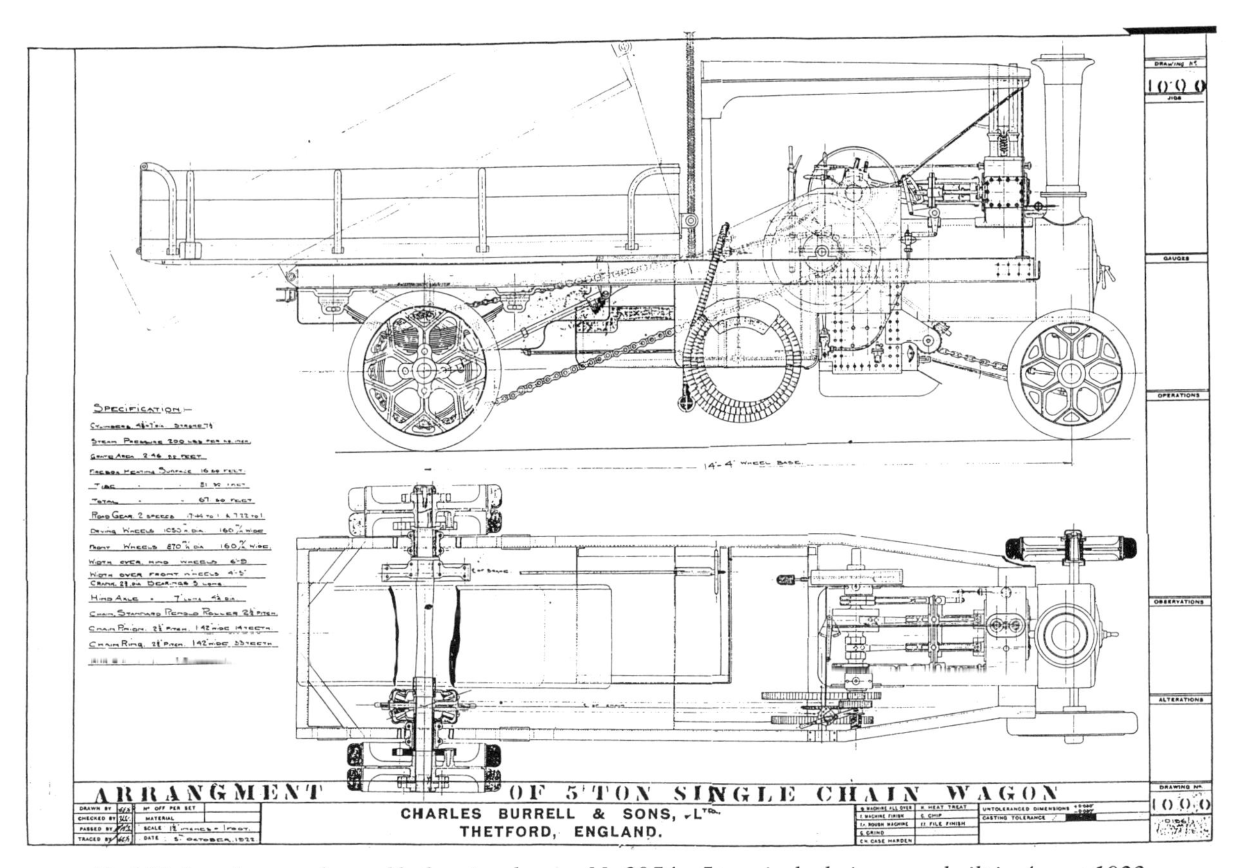

Fig 299 A works general assembly drawing showing No 3954 a 5 ton single chain wagon built in August 1923.

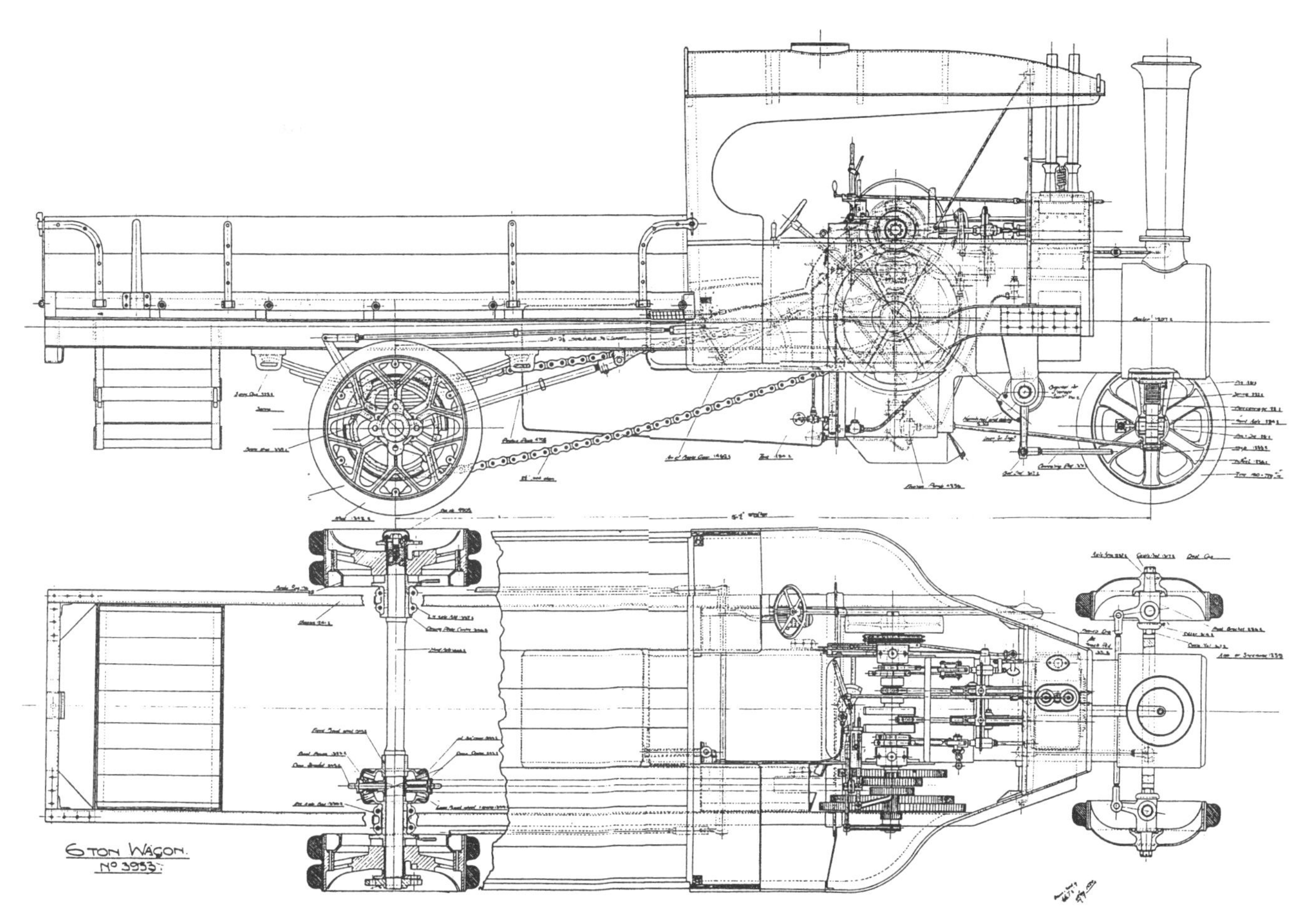

Fig 300 No 3953, the first Burrell 6 ton wagon introduced in December 1924.

additional fast speed ratio of 4.3 to 1 and all were driven through Hans Reynolds chains. Most were fitted with Bauley type wheels on solid rubbers. No 3793 had artillery type wheels on rubbers and No 4006 had National Steel Company cast steel dished front wheels and Bauley hind wheels. The works' General Assembly drawing of No 3954 is reproduced in Fig 299.

No 3883, completed in 1921, was the only Burrell wagon built specifically for the travelling showman complete with dynamo platform, long awning extending beyond the chimney and complete with twisted brass canopy supports. The much publicised photograph of the engine seen outside the Minstergate Paint Shop prior to deliver to Charles Summers of Norwich is reproduced in Fig 298. In the 1930s the engine was purchased secondhand by Smith Bros of Plymouth and sadly it was later destroyed by enemy action during the Blitz.

No 4006 was built specially for W Tatton of Leek. It had a number of special features including Ackerman steering and a 7 ft 1 ins wide hydraulically operated end tipping body. The boiler feed pump which provided the hydraulic pressure had a special friction drive instead of the usual eccentric driven direct drive.

Unfortunately, Mr Tatton was far from satisfied with his purchase and his strong letter of complaint remains extant. The main areas of dissatisfaction concerned the body, but his letter goes on to say, "The driver's position is too low and cramped. The footplate needs lifting and the level of the firehole door and the awning need raising accordingly. A second seat is required for the mate. The front of the boiler needs lagging and cleading in order to keep the driver cool. The motion side plates need alteration and doors should be fitted. The splash cover over the crankshaft requires alteration to facilitate oiling and adjustment. The brakes were useless and will not hold the wagon. The drive chains fouled a chassis cross-member. The double high pressure valve (the simpling valve) is also quite useless. There are no means of lubricating the Ackerman steering track rod, the front wheels have insufficient lock and the 13 leaf front springs are too weak." The letter ended by claiming that after only a few weeks' service the crankshaft had had to be lifted and the brasses refitted. Mr Tatton informed Burrells that he and his driver intended to visit the works upon completion of the alterations to inspect the work done. Suffice it to say that although some of the criticisms may be regarded as subjective only two more 5 ton wagons were built at St Nicholas Works. Undoubtedly after the take-over by AGE the new owners concentrated their sales effort on the Garrett wagon and the few orders Burrell were able to obtain were largely due to the personal contacts of Wilberforce Burrell.

Fig 301 No 4003 6 ton wagon with a new Garrett trailer prior to delivery to J Hancock & Son, Exeter – 1925.

Fig 302 No 4027 6 ton hydraulically operated 3-way tipping wagon supplied to John Hardie & Sons, Bo'ness in 1926.

Fig 303 No 4054, one of three 6 ton 3-way tipping wagons supplied to W J King of Bishops Lydeard, Somerset in 1920s.

Fig 304 No 4068 6 ton 3-way tipping wagon seen at the RASE Show in Newport prior to delivery to the Bottisham Haulage Company – 1927.

FINAL 5 TON DOUBLE CHAIN WAGONS BUILT AT ST NICHOLAS WORKS

No			
No 3963	Built	1923 – 4½″ × 7½″ × 8½″ DCC cyls.	
3981	"	1924 – 4⅛″ × 7″ × 7½″ DCC cyls.	

Both had the slightly larger 3.0 sq ft 200 PSI boilers used on the earlier double chain engines and both were 3-speed engines, Nos 3981 having special machine cut gears. No 3963 was fitted with differential locking gear which could be operated from the footplate. It was also fitted with expanding type brakes operating on the hind wheels, replacing the large contracting band type formerly fitted to the hind axle of double chain wagons. Additionally a separate tralier brake control was provided. Both engines had Bauley type wheels having 1050 mm × 110 mm solid rubber tyres. No 3981 was fitted with a hydraulically operated end tipping body and spent all its life on the East Coast of Scotland after being exhibited at the 1924 RASE and Perth Shows.

The first wagon to carry the AGE monogram was No 3844 built in 1920. Under the aegis of this ill-fated organisation St Nicholas Works introduced an entirely new 6 ton single chain wagon in December 1924. It was regarded by many as a last desperate attempt to retain a share of the fast dwindling market.

Fig 305 No 4078 6 ton wagon seen taking part in a 1000 mile promotional run organised by the 'Commercial Motor' in November 1927.

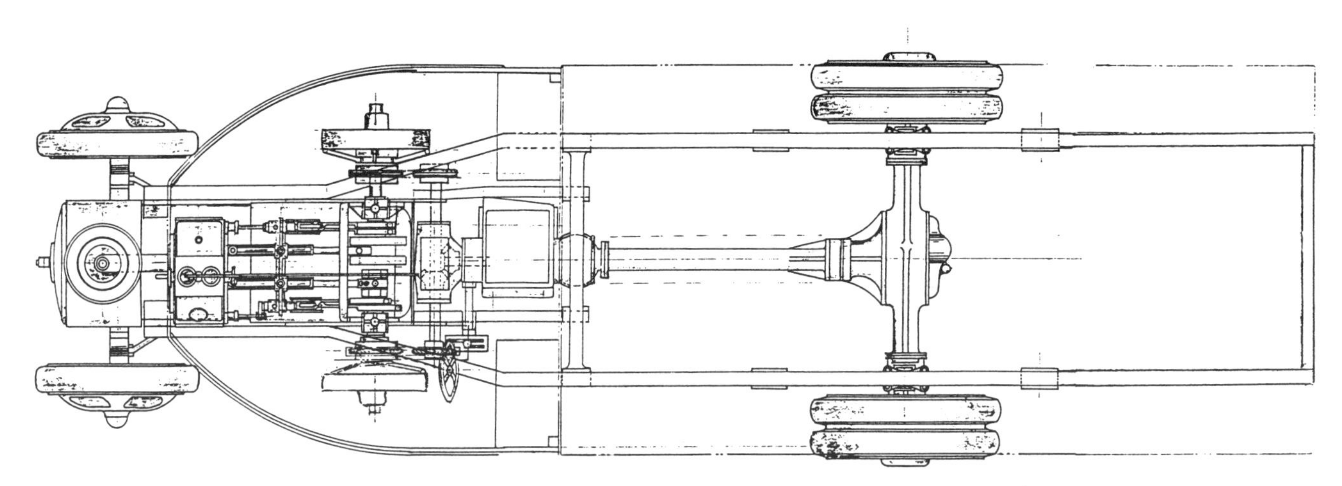

Fig 306 Plan elevation of proposed 6 ton wagon having 3-speed totally enclosed sliding mesh gearbox, cardan shaft drive and single reduction hind axle with differential gearing as drawn in 1924.

A new 220 PSI boiler was designed having a 3.5 sq ft grate, the total heating surface as 88.0 sq ft and sixty-four 1⅜ ins dia × 3 ft 9 ins long smoke tubes. Exhaust steam silencers were fitted to all except the first two engines and Nos 4035, 4054, 4068 & 4086 were fitted with feed water heaters. The smaller 4⅛ ins dia × 7 ins dia × 7½ ins stroke DCC cylinders were retained but a new double HP arrangement to drawing 7036 was incorporated in answer to Mr Tatton's earlier complaints. The engines were reputed to develop 30 BHP at 400 RPM. All were fitted with friction drive boiler feed pumps suitable also for providing the hydraulic pressure for operating tipping gear and a single injector. Nos 4082 & 4086 had roller bearings on the crankshaft and Nos 4001 & 4003 were experimentally fitted with Ransom & Marles roller bearings on the eccentrics. The 2 ft 0 ins dia × 4 ins wide flywheel was retained.

Three-speed gearing having various ratios to suit the duty to be performed were provided and the wagons were sprung for 7½ ton payloads. The single drive was by Hans Reynolds 110 link chain having 2.5 ins pitch and 9 ft 2 ins wheel centres. All had Ackerman type steering and rubber tyred cast steel wheels. All had expanding brakes on the hind axle and flywheel brakes. No 4003 supplied to J Hancock & Son, the Exeter brick and tile manufacturer went complete with a Garrett built 5/6 ton trailer (No 17057) and the wagon was fitted with special trailer brake gear. The unladen weight of the wagons was approximately 7 ton 4 cwt.

6 TON SINGLE CHAIN WAGON – 4⅛ ins × 7 ins × 7½ ins DCC CYLINDERS

No	Built	No	Built
No 3953	Built 1924	No 4054	Built 1927*
4001	1925*	4064	1927
4003	1925	4068	1928*
4027	1925*	4078	1927
4029	1926*	4082	1928*
4035	1926*	4086	1928
4036	1927*		

* Fitted with 3-Way hydraulic tipping bodies

Three of the 3-Way hydraulic tippers, Nos 4001, 4035 & 4054 went to the Somerset quarry owner W J King of Bishops Lydeard. Two others, Nos 4029 & 4036 went to the Norfolk road building contractors, Sommerfield & Thomas and both wagons eventually passed to the Boston RDC in South Lincolnshire. Nos 4064 & 4086 went to the Dalbeattie contractors, J Carswell & Son and spent their working lives on the East Coast of Scotland. No 4078 was supplied to Burrell's greatly valued old customer, John Charlton of Dumfries. Before being handed over in November 1927 the wagon took part in a 1000 mile convoy organised by the 'Commercial Motor' as part of a British Coal promotion. Reference to Fig 305 will show just how many of Mr Tatton's earlier criticisms had been implemented by the works in the 6 ton design, but unfortunately they came too late. Undoubtedly, however, they proved a thoroughly useful wagon well able to maintain the legal speed limit of 12 mph and more with a full payload.

Concurrently with the introduction of the 6 ton wagon the Drawing Office designed a wagon having a 3-speed gearbox, a cardan shaft drive and a conventional hind axle differential as shown in plan elevation in Fig 306. The wartime development of the standard W D petrol lorry manufactured by Leyland, AEC, Dennis and others had set a new vogue and by 1925 the road haulage industry was increasingly looking for new vehicles having internal combustion engines and the elimination of driving chains. A prototype cardan shaft wagon was built, but AGE aborted the project. Who knows, had events at St Nicholas Works been different in the post-war years, Charles Burrell might well have trod the same path Fodens of Sandbach so successfully trod in the 1930s.

CHAPTER EIGHTEEN

Finale under A.G.E.

The outbreak of war in August 1914 came suddenly and unexpectedly for the people of Thetford, although its young men were not slow in joining the Colours and most thought the crisis would be over by Christmas. Seen in retrospect, things were never quite the same again at St Nicholas Works. There is no evidence that the Directors, like many of their contemporaries, made any serious endeavour to secure work to aid the war effort. It was not until twelve months later in 1915 that the Government stepped in, compelling the company to undertake the manufacture of munitions. Throughout the war the production of the company's traditional products declined, which apart from a brief post-war boom, continued until the final closure of the works in 1928.

We have already considered DCC traction engines, Showmen's engines, road rollers, one-man operation tractors and steam wagons produced in the declining years. Finally, we now have to consider thirty-four single cylinder, twenty-nine single crank compound traction engines, and forty-one road locomotives built between 1915 and 1930, a total of 104 engines. Of this total just over half were built in the post-war period under the aegis of Agricultural & General Engineers Ltd.Two 6 NHP SC GP traction engines were built in the period under review. No 3766 built in July 1917 and No 3831 built in May 1920 were both generally as the double geared unsprung engines introduced in 1897 but with the boiler pressure increased to 180 PSI. No 3944 was built originally in 1922 as a double geared unsprung 7 NHP engine similar to those introduced in 1899 but having a boiler pressure of 175 PSI. In 1924 the cylinder bore was bushed down to 8 ins dia × 12 ins stroke and the engine was sold to Limerick CC Highways Deptartment as a 6 NHP engine. It was a particularly smart looking engine having a short awning and painted Quaker green with maroon wheels.

A total of fourteen 7 NHP SC double geared GP traction engines were built between 1916 and 1930. Those built during the war had 180 PSI boilers, thereafter the pressure was increased to 200 PSI.

7 NHP SC DOUBLE GEARED UNSPRUNG GP TRACTION ENGINES

No	Built	No	Built
No 3728	Built 1916	No 3922	Built 1921
3736	" 1916	3924	" 1922
3765	" 1917	3984	" 1924
3767	" 1917	4048	" 1926
3770	" 1917	4051	" 1926
3775	" 1917	4081	" 1928
3778	" 1918	4088	" 1930

Nos 3924, 4081 & 4088 were all given a Show finish and exhibited at various agricultural shows before being sold. They were painted olive green with brown wheels and engines built after 1921 all had short awnings. No 4081 was exhibited at Smithfield and was the very last engine to be built wholly at St Nicholas Works. Fortunately it survives today in Mr G. T. Cushing's fine collection of engines at Thursford. No 4088, supplied to Eggleton Bros in Norfolk had an enlarged asbestos lagged boiler having a 5.49 sq ft grate which increased the total heating surface to 134.5 sq ft. The smokebox was also special in that it was made suitable for the fitment of a road roller type forecarriage at a later date, although there is no evidence that this was ever done. The engine was one of the few GP traction engines to be fitted with a fully balanced crankshaft. Seven of these engines went to East Anglian customers who generally remained loyal to the Burrell marque until the works finally closed. Four went to Irish agriculturists and others went to Scotland and the West Country.

Eight similar 7 NHP SC double geared GP traction engines with springs on the hind axle only were also built in the period. All were generally as the 7 NHP sprung engines introduced in 1906 although the boiler pressures were progressively increased to 200 PSI. All built after 1920 carried the AGE motif on the hornplates and like their unsprung counterparts the majority of these engines went to customers in East Anglia and Scotland.

7 NHP SC DOUBLE GEARED SPRUNG AFT GP TRACTION ENGINES

No	Built	No	Built
No 3692	Built 1915	No 3855	Built 1920
3721	" 1916	3914	" 1921
3842	" 1920	3977	" 1924
3853	" 1920	4032	" 1925

Nos 3977 & 4032 and the 8 NHP SC engine No 4063 were fitted with a special form of Stephenson's link motion. The arm of the bell crank attached to the reversing lever had its radius link made adjustable. This was no doubt intended to give improved fine tuning of the valve setting whilst the engine was in steam. In the final decade of steam in agriculture most farmers found that the higher pressure 7 NHP GP traction engine was adequate for driving their threshing machines and other traditional farm duties.

Fig 307 The final post war design of the famous Burrell double geared SCC General Purpose traction engine.

8 NHP SC DOUBLE GEARED UNSPRUNG GP TRACTION ENGINES

No	Built	No	Built
No 3740	1916	No 4094	1932
3939	" 1922		

These were direct descendants of the famous type 'C' engines introduced in 1886 and apart from 200 PSI boilers, 6.0 sq ft grates, forty 2 ins dia × 5 ft 8 ins long smoke tubes and a total heating surface of 149.0 sq ft, little had altered in the intervening forty-six years, a remarkable testimony to the quality of the original Burrell design. No 4094 was built at Garretts of Leiston nearly four years after all production had ceased at St Nicholas Works and a few months after AGE Ltd had finally gone into voluntary liquidation. It was the very last engine built to carry the Burrell name and was given a special Show finish. It was painted olive green with brown wheels and was smartly lined out in green, black, red and yellow. Fortunately the engine survives today in preservation, named 'King George V'.

Six spring mounted versions of the 8 NHP SC double geared GP traction engine were built in the period 1917–1927. Both Nos 3882 & 4063 survive in preservation as fine examples of these excellent engines.

8 NHP SC DOUBLE GEARED SPRING MOUNTED GP TRACTION ENGINES

No	Built	No	Built
No 3750	1917	No 3870	1921
3797	" 1919	3882	" 1921
3803	" 1919	4063	" 1927

Nos 3797 & 3803 had the enlarged 6.6 sq ft grates whereas the remainder had 6.0 sq ft grates as the series first introduced in 1908. No 4063 unusually had the opening to the footplate on the right hand side or gear side of the engine and the forecarriage was set back several inches. Additionally the smokebox was lined, the boiler was asbestos lagged and a special guard was arranged over the governors. Two of these engines went to Burrell's old customers John Wyllie and John Charlton, both flour millers in Dumfries, and the remainder went to East Anglian customers.

We now consider the SCC GP traction engines of various sizes built between 1915 and 1924.

6 NHP SCC DOUBLE GEARED UNSPRUNG GP TRACTION ENGINES

No	Built	No	Built
No 3726	1916	No 3780	1918
3763	" 1917	3792	" 1918
3771	" 1917	3805	" 1919
3774	" 1917		

Six of the above 'Devonshire' type engines with $5\frac{1}{2}$ ins dia × 9 ins dia × 10 ins stroke SCC cylinders went to Irish customers, the seventh went to a West Country farmer. Ireland was at this time still part of the United Kingdom and everything possible was being done to increase food production to combat the havoc being caused by German submarines. Nos 3780, 3792 & 3805 were fitted with wood burning fireboxes in which the grate area was increased from 4.9 sq ft to 5.76 sq ft. This may very well be an indication that the engines were built-up from existing

Fig 308 No 3950 5 NHP DCC Road Locomotive supplied to Cox Bros of Abingdon in March 1924.

stocks. In the latter months of the war all materials were in short supply and allocations were difficult to obtain.

More or less concurrently, St Nicholas Works built seven spring mounted versions of the successful 'Devonshire' type engine.

6 NHP SCC DOUBLE GEARED SPRING MOUNTED GP TRACTION ENGINES

No	Built	No	Built
No 3609	Built 1915	No 3907	Built 1921
3657	" 1915	3918	" 1923
3676	" 1915	4033	" 1925
3854	" 1920		

These engines all went to haulage contractors scattered through East Anglia and the Shire Counties, mostly as repeat orders.

Only two 6 NHP SCC standard duty GP traction engines with 6 ins dia × 10 ins dia × 10 ins stroke cylinders were built in this final period. No 3873 was built in June 1921 for a Cornish farmer and fitted with a long awning. No 4087 was the first Burrell engine built entirely at Leiston in October 1928. It had a lengthened boiler increasing the total heating suface by 16 per cent. The Stephenson's link motion also had the adjustable radius link described earlier. It was a condition of this desperately needed order that the customer's driver should recieve forty-seven hours training at the works free of charge.

Six similar double geared engines with 6 ins dia × 10 ins dia × 10 ins stroke but spring mounted were built between 1915 and 1921, the majority going to East Anglian customers.

6 NHP SCC DOUBLE SPRING MOUNTED STANDARD DUTY GP TRACTION ENGINES

No	Built	No	Built
No 3665	Built 1915	No 3919	Built 1922
3755	" 1917	3920	" 1921
3818	" 1919	3983	" 1924

No 3818 was ordered to be supplied painted lead primer with plumished steel cleading on the boiler. No doubt the purchaser, Arthur Bird of Great Hodcham in Norfolk had his own ideas as to how an engine should be finished.

No 3841 built in June 1920 was the only 7 NHP SCC double geared unsprung GP traction engine built after 1914. In all respects it conformed with the majority of the seventy-six engines of this type built between 1897 and 1914 having 6 ins dia × 10 dia × 12 ins stroke cylinders. Five similar spring mounted engines were built between 1916 and 1924. So far as your author can trace none of this batch of engines has survived apart from 200 PSI boilers they were similar in all other respects to the series first introduced in 1903. No 3983 was re-numbered No 4050 and sold in 1924.

7 NHP SCC DOUBLE GEARED SPRING MOUNTED GP TRACTION ENGINES

No	Built	No	Built
No 3735	Built 1916	No 3860	Built 1920
3788	" 1918	3992	" 1920
3801	" 1919		

Two of these engines went to Scottish haulage contractors, two went to Yorkshire and No 3801 went to

Fig 309 No 3930 5 NHP DCC road locomotive photographed in the Works' yard, August 1922.

Thomas & Lanyon's Newlyn East Steam Threshing Company.

Finally, two 8 NHP SCC double geared but unsprung traction engines, Nos 3695 & 3761 were supplied to S J Rosbotham, the well known road rolling contractors of Bickerstaff in Lancashire. These heavy duty engines were akin to unpsrung road locomotives with 6½ ins dia × 11 ins dia × 12 ins stroke SCC cylinders. No 3695 was built in October 1915 and named 'Lord Derby', No 3761 was built in May 1917 and named 'Lord Stanley', father and son, big landowners in the area. The engines had long awnings and apart from the haulage of road stone in the area, they are believed to have been used as scarifying engines. In all major detail they were similar to the fifteen 8 NHP double geared sprung engines built between 1904 and 1916.

Only one SCC road locomotive was built after 1914 and this was very similar to the 6 NHP SC engine, No 3806 built in 1919. No 3937 built in July 1922 had a 6 ins dia × 10 ins dia × 10 ins stroke SCC cylinder. It was double geared with differential locking gear and was spring mounted. The hind wheels were 6 ft 6 ins dia × 16 ins wide and unlike No 3806 had 3-speed gearing. Both engines were employed upon haulage work on the East Coast of Scotland until the 1930s.

We consider next the nineteen 5 NHP DCC road locomotives which many felt were some of the most handsome engines ever produced at St Nicholas Works. The first four were described as 'Devonshire' engines but thereafter this well known and much respected name was dropped and AGE motifs were substituted.

5 NHP DCC 'DEVONSHIRE' TYPE 26 BHP ROAD LOCOMOTIVES

No	Built	No	Built
No 3708	Built 1916	No 3930	Built 1922
3777	" 1917	3941	" 1923
3809	" 1919	3950	" 1924
3821	" 1919	3996	" 1924
3824	" 1919	4010	" 1925
3832	" 1920	4026	" 1925
3845	" 1920	4066	" 1927
3849	" 1921	4074	" 1927
3856	" 1920	4093	" 1931
3858	" 1920		

No 3809, the first post war engine was exhibited at the 1919 RASE Show and was well received by both the technical press and the crowds looking for new developments after five years of war-time austerity. It was basically as the series first introduced in 1909 with 200 PSI boilers and originally much favoured by the travelling showmen who purchased nine of these 26 BHP engines between 1909 and 1915. In 1922 re-designed link motion was fitted, improved machine cut gearing was added and the engines were fitted with geared type boiler feed pumps.

Most of the engines went to haulage contractors in the West Country including two to W J King, the Bishop's Lydeard brick and tile manufacturers, and to the English Shires. Three were subsequently purchased by showmen and had dynamo platforms and full length canopies added. No 3845, after service with Harry Gardam, the Staines haulage contractor, was purchased by J Purchase of

Fig 310 No 4074 5 NHP Crane engine 'The Lark' en route from Thetford to Bury St Edmunds in 1927.

Surbiton. No 3858 was similarly purchased by White Bros of Cardiff and No 3950, originally exhibited at the 1923 RASE Show was purchased in 1932 by Robert Edwards & Sons of Swindon who variously operated as a threshing contractor, a haulage contractor and a travelling showman.

No 4074 was supplied with a 5 ton capacity swanneck crane jib and was the only crane engine in the series. It was supplied to Tom Reynolds, a Bury St Edmunds timber merchant, in November 1927 and named 'The Lark' after the river on which Bury stands. This smart 3-speed engine was somewhat unusual in that the 5 ft 10½ ins dia hind wheels were fitted with rubber strakes instead of continuous rubbers.

No 4011 was built originally as a unique double geared 5 NHP 3-speed showman's road locomotive and exhibited at the 1924 Royal Show. Obviously a customer could not be found and the engine was returned to the works and rebuilt as a 4 NHP traction engine. The cylinder was re-bored and fitted with a liner reducing the LP cylinder bore to 5¼ ins and the engine was sold to W.S. Dewing of Norwich.

Between 1915 and 1924 St Nicholas Works built thirteen 28 BHP 6 NHP road locomotives with 6 ins dia × 10 ins dia × 10 ins stroke DCC cylinders.

6 NHP DCC 28 BHP ROAD LOCOMOTIVES

No	Built	No	Built
No 3670	Built 1915	No 3799	Built 1919
3703	" 1915	3829	" 1920
3711	" 1916	3847	" 1920
3720	" 1916	3869	" 1920
3723	" 1916	3892	" 1921
3744	" 1916	3979	" 1924
3751	" 1917		

These engines were all exactly as the improved 6 NHP DCC road locomotives with 200 PSI boilers introduced in 1909. They were sold to customers widely scattered throughout the Kingdom and five were subsequently converted to Showman's type engines. No 3670 started life with the Hampshire haulage contractor Richard Pool and is said to have been shipped to Greece at an early date. No 3703 went to the renowned heavy haulage contractors Robert Wynn of Newport. The author recalls a conversation with Mr Wynn many years ago in which he emphasised his preference for 3-shaft engines and spoke in particular of his Burrell engines in glowing terms. Others went to loyal Burrell customers whose names have often been mentioned as the story of St Nicholas Works has unfolded. No 3744 went to W J King of Bishops Lydeard; No 3751 went to Samuel Jackson of Wistaston and Nos 3799 & 3892 went to Charles Tassell of North Kent. No 3829 went to T & W F Hooper of Liskeard in Cornwall, built as a crane engine, although no jib was ever supplied. Later in 1920 the engine was acquired by J Hickey & Sons of Richmond in Surrey.

The engines subsequently acquired by travelling showmen and fitted with full length canopies, dynamo platforms and other decorative embellishments so much beloved by the showman such as twisted brass canopy supports and stars and rings were:

No 3703 purchased 1921 by G Rogers, Chipping Sodbury
3711 " 1922 by T Whitelegg, Plymouth
3842 " 1921 by Mrs Hannah Parkin, Norwich
3869 " 1922 by Hibble & Mellors, Nottingham
3979 " 1930 by Mrs F Symonds, Gloucester

Similarly, all five of the 7 NHP 34 BHP DCC road locomotives built in the declining years of steam were subsequently converted to Showman's type engines.

7 NHP DCC 34 BHP ROAD LOCOMOTIVES

No	Built	No	Built
No 3651	Built 1915	No 3810	Built 1919
3682	" 1915	3897	" 1921
3804	" 1919		

Fig 311 No 4066 5 NHP DCC road locomotive with special rubber straked hind wheels outside the Paint Shop in Minstergate Street, April 1927.

These engines had $6\frac{1}{2}$ ins dia × 11 ins dia × 12 ins stroke DCC cylinders and were exactly as the series introduced in 1909 with 200 PSI boilers, double gearing and spring mountings. Originally they went to haulage contractors in East Anglia and the English Shires, but by 1923 all had been acquired by showmen and converted.

No			
No 3651	purchased	1923	by R Edwards & Sons, Swindon
3682	"	1919	by J W Fletcher, Cardiff
3804	"	1923	by Woolls Bros, Erith, Kent
3981	"	1923	by John Evans, Brecon
3897	"	1923	by John Evans, Brecon

In 1929 the Leiston Works completed a hybrid 8 NHP DCC double-geared spring mounted engine No 4090 having $6\frac{3}{4}$ ins × $11\frac{1}{4}$ ins × 12 ins cylinders. The engine was shipped to Australia through Aveling & Porter.

The very last engine to be considered in our review of Burrell products is the large 8 NHP crane engine, No 4039, built in 1926 for Screen Brothers of Oldbury, near Birmingham. It was based on the very successful series of forty-nine Showman's type road locomotives with $6\frac{3}{4}$ ins dia × $11\frac{1}{4}$ ins dia × 12 ins stroke DCC cylinders built between 1911 and 1930, but unlike the Showman's engines it had single drive gearing to the hind axle and long travel spring gear. The grate area was reduced from 6.6 sq ft to 6.0 sq ft and unlike the majority of the Showman's engines it had 5 ft 8 ins long smoke tubes which had the effect of reducing the total heating surface of the 200 PSI boiler to 149.0 sq ft.

It had 3-speed gearing having ratios of 30.5, 19.6 and 10.4 to 1 and the hind wheels mounted on Mackintosh solid rubber tyres were 6 ft 9 ins dia × $20\frac{1}{4}$ ins wide. The flywheel was reduced to 4 ft 4 ins dia × 6 ins wide since the engine was not required for working on the belt. The weight of the engine in working order was 16 ton 16 cwt.

The swanneck jib had a capacity of 10 tons maximum

Fig 312 Road locomotives Nos 3703 & 3810 after conversion to Showman's engines in the ownership of George Rogers of Chipping Sodbury – circa 1928.

and the bevel gear drive from the crankshaft to the worm driven winding drum mounted on the front of the smokebox will be clearly seen by reference to Fig 313. Often as a schoolboy your author has trailed this engine on his bicycle as it went about its many and varied heavy haulage duties in the Industrial Midlands. Sadly, the engine is no longer with us today, having gone the same way as other Burrell classics like 'Clyde' and 'Simplicity', but the ghosts of these magnificent engines will be with us for long.

At the start of 1919 the country optimistically began to adjust to peace time conditions and tens of thousands returned home from the armed forces. The Board of Charles Burrell & Sons Ltd comprised Charles II, his sons Herbert and Charles Wilberforce, Robert Burrell's widow, Ellen and Charles' unmarried sister Ella Burrell. William, Charles' younger brother who joined the Board upon Robert's death in 1904 had retired some time during the war.

Charles II was now over 70 years of age and Herbert, formerly the Company Secretary, was appointed Managing Director with the day to day control of the company's affairs. Charles Wilberforce, an extrovert character, had recently returned from distinguished service in the Royal Engineers with the rank of Lieut. Colonel and awarded an OBE. He was placed in charge of Sales. The ladies fulfilled a non-executive role.

At this time Robert Eden Burrell, Robert and Ellen's only son joined the firm. He had been educated at Oundle and enlisted in the Norfolk Regiment on August 4th 1914 at the age of 24. He saw service at Gallipoli attaining the rank of Captain. Later, whilst attached to the Royal Engineers he served as Wharfmaster on the Suez Canal. Finally, just before the Armistice he was posted to France where he received a mention in despatches posted by Sir Douglas Haigh, the British Field Commander. Upon his return home he was appointed the company's Personnel & Welfare Officer. It is said that relationships between Herbert and Robert Eden were not good, but clearly it was only a matter of time before he would have been given greater responsibility. Sadly on April 3rd 1921 he was killed in a motor accident whilst a passenger in a friend's car, at Kennett crossroads near Barton Mills in Suffolk. H R Corrin was the Works Manager at this time although he was later cavalierly dismissed by Herbert at a moments notice and replaced by H L Senior who had been in charge of the Drawing Office. Herbert C Edwards was the Company Secretary and Accountant and managed the General Office and Sales Office assisted by Duffield, Claydon, Horwood, Shaw and Hanniball. Billy Greenwood succeeded Senior in the Drawing Office and later went on to become a Senior Draughtsman at the Bristol Aircraft Company's engine works. Sydney Harrison, whose father had previously been the Chief Cashier and Buyer was the company's enormously popular outside Sales Engineer. He went on to make a great name for himself at John Fowler's in Leeds and with Scammell Lorries of Watford, where he was responsible for their famous 'Showtrac' Showman's tractor. The two most senior shopfloor foremen were Snelling in the Fitting Shop and Spencer in the Erecting Shop.

Unfortunately, we know little of the company's financial position during this period. We know that sales peaked in 1909 and presume that the company remained profitable at least until the Government munition contracts were terminated. It seems probable that the company moved into a loss position in 1920. We know that Garretts of Leiston, J & F Howard of Bedford, Marshalls of Gainsborough and John Fowler of Leeds and possibly others all recorded serious losses that year from which Garretts and Howards never recovered.

In 1919 a man named A W Maconochie promoted a new company, Agricultural & General Engineers Ltd (AGE) having an issued capital of £8 million with the intention of combating the enormous expansion in agricultural machinery and tractor production in the United States during the war. Maconochie, a man of good standing and a director of the Great Eastern Railway, was elected the company's first Chairman. He quickly secured the purchase of a dozen well known family owned engineering businesses in exchange for AGE shares and declared his ambition of building the new company into a £30 million empire. He understood that potentially the real assets and earning power of many small family owned manufacturing businesses was far greater than the value of their paid-up capital. He was one of the first 'Asset Strippers'. It transpired in later investigations that at the time of purchase he had helped himself to 5 per cent commission in shares on the purchase price of the companies he had persuaded to join the group.

The initial participants in AGE were:

Aveling & Porter Ltd, Rochester
Barford & Perkins Ltd, Peterborough
Richard Garrett & Sons Ltd, Leiston
J & F Howard Ltd, Bedford
Davey Paxman Ltd, Colchester
E H Bentall & Co Ltd, Heybridge
Blackstone & Co Ltd, Stamford
Peterbrotherhood Ltd, Peterborough
Clarke's Crank & Forge Ltd, Lincoln
E R & F Turner Ltd, Ipswich
Bull Motors Ltd

Most of the directors of AGE were the Chairmen of the member companies, which position they retained after the take-over of their family businesses. This had acted as a carrot, seemingly enabling them to remain the figurehead in their own companies whilst absolving them from any real financial responsibility. Edward Barford who later successfully founded Aveling & Barford Ltd from the ashes of the collapsed AGE empire in the 1930s wrote of these men, "Their grandfathers and great grandfathers had done their work and founded businesses on solid foundations. But long before 1919 many of these people had become country squires and didn't need to go to their workshops more often than they wanted. All they had to do was to pick a good manager. If the manager didn't seem to be doing as well as he might, the answer was simple – try another". Barford suggested these men were often more interested in their outside activities and being seen at events like the Royal Show, rather than delving deeper into affairs of business.

John Fowler, Marshalls of Gainsborough and the

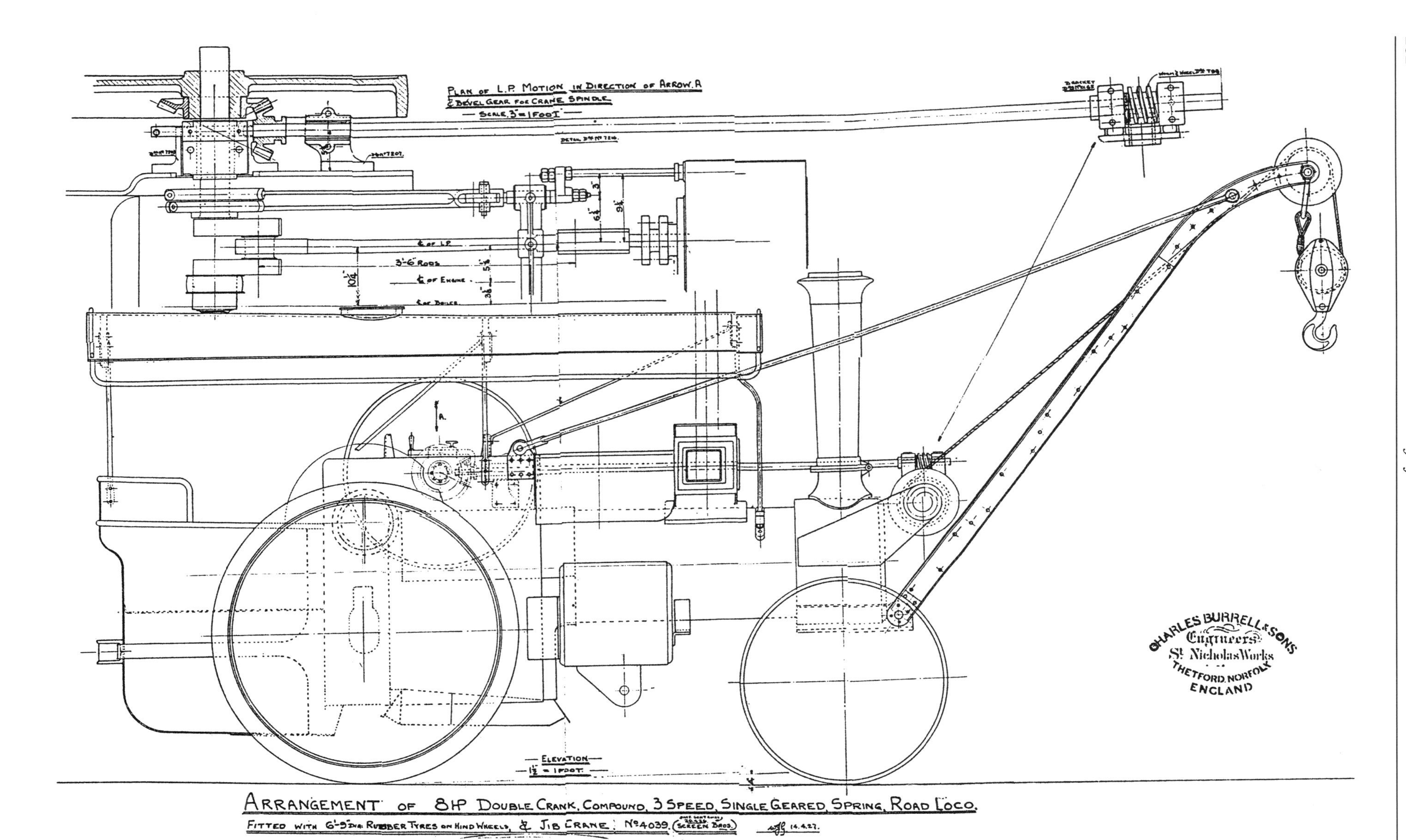

Fig 313 No 4039 8 NHP DCC single drive crane engine built for Screen Bros of Oldbury in 1926, showing shaft drive to crane drum in plan elevation.

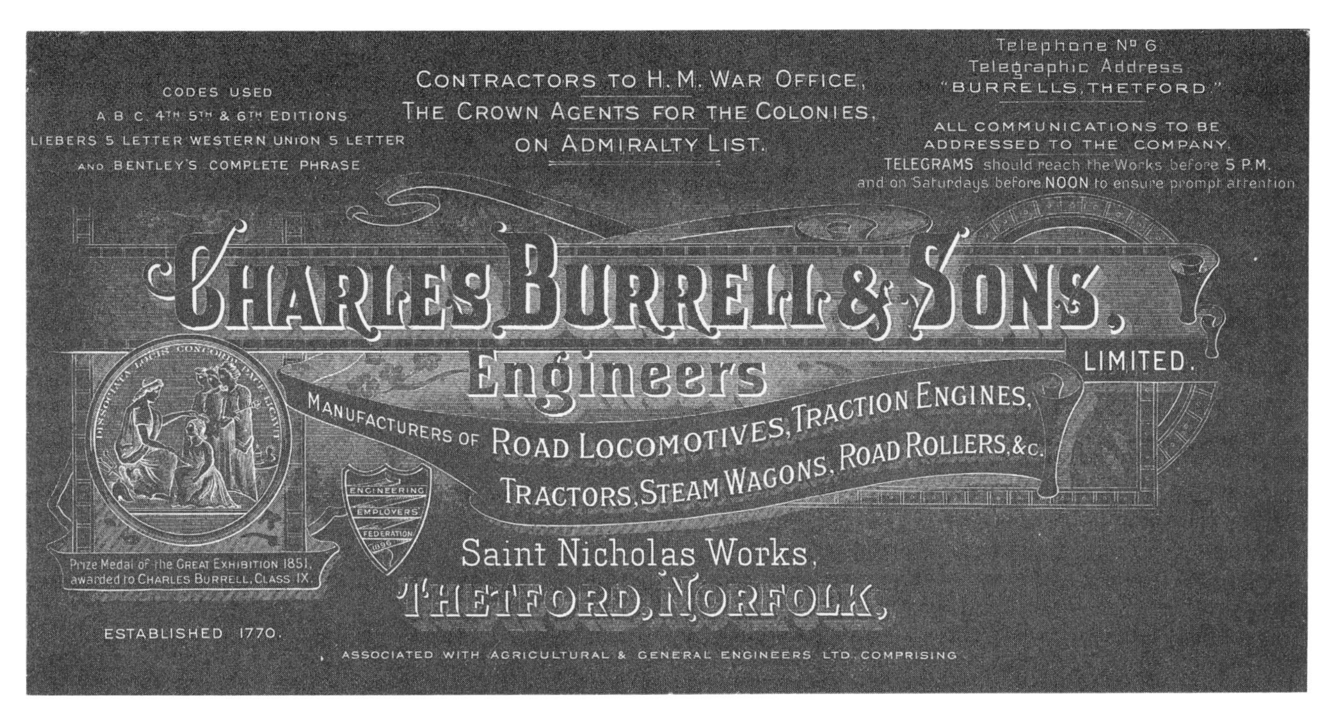

Fig 314 An example of Charles Burrell & Sons Ltd letterheading in 1920s.

Lincoln engine builders all resisted overtures to join the AGE group but in 1920 Charles II and his two sons agreed to sell 120 of the company's £10 shares to Maconochie. This was seen by some as the thin end of the wedge and was probably the main cause for Mrs Ellen Burrells' resignation from the Board. Subsequently, new Articles of Association were issued and a new Debenture for £73,000 was raised.

The 1921 slump hit both the group and Burrells very badly and Maconochie was replaced as Chairman by G E Rowland, an influential tax expert who was well connected in the City of London and at the Board of Trade. For the next decade Rowland ruled as a despot. Always hard working and tremendously enthusiastic, his scorn for his fellow directors was intense. Expensive endeavours to regain lost export markets failed, huge stocks were allowed to build up in some companies and enormous sums of money were expended upon the group's headquarters at Aldwych House. Irregularities with the recently formed Government owned Export Credits Guarantee Department and with Aldwych House Estates Ltd, which the group had leased from the LCC, were carefully concealed.

In July 1922 a serious fire at St Nicholas Works destroyed the north end of the boiler shop, temporarily disrupting production. The company's financial situation continued to deteriorate alarmingly and by 1924 the directors of Charles Burrell were left with little or no choice but to allow AGE to acquire the controlling interest in the company. AGE acquired 6319 £10 ordinary shares which left the Burrell family holding only four shares in the company.

In 1927 Arthur Leggett and Arthur Bennett were elected to the Burrell Board. Leggett was an AGE main board director and both he and Arthur Bennett were also directors of Richard Garrett and E H Bentall. Garretts had been making very serious losses for a number of years and clearly the purpose of the reconstruction was to arrange

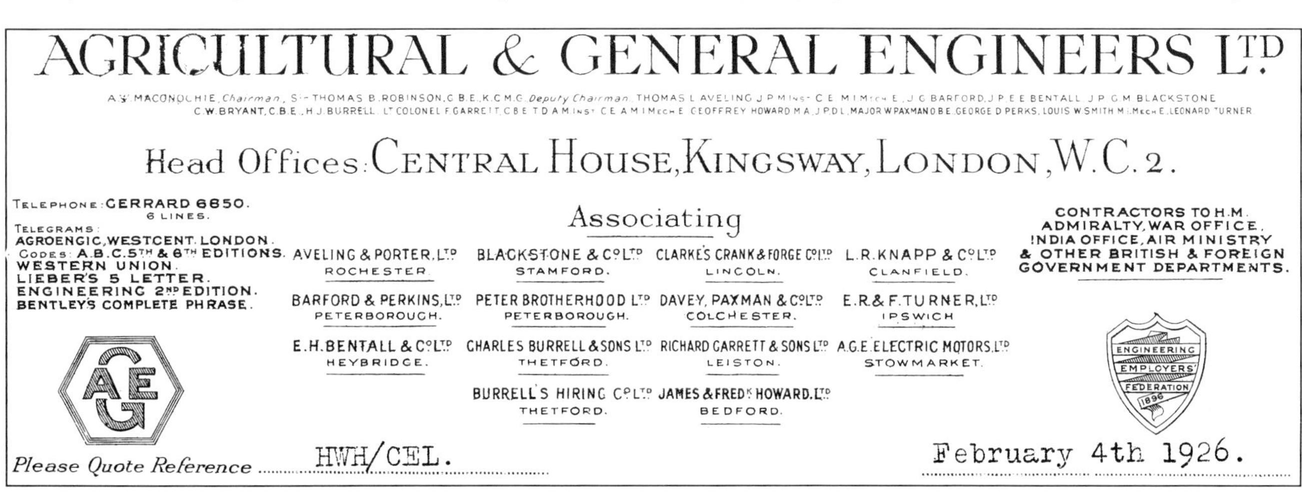

Fig 315 An example of AGE letterheading erroneously still listing A W Maconochie as Chairman in 1926.

The site of St Nicholas Works in the context of present day Thetford.

1 Smith's shop
2 Brass foundry
3 Iron foundry
4 Stores, drawing office above
5 General offices
6 Copper plating shop
7 Carpenter's shop
8 St Nicholas House
9 Site of original paint shop
10 Works yard
11 Original electricity generating station
12 Tool room
13 Machine shop (turnery)
14 Erecting shop
15 Boiler shop
16 New paint shop – *present museum*
17 Liddamore's office
18 Liddamore's store

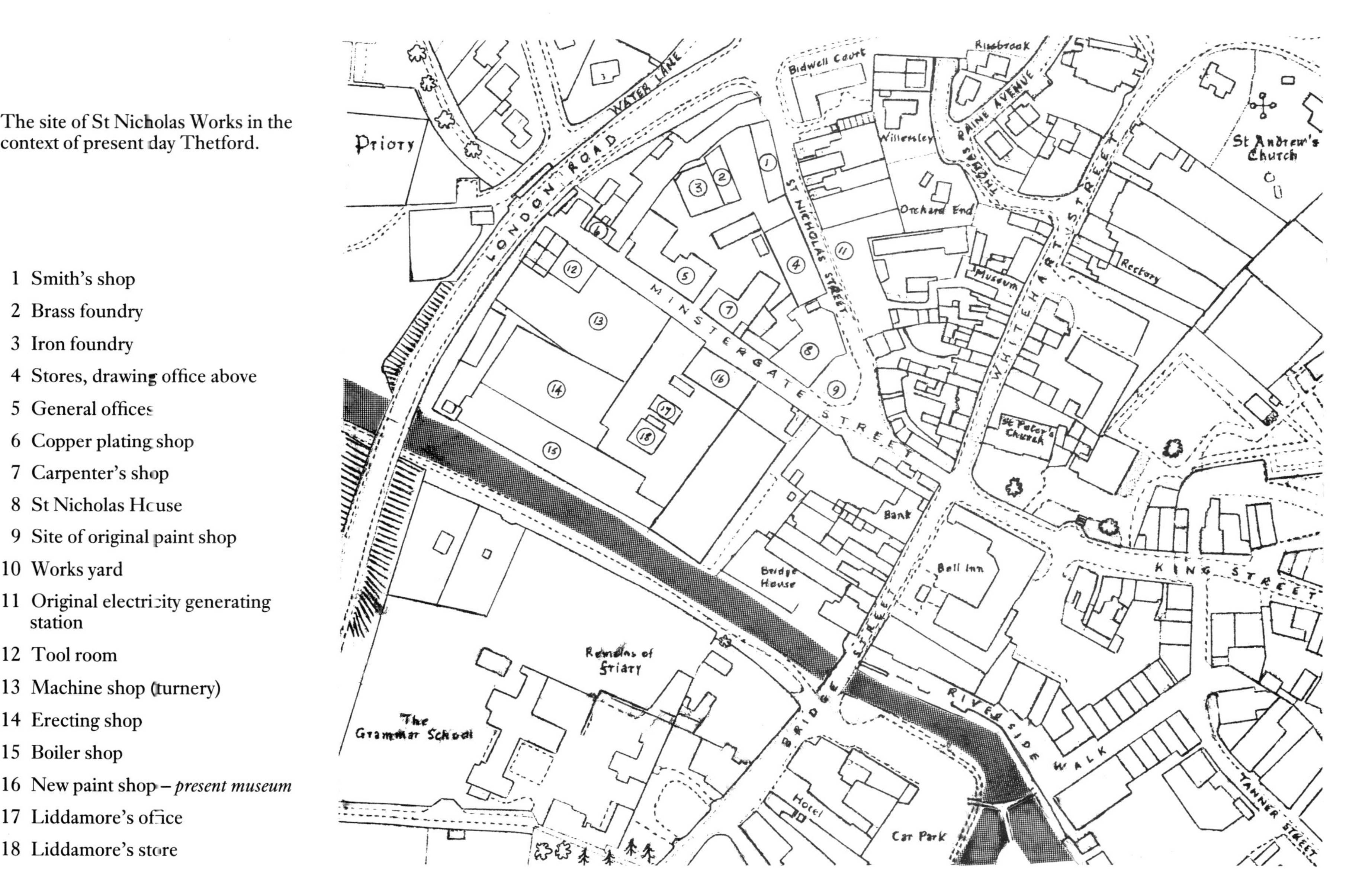

Fig 316 The site of St Nicholas Works in the context of present day Thetford.

Fig 317 The commemorative bronze plaque erected by public subscription in 1958 at the entrance to St Nicholas Works in Minstergate Street, Thetford.

the complete closure of St Nicholas Works and the transference of all production to Leiston. The loss of St Nicholas Works was a terrible blow to the people of Thetford as the company had been the principal employer and mainstay of the town for many years. Local agriculture was in a depressed state and the nation as a whole was on the verge of a major slump. Rearmament and the building of new airfields and other military installations in the area in the late 1930s brought some relief but Thetford never really recovered until after the war. In the 1950s the town was designated an official overspill area for London and new housing and industrial estates brought renewed prosperity to the district.

St Nicholas Works finally closed its gates for the last time on June 4th 1928 and in December 1930 the remaining plant and machinery was sold at a two day auction held by Hawker & Witton. Fortunately a surprising number of the machines sold at this auction have survived and are today on display at the splendid Burrell Museum now housed in the 'New' Paint Shop in Minstergate Street, Thetford.

We need not concern ourselves with the fate of AGE Ltd. Suffice it to say, Rowland resigned without warning in February 1932 and disappeared. A week later the banks appointed a Receiver and in November 1932 the company went into voluntary liquidation. It is said the sum total of cash recieved by the Burrell family following the collapse of AGE was £1600, considerably less than the value of James Burrell's estate when Charles I inherited the business in 1837, but what an extraordinary saga of technological innovation and dedication encapsulates the story of St Nicholas Works during its 125 years history.

Charles II died on November 12th 1929 in his 83rd year and was buried at his beloved St Mary's Church in the town. One can only imagine his feelings at the turn of events since he became persuaded to sell the family's birthright to AGE. To be fair he understood that the days of steam were numbered. He appreciated the need for change but realised that the existing management team lacked the technological skills, facilities and capital necessary in order to successfully enter the world of the internal combustion engine. He was a patriarch of the old school, but always fair and generous, if at times very severe.

He was greatly respected by all who knew him for his knowledge and understanding of all that went on in the works. His daily walk round the factory, always immaculately dressed with highly polished shoes became very much a feature of the St Nicholas Works routine. Throughout his life he always demonstrated his belief in the value of good health and good education. He did a great deal to promote sporting facilities in the town and was President of the local Mechanics Institute for many years. He rode with the Suffolk Foxhounds for over half a century and enjoyed all manner of country pursuits.

He had been elected to Thetford Council in 1874 and served for 55 years, much of the time as an Alderman. He became a Justice of the Peace in 1907 and was elected the town's mayor no less than six times. He served as a warden of St Mary's Church for over 50 years and at the time of his death he was the oldest member of the Bury St Edmunds Freemasons.

He was immensely proud when at the age of thirty-one he was elected a Member of the Institution of Mechanical Engineers. He served on the Council of the Smithfield Club from 1916 to 1925. He was adored by his large family and his home, 'Shrublands' was long remembered by them as a very happy place. He loved animals, especially horses and always had bulldogs and pugs in the house. He never lost his great passion for Harry Lauder records and had a huge collection which he played at every opportunity.

Perhaps there are still some people in the town who remember his habit at Christmas of walking the streets of Thetford handing new shilling pieces to the townsfolk. It can be truly said of him that he was, "A gentleman of sound understanding, a sincere heart and plain open behaviour".

Charles Burrell II (1847–1929) photographed during his daily tour of the works. Circa 1923

Numerical Listing of Engines

ABBREVIATIONS USED

TE (C) – Traction Engine, chain driven
TE – Traction Engine, geared drive
TE (S) – Traction Engine, showland ownership
TE (CRL) – Traction Engine, with forward jib crane
TE (DIG) – Traction Engine, fitted digging machine
RL (C) – Road Locomotive, chain driven
RL – Road Locomotive, geared drive
SRL – Showman's Road Locomotive
SRL (SC) – Showman's Road Locomotive, built as scenic type
SRL (CSC) – Showman's Road Locomotive, converted to scenic type
RL (S) – Road Locomotive, converted to Showman's type engine
CRL – Crane Road Locomotive
SRL (TC) – Showman's traction centre engine
RR – Road Roller
RR/NW – Road Roller, supplied without rollers
RR/TE – Convertible RR/TE
PE (C) – Ploughing Engine, chain driven
PE – Ploughing Engine, geared horizontal drum
PE (U) – Ploughing Engine, geared universal drum
TR – Tractor
STR – Showman's type tractor
TR (CRL) – Tractor fitted with forward jib crane
W – Wagon (5 ton or 6 ton) (SC – single chain; DC – double chain)
SW – Showman's type wagon
TRS – Thomson Road Steamer, vertical boiler
BRS – Burrell Road Steamer, horizontal boiler
PORT – Portable Engine
PORT (S/B) – Portable Engine with straw burning apparatus
OTE – Over-type semi-portable engine
UTE – Under-type semi-portable engine
MARINE – Marine Engine
H STAT E – Horizontal Stationary Engine
V STAT E – Vertical Stationary Engine
W(SC) Wagon – Single Chain
W(DC) Wagon – Double Chain
S/chain – Single chain
L/chain – Long chain
D/chain – Double chain
Com. – Composite
sft – shaft
uni. – universal

CYLINDERS: SC, single; SCC, single crank compound; DCC, double crank compound; DUPLEX, Duplex cylinder.
TRANSMISSION: SD, single drive; DG, double geared; US, unsprung; SPR, spring mounted.

Engine No.	Page Ref.	Date Built	Type	NHP	Cyl
395	33	1867	TE (C)	12	Duplex
396	40	1867	PORT	8	SC
397	36	1867	PE 'PEW'	10	SC
398	36	1867	PE 'PEW'	10	SC
399	40	1867	PORT	8	SC
400	40	1867	PORT	8	SC
401	40	1867	PORT	10	SC
402	40	1867	PORT	8	SC
403	40	1867	PORT	8	SC
404	40	1867	PORT	8	SC
405	32	1867	TE (C)	10	SC
406	40	1868	PORT	8	SC
407	40	1868	PORT	8	SC
408	28	1868	TE (C) S/Chain	8	SC
409	40	1868	PORT	8	SC
410	40	1868	PORT	8	SC
411	40	1868	PORT	7	SC
412	40	1868	PORT	12	SC
413	37	1868	PE L/Chain	12	SC

* Indicates engine survives.

Engine No.	Page Ref.	Date Built	Type	NHP	Cyl
414	32	1868	TE (C)	10	SC
415	40	1868	PORT	8	SC
416	37	1868	PE L/Chain	12	SC
417	28	1868	TE (C)/Chain	8	SC
418	40	1868	PORT	8	SC
419	40	1868	PORT	8	SC
420	128	1868	H.STAT.E	16	SC
421	37	1868	PE L/Chain	12	SC
422	37	1868	PE L/Chain	12	SC
423	37	1868	PE L/Chain	12	SC
424	37	1868	PE L/Chain	12	SC
425	37	1868	PE L/Chain	12	SC
426	37	1868	PE L/Chain	12	SC
427	28	1868	TE (C) S/Chain	8	SC
428	40	1868	PORT	8	SC
429	40	1868	PORT	10	SC
430	32	1868	TE (C)	10	SC
431	40	1868	PORT	8	SC
432	40	1868	PORT	10	SC
433	40	1869	PORT	8	SC
434	40	1869	PORT	8	SC
435	37	1869	PE L/Chain	12	SC
436	37	1869	PE L/Chain	12	SC
437	40	1869	PORT	8	SC
438	37	1869	PE L/Chain	12	SC
439	37	1869	PE L/Chain	12	SC
440	40	1869	PORT	8	SC
441	40	1869	PORT	8	SC
442	33	1869	TE (C)	12	Duplex
443	32	1869	TE (C)	10	SC
444	28	1869	TE (C)	8	SC
445	40	1869	PORT	8	SC
446	37	1869	PE L/Chain	12	SC
447	37	1869	PE L/Chain	12	SC
448	40	1869	PORT	8	SC
449	40	1869	PORT	8	SC
450	40	1869	PORT	8	SC
451	40	1869	PORT	8	SC
452	28	1869	TE (C) D/Chain	8	SC
453	37	1869	PE L/Chain	12	SC
454	37	1870	PE L/Chain	12	SC
455	28	1870	TE (C) S/Chain	8	SC
456	36	1870	PE 'AW'	14	SC
457	128	1870	H.STAT.E	8	SC
458	40	1870	PORT	8	SC
459	40	1870	PORT	8	SC
460	40	1870	PORT	8	SC
461	40	1870	PORT	8	SC
462	40	1870	PORT	10	SC
463	28	1870	TE (C) D/Chain	8	SC
464	28	1870	TE (C) D/Chain	8	SC
465	40	1870	PORT	8	SC
466	40	1870	PORT	8	SC
467	40	1870	PORT	8	SC
468	40	1870	PORT	8	SC
469	40	1870	PORT	10	SC
470	40	1870	PORT	8	SC
471	28	1870	TE (C)	8	SC
472	28	1870	TE (C)	8	SC
473	28	1870	TE (C)	8	SC
474	40	1870	PORT	8	SC
475	40	1870	PORT	8	SC
476	40	1870	PORT	8	SC
477	40	1870	PORT	7	SC
478	32	1870	TE (C)	10	SC
479	40	1870	PORT	8	SC
480	40	1871	PORT	8	SC
481	40	1871	PORT	8	SC
482	40	1871	PORT	8	SC
483	40	1871	PORT	8	SC
484	28	1870	TE (C)	8	SC
485	28	1870	TE (C)	8	SC
486	28	1870	TE (C)	8	SC
487	32	1870	TE (C)	10	SC
488	32	1870	TE (C)	10	SC
489	–	–	NO INFO	–	–
490	40	1870	PORT	7	SC
491	51	1871	TRS	8	Duplex
492	51	1871	TRS	8	Duplex
493	51	1871	TRS	8	Duplex
494	51	1871	TRS	8	Duplex
495	28	1871	TE (C)	8	SC
496	28	1871	TE (C)	8	SC
497	28	1871	TE (C)	8	SC
498	32	1871	TE (C)	10	Duplex
499	40	1871	PORT	10	SC
500	40	1871	PORT	10	SC
501	40	1871	PORT	8	SC
502	40	1871	PORT	8	SC
503	40	1871	PORT	8	SC
504	40	1871	PORT	8	SC
505	40	1871	PORT	8	SC
506	40	1871	PORT	8	SC
507	40	1871	PORT	8	SC
508	40	1871	PORT	8	SC
509	51	1871	TRS	8	Duplex
510	55	1871	BRS	12	Duplex
511	56	1871	BRS	8	SC
512	51	1871	TRS	8	Duplex
513	51	1871	TRS	8	Duplex
514	55	1871	BRS	8	Duplex
515	40	1871	PORT	8	SC
516	40	1871	PORT	8	SC
517	40	1871	PORT	8	SC
518	40	1871	PORT	8	SC
519	40	1871	PORT	8	SC
520	40	1871	PORT	8	SC
521	128	1872	H.STAT.E	8	SC
522	28	1871	TE (C)	8	SC
523	28	1872	TE (C)	8	SC
524	28	1872	TE (C)	8	SC
525	40	1872	PORT	8	SC
526	40	1872	PORT	8	SC
527	40	1872	PORT	8	SC
528	40	1872	PORT	8	SC
529	40	1872	PORT	8	SC
530	40	1872	PORT	8	SC
531	32	1871	TE (C)	10	SC
532	61	1872	TE	10	SC
533	61	1872	TE	10	SC
534	40	1872	PORT	8	SC
535	40	1872	PORT	8	SC
536	40	1872	PORT	8	SC
537	40	1872	PORT	8	SC
538	40	1872	PORT	8	SC
539	40	1872	PORT	8	SC
540*	56	1872	BRS	8	SC
541	37	1871	PE L/Chain	12	SC
542	56	1872	BRS	8	SC
543	32	1873	TE (C)	10	SC
544	28	1872	TE (C)	8	SC
545	40	1872	PORT	8	SC
546	40	1872	PORT	8	SC
547	40	1872	PORT	8	SC
548	40	1872	PORT	8	SC
549	40	1872	PORT	8	SC
550	40	1872	PORT	8	SC
551	40	1872	PORT	10	SC
552	61	1872	TE	10	SC
553	61	1872	TE	10	SC
554	58	–	BRS (Scrapped)	–	–
555	40	1872	PORT	10	SC
556	40	1873	PORT	8	SC
557	40	1873	PORT	8	SC
558	40	1873	PORT	8	SC
559	40	1873	PORT	8	SC
560	40	1873	PORT	8	SC
561	40	1873	PORT	8	SC
562	40	1873	PORT	8	SC
563	40	1873	PORT	8	SC
564	40	1873	PORT	8	SC
565	40	1873	PORT	8	SC
566	40	1873	PORT	8	SC
567	40	1873	PORT	8	SC
568	28	1873	TE (C)	8	SC
569	29	1873	TE (C)	8	SC
570	31	1873	TE (C)	8	SC
571	31	1873	TE (C)	8	SC
572	31	1873	TE (C)	8	SC
573	31	1874	TE (C)	8	SC
574	58	1873	BRS	10	Duplex
575	40	1873	PORT	10	SC
576	40	1873	PORT	10	SC
577	40	1873	PORT	10	SC
578	40	1873	PORT	10	SC
579	40	1873	PORT	10	SC
580	40	1873	PORT	10	SC
581	40	1873	PORT	10	Duplex
582	37	1873	PE L/Chain	12	SC
583	40	1873	PORT	8	SC
584	40	1873	PORT	8	SC
585	40	1873	PORT	8	SC
586	40	1873	PORT	8	SC
587	40	1873	PORT	8	SC
588	40	1873	PORT	8	SC
589	40	1873	PORT	8	SC
590	40	1873	PORT	8	SC
591	40	1873	PORT	8	SC
592	40	1873	PORT	8	SC
593	40	1873	PORT	8	SC
594	40	1873	PORT	8	SC
595	31	1874	TE (C)	8	SC
596	31	1874	TE (C)	8	SC
597	28	1874	TE (C)	8	SC
598	40	1873	PORT	8	SC
599	40	1873	PORT	8	SC
600	40	1873	PORT	8	SC
601	40	1874	PORT	8	SC
602	40	1874	PORT	8	SC
603	40	1874	PORT	8	SC
604	40	1874	PORT	8	SC
605	40	1874	PORT	8	SC
606	40	1874	PORT (S/B)	8	SC
607	40	1874	PORT (S/B)	8	SC
608	40	1874	PORT (S/B)	8	SC
609	40	1874	PORT (S/B)	8	SC
610	40	1874	PORT (S/B)	12	Duplex
611	40	1874	PORT (S/B)	10	SC
612	40	1874	PORT (S/B)	10	SC
613	40	1874	PORT (S/B)	10	SC
614	40	1874	PORT (S/B)	10	SC
615	40	1874	PORT (S/B)	10	SC
616	40	1874	PORT	10	SC
617	40	1874	PORT (S/B)	8	SC
618	40	1874	PORT	8	SC
619	40	1874	PORT	8	SC
620	40	1874	PORT	8	SC
621	40	1874	PORT	8	SC
622	40	1874	PORT	8	SC
623	40	1874	PORT	8	SC
624	40	1874	PORT	8	SC
625	40	1874	PORT	8	SC
626	40	1874	PORT	8	SC
627	40	1874	PORT	8	SC
628	40	1875	PORT	8	SC
629	40	1874	PORT (S/B)	10	SC
630	40	1874	PORT (S/B)	10	SC
631	40	1874	PORT (S/B)	10	SC
632	40	1874	PORT (S/B)	10	SC
633	40	1874	PORT (S/B)	10	SC
634	40	1874	PORT (S/B)	10	SC
635	40	1875	PORT	8	SC
636	40	1875	PORT	8	SC
637	40	1875	PORT	8	SC
638	40	1875	PORT	8	SC
639	40	1875	PORT	8	SC
640	40	1875	PORT	8	SC
641	40	1875	PORT	8	SC
642	40	1875	PORT	8	SC
643	40	1875	PORT	8	SC
644	40	1875	PORT	8	SC
645	40	1875	PORT	8	SC
646	40	1875	PORT	8	SC
647	40	1875	PORT	8	SC
648	40	1875	PORT	8	SC
649	40	1875	PORT	8	SC
650	40	1875	PORT	8	SC
651	40	1875	PORT	8	SC
652	40	1875	PORT	8	SC
653	40	1875	PORT	8	SC
654	40	1875	PORT	8	SC
655	40	1875	PORT	8	SC
656	40	1875	PORT	8	SC
657	40	1875	PORT	8	SC
658	40	1875	PORT	8	SC
659	37	1875	PE L/Chain	12	SC
660	37	1875	PE L/Chain	12	SC
661	40	1875	PORT	6	SC
662	40	1875	PORT	7	SC
663	–	–	NO INFO	–	–
664	40	1874	PORT	10	SC
665	40	1874	PORT	10	SC
666	40	1875	PORT	10	SC
667	40	1875	PORT	10	SC
668	40	1875	PORT	10	SC
669	40	1876	PORT (S/B)	10	SC
670	128	1874	H STAT E	20	–
671	40	1874	PORT	7	SC
672	32	1875	TE (C)	8	SC
673	32	1875	TE (C)	8	SC
674	61	1875	TE	10	SC
675	40	1875	PORT	16	SC
676	40	1875	PORT	10	SC
677	40	1875	PORT	10	SC
678	40	1871	PORT	10	SC
679	40	1876	PORT	10	SC
680	40	1876	PORT	10	SC
681	40	1877	PORT	10	SC
682	40	1875	PORT	12	SC
683	40	1875	PORT	12	Duplex

Engine No.	Page Ref.	Date Built	Type	NHP	Cyl
684	40	1875	PORT	12	Duplex
685	40	1875	PORT	12	Duplex
686	40	1875	PORT	12	Duplex
687	37	1875	PE L/Chain	12	SC
688	37	1875	PE L/Chain	12	SC
689	39	1875	PE S/Chain	14	SC
690	36	1875	PE S/Chain	14	SC
691	62	1876	TE	6	SC
692	32	1875	TE (C)	8	SC
693	32	1876	TE (C)	8	SC
694	40	1876	PORT	8	SC
695	40	1876	PORT	8	SC
696	40	1876	PORT	8	SC
697	40	1876	PORT	8	SC
698	40	1876	PORT	8	SC
699	40	1876	PORT	8	SC
700	40	1876	PORT	8	SC
701	40	1876	PORT	8	SC
702	40	1877	PORT	8	SC
703	40	1877	PORT	8	SC
704	40	1877	PORT	8	SC
705	40	1877	PORT	8	SC
706	40	1875	PORT	6	SC
707	40	1875	PORT	6	SC
708	62	1875	TE	12	SC
709	40	1877	PORT	8	SC
710	40	1877	PORT	8	SC
711	40	1877	PORT	8	SC
712	40	1877	PORT	8	SC
713	40	1877	PORT	8	SC
714	40	1877	PORT	8	SC
715	40	1877	PORT	8	SC
716	40	1877	PORT	8	SC
717	40	1877	PORT	8	SC
718	40	1877	PORT	8	SC
719	40	1877	PORT	8	SC
720	40	1877	PORT	8	SC
721	32	1876	TE (C)	8	SC
722	32	1876	TE (C)	8	SC
723	36	1876	PE S/Chain	14	SC
724	36	1876	PE S/Chain	14	SC
725	61	1875	TE	10	SC
726	39	1876	PE S/Chain	12	SC
727	39	1876	PE S/Chain	12	SC
728	39	1876	PE S/Chain	12	SC
729	39	1876	PE S/Chain	12	SC
730	39	1876	PE S/Chain	12	SC
731	39	1876	PE S/Chain	12	SC
732	62	1876	TE Rigid US	6	SC
733	62	1876	TE Rigid US	6	SC
734	32	1876	TE (C)	10	SC
735	61	1876	TE	10	SC
736	40	1876	PORT	7	SC
737	32	1876	TE (C)	10	SC
738	32	1876	TE (C) 'J'	8	SC
739	32	1876	TE (C) 'J'	8	SC
740	32	1876	TE (C) 'J'	8	SC
741	62	1876	TE SD US	6	SC
742	62	1877	TE SD US	6	SC
743	40	1877	PORT	7	SC
744	67	1876	TE SD US	8	SC
745	67	1876	TE SD US	8	SC
746	67	1877	TE SD US	8	SC
747	32	1877	TE (C)	8	SC
748*	32	1878	TE (C)	8	SC
749	32	1878	TE (C)	8	SC
750	67	1877	TE SD US	8	SC
751	143	1877	RL SD US	8	SC
752	67	1877	TE SD US	8	SC
753	67	1877	TE SD US	8	SC
754	67	1877	TE SD US	8	SC
755	67	1878	TE SD US	8	SC
756	39	1877	PE S/Chain	14	SC
757	39	1877	PE S/Chain	14	SC
758	62	1877	TE SD US	6	SC
759	62	1877	TE SD US	6	SC
760	62	1877	TE SD US	6	SC
761	37	1877	PE L/Chain	12	SC
762	37	1877	PE L/Chain	12	SC
763	62	1877	TE SD US	6	SC
764	62	1878	TE (CRL) SD US	6	SC
765	62	1878	TE SD US	6	SC
766	107	1877	PE 'M'	8	SC
767	107	1877	PE 'M'	8	SC
768	40	1878	PORT	8	SC
769	32	1877	TE (C)	10	SC
770	33	1877	RL (C)	10	SC
771	40	1877	PORT	7	SC
772	40	1878	PORT	10	SC
773	40	1878	PORT	8	SC
774	40	1878	PORT	10	SC
775	107	1879	PE 'M'	8	SC
776*	107	1879	PE 'M'	8	SC
777*	107	1879	PE 'M'	8	SC
778	39	1878	PE S/Chain	14	SC
779	39	1878	PE S/Chain	14	SC
780	67	1878	TE SD US	8	SC
781	67	1878	TE SD US	8	SC
782	67	1878	TE SD US	8	SC
783	62	1878	TE SD US	6	SC
784	62	1878	TE SD US	6	SC
785	62	1878	TE SD US	6	SC
786	40	1878	PORT	10	SC
787	32	1878	TE (C)	8	SC
788	32	1878	TE (C)	8	SC
789	143	1878	RL SD US	10	SC
790	40	1878	PORT	8	SC
791	40	1878	PORT	8	SC
792	40	1878	PORT	8	SC
793	40	1878	PORT	8	SC
794	40	1878	PORT	8	SC
795	40	1878	PORT	8	SC
796	40	1878	PORT	8	SC
797	40	1878	PORT	10	SC
798	40	1878	PORT	8	SC
799	40	1878	PORT	8	SC
800	61	1878	TE	10	Duplex
801	39	1878	PE S/Chain	14	SC
802	39	1878	PE S/Chain	14	SC
803	–	–	NO INFO	–	–
804	67	1879	TE SD US	8	SC
805	67	1879	TE SD US	8	SC
806	62	1878	TE SD US	6	SC
807	62	1879	TE SD US	6	SC
808	62	1879	TE SD US	6	SC
809	40	1878	PORT	8	SC
810	40	1878	PORT	8	SC
811	40	1878	PORT	8	SC
812	40	1878	PORT	8	SC
813	40	1878	PORT	10	SC
814	108	1879	PE 'N'	14	SC
815	108	1879	PE 'N'	14	SC
816	32	1879	TE (C)	8	SC
817	32	1879	TE (C)	8	SC
818	40	1879	PORT	10	SC
819	40	1879	PORT	10	SC
820	40	1878	PORT	8	SC
821	40	1878	PORT	8	SC
822	40	1878	PORT	8	SC
823	40	1878	PORT	8	SC
824	40	1879	PORT	8	SC
825	40	1879	PORT	8	SC
826	143	1879	RL SD US	6	SC
827	62	1879	TE SD US	6	SC
828	62	1879	TE SD US	6	SC
829	62	1880	TE SD US	6	SC
830	62	1880	TE SD US	6	SC
831	62	1880	TE SD US	6	SC
832	32	1879	TE (C)	8	SC
833	32	1879	TE (C)	8	SC
834	32	1879	TE (C)	8	SC
835	40	1879	PORT	8	SC
836	40	1879	PORT	8	SC
837	40	1879	PORT	8	SC
838	40	1879	PORT	8	SC
839	40	1879	PORT	8	SC
840	40	1879	PORT	8	SC
841	61	1879	TE	10	SC
842	40	1879	PORT	10	SC
843	40	1879	PORT	10	SC
844	40	1879	PORT	10	SC
845	40	1879	PORT	10	SC
846	40	1879	PORT	10	SC
847	40	1879	PORT	10	SC
848	67	1878	TE SD US	8	SC
849	111	1881	PE	16	SC
850	111	1881	PE	16	SC
851	40	1880	PORT	8	SC
852	40	1880	PORT	8	SC
853	40	1880	PORT	8	SC
854	40	1880	PORT	8	SC
855	40	1880	PORT	8	SC
856	40	1880	PORT	8	SC
857	32	1879	TE (C)	8	SC
858	32	1880	TE (C)	8	SC
859	32	1880	TE (C)	8	SC
860	40	1880	PORT	9	SC
861	107	1879	PE 'M'	8	SC
862	107	1879	PE 'M'	8	SC
863	40	1879	PORT	10	SC
864	40	1879	PORT	10	SC
865	40	1879	PORT	10	SC
866	40	1879	PORT	10	SC
867	40	1879	PORT	10	SC
868	40	1879	PORT	10	SC
869	67	1879	TE SD US	7	SC
870	67	1879	TE SD US	8	SC
871	67	1881	TE SD US	8	SC
872	67	1880	TE SD US	8	SC
873	40	1880	PORT	8	SC
874	40	1880	PORT	8	SC
875	40	1880	PORT	8	SC
876	118	1881	PORT	10	SC
877	118	1881	PORT	10	SC
878	118	1881	PORT	10	SC
879	40	1880	PORT	8	SC
880	128	1879	OTE	6	SC
881	67	1881	TE SD US	8	SC
882	67	1881	TE SD US	8	SC
883	67	1881	TE SD US	8	SC
884	143	1880	RL 4-shaft SD US	12	SC
885	67	1880	TE SD US	7	SC
886	67	1880	TE SD US	7	SC
887	67	1880	TE SD US	7	SC
888	109	1880	PE 2 drum uni.	8	SC
889	40	1880	PORT	12	SC
890	65	1881	TE SD US	6	SC
891	65	1881	TE SD US	6	SC
892	65	1881	TE SD US	6	SC
893	118	1881	PORT	10	SC
894	110	1882	PE 2 drum uni.	10	SC
895	110	1883	PE 1 drum uni.	10	SC
896	78	1881	TE 'C' SD US	8	SC
897	78	1881	TE 'C' SD US	8	SC
898	40	1880	PORT	8	SC
899	118	1881	PORT	8	SC
900	118	1881	PORT	8	SC
901	78	1881	TE 'C' SD US	8	SC
902	78	1881	TE 'C' SD US	8	SC
903	78	1881	TE 'C' SD US	8	SC
904	118	1881	PORT	7	SC
905	65	1881	TE SD US	6	SC
906	65	1881	TE SD US	6	SC
907	65	1881	TE SD US	6	SC
908	75	1881	TE 'T' SD US	7	SC
909	75	1881	TE 'T' SD US	7	SC
910	75	1881	TE 'T' SD US	7	SC
911	145	1882	RL 'F' DG US	8	SC
912	75	1881	TE 'T' SD US	7	SC
913	75	1881	TE 'T' SD US	7	SC
914	75	1881	TE 'T' SD US	7	SC
915	78	1881	TE 'C' SD US	8	SC
916	78	1881	TE 'C' SD US	8	SC
917	78	1882	TE 'C' SD US	8	SC
918	78	1882	TE 'C' SD US	8	SC
919	118	1881	PORT	8	SC
920	118	1881	PORT	8	SC
921	118	1881	PORT	8	SC
922	118	1881	PORT	8	SC
923	118	1881	PORT	14	Duplex
924	118	1881	PORT	1½	SC
925	118	1882	PORT	1½	SC
926	118	1882	PORT	1½	SC
927	118	1882	PORT	1½	SC
928	118	1882	PORT	1½	SC
929	118	1882	PORT	1½	SC
930	65	1881	TE 'T' SD US	6	SC
931	65	1881	TE 'T' SD US	6	SC
932	65	1882	TE 'T' SD US	6	SC
933	118	1881	PORT	6	SC
934	–	–	Became 1082	–	–
935	–	–	Never Used	–	–
936	118	1881	PORT	6	SC
937	118	1882	PORT	6	SC
938	118	1882	PORT	8	SC
939	118	1882	PORT	8	SC
940	118	1882	PORT	8	SC
941	118	1882	PORT	8	SC
942	118	1882	PORT	8	SC
943	118	1882	PORT	8	SC
944	118	1882	PORT	8	SC
945	118	1882	PORT	8	SC
946	118	1882	PORT	8	SC
947	118	1882	PORT (S/B)	8	SC
948	118	1882	PORT	10	SC
949	118	1882	PORT	10	SC
950	118	1882	PORT	10	SC
951	65	1882	TE 'T' SD US	6	SC
952	65	1882	TE 'T' SD US	6	SC
953	65	1882	TE 'T' SD US	6	SC

Engine No.	Page Ref.	Date Built	Type	NHP	Cyl
954	65	1882	TE SD US	6	SC
955	65	1882	TE SD US	6	SC
956	65	1882	TE SD US	6	SC
957	118	1883	PORT	6	SC
958	–	–	NO INFO	–	–
959	–	–	NO INFO	–	–
960	118	1882	PORT	10	SC
961	118	1882	PORT	10	SC
962	118	1882	PORT	10	SC
963	118	1882	PORT	10	SC
964	118	1882	PORT	10	SC
965	118	1882	PORT	10	SC
966	118	1882	PORT	8	SC
967	118	1882	PORT	8	SC
968	118	1882	PORT	8	SC
969	118	1882	PORT	8	SC
970	118	1882	PORT	8	SC
971	118	1882	PORT	8	SC
972	145	1882	RL SD US	8	SC
973	78	1882	TE 'C' SD US	8	SC
974	78	1882	TE 'C' SD US	8	SC
975	65	1882	TE (T) SD US	6	SC
976	65	1883	TE (T) SD US	6	SC
977	65	1883	TE (T) SD US	6	SC
978	65	1883	TE SPECIAL	6	SC
979	75	1883	TE (T) SD US	7	SC
980	75	1883	TE (T) SD US	7	SC
981	118	1882	PORT	10	SC
982	118	1882	PORT	10	SC
983	118	1883	PORT	10	SC
984	118	1883	PORT	10	SC
985	118	1883	PORT	10	SC
986	118	1883	PORT	10	SC
987	118	1883	PORT	6	SC
988	118	1883	PORT	6	SC
989	118	1883	PORT	6	SC
990	118	1883	PORT	6	SC
991	118	1883	PORT	6	SC
992	118	1884	PORT	6	SC
993	118	1882	PORT	8	SC
994	118	1882	PORT	8	SC
995	118	1882	PORT	8	SC
996	118	1882	PORT	8	SC
997	118	1882	PORT	8	SC
998	118	1883	PORT	8	SC
999	118	1882	PORT	12	Duplex
1000	78	1882	TE 'C' SD US	8	SC
1001	145	1882	RL (S) SD US	8	SC
1002	145	1882	RL SD US	8	SC
1003	78	1882	TE 'C' SD US	8	SC
1004	78	1883	TE 'C' SD US	8	SC
1005	78	1883	TE 'C' SD US	8	SC
1006	145	1883	RL SD US	8	SC
1007	78	1883	TE 'C' SD US	8	SC
1008	78	1883	TE 'C' SD US	8	SC
1009	129	1886	UTE	14	DCC
1010	–	–	NO INFO	–	–
1011	–	–	NO INFO	–	–
1012	–	–	NO INFO	–	–
1013	–	–	NO INFO	–	–
1014	–	–	NO INFO	–	–
1015	107	1882	PE 'M'	8	SC
1016	107	1882	PE 'M'	8	SC
1017	–	–	NO INFO	–	–
1018	–	–	NO INFO	–	–
1019	–	–	NO INFO	–	–
1020	–	–	NO INFO	–	–
1021	118	1882	PORT	8	SC
1022	118	1883	PORT	8	SC
1023	118	1883	PORT	8	SC
1024	118	1883	PORT	8	SC
1025	118	1883	PORT	8	SC
1026	118	1883	PORT	8	SC
1027	78	1883	TE 'C' SD US	8	SC
1028	145	1884	RL SD US	8	SC
1029	145	1884	RL SD US	8	SC
1030	118	1883	PORT	8	SC
1031	118	1883	PORT	8	SC
1032	118	1883	PORT	8	SC
1033	118	1883	PORT	8	SC
1034	118	1883	PORT	8	SC
1035	118	1883	PORT	8	SC
1036	118	1883	PORT	8	SC
1037	118	1883	PORT	8	SC
1038	118	1883	PORT	8	SC
1039	118	1883	PORT	8	SC
1040	118	1883	PORT	8	SC
1041	118	1883	PORT	8	SC
1042	118	1883	PORT	10	SC
1043	118	1884	PORT	10	SC
1044	118	1884	PORT	10	SC
1045	118	1884	PORT	10	SC
1046	118	1884	PORT	10	SC
1047	118	1884	PORT	10	SC
1048	118	1883	PORT	8	SC
1049	118	1883	PORT	8	SC
1050	118	1884	PORT	8	SC
1051	118	1884	PORT	8	SC
1052	118	1884	PORT	8	SC
1053	118	1883	PORT	8	SC
1054	118	1883	PORT	8	SC
1055	118	1883	PORT	8	SC
1056	118	1884	PORT	8	SC
1057	118	1884	PORT	8	SC
1058	118	1886	PORT	8	SC
1059	118	1884	PORT	8	SC
1060	133	–	MARINE	32	–
1061	34	1883	RL (C)	8	SC
1062	118	1884	PORT	8	SC
1063	118	1884	PORT	8	SC
1064	118	1884	PORT	8	SC
1065	118	1884	PORT	8	SC
1066	118	1884	PORT	8	SC
1067	118	1884	PORT	8	SC
1068	145	1884	RL DG US	8	SC
1069	145	1885	RL DG US	8	SC
1070	118	1885	PORT	12	Duplex
1071	112	1883	PE	16	SC
1072	112	1883	PE	16	SC
1073	118	1884	PORT	10	SC
1074	118	1884	PORT	10	SC
1075	118	1885	PORT	10	SC
1076	118	1884	PORT	10	SC
1077	118	1884	PORT	10	SC
1078	118	1886	PORT	10	SC
1079	118	1883	PORT	20	DCC
1080	75	1883	TE 'T' SD US	7	SC
1081	–	–	NO INFO	–	–
1082	68	1884	'R' TE DG US	4	SC
1083	78	1884	TE 'C' SD US	8	SC
1084	78	1884	TE 'C' SD US	8	SC
1085	78	1884	TE 'C' SD US	8	SC
1086	75	1884	TE 'T' SD US	7	SC
1087	75	1884	TE 'T' SD US	7	SC
1088	75	1884	TE 'T' SD US	7	SC
1089	119	1885	PORT	8	DCC
1090	129	1888	UTE	8	DCC
1091	119	–	Became 1379	–	–
1092	129	1884	UTE	8	DCC
1093	118	1885	PORT	10	TCC
1094	–	–	Became 1357	–	–
1095	–	–	NO INFO	–	–
1096	118	1884	PORT	6	SC
1097	118	1885	PORT	6	SC
1098	118	1885	PORT	6	SC
1099	118	1885	PORT	6	SC
1100	118	1885	PORT	6	SC
1101	118	1886	PORT	6	SC
1102	78	1884	TE 'C' SD US	8	SC
1103	78	1885	TE 'C' SD US	8	SC
1104	78	1885	TE 'C' SD US	8	SC
1105	133	–	MARINE	–	–
1106	–	–	NO INFO	–	–
1107	118	1885	PORT	8	SC
1108	118	1884	PORT	8	SC
1109	118	1884	PORT	8	SC
1110	–	–	NO INFO	–	–
1111	118	1884	PORT	8	SC
1112	118	1884	PORT	8	SC
1113	118	1885	PORT	8	SC
1114	118	1885	PORT	8	SC
1115	118	1885	PORT	8	SC
1116	118	1885	PORT	8	SC
1117	118	1884	PORT	8	SC
1118	–	–	Became 1226	–	–
1119	133	–	MARINE	–	–
1120	118	1886	PORT	10	SC
1121	118	1885	PORT	10	SC
1122	118	1887	PORT	10	SC
1123	118	1887	PORT	10	SC
1124	118	1888	PORT	10	SC
1125	118	1888	PORT	10	SC
1126	75	1884	TE 'T' SD US	7	SC
1127*	75	1884	TE 'T' SD US	7	SC
1128	75	1885	TE 'T' SD US	7	SC
1129	133	–	MARINE	–	–
1130	–	–	NO INFO	–	–
1131	–	–	NO INFO	–	–
1132	–	–	NO INFO	–	–
1133	78	1885	TE 'C' SD US	8	SC
1134	78	1885	TE 'C' SD US	8	SC
1135	78	1885	TE 'C' SD US	8	SC
1136	118	1885	PORT	8	SC
1137	118	1885	PORT	8	SC
1138	118	1885	PORT	8	SC
1139	118	1885	PORT	8	SC
1140	–	–	Became 1256	–	–
1141	118	1885	PORT	8	SC
1142	133	–	MARINE	32	–
1143	65	1884	TE 'T' SD US	6	SC
1144	65	1884	TE 'T' SD US	6	SC
1145	118	1885	PORT	8	SC
1146	118	1885	PORT	8	SC
1147	118	1885	PORT	8	SC
1148	118	1885	PORT	8	SC
1149	118	1885	PORT	8	SC
1150	118	1886	PORT	8	SC
1151	–	–	NO INFO	–	–
1152	–	–	NO INFO	–	–
1153	–	–	NO INFO	–	–
1154	65	1885	TE 'T' SD US	6	SC
1155	65	1885	TE 'T' SD US	6	SC
1156	65	1885	TE 'T' SD US	6	SD
1157	75	1885	TE 'T' SD US	7	SC
1158	75	1885	TE 'T' SD US	7	SC
1159	75	1885	TE 'T' SD US	7	SC
1160	118	1885	PORT	10	SC
1161	112	1889	PE	9	SC
1162	112	1889	PE	9	SC
1163	–	–	NO INFO	–	–
1164	–	–	NO INFO	–	–
1165	–	–	NO INFO	–	–
1166	–	–	NO INFO	–	–
1167	–	–	NO INFO	–	–
1168	–	–	NO INFO	–	–
1169	–	–	NO INFO	–	–
1170	118	1886	PORT	8	SC
1171	118	1886	PORT	8	SC
1172	118	1886	PORT	8	SC
1173	–	–	Became 1472	–	–
1174	118	1886	PORT	8	SC
1175	118	1886	PORT	8	SC
1176	78	1885	TE 'C' SD US	8	SC
1177	78	1885	TE 'C' SD US	8	SC
1178	78	1886	TE 'C' SD US	8	SC
1179	75	1885	TE 'T' SD US	7	SC
1180	75	1885	TE 'T' SD US	7	SC
1181	75	1885	TE 'T' SD US	7	SC
1182	65	1886	TE 'T' SD US	6	SC
1183	65	1886	TE 'T' SD US	6	SC
1184	65	1886	TE 'T' SD US	6	SC
1185	133	1886	MARINE	–	–
1186	129	1885	UTE	20	DCC
1187	68	1885	TE 'R' TYPE	4	SC
1188	68	1887	TE 'R' TYPE	4	SC
1189	68	1886	TE 'R' TYPE	4	SC
1190	–	–	NO INFO	–	–
1191	118	1885	PORT	10	SC
1192	–	–	NEVER USED	–	–
1193	–	–	NEVER USED	–	–
1194	–	–	NEVER USED	–	–
1195	–	–	NEVER USED	–	–
1196	–	–	NEVER USED	–	–
1197	–	–	NEVER USED	–	–
1198	133	–	MARINE	–	–
1199	119	1885	PORT	8	SC
1200	75	1885	TE 'T' SD US	7	SC
1201	75	1886	TE 'T' SD US	7	SC
1202	75	1886	TE 'T' SD US	7	SC
1203	118	1886	PORT	8	SC
1204	118	1886	PORT	8	SC
1205	118	1886	PORT	8	SC
1206	118	1886	PORT	8	SC
1207	118	1886	PORT	8	SC
1208	118	1886	PORT	8	SC
1209	118	1885	PORT	7	SC
1210	118	1885	PORT	7	SC
1211	118	1886	PORT	4	SC
1212*	78	1886	TE 'C' SD US	8	SC
1213	–	–	NO INFO	–	–
1214	118	1890	PORT	4	SC
1215	–	–	NO INFO	–	–
1216	78	1886	TE 'C' SD US	8	SC
1217	118	1886	PORT	4	SC
1218	118	1886	PORT	6	SC
1219	118	1886	PORT	4	SC
1220	118	1886	PORT	4	SC
1221	71	1886	TE 'T' (CRL) SD US	6	SC

Engine No.	Page Ref.	Date Built	Type	NHP	Cyl
1222	71	1887	TE 'T' (CRL) SD US	6	SC
1223	78	1886	TE 'C' SD US	8	SC
1224	118	1886	PORT	6	SC
1225	75	1886	TE 'T' SD US	7	SC
1226	118	1886	PORT	8	SC
1227	129	1886	UTE	20	DCC
1228	129	1886	UTE	20	DCC
1229	75	1886	TE 'T' SD US	7	SC
1230	78	1886	TE 'C' SD US	8	SC
1231	118	1886	PORT	8	SC
1232	118	1886	PORT	8	SC
1233	118	1886	PORT	5	SC
1234	118	1886	PORT	4	SC
1235	118	1886	PORT	4	SC
1236	75	1886	TE 'T' SD US	7	SC
1237	118	1886	PORT	8	SC
1238	118	1886	PORT	6	SC
1239	118	1886	PORT	8	SC
1240	78	1886	TE 'C' SD US	8	SC
1241	118	1887	PORT	6	SC
1242	118	1886	PORT	8	SC
1243	75	1886	TE 'T' SD US	7	SC
1244*	80	1886	TE 'C' DG US	8	SC
1245	118	1886	PORT	8	SC
1246	75	1886	TE 'T' SD US	7	SC
1247	118	1886	PORT	8	SC
1248	68	1886	DIGGING 'R' TE DG US	4	SC
1249	118	1886	PORT	8	SC
1250	75	1886	TE 'T' SD US	7	SC
1251	71	1886	TE 'T' DG US	6	SC
1252	118	1886	PORT	8	SC
1253	80	1887	TE 'C' DG US	8	SC
1254	118	1886	PORT	10	SC
1255	118	1886	PORT	8	SC
1256	118	1886	PORT	8	SC
1257	112	1886	PE 'N'	18	DCC
1258	112	1886	PE 'N'	18	DCC
1259	118	1887	PORT	8	SC
1260	118	1887	PORT	4	SC
1261	71	1887	TE 'T' SD US	6	SC
1262	118	1887	PORT	8	SC
1263	118	1887	PORT	8	SC
1264	118	1887	PORT	6	SC
1265	118	1887	PORT	6	SC
1266	80	1887	TE 'C' DG US	8	SC
1267	71	1887	TE 'T' SD US	6	SC
1268	75	1887	TE 'T' SD US	7	SC
1269	118	1887	PORT	8	SC
1270	118	1887	PORT	4	SC
1271	118	1887	PORT	8	SC
1272	68	1887	DIGGING 'R' TE DG US	4	SC
1273	80	1887	TE 'C' DG US	8	SC
1274	80	1887	TE 'C' DG US	8	SC
1275	75	1887	TE 'T' SD US	7	SC
1276	118	1887	PORT	8	SC
1277	118	1888	PORT	4	SC
1278	75	1887	TE 'T' SD US	7	SC
1279	118	1887	PORT	6	SC
1280	118	1887	PORT	4	SC
1281	118	1887	PORT	8	SC
1282	129	1887	UTE	20	DCC
1283	118	1887	PORT	7	SC
1284	–	–	NO INFO	–	–
1285	71	1887	TE 'T' SD US	6	SC
1286	71	1887	TE 'T' SD US	6	SC
1287	80	1887	TE (S) 'C' DG US	8	SC
1288	71	1887	TE 'T' SD US	6	SC
1289	118	1887	PORT	8	SC
1290	87	1887	TE (DIG) SD US	8	SCC
1291	88	1887	TE SD SPR	7	SCC
1292	80	1887	TE 'C' DG US	8	SC
1293	80	1887	TE 'C' DG US	8	SC
1294	76	1887	TE 'T' SD SPR	7	SC
1295	80	1887	TE 'C' DG US	8	SC
1296	118	1887	PORT	8	SC
1297	76	1887	TE (T) SD US	7	SC
1298	80	1888	TE 'C' DG US	8	SC
1299	80	1888	TE 'C' DG US	8	SC
1300	76	1887	TE (T) SD SPR	7	SC
1301	118	1889	PORT	4	SC
1302	118	1888	PORT	8	SC
1303	118	1887	PORT	8	SC
1304	80	1887	TE SD US	7/8	SC
1305	129	1887	UTE	10	SC
1306	118	1888	PORT	8	SC
1307	71	1888	TE (T) SD US	6	SC
1308	118	1888	PORT	8	SC
1309	76	1887	TE (T) SD SPR	7	SC
1310	71	1888	TE (T) SD US	6	SC
1311	71	1888	TE (T) SD US	6	SC
1312	76	1888	TE (T) SD US	7	SC
1313	118	1889	PORT	8	SC
1314	70	1887	TE DG US	5	SC
1315	–	–	NO INFO	–	–
1316	118	1888	PORT	8	SC
1317	76	1888	TE (T) SD US	7	SC
1318	80	1888	TE 'C' DG US	8	SC
1319	80	1888	TE 'C' DG US	8	SC
1320	80	1888	TE 'C' DG US	8	SC
1321	76	1888	TE (T) SD US	7	SC
1322	70	1888	TE DG US	5	SC
1323	118	1888	PORT	8	SC
1324	118	1888	PORT	8	SC
1325	70	1888	TE DG US	5	SC
1326	129	1888	UTE	14	DCC
1327	118	1888	PORT	8	SC
1328	118	1889	PORT	8	SC
1329	80	1888	TE 'C' DG US	8	SC
1330	76	1888	TE (T) SD SPR	7	SC
1331	76	1888	TE 'T' SD SPR	7	SC
1332	76	1888	TE 'T' SD SPR	7	SC
1333	80	1888	TE 'C' DG US	8	SC
1334	118	1888	PORT	6	SC
1335	73	1888	TE 'T' SD SPR	6	SC
1336	70	1888	DIGGING TE SD US	5	SC
1337	128	1890	OTE	10	SC
1338	118	1888	PORT	10	SC
1339	118	1889	PORT	8	SC
1340	80	1888	TE 'C' DG US	8	SC
1341	81	1888	TE 'C' SD SPR	8	SC
1342	118	1888	PORT	6	SC
1343	118	1888	PORT	6	SC
1344	118	1888	PORT	8	SC
1345	129	1888	UTE	12	DCC
1346	118	1888	PORT	7	SC
1347	–	–	NO INFO	–	–
1348	118	1888	PORT	8	SC
1349	71	1888	TE 'T' SD US	6	SC
1350	76	1888	TE 'T' SD US	7	SC
1351	73	1888	TE 'T' SD SPR	6	SC
1352	81	1888	TE 'C' SD SPR	8	SC
1353	118	1888	PORT	8	SC
1354	118	1888	PORT	10	SC
1355	76	1888	TE 'T' SD SPR	7	SC
1356	118	1888	PORT	6	SC
1357	118	1888	PORT	20	DCC
1358	118	1888	PORT	6	SC
1359	118	1888	PORT	10	SC
1360	118	1888	PORT	4	SC
1361	80	1888	TE 'C' DG US	8	SC
1362	71	1888	TE 'T' SD US	6	SC
1363	76	1888	TE 'T' SD US	7	SC
1364	118	1888	PORT	6	SC
1365	129	1888	UTE	8	DCC
1366	76	1888	TE 'T' SD SPR	7	SC
1367	76	1888	TE 'T' SD US	7	SC
1368	118	1888	PORT	10	SC
1369	129	1888	UTE	16	DCC
1370	–	–	NO INFO	–	–
1371	118	1889	PORT	4	SC
1372	118	1888	PORT	8	SC
1373	118	1888	PORT	6	SC
1374	118	1888	PORT	8	SC
1375	118	1889	PORT	10	SC
1376	–	–	NO INFO	–	–
1377	–	–	NO INFO	–	–
1378	71	1889	TE 'T' SD US	6	SC
1379	119	1889	PORT	8	DCC
1380	–	–	NO INFO	–	–
1381	118	1889	PORT	10	SC
1382	–	–	NO INFO	–	–
1383	76	1889	TE 'T' SD US	7	SC
1384	118	1889	PORT	6	SC
1385	118	1889	PORT	8	SC
1386	88	1889	TE (CRL) SD SPR	8	SCC
1387	87	1889	TE (DIG) SD US	8	SCC
1388	118	1889	PORT	4	SC
1389	76	1889	TE 'T' SD SPR	7	SC
1390	118	1889	PORT	8	SC
1391	–	–	NO INFO	–	–
1392	–	–	NO INFO	–	–
1393	128	1889	H STAT E	10	SC
1394	129	1889	UTE	16	DCC
1395	73	1889	TE 'T' SD SPR	6	SC
1396	76	1889	TE 'T' SD SPR	7	SC
1397	129	1889	UTE	16	DCC
1398	129	1889	UTE	20	DCC
1399	128	1889	V STAT E	–	SC
1400	129	1889	UTE	10	DCC
1401	71	1889	TE 'T' SD US	6	SC
1402	118	1889	PORT	6	SC
1403	118	1889	PORT	8	SC
1404	118	1889	PORT	6	SC
1405	118	1889	PORT	10	SC
1406	118	1889	PORT	6	SC
1407	–	–	NO INFO	–	–
1408	76	1889	TE (T) SD SPR	7	SC
1409	88	1889	TE (CRL) SD SPR	8	SCC
1410	118	1889	PORT	10	SC
1411	81	1889	TE 'C' SD SPR	8	SC
1412	129	1889	UTE	20	DCC
1413	129	1889	UTE	16	DCC
1414	118	1889	PORT	4	SC
1415	157	1890	RL (SPECIAL) SD SPR	8	SC
1416	118	1889	PORT	5	SC
1417	118	1889	PORT	8	SC
1418	118	1890	PORT	8	SC
1419	118	1889	PORT	10	SC
1420	118	1889	PORT	8	SC
1421	80	1889	TE 'C' DG US	8	SC
1422	76	1889	TE (T) SD US	7	SC
1423	118	1889	PORT	4	SC
1424	118	1889	PORT	10	SC
1425	118	1889	PORT	8	SC
1426*	76	1889	TE (T) SD SPR	7	SC
1427	80	1889	TE 'C' DG US	8	SC
1428	81	1889	TE 'C' SD SPR	8	SC
1429	118	1889	PORT	8	SC
1430	118	1889	PORT	6	SC
1431	118	1889	PORT	10	SC
1432*	73	1889	TE (T) SD SPR	6	SC
1433	76	1889	TE (T) SD SPR	7	SC
1434	118	1889	PORT	6	SC
1435	71	1889	TE (T) SD US	6	SC
1436	81	1889	TE 'C' SD SPR	8	SC
1437	118	1889	PORT	10	SC
1438	80	1889	TE 'C' DG US	8	SC
1439	118	1889	PORT	10	SC
1440	76	1889	TE (T) SD SPR	7	SC
1441	118	1892	PORT	4	SC
1442	118	1889	PORT	10	SC
1443	80	1889	TE 'C' DG US	8	SC
1444	118	1889	PORT	10	SC
1445*	128	1889	OTE	12	SC
1446	80	1889	TE 'C' DG US	8	SC
1447	129	1889	UTE	10	DCC
1448	118	1889	PORT	12	SC
1449	118	1889	PORT	8	SC
1450	80	1889	TE 'C' DG US	8	SC
1451	81	1889	TE (S) 'C' SD SPR	8	SC
1452	118	1889	PORT	8	SC
1453	76	1889	TE (T) SD SPR	7	SC
1454	118	1889	PORT	10	SC
1455	118	1889	PORT	12	SC
1456	–	–	NO INFO	–	–
1457	118	1889	PORT	6	SC
1458	76	1889	TE (T) SD SPR	7	SC
1459	118	1890	PORT	8	SC
1460	118	1890	PORT	10	SC
1461	80	1890	TE 'C' DG US	8	SC
1462	118	1890	PORT	6	SC
1463	118	1890	PORT	8	SC
1464	129	1891	UTE	16	DCC
1465	118	1890	PORT	8	SC
1466	118	1890	PORT	8	SC
1467	118	1890	PORT	6	SC
1468	118	1890	PORT	10	SC
1469	118	1890	PORT	10	SC
1470	176	1890	RL (S) SD SPR	7/8	SC
1471	73	1890	TE (T) SD SPR	6	SC
1472	118	1886	PORT	8	SC
1473	76	1890	TE (T) SD SPR	7	SC
1474	118	1890	PORT	10	SC
1475*	118	1890	PORT	8	SC
1476	118	1890	PORT	12	SC
1477	118	1890	PORT	8	SC
1478	129	1890	UTE	8	DCC
1479	81	1890	TE 'C' SD SPR	8	SC
1480	147	1890	RL SD SPR	8	SCC
1481	147	1890	RL (S) SD SPR	8	SCC
1482	71	1890	TE 'T' SD US	6	SC
1483	81	1890	TE 'C' SD SPR	8	SC

Engine No.	Page Ref.	Date Built	Type	NHP	Cyl
1484	–	–	Became 2771	–	–
1485	147	1890	RL 4-sft SD SPR	8	SCC
1486	118	1890	PORT	6	SC
1487	113	1890	Ex-Fowler 1024	20	DCC
1488	113	1890	Ex-Fowler 1025	20	DCC
1489	73	1890	TE 'T' SD SPR	6	SC
1490	80	1890	TE 'C' DG US	8	SC
1491	76	1890	TE 'T' SD US	7	SC
1492	118	1890	PORT	8	SC
1493	118	1890	PORT	8	SC
1494	88	1890	TE SD SPR	7	SCC
1495	118	1890	PORT	8	SC
1496	118	1890	PORT	8	SC
1497	147	1890	CRL SD SPR	8	SCC
1498	145	1890	RL 4-sft SD SPR	8	SC
1499	76	1890	TE 'T' SD US	7	SC
1500	118	1890	PORT	8	SC
1501	80	1890	TE 'C' DG US	8	SC
1502	70	1890	TE DG US	5	SC
1503	89	1890	TE DG US	5	SCC
1504	76	1890	TE SD SPR	7	SC
1505	80	1890	TE 'C' DG US	8	SC
1506	128	1890	V STAT E		DCC
1507	118	1890	PORT	8	SC
1508	71	1890	TE 'T' SD US	6	SC
1509	73	1890	TE 'T' SD SPR	6	SC
1510	118	1890	PORT	8	SC
1511	76	1890	TE 'T' SD US	7	SC
1512	80	1890	TE 'C' DG US	8	SC
1513	88	1890	TE SD SPR	8	SCC
1514	71	1891	TE 'T' SD US	6	SC
1515	118	1891	PORT	6	SCC
1516	118	1890	PORT	8	SC
1517	118	1891	PORT	8	SC
1518	80	1890	TE 'C' DG US	8	SC
1519	76	1891	TE 'T' SD US	7	SC
1520	–	–	NO INFO	–	–
1521	–	–	NO INFO	–	–
1522*	81	1891	TE 'C' SD SPR	8	SC
1523	88	1891	TE SD SPR	8	SCC
1524	80	1891	TE 'C' DG US	8	SC
1525	150	1891	CRL SD SPR	10	SCC
1526	118	1891	PORT	4	SC
1527	76	1891	TE 'T' SD US	7	SC
1528	118	1891	PORT	10	SC
1529	118	1891	PORT	6	SC
1530	147	1891	RL SD SPR	8	SCC
1531	71	1891	TE 'T' SD US	6	SC
1532	128	1891	OTE	12	SC
1533	76	1891	TE 'T' SD US	7	SC
1534	118	1891	PORT	8	SC
1535	240	1891	R.R. 4-sft	6	SCC
1536	129	1891	UTE	8	DCC
1537	118	1891	PORT	10	SC
1538	81	1891	TE 'C' SD SPR	8	SC
1539	129	1891	UTE	20	DCC
1540	89	1891	TE DG US	6	SCC
1541	118	1891	PORT	10	SC
1542	147	1891	RL (S) SD SPR	8	SCC
1543	70	1891	TE DG US	5	SC
1544	80	1891	TE 'C' DG US	8	SC
1545	73	1891	TE 'T' SD SPR	6	SC
1546	177	1891	SRL SD SPR	8	SCC
1547	118	1891	PORT	16	Duplex
1548	118	1891	PORT	8	SC
1549	80	1881	TE 'C' DG US	8	SC
1550	118	1892	PORT	8	SC
1551	118	1891	PORT	8	SC
1552	76	1891	TE (T) SD SPR	7	SC
1553	118	1891	PORT	8	SC
1554	118	1891	PORT	8	SC
1555	71	1891	TE (T) SD US	6	SC
1556	81	1891	TE 'C' SD SPR	8	SC
1557	76	1891	TE (T) SD US	7	SC
1558	80	1891	TE 'C' DG US	8	SC
1559	88	1891	TE SD SPR	8	SCC
1560	76	1891	TE (T) SD US	7	SC
1561	73	1891	TE (T) SD SPR	6	SC
1562	118	1891	PORT	6	SC
1563*	80	1891	TE 'C' DG US	8	SC
1564	76	1891	TE (T) SD US	7	SC
1565	96	1891	TE SD SPR	6	SCC
1566	80	1891	TE 'C' DG US	8	SC
1567	73	1891	TE (T) SD SPR	6	SC
1568	118	1891	PORT	6	SC
1569	96	1891	TE SD SPR	6	SCC
1570	76	1891	TE (T) SD US	7	SC
1571	118	1891	PORT	8	SC
1572	76	1891	TE (T) SD SPR	7	SC
1573	96	1891	TE SD SPR	6	SCC

Engine No.	Page Ref.	Date Built	Type	NHP	Cyl
1574	81	1891	TE 'C' SD SPR	8	SC
1575	177	1892	SRL SD SPR	8	SCC
1576	80	1891	TE 'C' DG US	8	SC
1577	93	1891	TE SD US	6	SCC
1578	88	1891	TE SD SPR	8	SCC
1579	118	1891	PORT	7	SC
1580	76	1891	TE (T) SD US	7	SC
1581	96	1891	TE SD SPR	6	SCC
1582	128	1892	OTE	10	SC
1583	147	1892	RL SD SPR	8	SCC
1584	96	1891	TE SD SPR	6	SCC
1585	129	1892	UTE	8	DCC
1586	129	1892	UTE	10	DCC
1587	80	1892	TE 'C' DG US	8	SC
1588	118	1892	PORT	8	SC
1589	96	1891	TE SD SPR	6	SCC
1590	96	1891	TE SD SPR	6	SCC
1591	118	1892	PORT	6	SC
1592	76	1892	TE (T) SD SPR	7	SC
1593	118	1892	PORT	6	SC
1594	80	1892	TE 'C' DG US	8	SC
1595	76	1892	TE (T) SD US	7	SC
1596	71	1892	TE (T) SD US	6	SC
1597	96	1892	TE SD SPR	6	SCC
1598	240	1892	RR 4-sft	6	SCC
1599	89	1892	TE DG US	6	SCC
1600	147	1892	CRL SD SPR	8	SCC
1601	71	1892	TE (T) SD US	6	SC
1602	80	1892	TE 'C' DG US	8	SC
1603	96	1892	TE SD SPR	6	SCC
1604	73	1892	TE (T) SD SPR	6	SC
1605	76	1892	TE (T) SD US	7	SC
1606*	81	1892	TE 'C' SD SPR	8	SC
1607	89	1892	TE DG US	6	SCC
1608	240	1892	RR 4-sft	6	SCC
1609	96	1892	TE SD SPR	6	SCC
1610	76	1892	TE SD US	7	SC
1611	80	1892	TE 'C' DG US	8	SC
1612	96	1892	TE SD SPR	6	SCC
1613	240	1892	RR 4-sft	6	SCC
1614	80	1892	TE 'C' DG US	8	SC
1615	80	1892	TE 'C' DG US	8	SC
1616	118	1892	PORT	8	SC
1617	93	1892	TE SD US	6	SCC
1618	96	1892	TE SD SPR	6	SCC
1619	118	1892	PORT	8	SC
1620	71	1892	TE 'T' SD US	6	SC
1621	96	1892	TE SD SPR	6	SCC
1622	96	1892	TE SD SPR	6	SCC
1623	96	1892	TE SD SPR	6	SCC
1624	118	1892	PORT	8	SC
1625	118	1892	PORT	8	SC
1626	118	1892	PORT	8	SC
1627	118	1892	PORT	8	SC
1628	147	1892	RL(S) SD SPR	8	SCC
1629	214	1892	SRL SD SPR	7/8	SCC
1630	76	1892	TE SD US	7	SC
1631	118	1892	PORT	8	SC
1632	88	1892	TE SD SPR	7/8	SCC
1633	–	–	NO INFO	–	–
1634	76	1892	TE SD SPR	7	SC
1635	81	1892	TE 'C' SD SPR	8	SC
1636	80	1892	TE 'C' DG US	8	SC
1637	118	1892	PORT	8	SC
1638	118	1892	PORT	8	SC
1639	118	1892	PORT	6	SC
1640	76	1892	TE SD US	7	SC
1641	71	1892	TE 'T' SD US	6	SC
1642	81	1892	TE 'C' SD SPR	8	SC
1643	71	1892	TE 'T' SD US	6	SC
1644	118	1892	PORT	8	SC
1645	118	1892	PORT	6	SC
1646	93	1892	TE SD US	6	SCC
1647	93	1892	TE SD US	6	SCC
1648	80	1892	TE 'C' DG US	8	SC
1649	76	1892	TE SD US	7	SC
1650	118	1892	PORT	8	SC
1651	93	1893	TE SD US	6	SCC
1652	88	1892	TE SD SPR	7	SCC
1653	240	1892	RR 4-sft	6	SCC
1654	147	1893	RL 4-sft SD SPR	8	SCC
1655	147	1892	RL(S) SD SPR	8	SCC
1656	89	1892	TE DG US	6	SCC
1657	152	1893	RL SD SPR	6	SCC
1658	80	1892	TE 'C' DG US	8	SC
1659	81	1892	TE 'C' SD SPR	8	SC
1660	76	1892	TE SD US	7	SC
1661	118	1893	PORT	8	SC
1662	96	1893	TE SD SPR	6	SCC
1663	89	1892	TE DG US	6	SCC

Engine No.	Page Ref.	Date Built	Type	NHP	Cyl
1664	–	–	NO INFO	–	–
1665	118	1893	PORT	10	SC
1666	147	1893	RL SD SPR	8	SCC
1667	147	1893	RL SD SPR	8	SCC
1668	101	1893	TE DG US	8	SCC
1669	93	1893	TE SD US	6	SCC
1670	118	1893	PORT	10	SC
1671	89	1893	TE DG US	6	SCC
1672	96	1893	TE SD SPR	6	SCC
1673	240	1893	RR 4-sft	6	SCC
1674	147	1893	RL(S) SD SPR	8	SCC
1675	96	1895	TE SD SPR	6	SCC
1676	93	1893	TE SD US	6	SCC
1677	93	1893	TE SD US	6	SCC
1678	89	1893	TE DG US	6	SCC
1679	96	1893	TE SD SPR	6	SCC
1680	96	1893	TE SD SPR	6	SCC
1681	240	1893	RR 4-sft	6	SCC
1682	152	1893	RL SD SPR	6	SCC
1683	88	1893	TE SD SPR	8	SCC
1684	89	1893	TE DG US	6	SCC
1685	89	1893	TE DG US	6	SCC
1686	80	1893	TE 'C' DG US	8	SC
1687*	93	1893	TE SD US	6	SCC
1688	147	1893	RL SD SPR	8	SCC
1689	101	1893	TE DG US	8	SCC
1690	71	1893	TE 'T' SD US	6	SC
1691	76	1893	TE SD US	7	SC
1692	129	1893	UTE	16	DCC
1693	101	1893	TE DG US	8	SCC
1694*	80	1893	TE 'C' DG US	8	SC
1695	101	1893	TE DG US	8	SCC
1696	96	1893	TE SD SPR	6	SCC
1697	–	–	NO INFO	–	–
1698	93	1893	TE SD US	6	SCC
1699	93	1893	TE SD US	6	SCC
1700	152	1893	RL(S) SD SPR	6	SCC
1701	147	1893	RL(S) SD SPR	8	SCC
1702	118	1893	PORT	6/7	SC
1703	76	1893	TE SD US	7	SC
1704	76	1893	TE SD US	7	SC
1705	73	1893	TE 'T' SD SPR	6	SC
1706	89	1893	TE DG US	6	SCC
1707	118	1893	PORT	8	SC
1708	88	1893	TE (DIG) SD US	8	SCC
1709	147	1893	RL(S) SD SPR	8	SCC
1710	88	1893	TE SD SPR	7/8	SCC
1711	93	1893	TE SD US	6	SCC
1712	80	1893	TE 'C' DG US	8	SC
1713	240	1893	RR 4-sft	6	SCC
1714	72	1893	TE 'T' SD US	6	SC
1715	93	1893	TE SD US	6	SCC
1716	113	1893	PE Universal	12	SCC
1717	113	1893	PE Universal	12	SCC
1718	113	1893	PE Universal	12	SCC
1719	113	1893	PE Universal	12	SCC
1720	101	1893	TE DG US	8	SCC
1721	118	1893	PORT	8	SC
1722	101	1893	TE DG US	8	SCC
1723	118	1893	PORT	8	SC
1724	89	1893	TE DG US	6	SCC
1725	103	1893	TE SD SPR	8	SCC
1726	152	1893	RL SD SPR	6	SCC
1727	149	1893	RL SD SPR	8	SCC
1728	145	1893	RL SD SPR	8	SC
1729	177	1894	SRL SD SPR	8	SCC
1730	101	1893	TE DG US	8	SCC
1731	72	1894	TE 'T' SD US	6	SC
1732	96	1894	TE SD SPR	6	SCC
1733	153	1894	RL SD SPR	6	SCC
1734	118	1894	PORT	8	SC
1735	149	1894	RL SD SPR	8	SCC
1736	150	1894	RL(S) SD SPR	10	SCC
1737	240	1894	RR 4-sft	6	SCC
1738	96	1894	TE SD SPR	6	SCC
1739	93	1894	TE SD US	6	SCC
1740	178	1894	SRL SD SPR	10	SCC
1741	214	1894	SRL SD SPR	6	SCC
1742	93	1894	TE SD US	6	SCC
1743	177	1894	RL SD SPR	8	SCC
1744	96	1894	TE SD SPR	6	SCC
1745	114	1894	PE Universal	14	SCC
1746	114	1894	PE Universal	14	SCC
1747	114	1894	PE Universal	14	SCC
1748	114	1894	PE Universal	14	SCC
1749	153	1894	RL SD SPR	6	SCC
1750	89	1894	TE DG US	6	SCC
1751	93	1894	TE SD US	6	SCC
1752	89	1894	TE DG US	6	SCC
1753	240	1894	RR 4-sft	6	SCC

Engine No.	Page Ref.	Date Built	Type	NHP	Cyl
1754	114	1894	PE Universal	14	SCC
1755	114	1894	PE Universal	14	SCC
1756	89	1894	TE DG US	6	SCC
1757	149	1894	RL SD SPR	8	SCC
1758	96	1894	TE SD SPR	6	SCC
1759	72	1894	TE 'T' SD US	6	SC
1760	101	1894	TE DG US	8	SCC
1761	89	1894	TE DG US	6	SCC
1762	76	1894	TE SD US	7	SC
1763	93	1894	TE SD US	6	SCC
1764	153	1894	RL SD SPR	6	SCC
1765	96	1894	TE SD SPR	6	SCC
1766	82	1894	TE DG US	8	SC
1767	118	1894	PORT	8	SC
1768	101	1894	TE DG US	8	SCC
1769	118	1894	PORT	16	Duplex
1770	103	1894	TE SD SPR	8	SCC
1771	96	1894	TE SD SPR	6	SCC
1772	89	1894	TE DG US	6	SCC
1773	93	1894	TE SD US	6	SCC
1774	118	1894	PORT	6	SC
1775	101	1894	TE DG US	8	SCC
1776	103	1894	TE SD SPR	8	SCC
1777	178	1894	SRL SD SPR	10	SCC
1778	76	1894	TE SD US	7	SC
1779	82	1894	TE DG US	8	SC
1780	93	1894	TE SD US	6	SCC
1781	82	1894	TE DG US	8	SC
1782	93	1894	TE SD US	6	SCC
1783	114	1894	PE Universal	20	SCC
1784	114	1894	PE Universal	20	SCC
1785	89	1894	TE DG US	6	SCC
1786	93	1894	TE SD US	6	SCC
1787	93	1894	TE SD US	6	SCC
1788	118	1894	PORT	8	SC
1789	89	1894	TE DG US	6	SCC
1790	149	1894	RL DG US	8	SCC
1791	82	1894	TE DG US	8	SC
1792	93	1894	TE SD US	6	SCC
1793	76	1894	TE SD US	7	SC
1794	234	1894	Spec. straw burner	8	SC
1795	89	1894	TE DG US	6	SCC
1796	177	1894	SRL SD SPR	8	SCC
1797	82	1894	TE DG US	8	SC
1798	96	1894	TE SD SPR	6	SCC
1799	93	1894	TE SD US	6	SCC
1800	93	1894	TE SD US	6	SCC
1801	96	1894	TE SD SPR	6	SCC
1802	114	1894	PE Universal	20	SCC
1803	114	1894	PE Universal	20	SCC
1804	76	1894	TE SD US	7	SC
1805	89	1895	TE DG US	6	SCC
1806	93	1894	TE SD US	6	SCC
1807	82	1894	TE DG US	8	SC
1808	76	1894	TE SD US	7	SC
1809	82	1894	TE DG US	8	SC
1810	177	1895	SRL SD SPR	8	SCC
1811	72	1894	TE 'T' SD US	6	SC
1812	93	1894	TE SD US	6	SCC
1813	89	1894	TE DG US	6	SCC
1814	101	1894	TE DG US	8	SCC
1815	93	1895	TE SD US	6	SCC
1816	93	1895	TE SD US	6	SCC
1817	149	1895	RL SD SPR	8	SCC
1818	93	1894	TE SD US	6	SCC
1819	177	1894	SRL SD SPR	8	SCC
1820	177	1895	SRL SD SPR	8	SCC
1821	150	1894	RL SD SPR	10	SCC
1822	93	1894	TE SD US	6	SCC
1823	89	1894	TE DG US	6	SCC
1824	249	1895	RR/TE	6	SCC
1825	153	1895	RL SD SPR	6	SCC
1826	82	1895	TE DG US	8	SC
1827	76	1895	TE SD US	7	SC
1828	89	1895	TE SD US	6	SCC
1829	93	1895	TE SD US	6	SCC
1830	89	1895	TE DG US	6	SCC
1831	89	1895	TE DG US	6	SCC
1832	93	1895	TE SD US	6	SCC
1833	82	1895	TE DG US	8	SC
1834	82	1895	TE DG US	8	SC
1835	101	1895	TE DG US	8	SCC
1836	241	1895	RR 10 ton	6	SCC
1837	93	1895	TE SD US	6	SCC
1838	82	1895	TE DG US	8	SC
1839	118	1895	PORT	8	SC
1840*	72	1895	TE 'T' SD US	6	SC
1841	153	1895	RL SD SPR	6	SCC
1842	118	1895	PORT	8	SC
1843	93	1895	TE SD US	6	SCC
1844	101	1895	TE DG US	8	SCC
1845	178	1895	SRL SD SPR	10	SCC
1846	93	1895	TE SD US	6	SCC
1847	76	1895	TE SD US	7	SC
1848	96	1895	TE SD SPR	6	SCC
1849	149	1896	RL SD SPR	8	SCC
1850	89	1895	TE DG US	6	SCC
1851	72	1895	TE 'T' SD US	6	SC
1852	119	1895	PORT	8	SCC
1853	118	1895	PORT	6	SC
1854	101	1895	TE DG US	8	SCC
1855	76	1895	TE SD US	7	SC
1856	76	1895	TE SD US	7	SC
1857	118	1895	PORT	6	SC
1858	93	1895	TE SD US	6	SCC
1859	101	1895	TE DG US	8	SCC
1860	93	1895	TE SD US	6	SCC
1861*	93	1895	TE SD US	6	SCC
1862	89	1895	TE DG US	6	SCC
1863	73	1895	TE 'T' SD SPR	6	SC
1864	76	1895	TE SD US	7	SC
1865	101	1895	TE DG US	8	SCC
1866	72	1896	TE 'T' SD US	6	SC
1867	250	1895	RR 10 ton	5	SC
1868	241	1895	RR 10 ton	6	SCC
1869	118	1895	PORT	6	SC
1870	149	1895	RL Com. DG US	8	SCC
1871	89	1895	TE DG US	6	SCC
1872	93	1895	TE SD US	6	SCC
1873	82	1895	TE DG US	8	SC
1874	93	1895	TE SD US	6	SCC
1875	76	1895	TE SD US	7	SC
1876*	178	1895	SRL SD SPR	10	SCC
1877	241	1895	RR 10 ton	6	SCC
1878	153	1895	RL SD SPR	6	SCC
1879	93	1895	TE SD US	6	SCC
1880	241	1895	RR 10 ton	6	SCC
1881	76	1895	TE SD SPR	7	SC
1882	82	1895	TE DG US	8	SC
1883	101	1895	TE DG US	8	SCC
1884	149	1895	RL SD SPR	8	SCC
1885	93	1895	TE SD US	6	SCC
1886	249	1895	RR/TE	6	SCC
1887	178	1895	SRL SD SPR	10	SCC
1888	178	1897	SRL SD SPR	10	SC
1889	118	1895	PORT	8	SC
1890	–	–	NO INFO	–	–
1891	93	1895	TE SD US	6	SCC
1892	150	1895	RL DG US	10	SCC
1893	128	1893	OTE	12	SC
1894	241	1895	RR/NW	6	SCC
1895	241	1895	RR/NW	6	SCC
1896	241	1896	RR/NW	6	SCC
1897	241	1896	RR/NW	6	SCC
1898	118	1896	PORT	6	SC
1899	82	1896	TE DG US	8	SC
1900	250	1896	RR 10 ton	5	SC
1901	241	1896	RR 10 ton	6	SCC
1902	149	1896	CRL SD SPR	8	SCC
1903	118	1895	PORT	8	SC
1904	241	1896	RR/NW	6	SCC
1905	177	1896	SRL SD SPR	8	SCC
1906	247	1896	RR/NW 16½ ton	7	SCC
1907	177	1896	SRL SD SPR	8	SCC
1908	178	1896	SRL SD SPR	10	SCC
1909	177	1896	SRL SD SPR	8	SCC
1910	177	1896	SRL SD SPR	8	SCC
1911	117	1896	PE Universal	16	SCC
1912	117	1896	PE Universal	16	SCC
1913	117	1896	PE Universal	16	SCC
1914	117	1896	PE Universal	16	SCC
1915	177	1896	SRL SD SPR	8	SCC
1916	93	1896	TE SD US	6	SCC
1917	82	1896	TE DG US	8	SC
1918	82	1896	TE DG US	8	SC
1919	89	1897	TE DG US	6	SCC
1920	82	1896	TE DG US	8	SC
1921	101	1896	TE DG US	8	SCC
1922	89	1896	TE DG US	6	SCC
1923	76	1896	TE SD US	7	SC
1924	82	1895	TE DG US	8	SC
1925	76	1896	TE SD US	7	SC
1926	241	1896	RR/NW	6	SCC
1927	89	1896	TE DG US	6	SCC
1928	93	1896	TE SD US	6	SCC
1929	101	1896	TE DG US	8	SCC
1930	93	1896	TE SD US	6	SCC
1931	96	1896	TE SD SPR	6	SCC
1932	241	1896	RR 10 ton	6	SCC
1933	93	1896	TE SD US	6	SCC
1934	127	1896	SRL(TC) SD SPR	6	SCC
1935	150	–	Became 1972	–	–
1936	76	1896	TE SD US	7	SC
1937	118	1896	PORT	8	SC
1938	103	1896	TE SD SPR	8	SCC
1939	247	1896	RR 'C' 16 ton	7	SCC
1940	82	1896	TE DG US	8	SC
1941*	70	1896	TE DG US	5	SC
1942	247	1896	RR 'C' 15 ton	7	SCC
1943	149	1896	RL(S) SD SPR	8	SCC
1944	82	1896	TE DG US	8	SC
1945*	93	1896	TE SD US	6	SCC
1946	82	1896	TE DG US	8	SC
1947	159	1896	RL SD SPR	10	DCC
1948	241	1896	RR/NW	6	SCC
1949	96	1896	TE SD SPR	6	SCC
1950	93	1896	TE SD US	6	SCC
1951	72	1896	TE 'T' SD US	6	SC
1952	249	1896	RR/TE	6	SCC
1953	149	1896	RL SD SPR	8	SCC
1954	73	1896	TE 'T' SD SPR	6	SC
1955	153	1896	RL SD SPR	6	SCC
1956	82	1896	TE DG US	8	SC
1957	103	1896	TE SD SPR	8	SCC
1958	241	1896	RR 10 ton	6	SCC
1959	101	1896	TE DG US	8	SCC
1960	249	1896	RR/TE	6	SCC
1961	153	1896	RL SD SPR	6	SCC
1962	93	1896	TE SD US	6	SCC
1963	93	1896	TE SD US	6	SCC
1964	249	1896	RR/TE	6	SCC
1965	241	1896	RR 10 ton	6	SCC
1966	93	1896	TE SD US	6	SCC
1967	149	1896	RL SD SPR	8	SCC
1968	93	1896	TE SD US	6	SCC
1969	241	1896	RR 10 ton	6	SCC
1970	76	1896	TE SD US	7	SC
1971	182	1897	SRL SD SPR	10	DCC
1972	159	1896	CRL SD SPR	10	DCC
1973	247	1896	RR 'C' 16 ton	7	SCC
1974	241	1896	RR 10 ton	6	SCC
1975	103	1896	TE SD SPR	8	SCC
1976	76	1897	TE SD US	7	SC
1977	93	1897	TE SD US	6	SCC
1978	96	1897	TE SD SPR	6	SCC
1979	242	1897	RR 10 ton	6	SCC
1980	182	1897	SRL SD SPR	10	DCC
1981	242	1897	RR/NW 13 ton	6	SCC
1982	241	1897	RR 10 ton	6	SCC
1983	93	1897	TE SD US	6	SCC
1984	242	1897	RR 13¾ ton	6	SCC
1985	177	1897	SRL SD SPR	8	SCC
1986	118	1897	PORT	8	SC
1987	247	1897	RR/NW 16 ton	7	SCC
1988	76	1897	TE SD SPR	7	SC
1989	118	1897	PORT	12	SC
1990	247	1897	RR/NW 18½ ton	7	SCC
1991	93	1897	TE SD US	6	SCC
1992	76	1897	TE SD US	7	SC
1993	178	1897	SRL SD SPR	8	SCC
1994	118	1897	PORT	8	SC
1995	91	1897	TE SD SPR	6	SCC
1996	242	1897	RR 10 ton	6	SCC
1997	183	1897	SRL SD SPR	10	DCC
1998	80	1897	TE SD SPR	8	SC
1999	188	1897	SRL SD SPR	8	DCC
2000	242	1897	RR 14½ ton	6	SCC
2001	247	1897	RR 'C' 17 ton	7	SCC
2002	73	1897	TE 'T' SD SPR	6	SC
2003*	93	1897	TE SD US	6	SCC
2004	119	1897	PORT	8	SCC
2005	214	1897	SRL SD SPR	6	SCC
2006	117	1897	PE Universal	16	SCC
2007	117	1897	PE Universal	16	SCC
2008	96	1897	TE DG US	6	SCC
2009	247	1897	RR 'C' 15 ton	7	SCC
2010	183	1897	SRL SD SPR	8	DCC
2011	149	1897	RL(S) SD SPR	8	SCC
2012	82	1897	TE DG US	8	SC
2013	82	1897	TE DG US	8	SC
2014	82	1897	TE DG US	8	SC
2015	76	1897	TE SD US	7	SC
2016	72	1897	TE 'T' SD US	6	SC
2017	150	1897	RL SD SPR	8	SCC
2018	114	1897	PE Universal	20	SCC
2019	114	1897	PE Universal	20	SCC
2020	242	1897	RR/NW 10 ton	6	SCC
2021	96	1897	TE DG US	6	SCC
2022	149	1897	RL(S) SD SPR	8	SCC
2023	242	1897	RR/NW 10 ton	6	SCC

Engine No.	Page Ref.	Date Built	Type	NHP	Cyl
2024	96	1897	TE DG US	6	SCC
2025	118	1897	PORT	8	SC
2026	82	1897	TE DG US	8	SC
2027	99	1897	TE DG US	7	SCC
2028	245	1898	RR 8 ton	6	SCC
2029	96	1897	TE DG US	6	SCC
2030	159	1897	CRL SD SPR	10	DCC
2031	90	1897	TE DG US	6	SCC
2032	82	1897	TE DG US	8	SC
2033	90	1897	TE DG US	6	SCC
2034	82	1897	TE DG US	8	SC
2035	159	1898	CRL SD SPR	10	DCC
2036	82	1897	TE DG US	8	SC
2037	242	1897	RR 12½ ton	6	SCC
2038	149	1897	RL SD SPR	8	SCC
2039	76	1897	TE SD SPR	7	SC
2040	247	1898	RR 'C' 15 ton	7	SCC
2041	159	1897	RL SD SPR	10	DCC
2042	100	1897	TE SD SPR	7	SCC
2043	82	1897	TE DG US	8	SC
2044	96	1897	TE DG US	6	SCC
2045	118	1897	PORT	8	SC
2046	74	1897	TE DG US	6	SC
2047	96	1897	TE DG US	6	SCC
2048	118	1897	PORT	8	SC
2049	242	1897	RR 10 ton	6	SCC
2050	118	1897	PORT	8	SC
2051	82	1897	TE DG US	8	SC
2052	153	1897	RL SD SPR	6	SCC
2053	152	1897	CRL DG SPR	6	SCC
2054	101	1898	TE(S) DG US	8	SCC
2055	159	1897	CRL(S) SD SPR	10	DCC
2056	96	1897	TE DG US	6	SCC
2057	167	1897	RL(S) SD SPR	8	DCC
2058	242	1897	RR 12½ ton	6	SCC
2059	119	1897	PORT	8	SCC
2060	101	1897	TE DG US	8	SCC
2061	99	1898	TE DG US	7	SCC
2062	167	1898	RL SD SPR	8	DCC
2063	76	1898	TE SD SPR	7	SC
2064	153	1898	RL SD SPR	6	SCC
2065	242	1898	RR/NW 10 ton	6	SCC
2066	96	1898	TE DG US	6	SCC
2067	188	1898	SRL SD SPR	8	DCC
2068	188	1898	SRL SD SPR	8	DCC
2069	162	1898	CRL SD SPR	14	DCC
2070	118	1898	PORT	8	SC
2071	101	1898	TE DG US	8	SCC
2072*	188	1898	SRL SD SPR	8	DCC
2073	247	1898	RR/NW 18½ ton	7	SCC
2074	76	1898	TE SD US	7	SC
2075	167	1898	RL SD SPR	8	DCC
2076	188	1898	SRL SD SPR	8	DCC
2077	149	1898	CRL SD SPR	8	SCC
2078	153	1898	RL SD SPR	6	SCC
2079	96	1898	TE DG US	6	SCC
2080	242	1898	RR 10 ton	6	SCC
2081	167	1898	RL(S)	8	DCC
2082	101	1898	TE DG US	8	SCC
2083	167	1898	RL SD SPR	8	DCC
2084	118	1898	PORT	6/7	SC
2085	242	1898	RR 10 ton	6	SCC
2086	96	1898	TE DG US	6	SCC
2087	96	1898	TE SD SPR	6	SCC
2088	167	1898	RL SD SPR	8	DCC
2089	99	1898	TE DG US	7	SCC
2090	242	1898	RR/NW 10 ton	6	SCC
2091	90	1898	TE DG US	6	SCC
2092	96	1898	TE DG US	6	SCC
2093*	82	1898	TE DG US	8	SC
2094	90	1898	TE DG US	6	SCC
2095	247	1898	RR/NW 18½ ton	7	SCC
2096	242	1898	RR 12½ ton	6	SCC
2097	242	1898	RR 14½ ton	6	SCC
2098	76	1898	TE SD US	7	SC
2099	101	1898	TE DG US	8	SCC
2100	76	1898	TE SD US	7	SC
2101	159	1898	RL SD SPR	10	DCC
2102	96	1898	TE SD SPR	6	SCC
2103	117	1898	PE Universal	16	SCC
2104	117	1898	PE Universal	16	SCC
2105	159	1898	RL SD SPR	10	DCC
2106	82	1898	TE DG US	8	SC
2107	101	1898	TE DG US	8	SCC
2108	99	1898	TE DG US	7	SCC
2109	247	1898	RR/NW 18½ ton	7	SCC
2110	242	1898	RR/NW 10 ton	6	SCC
2111	245	1898	RR 8 ton	6	SCC
2112*	74	1898	TE DG US	6	SC
2113	96	1898	TE DG US	6	SCC
2114	82	1898	TE DG US	8	SC
2115	74	1898	TE DG US	6	SC
2116	188	1898	SRL SD SPR	8	DCC
2117	249	1898	RR/TE	6	SCC
2118	118	1898	PORT	8	SC
2119	99	1898	TE DG US	7	SCC
2120	82	1898	TE DG US	8	SC
2121	74	1898	TE DG US	6	SC
2122	96	1898	TE SD SPR	6	SCC
2123	249	1898	RR/TE	6	SCC
2124	99	1898	TE DG US	7	SCC
2125	118	1898	PORT	8	SC
2126	153	1898	RL(S) SD SPR	6	SCC
2127	103	1898	TE SD SPR	8	SCC
2128	74	1898	TE DG US	6	SC
2129	99	1898	TE DG US	7	SCC
2130	103	1898	TE SD SPR	8	SCC
2131	96	1898	TE DG US	6	SCC
2132	118	1898	PORT	8	SC
2133	82	1898	TE DG US	8	SC
2134	159	1898	RL(S) SD SPR	10	DCC
2135	82	1898	TE DG US	8	SC
2136	82	1898	TE DG US	8	SC
2137	242	1898	RR 10 ton	6	SCC
2138	242	1898	RR 12½ ton	6	SCC
2139	100	1898	TE SD SPR	7	SCC
2140	82	1898	TE DG US	8	SC
2141	242	1898	RR/NW 10 ton	6	SCC
2142	74	1898	TE DG US	6	SC
2143	96	1898	TE DG US	6	SCC
2144	99	1899	TE DG US	7	SCC
2145	249	1898	RR/TE	6	SCC
2146	118	1898	PORT	8	SC
2147*	96	1898	TE SD SPR	6	SCC
2148	99	1898	TE DG US	7	SCC
2149	96	1898	TE DG US	6	SCC
2150	167	1898	SRL SD SPR	8	DCC
2151	242	1899	RR/NW 10 ton	6	SCC
2152	90	1898	TE DG US	6	SCC
2153	82	1898	TE DG US	8	SC
2154	242	1898	RR 10 ton	6	SCC
2155	96	1899	TE DG US	6	SCC
2156	96	1899	TE DG US	6	SCC
2157	242	1899	RR/NW	6	SCC
2158	77	1899	TE DG US	7	SC
2159*	77	1899	TE DG US	7	SC
2160	167	1899	RL SD SPR	8	DCC
2161	251	1899	RR	5	SC
2162	99	1899	TE DG US	7	SCC
2163	100	1899	TE SD SPR	7	SCC
2164	153	1899	RL SD SPR	6	SCC
2165	242	1899	RR 12½ ton	6	SCC
2166	150	1899	RL SD SPR	8	SCC
2167	96	1899	TE DG US	6	SCC
2168	242	1899	RR/NW 10 ton	6	SCC
2169	80	1899	TE SD SPR	8	SC
2170	188	1899	SRL SD SPR	8	DCC
2171	101	1899	TE(S) DG US	8	SCC
2172	74	1899	TE DG US	6	SC
2173	215	1899	SRL SD SPR	6	SCC
2174	242	1899	RR 14½ ton	6	SCC
2175	242	1899	RR 10 ton	6	SCC
2176	242	1899	RR 10 ton	6	SCC
2177	118	1899	PORT	4	SC
2178	101	1899	TE DG US	8	SCC
2179	101	1899	TE DG US	8	SCC
2180	100	1899	TE SD SPR	7	SCC
2181	96	1899	TE DG US	6	SCC
2182	101	1899	TE SD US	8	SCC
2183	82	1899	TE DG US	8	SC
2184	242	1899	RR/NW 10 ton	6	SCC
2185	90	1899	TE DG US	6	SCC
2186	82	1899	TE DG US	8	SC
2187	159	1899	RL SD SPR	10	DCC
2188	96	1899	TE DG US	6	SCC
2189*	100	1899	TE SD SPR	7	SCC
2190	100	1899	TE SD SPR	7	SCC
2191	99	1899	TE DG US	7	SCC
2192	220	1899	TE SD SPR	8	DCC
2193	242	1896	RR 10 ton	6	SCC
2194	167	1899	RL(S) SD SPR	8	DCC
2195	215	1899	SRL SD SPR	6	SCC
2196	90	1899	TE DG US	6	SCC
2197	77	1899	TE DG US	7	SC
2198	96	1899	TE DG US	6	SCC
2199	242	1899	RR/NW 10 ton	6	SCC
2200	242	1899	RR 10 ton	6	SCC
2201	82	1899	TE DG US	8	SC
2202	82	1899	TE DG US	8	SC
2203	74	1899	TE DG US	6	SC
2204	114	1899	PE Universal	20	SCC
2205	114	1899	PE Universal	20	SCC
2206	96	1899	TE DG US	6	SCC
2207	82	1899	TE DG US	8	SC
2208	74	1899	TE DG US	6	SC
2209	118	1899	PORT	7	SC
2210	118	1899	PORT	7	SC
2211	74	1899	TE DG US	6	SC
2212	99	1899	TE DG US	7	SCC
2213	118	1899	PORT	8	SC
2214	74	1899	TE DG US	6	SC
2215	82	1899	TE DG US	8	SC
2216	82	1899	TE DG US	8	SC
2217	101	1899	TE DG US	8	SCC
2218	99	1899	TE DG US	7	SCC
2219	96	1899	TE DG US	6	SCC
2220	100	1899	TE SD SPR	7	SCC
2221	96	1899	TE SD SPR	6	SCC
2222	188	1899	SRL SD SPR	8	DCC
2223	153	1899	RL(S) SD SPR	6	SCC
2224	162	1899	RL SD SPR	14	DCC
2225	118	1899	PORT	8	SC
2226	82	1899	TE DG US	8	SC
2227	100	1899	TE SD SPR	7	SCC
2228	–	–	Became 2200	–	–
2229	96	1899	TE DG US	6	SCC
2230	242	1899	RR/NW 10 ton	6	SCC
2231	82	1899	TE DG US	8	SC
2232	245	1899	RR 'A' 8 ton	6	SCC
2233	99	1899	TE DG US	7	SCC
2234	249	1899	RR/TE	6	SCC
2235	242	1899	RR/NW 10 ton	6	SCC
2236	99	1899	TE DG US	7	SCC
2237	242	1899	RR 10 ton	6	SCC
2238	242	1900	RR/NW 12½ ton	6	SCC
2239	153	1899	RL SD SPR	6	SCC
2240	247	1900	RR/NW 'C'	7	SCC
2241	96	1899	TE DG US	6	SCC
2242	242	1899	RR 12½ ton	6	SCC
2243	100	1899	TE SD SPR	7	SCC
2244	99	1899	TE DG US	7	SCC
2245	118	1899	PORT	6	SC
2246	99	1899	TE DG US	7	SCC
2247	167	1899	RL(S) SD SPR	8	DCC
2248	101	1900	TE DG US	8	SCC
2249	–	–	NO INFO	–	–
2250*	100	1899	TE SD SPR	7	SCC
2251	74	1899	TE DG US	6	SC
2252	103	1899	TE SD SPR	8	SCC
2253	249	1899	RR/TE	6	SCC
2254	96	1900	TE DG US	6	SCC
2255	101	1900	TE DG US	8	SCC
2256	99	1900	TE DG US	7	SCC
2257	99	1900	TE DG US	7	SCC
2258	245	1900	RR 'A' 10 ton	6	SCC
2259	242	1900	RR/NW 10 ton	6	SCC
2260	82	1900	TE DG US	8	SC
2261*	249	1900	RR/TE	6	SCC
2262	90	1900	TE DG US	6	SCC
2263	100	1900	TE(S) SD SPR	7	SCC
2264	96	1900	TE SD SPR	6	SCC
2265	118	1900	PORT	8	SC
2266	245	1900	RR 'A' 8 ton	6	SCC
2267	90	1900	TE DG US	6	SCC
2268	188	1900	SRL SD SPR	8	DCC
2269	242	1900	RR 10 ton	6	SCC
2270	103	1900	TE SD SPR	8	SCC
2271	101	1900	TE DG US	8	SCC
2272	118	1900	PORT	8	SC
2273	242	1900	RR 'B' 10 ton	6	SCC
2274	242	1900	RR 'B' 10 ton	6	SCC
2275	90	1900	TE DG US	6	SCC
2276	82	1900	TE DG US	8	SC
2277	82	1900	TE DG US	8	SC
2278	82	1900	TE DG US	8	SC
2279	155	1900	RL SD SPR	7	SCC
2280	167	1900	RL SD SPR	8	DCC
2281	167	1900	RL(S) SD SPR	8	DCC
2282	90	1900	TE DG US	6	SCC
2283	153	1900	RL SD SPR	6	SCC
2284	–	–	Became 2451	–	–
2285	230	1900	TE (D/T PE) DG US	10	SCC
2286	96	1900	TE DG US	6	SCC
2287	117	1900	PE Universal	16	SCC
2288	117	1900	PE Universal	16	SCC
2289	103	1900	TE SD SPR	8	SCC
2290	96	1900	TE SD SPR	6	SCC
2291	242	1900	RR 'B' 10 ton	6	SCC
2292	99	1900	TE DG US	7	SCC

Engine No.	Page Ref.	Date Built	Type	NHP	Cyl
2293	153	1900	RL SD SPR	6	SCC
2294	90	1900	TE DG US	6	SCC
2295	82	1900	TE DG US	8	SC
2296	82	1900	TE DG US	8	SC
2297	82	1900	TE DG US	8	SC
2298*	77	1900	TE DG US	7	SC
2299	96	1900	TE DG US	6	SCC
2300	96	1900	TE DG US	6	SCC
2301	100	1900	TE SD SPR	7	SCC
2302	100	1900	TE SD SPR	7	SCC
2303	118	1900	PORT	8	SC
2304	114	1900	PE Universal	20	SCC
2305	114	1900	PE Universal	20	SCC
2306	82	1900	TE DG US	8	SC
2307	90	1900	TE DG US	6	SCC
2308	96	1900	TE DG US	6	SCC
2309	90	1900	TE DG US	6	SCC
2310	99	1900	TE DG US	7	SCC
2311	99	1900	TE DG US	7	SCC
2312	91	1900	TE SD SPR	6	SCC
2313	77	1900	TE DG US	7	SC
2314	74	1900	TE DG US	6	SC
2315	242	1900	RR 'B' 10 ton	6	SCC
2316	245	1900	RR 'A' 8 ton	6	SCC
2317	99	1900	TE DG US	7	SCC
2318	90	1900	TE DG US	6	SCC
2319*	96	1900	TE DG US	6	SCC
2320	245	1900	RR 'A' 8 ton	6	SCC
2321	101	1900	TE DG US	8	SCC
2322	99	1900	TE DG US	7	SCC
2323	247	1900	RR/NW 'C'	7	SCC
2324	99	1900	TE DG US	7	SCC
2325	242	1900	RR 'B'	6	SCC
2326	101	1900	TE DG US	8	SCC
2327	103	1900	TE SD SPR	7/8	SCC
2328	245	1900	RR 'A' 8 ton	6	SCC
2329	96	1900	TE DG US	6	SCC
2330	96	1900	TE DG US	6	SCC
2331	82	1900	TE DG US	8	SC
2332	82	1900	TE DG US	8	SC
2333	90	1900	TE DG US	6	SCC
2334	105	1900	TE SD SPR	10	SCC
2335	99	1900	TE DG US	7	SCC
2336*	101	1900	TE DG US	8	SCC
2337	167	1900	RL SD SPR	8	DCC
2338	242	1900	RR 'B'	6	SCC
2339	153	1900	RL SD SPR	6	SCC
2340	96	1900	TE SD SPR	6	SCC
2341	99	1901	TE DG US	7	SCC
2342*	167	1900	RL SD SPR	8	DCC
2343	103	1900	TE SD SPR	8	SCC
2344	247	1900	RR 'C'	7	SCC
2345	167	1900	CRL SD SPR	8	DCC
2346	159	1900	RL SD SPR	10	DCC
2347	242	1901	RR/NW 'B'	6	SCC
2348	100	1901	TE SD SPR	7	SCC
2349	247	1901	RR/NW 'C'	7	SCC
2350	188	1901	SRL SD SPR	8	DCC
2351*	188	1901	SRL SD SPR	8	DCC
2352	159	1901	RL SD SPR	10	DCC
2353	242	1901	RR 'B'	6	SCC
2354	215	1901	SRL SD SPR	6	SCC
2355	188	1901	SRL SD SPR	8	DCC
2356	242	1901	RR/NW	6	SCC
2357	242	1901	RR/NW	6	SCC
2358	245	1901	RR 'A' 8 ton	6	SCC
2359	242	1901	RR/NW	6	SCC
2360	242	1901	RR/NW	6	SCC
2361	100	1901	TE SD SPR	7	SCC
2362	167	1901	RL SD SPR	8	DCC
2363*	118	1901	PORT	10	SCC
2364	153	1901	RL SD SPR	6	SCC
2365*	74	1901	TE DG US	6	SC
2366*	82	1901	TE DG US	8	SC
2367	103	1901	TE SD SPR	8	SCC
2368	118	1901	PORT	8	SC
2369	188	1901	SRL SD SPR	8	DCC
2370	167	1901	RL SD SPR	7/8	DCC
2371	114	1901	PE Universal	20	SCC
2372	114	1901	PE Universal	20	SCC
2373	242	1901	RR 'B'	6	SCC
2374	245	1901	RR 'A' 8 ton	6	SCC
2375	101	1901	TE DG US	8	SCC
2376	96	1901	TE DG US	6	SCC
2377	103	1901	TE SD SPR	8	SCC
2378	101	1901	TE DG US	8	SCC
2379	188	1901	SRL SD SPR	8	DCC
2380	100	1901	TE SD SPR	7	SCC
2381	114	1901	PE Universal	20	SCC
2382	114	1901	PE Universal	20	SCC
2383	96	1901	TE DG US	6	SCC
2384	242	1901	RR 'B'	6	SCC
2385	153	1901	RL SD SPR	6	SCC
2386*	99	1901	TE DG US	7	SCC
2387	167	1901	RL SD SPR	8	DCC
2388	90	1901	TE DG US	6	SCC
2389	103	1901	TE(S) SD SPR	8	SCC
2390	91	1901	TE SD SPR	6	SCC
2391	96	1901	TE DG US	6	SCC
2392	82	1901	TE DG US	8	SC
2393	82	1901	TE DG US	8	SC
2394	82	1901	TE DG US	8	SC
2395	242	1901	RR/NW 'B'	6	SCC
2396	101	1901	TE DG US	8	SCC
2397	76	1901	TE SD SPR	7	SC
2398	159	1901	RL SD SPR	10	DCC
2399	99	1901	TE DG US	7	SCC
2400	99	1901	TE DG US	7	SCC
2401	242	1901	RR 'B'	–	SCC
2402	77	1901	TE DG US	7	SC
2403	245	1901	RR 'A' 8 ton	6	SCC
2404	159	1901	RL SD SPR	10	DCC
2405	96	1891	TE DG US	6	SCC
2406*	74	1901	TE DG US	6	SC
2407	90	1901	TE DG US	6	SCC
2408	90	1901	TE DG US	6	SCC
2409	96	1901	TE DG US	6	SCC
2410	153	1901	RL SD SPR	6	SCC
2411	82	1901	TE DG US	8	SC
2412	74	1901	TE DG US	6	SC
2413	114	1901	PE Universal	20	SCC
2414	114	1901	PE Universal	20	SCC
2415	96	1901	TE DG US	6	SCC
2416	100	1901	TE SD SPR	7	SCC
2417*	249	1901	RR/TE	6	SCC
2418	96	1901	TE DG US	6	SCC
2419	101	1901	TE DG US	8	SCC
2420	99	1901	TE DG US	7	SCC
2421*	76	1901	TE SD SPR	7	SC
2422	90	1901	TE DG US	6	SCC
2423	100	1901	TE SD SPR	7	SCC
2424	91	1901	TE SD SPR	6	SCC
2425*	82	1901	TE DG US	8	SC
2426*	96	1901	TE SD SPR	6	SCC
2427	247	1901	RR/NW 'C'	7	SCC
2428	242	1901	RR 'B'	6	SCC
2429	101	1901	TE DG US	8	SCC
2430	150	1901	RL SD SPR	8	SCC
2431	153	1901	RL SD SPR	6	SCC
2432	–	1901	PORT	8	SC
2433	100	1901	TE SD SPR	7	SCC
2434	245	1901	RR 'A' 8 ton	6	SCC
2435	101	1901	TE DG US	8	SCC
2436	167	1901	RL SD SPR	8	DCC
2437	167	1901	RL SD SPR	8	DCC
2438	215	1901	SRL SD SPR	6	SCC
2439	99	1901	TE DG US	7	SCC
2440	167	1901	RL SD SPR	8	DCC
2441	74	1901	TE DG US	6	SC
2442	99	1901	TE DG US	7	SCC
2443	80	1901	TE SD SPR	8	SC
2444	167	1901	CRL SD SPR	8	DCC
2445	249	1901	RR/TE	7	SC
2446	159	1901	RL DG SPR	10	DCC
2447	242	1902	RR/NW 'B'	6	SCC
2448	242	1902	RR/NW 'B'	6	SCC
2449	96	1902	TE DG US	6	SCC
2450	167	1902	RL SD SPR	8	DCC
2451	96	1902	TE DG US	6	SCC
2452	159	1902	CRL SD SPR	10	DCC
2453	96	1902	TE DG US	6	SCC
2454	96	1902	TE DG US	6	SCC
2455	215	1902	SRL SD SPR	6	SCC
2456	188	1902	SRL SD SPR	8	DCC
2457	242	1902	RR/NW 'B'	6	SCC
2458	242	1902	RR/NW 'B'	6	SCC
2459	100	1902	TE SD SPR	7	SCC
2460	245	1902	RR 'A' 8 ton	6	SCC
2461	245	1902	RR 'A' 8 ton	6	SCC
2462	100	1902	TE(S) SD SPR	7	SCC
2463	188	1902	SRL SD SPR	8	DCC
2464	150	1902	RL SD SPR	8	SCC
2465	90	1902	TE DG US	6	SCC
2466	242	1902	RR/NW 'B'	6	SCC
2467	242	1902	RR 'B'	6	SCC
2468	159	1902	RL SD SPR	10	DCC
2469	80	1902	TE SD SPR	8	SC
2470	167	1902	RL SD SPR	8	DCC
2471	215	1902	SRL SD SPR	6	SCC
2472	167	1902	RL SD SPR	8	DCC
2473*	101	1902	TE(DIG) DG US	8	SCC
2474	96	1902	TE DG US	6	SCC
2475	100	1902	TE SD SPR	7	SCC
2476	99	1902	TE DG US	7	SCC
2477	114	1902	PE Universal	20	SCC
2478	114	1902	PE Universal	20	SCC
2479*	101	1902	TE DG US	8	SCC
2480	90	1902	TE DG US	6	SCC
2481	101	1902	TE DG US	8	SCC
2482	82	1902	TE DG US	8	SC
2483	101	1902	TE DG US	8	SCC
2484	101	1902	TE DG US	8	SCC
2485	82	1902	TE DG US	8	SC
2486	90	1902	TE DG US	6	SCC
2487	96	1902	TE DG US	6	SCC
2488	100	1902	TE SD SPR	7	SCC
2489	167	1902	RL SD SPR	8	DCC
2490	118	1902	PORT	8	SC
2491	245	1902	RR 'A' 8 ton	6	SCC
2492	96	1902	TE DG US	6	SCC
2493	153	1902	RL SD SPR	6	SCC
2494	118	1902	PORT	10	SCC
2495	96	1902	TE (S) SD SPR	6	SCC
2496	100	1902	TE SD SPR	7	SCC
2497	188	1902	SRL SD SPR	8	DCC
2498	159	1902	CRL SD SPR	10	DCC
2499	96	1902	TE DG US	6	SCC
2500	96	1902	TE DG US	6	SCC
2501	82	1902	TE DG US	8	SC
2502	82	1902	TE DG US	8	SC
2503	82	1902	TE DG US	8	SC
2504	96	1902	TE DG US	6	SCC
2505*	99	1902	TE DG US	7	SCC
2506	90	1902	TE DG US	6	SCC
2507*	77	1902	TE DG US	7	SC
2508	96	1902	TE DG US	6	SCC
2509	77	1902	TE DG US	7	SC
2510	101	1902	TE DG US	8	SCC
2511	99	1902	TE DG US	7	SCC
2512*	90	1902	TE DG US	6	SCC
2513*	90	1902	TE DG US	6	SCC
2514	99	1902	TE DG US	7	SCC
2515	159	1902	CRL SD SPR	10	DCC
2516	242	1902	RR/NW 'B'	6	SCC
2517	74	1902	TE DG US	6	SC
2518	96	1902	TE DG US	6	SCC
2519	249	1902	RR/TE	6	SCC
2520	100	1902	TE SD SPR	7	SCC
2521	99	1902	TE DG US	7	SCC
2522	242	1902	RR 'B'	6	SCC
2523	96	1902	TE SD SPR	6	SCC
2524	163	1902	CRL SD SPR	12	DCC
2525	77	1902	TE DG US	7	SC
2526	242	1902	RR/NW 'B'	6	SCC
2527	167	1902	RL SD SPR	8	DCC
2528	242	1902	RR 'B'	6	SCC
2529	249	1902	RR/TE	6	SCC
2530	82	1902	TE DG US	8	SC
2531	99	1902	TE DG US	7	SCC
2532	103	1902	TE SD SPR	8	SCC
2533	103	1902	TE SD SPR	8	SCC
2534	91	1902	TE DG US	6	SCC
2535	245	1902	RR 'A' 8 ton	6	SCC
2536*	96	1903	TE DG US	6	SCC
2537	167	1902	RL(S) SD SPR	8	DCC
2538	96	1902	TE DG US	6	SCC
2539	91	1902	TE DG US	6	SCC
2540	74	1902	TE DG US	6	SC
2541	159	1902	RL SD SPR	10	DCC
2542	159	1903	CRL SD SPR	10	DCC
2543	82	1902	TE DG US	8	SC
2544	96	1902	TE DG US	6	SCC
2545	96	1902	TE DG US	6	SCC
2546	101	1903	TE(DIG) DG US	8	SCC
2547*	167	1903	RL(S) SD SPR	8	DCC
2548	167	1903	RL DG SPR	8	DCC
2549	167	1903	RL SD SPR	8	DCC
2550	249	1903	RR/TE	6	SCC
2551	242	1903	RR 'B'	6	SCC
2552	118	1903	PORT	8	SC
2553	159	1903	CRL SD SPR	10	DCC
2554	82	1903	TE DG US	8	SC
2555	242	1903	RR/NW 'B'	6	SCC
2556	242	1903	RR/NW 'B'	6	SCC
2557	150	1903	RL SD SPR	10	SCC
2558*	245	1903	RR 'A' 8 ton	6	SCC
2559	163	1903	CRL SD SPR	12	DCC
2560	91	1903	TE DG US	6	SCC
2561	245	1903	RR 'A' 8 ton	6	SCC
2562	167	1903	RL(S) SD SPR	8	DCC

Engine No.	Page Ref.	Date Built	Type	NHP	Cyl
2563	247	1903	RR 'C'	7	SCC
2564	242	1903	RR/NW 'B'	6	SCC
2565	242	1903	RR/NW 'B'	6	SCC
2566	153	1903	RL(S) SD SPR	6	SCC
2567	77	1903	TE DG US	7	SC
2568	114	1903	PE Universal	20	SCC
2569	114	1903	PE Universal	20	SCC
2570	242	1903	RR 'B'	6	SCC
2571	167	1903	RL SPR	8	DCC
2572	91	1903	TE DG US	6	SCC
2573	96	1903	TE SD SPR	6	SCC
2574	103	1903	TE SD SPR	8	SCC
2575*	96	1903	TE SD SPR	6	SCC
2576	167	1903	RL SD SPR	8	DCC
2577	91	1903	TE DG US	6	SCC
2578	99	1903	TE DG US	7	SCC
2579	91	1903	TE SD SPR	6	SCC
2580	245	1903	RR 'A' 8 ton	6	SCC
2581	77	1903	TE DG US	7	SC
2582	77	1903	TE DG US	7	SC
2583	101	1903	TE DG US	8	SCC
2584	167	1903	RL(S) SD SPR	8	DCC
2585	82	1903	TE DG US	8	SC
2586	96	1903	TE DG US	6	SCC
2587	91	1903	TE DG US	6	SCC
2588	242	1904	RR 'B'	6	SCC
2589	242	1903	RR 'B'	6	SCC
2590	96	1903	TE DG US	6	SCC
2591	247	1903	RR/NW 'C'	7	SCC
2592	100	1903	TE SD SPR	7	SCC
2593	167	1903	RL(S) SD SPR	8	DCC
2594	74	1903	TE DG US	6	SC
2595	242	1903	RR/NW 'B'	6	SCC
2596	232	1903	TE DG US	10	DCC
2597	99	1903	TE DG US	7	SCC
2598	77	1903	TE DG US	7	SC
2599	91	1903	TE DG US	6	SCC
2600	103	1903	TE SD SPR	8	SCC
2601	104	1903	TE DG SPR	8	SCC
2602*	104	1903	TE DG SPR	8	SCC
2603	104	1903	TE DG SPR	8	SCC
2604	91	1903	TE DG US	6	SCC
2605	99	1903	TE DG US	7	SCC
2606	91	1903	TE DG US	6	SCC
2607	99	1903	TE DG US	7	SCC
2608	82	1903	TE DG US	8	SC
2609	91	1903	TE DG US	6	SCC
2610	82	1903	TE DG US	8	SC
2611	91	1903	TE DG US	6	SCC
2612	96	1903	TE SD SPR	6	SCC
2613*	74	1903	TE DG US	6	SC
2614	77	1903	TE DG US	7	SC
2615	96	1903	TE DG US	6	SCC
2616	103	1903	TE SD SPR	8	SCC
2617	91	1903	TE DG US	6	SCC
2618	220	1903	TE DG SPR	7	DCC
2619	220	1903	TE DG SPR	7	DCC
2620	82	1903	TE DG US	8	SC
2621	98	1903	TE DG SPR	6	SCC
2622	101	1903	TE DG US	8	SCC
2623*	245	1903	RR 'A' 8 ton	6	SCC
2624	91	1903	TE DG US	6	SCC
2625*	215	1904	SRL SD SPR	7	DCC
2626*	249	1903	RR/TE	6	SCC
2627	82	1903	TE DG US	8	SC
2628	104	1903	TE DG SPR	8	SCC
2629	82	1903	TE DG US	8	SC
2630	99	1903	TE DG US	7	SCC
2631	188	1903	SRL SD SPR	8	DCC
2632	82	1903	TE DG US	8	SC
2633	220	1903	TE(S) SD SPR	7	DCC
2634	82	1903	TE DG US	8	SC
2635	101	1903	TE DG SPR	7	SCC
2636*	220	1903	TE DG SPR	8	DCC
2637	82	1903	TE DG US	8	SC
2638	220	1903	TE DG US	8	DCC
2639	220	1903	TE DG SPR	8	DCC
2640	159	1904	CRL SD SPR	10	DCC
2641	159	1904	CRL SD SPR	10	DCC
2642*	242	1904	RR 'B'	6	SCC
2643	174	1904	RL SD SPR	7	DCC
2644*	91	1904	TE DG US	6	SCC
2645	91	1904	TE DG US	6	SCC
2646*	155	1904	RL SD SPR	7	SCC
2647	174	1904	RL DG SPR	7	DCC
2648	103	1904	TE SD SPR	8	SCC
2649*	242	1904	RR 'B'	6	SCC
2650	188	1904	SRL SD SPR	8	DCC
2651*	188	1904	SRL SD SPR	8	DCC
2652	217	1904	SRL SD SPR	6	DCC
2653	242	1904	RR/NW 'B'	6	SCC
2654	242	1904	RR/NW 'B'	6	SCC
2655	242	1904	RR/NW 'B'	6	SCC
2656	245	1904	RR 'A' 8 ton	6	SCC
2657	167	1904	RL SD SPR	8	DCC
2658	242	1904	RR/NW 'B'	6	SCC
2659	101	1904	TE DG SPR	7	SCC
2660	167	1904	RL SD SPR	8	DCC
2661	150	1904	RL 4-sft SD SPR	10	SCC
2662*	96	1904	TE DG US	6	SCC
2663	96	1904	TE DG US	6	SCC
2664	77	1904	TE DG US	7	SC
2665	96	1904	TE DG US	6	SCC
2666	91	1904	TE DG US	6	SCC
2667	–	–	Became 2735	–	–
2668*	188	1904	SRL SD SPR	8	DCC
2669	82	1904	TE DG US	8	SC
2670	–	–	Became 2829	–	–
2671	91	1904	TE DG US	6	SCC
2672	101	–	Became 2755	–	–
2673	77	1904	TE DG US	7	SC
2674	99	1904	TE DG US	7	SCC
2675	153	1904	RL SD SPR	6	SCC
2676	167	1904	RL SD SPR	8	DCC
2677	217	1904	SRL SD SPR	6	DCC
2678	117	1904	PE Universal	16	SCC
2679	117	1904	PE Universal	16	SCC
2680	–	–	Became 2753	–	–
2681	104	1904	TE DG SPR	8	SCC
2682	100	1904	TE SD SPR	7	SCC
2683	247	1904	RR/NW 'C'	7	SCC
2684	96	1904	TE DG US	6	SCC
2685	74	1904	TE DG US	6	SC
2686	104	1904	TE DG SPR	8	SCC
2687	104	1904	TE DG SPR	8	SCC
2688	104	1904	TE DG SPR	8	SCC
2689	104	1904	TE DG SPR	8	SCC
2690	172	1904	RL(S) SD SPR	6	DCC
2691	–	–	Became 2749	–	–
2692	245	1904	RR 'A' 8 ton	6	SCC
2693*	99	1904	TE DG US	7	SCC
2694	82	1904	TE DG US	8	SC
2695	82	1904	TE DG US	8	SC
2696*	221	1904	TE DG SPR	8	DCC
2697	104	1904	TE DG SPR	8	SCC
2698	221	1904	TE DG SPR	8	DCC
2699	99	1904	TE DG US	7	SCC
2700	96	1904	TE DG US	6	SCC
2701*	167	1904	RL(S) SD SPR	8	DCC
2702	245	1904	RR 'A' 8 ton	6	SCC
2703	167	1904	RL SD SPR	8	DCC
2704	174	1904	RL DG SPR	7	DCC
2705	172	1904	RL SD SPR	6	DCC
2706*	91	1904	TE DG US	6	SCC
2707	99	1904	TE DG US	7	SCC
2708	249	1904	RR/TE	6	SCC
2709	188	1904	SRL SD SPR	8	DCC
2710	–	–	Became 2739	–	–
2711	104	1904	TE DG SPR	8	SCC
2712	172	1904	RL SD SPR	6	DCC
2713	188	1904	SRL SD SPR	8	DCC
2714	217	1904	SRL SD SPR	6	DCC
2715	91	1904	TE DG US	6	SCC
2716	188	1904	SRL SD SPR	8	DCC
2717	245	1904	RR 'A' 8 ton	6	SCC
2718	74	1905	TE DG US	6	SC
2719	242	1905	RR/NW 'B'	6	SCC
2720	242	1905	RR/NW 'B'	6	SCC
2721	188	1905	SRL SD SPR	8	DCC
2722	188	1905	SRL SD SPR	8	DCC
2723	188	1905	SRL SD SPR	8	DCC
2724	188	1905	SRL SD SPR	8	DCC
2725	245	1905	RR 'A' 8 ton	6	SCC
2726	245	1905	RR/NW	6	SCC
2727	242	1905	RR/NW 'B'	6	SCC
2728	100	1905	TE SD SPR	7	SCC
2729	245	1905	RR 'A' 8 ton	6	SCC
2730	245	1905	RR 'A' 8 ton	6	SCC
2731	91	1905	TE DG US	6	SCC
2732	96	1905	TE DG US	6	SCC
2733	188	1905	SRL SD SPR	8	DCC
2734	242	1905	RR/NW 'B'	6	SCC
2735	91	1905	TE DG US	6	SCC
2736	172	1905	RL SD SPR	6	DCC
2737	96	1905	TE DG US	6	SCC
2738	99	1905	TE DG US	7	SCC
2739	91	1905	TE DG US	6	SCC
2740	188	1905	SRL SD SPR	8	DCC
2741	74	1905	TE DG US	6	SC
2742	97	1905	TE DG SPR	6	SCC
2743	77	1905	TE DG US	7	SC
2744	188	1905	SRL SD SPR	8	DCC
2745	82	1905	TE DG US	8	SC
2746	172	1906	RL(S) SD SPR	6	SC
2747	104	1906	TE DG SPR	8	SCC
2748	251	1905	RR/NW	6	SC
2749	82	1905	TE DG US	8	SC
2750	100	1905	TE SD SPR	7	SCC
2751	77	1905	TE DG US	7	SC
2752	–	–	Became 2829	–	–
2753	118	1908	PORT	10	SCC
2754	–	–	Became 2807	–	–
2755	82	1905	TE DG US	8	SC
2756	245	1905	RR 'A' 8 ton	6	SCC
2757	104	1905	TE DG SPR	8	SCC
2758	118	1905	PORT	8	SC
2759	188	1905	SRL SD SPR	8	DCC
2760	–	–	Became 2828	–	–
2761	101	1905	TE DG US	8	SCC
2762	82	1905	TE DG US	8	SC
2763	82	1905	TE DG US	8	SC
2764*	221	1905	TE DG SPR	8	DCC
2765	245	1905	RR 'A' 8 ton	6	DCC
2766	99	1905	TE DG US	7	SCC
2767*	96	1905	TE DG US	6	SCC
2768	159	1905	RL SD SPR	10	DCC
2769	245	1905	RR 'A' 8 ton	6	SCC
2770	96	1905	TE SD SPR	6	SCC
2771	129	1905	UTE	20	DCC
2772	77	1905	TE DG US	7	SC
2773	250	1905	RR 'A'	5	SC
2774	75	1905	TE DG SPR	6	SC
2775	75	1905	TE DG SPR	6	SC
2776	99	1905	TE DG US	7	SCC
2777	245	1905	RR 'A' 8 ton	6	SCC
2778	221	1905	TE DG SPR	8	DCC
2779	165	1905	RL SD SPR	8	DCC
2780*	183	1905	SRL SD SPR	8	DCC
2781	100	1905	TE SD SPR	7	SCC
2782	74	1905	TE DG US	6	SC
2783	174	1906	RL SD SPR	7	DCC
2784	77	1905	TE DG US	7	SC
2785	91	1905	TE DG US	6	SCC
2786	99	1905	TE DG US	7	SCC
2787	256	–	Became 2805	–	–
2788*	183	1906	SRL SD SPR	8	DCC
2789*	183	1905	SRL SD SPR	8	DCC
2790	249	1905	RR/TE	6	SCC
2791	99	1906	TE DG US	7	SCC
2792	249	1906	RR/TE	6	SCC
2793	183	1906	SRL SD SPR	8	DCC
2794	242	1906	RR/NW 'B'	6	SCC
2795	91	1906	TE DG US	6	SCC
2796	183	1906	RL(S) SD SPR	8	DCC
2797	256	1906	TR 5T	4	SC
2798	97	1906	TE(S) DG SPR	6	SCC
2799	97	1906	TE(S) DG SPR	6	SCC
2800	104	1906	TE DG SPR	8	SCC
2801	183	1906	SRL SD SPR	8	DCC
2802	257	1906	STR 5T	4	DCC
2803	257	1906	STR 5T	4	DCC
2804*	183	1906	SRL SD SPR	8	DCC
2805	256	1909	TR (2787) 5T	4	SC
2806	217	1906	SRL SD SPR	6	DCC
2807	91	1906	TE DG US	6	SCC
2808	259	–	Became 2996	–	–
2809	245	1906	RR 'A' 8 ton	6	SCC
2810	82	1906	TE DG US	8	SC
2811	96	1906	TE DG US	6	SCC
2812	165	1906	RL DG SPR	8	DCC
2813	245	1906	RR 'A' 8 ton	6	SCC
2814	114	1906	PE Universal	20	SCC
2815	114	1906	PE Universal	20	SCC
2816	91	1906	TE DG US	6	SCC
2817	74	1906	TE DG US	6	SC
2818	183	1906	SRL DG SPR	8	DCC
2819*	100	1906	TE SD SPR	7	SCC
2820	77	1906	TE DG US	7	SC
2821	96	1906	TE DG US	6	SCC
2822	82	1906	TE DG US	8	SC
2823	245	1906	RR 'A' 8 ton	6	SCC
2824*	174	1906	RL DG SPR	7	DCC
2825	165	1906	RL SD SPR	8	DCC
2826	99	1906	TE DG US	7	SCC
2827	172	1906	RL SD SPR	6	DCC
2828	–	–	Became 2838	–	–
2829	242	1906	RR 'B'	6	SCC
2830	259	1906	TR 5T	4	DCC
2831	259	1906	TR 5T	4	DCC
2832	242	1906	RR/NW 'B'	6	SCC

Engine No.	Page Ref.	Date Built	Type	NHP	Cyl
2833	78	1906	TE DG SPR	7	SC
2834	97	1907	TE DG SPR	6	SCC
2835	82	1906	TE DG US	8	SC
2836	99	1906	TE DG US	7	SCC
2837	118	1906	PORT	8	SC
2838	91	1906	TE DG US	6	SCC
2839	245	1906	RR 'A' 8 ton	6	SCC
2840	82	1906	TE DG US	8	SC
2841	174	1906	RL DG SPR	7	DCC
2842	259	1906	TR 5T	4	DCC
2843	96	1906	TE DG US	6	SCC
2844	253	1906	RR/NW 'C'	7	SC
2845	104	1906	TE(S) DG SPR	8	SCC
2846	91	1906	TE DG US	6	SCC
2847	259	1906	TR 5T	4	DCC
2848	73	1906	TE 'T' SD SPR	6	SC
2849	245	1906	RR 'A' 8 ton	6	SCC
2850	222	1906	TE DG SPR	6	DCC
2851	104	1906	TE DG SPR	8	SCC
2852	221	1906	TE DG SPR	8	DCC
2853	98	1906	TE DG SPR	6	SCC
2854	222	1906	TE DG SPR	6	DCC
2855*	82	1906	TE DG US	8	SC
2856	100	1906	TE SD SPR	7	SCC
2857	98	1906	TE DG SPR	6	SCC
2858	245	1906	RR 'A' 8 ton	6	SCC
2859	104	1906	TE DG SPR	8	SCC
2860	97	1907	TE DG SPR	6	SCC
2861	259	1906	TR 5T	4	DCC
2862	118	1906	PORT	6	SC
2863	245	1906	RR 'A'	6	SCC
2864	91	1906	TE SD US	6	SCC
2865	174	1906	RL DG SPR	7	DCC
2866	259	1906	TR 5T	4	DCC
2867	165	1907	RL(S) SD SPR	8	DCC
2868	217	1906	SRL SD SPR	6	DCC
2869	104	1906	TE DG SPR	8	SCC
2870	259	1906	TR 5T	4	DCC
2871	165	1907	RL(S) SD SPR	8	DCC
2872	91	1906	TE DG US	6	SCC
2873	99	1906	TE DG US	7	SCC
2874	217	1906	SRL DG SPR	6	DCC
2875	104	1906	TE(S)	8	SCC
2876*	259	1907	TR 5T	4	DCC
2877*	188	1907	SRL DG SPR	8	DCC
2878	221	1907	TE DG SPR	8	DCC
2879*	217	1907	SRL SD SPR	7	DCC
2880	259	1907	STR 5T	4	DCC
2881	259	1907	STR 5T	4	DCC
2882	259	1907	TR 5T	4	DCC
2883	259	1907	TR 5T	4	DCC
2884	–	–	Became 3004	–	–
2885	259	1907	TR 5T	4	DCC
2886*	221	1907	TE DG SPR	8	DCC
2887	247	1907	RR 'C'	7	SCC
2888	242	1907	RR 'B' 14 ton	6	SCC
2889	117	1907	PE Universal	16	SCC
2890	117	1907	PE Universal	16	SCC
2891	251	1907	RR/NW	6	SC
2892	251	1907	RR/NW	6	SC
2893	91	1907	TE DG US	6	SCC
2894*	188	1907	SRL DG SPR	8	DCC
2895	242	1907	RR/NW 'B'	6	SCC
2896*	253	1907	RR 'A'	5	DCC
2897	104	1907	TE DG SPR	8	SCC
2898	188	1908	SRL DG SPR	8	DCC
2899	259	1907	TR 5T	4	DCC
2900	249	1907	RR/TE	6	SCC
2901	101	1907	TE DG SPR	7	SCC
2902	234	1907	TE 'Colonist' DG SPR	5	SCC
2903	96	1907	TE SD SPR	6	SCC
2904	259	1907	TR 5T	4	DCC
2905	91	1907	TE DG US	6	SCC
2906	96	1907	TE DG US	6	SCC
2907	172	1907	RL	6	DCC
2908	91	1907	TE DG US	6	SCC
2909*	91	1907	TE SD SPR	6	SCC
2910	82	1907	TE DG US	8	SC
2911	114	1907	PE Universal	20	SCC
2912	114	1907	PE Universal	20	SCC
2913	259	–	Became 3119	–	–
2914	99	1907	TE DG US	7	SCC
2915	245	1907	RR 'A' 10¼ ton	6	SCC
2916	245	1907	RR 'A' 10¼ ton	6	SCC
2917	188	1907	SRL DG SPR	8	DCC
2918	77	1907	TE DG US	7	SC
2919	220	1907	TE DG SPR	7	DCC
2920	220	1907	TE DG SPR	7	DCC
2921*	101	1907	TE DG SPR	7	SCC
2922	253	1907	RR 8 ton	4	DCC
2923	253	1907	RR 8 ton	4	DCC
2924	220	1907	TE DG SPR	7	DCC
2925	259	1907	TR 5T	4	DCC
2926	82	1907	TE DG US	8	SC
2927	98	1907	TE DG SPR	6	SCC
2928	242	1907	RR/NW 'B'	6	SCC
2929	259	1907	TR 5T	4	DCC
2930	98	1907	TE DG SPR	6	SCC
2931	98	1907	TE DG SPR	6	SCC
2932	259	1908	TR 5T	4	DCC
2933*	97	1907	TE DG SPR	6	SCC
2934	251	1907	RR/NW	6	SC
2935	253	1907	RR 8 ton	4	DCC
2936	220	1907	TE DG US	7	DCC
2937	150	1907	RL DG SPR	8	SCC
2938	82	1907	TE DG US	8	SC
2939	221	1907	TE DG SPR	8	DCC
2940	221	1907	TE DG SPR	8	DCC
2941	221	1907	TE DG SPR	8	DCC
2942	91	1907	TE DG SPR	6	SCC
2943	101	1907	TE DG SPR	7	SCC
2944	91	1907	TE DG SPR	6	SCC
2945	234	1907	TE 'Colonist' DG SPR	5	SC
2946	101	1907	TE DG SPR	7	SCC
2947	99	1907	TE DG US	7	SCC
2948*	82	1907	TE DG US	8	SC
2949	220	1907	TE DG SPR	7	DCC
2950*	91	1907	TE DG US	6	SCC
2951	77	1907	TE DG US	7	SC
2952	96	1907	TE DG US	6	SCC
2953	77	1907	TE DG US	7	SC
2954	247	1907	RR/NW 'C'	7	SCC
2955	259	1907	TR 5T	4	DCC
2956	82	1907	TE DG US	8	SC
2957	221	1907	TE DG SPR	8	DCC
2958	247	1907	RR/NW 'C'	7	SCC
2959	101	1907	TE DG SPR	7	SCC
2960	174	1907	RL DG SPR	7	DCC
2961	99	1907	TE DG US	7	SCC
2962	249	1907	RR 8 ton	5	SC
2963*	77	1908	TE DG US	7	SC
2964	91	1907	TE DG US	6	SCC
2965	96	1907	TE DG US	6	SCC
2966	220	1907	TE DG SPR	7	DCC
2967	247	1908	RR/NW 'C'	7	SCC
2968	247	1908	RR/NW 'C'	7	SCC
2969	251	1908	RR/NW	6	SC
2970	242	1908	RR/NW 'B'	6	SCC
2971	247	1908	RR/NW 'C'	7	SCC
2972	247	1908	RR/NW	7	SCC
2973	242	1908	RR 'B'	6	SCC
2974	247	1908	RR/NW	7	SCC
2975	259	1908	TR WD 5T	4	DCC
2976	259	1908	TR WD 5T	4	DCC
2977	259	1908	TR 5T	4	DCC
2978	259	1908	TR 5T	4	DCC
2979	188	1908	Became 3038	–	–
2980	242	1908	RR 'B'	6	SCC
2981	234	1908	TE SD US	5	SC
2982	259	1908	STR 5T	4	DCC
2983	188	1908	SRL DG SPR	8	DCC
2984	217	1908	SRL DG SPR	7	DCC
2985	83	1908	TE DG SPR	8	SC
2986	172	1908	RL(S) DG SPR	6	DCC
2987	220	1908	TE DG SPR	7	DCC
2988	188	1908	SRL DG SPR	8	DCC
2989	146	1908	RL DG SPR	8	SC
2990	234	1908	TE 'Colonist' DG US	5	SC
2991	242	1908	RR 'B' 14 ton	6	SCC
2992	114	1908	PE Universal	20	SCC
2993	114	1908	PE Universal	20	SCC
2994	–	–	Became 3109	–	–
2995	91	1908	TE DG US	6	SCC
2996	259	1906	TR (2808) 5T	4	DCC
2997	146	1908	RL DG SPR	8	SC
2998	245	1908	RR 'A' 10 ton	6	SCC
2999	91	1908	TE DG US	6	SCC
3000	99	1908	TE DG US	7	SCC
3001	82	1908	TE DG US	8	SC
3002	101	1908	TE DG SPR	7	SCC
3003	96	1908	TE DG US	6	SCC
3004	258	1908	TR 4¾ ton	4	DCC
3005	78	1908	TE DG SPR	7	SC
3006	–	–	Became 3057	–	–
3007	217	1908	SRL DG SPR	7	DCC
3008	222	1908	TE DG SPR	6	DCC
3009	156	1908	RL DG SPR	7	SCC
3010	91	1910	TE DG US	6	SCC
3011	82	1908	TE DG US	8	SC
3012	251	1908	RR/NW	6	SC
3013	242	1908	RR/NW 'B'	6	SCC
3014	97	1908	TE DG SPR	6	SCC
3015	188	1908	SRL DG SPR	8	DCC
3016	245	1908	RR 'A' 10 ton	6	SCC
3017*	96	1908	TE DG US	6	SCC
3018	245	1908	RR 'A' 10 ton	6	SCC
3019	165	1908	RL(S) DG SPR	8	DCC
3020	222	1908	TE DG SPR	6	DCC
3021	245	1908	RR/NW 10 ton	6	SCC
3022	114	1908	PE Universal	20	SCC
3023	114	1908	PE Universal	20	SCC
3024	101	1908	TE DG SPR	7	SCC
3025	78	1908	TE DG SPR	7	SC
3026	83	1908	TE DG SPR	8	SC
3027	91	1908	TE DG SPR	6	SCC
3028	259	1908	TR 5T	4	DCC
3029	91	1908	TE DG SPR	6	SCC
3030	222	1908	TE DG SPR	6	DCC
3031	91	1908	TE DG US	6	SCC
3032	82	1908	TE DG US	8	SC
3033*	221	1908	TE DG SPR	8	DCC
3034*	96	1908	TE DG US	6	SCC
3035	91	1908	TE DG US	6	SCC
3036*	96	1908	TE DG US	6	SCC
3037	259	1909	TR 5T	4	DCC
3038	188	1908	SRL DG SPR	8	DCC
3039	82	1908	TE DG US	8	SC
3040	222	1908	TE DG SPR	6	DCC
3041	256	1908	TR 5T	4	SC
3042	75	1908	TE DG SPR	6	SC
3043	101	1903	TE DG SPR	7	SCC
3044	–	–	Became 3108	–	–
3045	220	1908	TE DG SPR	7	DCC
3046	104	1908	TE DG SPR	8	SCC
3047*	253	1908	RR 'A' 10 ton	5	DCC
3048*	99	1908	TE DG US	7	SCC
3049	82	1908	TE DG US	8	SC
3050*	104	1908	TE DG SPR	8	SCC
3051*	82	1908	TE DG US	8	SC
3052	99	1908	TE DG US	7	SCC
3053	234	1908	S.America S.B.	12	SC
3054	91	1908	TE DG SPR	6	SCC
3055	74	1908	TE DG US	6	SC
3056	–	–	Became 3107	–	–
3057*	174	1908	RL DG SPR	7	DCC
3058	146	1908	RL DG SPR	8	SC
3059	82	1908	TE DG US	8	SC
3060	222	1908	TE DG SPR	6	DCC
3061	223	1908	TE DG US	6	DCC
3062	249	1909	RR/TE	6	SCC
3063	217	1909	SRL DG SPR	6	DCC
3064	259	1908	TR 5T	4	DCC
3065	99	1908	TE DG US	7	SCC
3066	98	1908	TE DG SPR	6	SCC
3067	99	1908	TE DG US	7	SCC
3068*	77	1909	TE DG US	7	SC
3069	251	1908	RR/NW	6	SC
3070	242	1908	RR/NW 'B'	6	SCC
3071	91	1909	TE DG US	6	SCC
3072	188	1909	SRL DG SPR	8	DCC
3073	223	1909	TE DG SPR	6	DCC
3074	220	1909	TE DG SPR	7	DCC
3075*	188	1909	SRL DG SPR	8	DCC
3076	242	1909	RR/NW 'B'	6	SCC
3077	242	1909	RR/NW 'B'	6	SCC
3078	217	1909	SRL DG SPR	7	DCC
3079	82	1909	TE DG US	8	SC
3080	242	1909	RR/NW 'B'	6	SCC
3081	217	1909	SRL DG SPR	7	DCC
3082	91	1909	TE DG SPR	6	SCC
3083	242	1909	RR/NW 14 ton	6	SCC
3084	247	1909	RR/NW 'C'	7	SCC
3085	245	1909	RR 'A' 12 ton	6	SCC
3086	259	1909	TR 5T	4	DCC
3087	101	1909	TE DG SPR	7	SCC
3088	217	1909	SRL DG SPR	7	DCC
3089	217	1909	SRL DG SPR	7	DCC
3090*	215	1909	SRL DG SPR	5	DCC
3091	242	1909	RR 'B'	6	SCC
3092*	92	1909	TE 'Irish' DG US	5	SCC
3093*	188	1909	SRL DG SPR	8	DCC
3094	114	1909	PE Universal	20	SCC
3095	114	1909	PE Universal	20	SCC
3096	242	1909	RR/NW 'B'	6	SCC
3097	242	1909	RR/NW 'B'	6	SCC
3098*	172	1909	RL DG SPR	6	DCC
3099	245	1909	RR 'A' 10 ton	6	SCC

Engine No.	Page Ref.	Date Built	Type	NHP	Cyl
3100	78	1909	TE DG SPR	7	SC
3101	245	1909	RR/NW 10 ton	6	SCC
3102	259	1909	TR 5T	4	DCC
3103*	172	1909	RL(S)	6	DCC
3104	242	1909	RR 'B'	6	SCC
3105	259	1909	TR 5T	4	DCC
3106*	82	1909	TE DG US	8	SC
3107	98	1909	TE DG SPR	6	SCC
3108	91	1909	TE DG US	6	SCC
3109	258	1909	TR 4¾ ton	4	DCC
3110	–	–	Became 3185	–	–
3111	77	1909	TE DG US	7	SC
3112*	99	1909	TE DG US	7	SCC
3113	259	1909	TR 5T	4	DCC
3114	82	1909	TE DG US	8	SC
3115	242	1909	RR 'B'	6	SCC
3116	91	1909	TE DG US	6	SCC
3117	91	1907	TE DG US	6	SCC
3118*	174	1909	RL(S) DG SPR	7	DCC
3119	259	1907	TR (2913) 5T	4	DCC
3120	245	1909	RR 'A' 10¼ ton	6	SCC
3121*	82	1909	TE DG US	8	SC
3122	259	1909	TR 5T	4	DCC
3123	98	1909	TE DG SPR	6	SCC
3124	78	1909	TE DG SPR	7	SC
3125*	96	1908	TE DG US	6	SCC
3126*	98	1909	TE DG SPR	6	SCC
3127	242	1909	RR 'B' 13 ton	6	SCC
3128	245	1909	RR 'A'	6	SCC
3129	174	1909	RL DG SPR	7	DCC
3130*	233	1909	TE DG SPR	10	DCC
3131*	221	1909	TE DG SPR	8	DCC
3132	83	1909	TE DG SPR	8	SC
3133	99	1909	TE DG US	7	SCC
3134	96	1909	TE DG US	6	SCC
3135*	91	1909	TE DG US	6	SCC
3136	98	1909	TE DG SPR	6	SCC
3137	99	1909	TE DG US	7	SCC
3138	99	1909	TE DG US	7	SCC
3139	99	1909	TE DG US	7	SCC
3140	249	1909	RR/TE	6	SCC
3141	259	1909	TR 5T	4	DCC
3142	221	1909	TE DG SPR	8	DCC
3143	96	1909	TE DG US	6	SCC
3144*	83	1909	TE DG SPR	8	SC
3145	96	1909	TE DG US	6	SCC
3146	91	1909	TE DG US	6	SCC
3147	259	1909	TR 5T	4	DCC
3148*	82	1909	TE DG US	8	SC
3149	83	1909	TE DG SPR	8	SC
3150	245	1909	RR 'A' 12 ton	6	SCC
3151	82	1909	TE DG US	8	SC
3152	82	1909	TE DG US	8	SC
3153	82	1909	TE DG US	8	SC
3154	77	1909	TE DG US	7	SC
3155	91	1909	TE DG US	6	SCC
3156	259	1909	TR 5T	4	DCC
3157	78	1909	SRL DG SPR	7	SC
3158	101	1909	TE DG SPR	7	SCC
3159*	217	1909	SRL DG SPR	7	DCC
3160	82	1909	TE DG US	8	SC
3161	146	1909	RL DG SPR	7	SC
3162	259	1909	TR 5T	4	DCC
3163	188	1910	SRL DG SPR	8	DCC
3164*	99	1909	TE DG US	7	SCC
3165	221	1909	TE DG SPR	8	DCC
3166	172	1909	CRL DG SPR	6	DCC
3167	215	1910	SRL DG SPR	5	DCC
3168	220	1910	TE DG US	7	DCC
3169	220	1910	TE DG SPR	7	DCC
3170	250	1909	RR/NW 'A'	5	SC
3171	245	1909	RR/NW	6	SCC
3172	251	1909	RR/NW	6	SC
3173	242	1909	RR/NW 'B'	6	SCC
3174	242	1909	RR/NW 'B'	6	SCC
3175	242	1909	RR/NW 'B'	6	DCC
3176	91	1910	TE DG US	6	SCC
3177	259	1910	TR(S) 5T	4	DCC
3178	217	1910	SRL DG SPR	7	DCC
3179	91	1910	TE DG SPR	6	SCC
3180	174	1910	RL DG SPR	7	DCC
3181	245	1910	RR 'A' 12 ton	6	SCC
3182	253	1910	RR 'A' 10 ton	5	DCC
3183	217	1910	SRL DG SPR	7	DCC
3184	101	1910	TE DG SPR	7	SCC
3185	258	1910	STR 4¾ ton	4	DCC
3186	259	1910	TR WD 5T	4	DCC
3187	259	1910	TR WD 5T	4	DCC
3188	82	1910	TE DG US	8	SC
3189	91	1910	TE DG US	6	SCC
3190	259	1910	TR (W D CRL)	4	DCC
3191*	259	1910	TR (W D CRL)	4	DCC
3192*	259	1910	TR (W D CRL)	4	DCC
3193	259	1910	TR (W D CRL)	4	DCC
3194	259	1910	TR (W D CRL)	4	DCC
3195*	92	1911	TE 'Irish' DG STR	5	SCC
3196	91	1910	TE DG SPR	6	SCC
3197*	174	1910	CRL DG SPR	7	DCC
3198	242	1910	RR 'B' 15 ton	6	SCC
3199	259	1910	TR 5T	4	DCC
3200*	188	1910	SRL DG SPR	8	DCC
3201*	101	1910	TE DG SPR	7	SCC
3202*	171	1910	RL DG SPR	5	DCC
3203	259	1910	TR 5T	4	DCC
3204	245	1910	RR 'A'	6	SCC
3205	96	1910	TE DG US	6	SCC
3206	242	1910	RR 'B'	6	SCC
3207	242	1910	RR 'B'	6	SCC
3208	77	1910	TE DG US	7	SC
3209	96	1910	TE DG US	6	SCC
3210	156	1910	RL DG SPR	7	SCC
3211	172	1911	RL DG SPR	6	DCC
3212	172	1910	RL(S) DG SPR	6	DCC
3213	104	1910	TE DG SPR	8	SCC
3214	259	1910	TR 5T	4	DCC
3215	98	1910	TE DG SPR	6	SCC
3216	91	1910	TE DG US	6	SCC
3217	245	1910	RR 'A' 11½ ton	6	SCC
3218*	101	1910	TE DG SPR	7	SCC
3219	255	1910	RR/TE	5	DCC
3220*	242	1910	RR 'B'	6	SCC
3221	99	1910	TE DG US	7	SCC
3222	172	1910	RL DG SPR	6	DCC
3223	259	1910	TR 5T	4	DCC
3224	96	1910	TE DG US	6	SCC
3225	256	1910	TR 5T	4	SC
3226	259	1910	TR (CRL) WD	5	DCC
3227*	221	1910	TE DG SPR	8	DCC
3228	221	1910	TE DG SPR	8	DCC
3229*	221	1910	TE DG SPR	8	DCC
3230	91	1910	TE DG SPR	6	SCC
3231	77	1910	TE DG US	7	SC
3232	223	1910	TE DG SPR	6	DCC
3233*	96	1910	TE DG US	6	SCC
3234	259	1910	TR 5T	4	DCC
3235	82	1910	TE DG US	8	SCC
3236	83	1910	TE DG SPR	8	SC
3237	82	1910	TE DG US	8	SC
3238	222	1910	TE DG SPR	6	DCC
3239	220	1910	TE DG SPR	7/8	DCC
3240	96	1910	TE DG US	6	SCC
3241	99	1910	TE DG US	7	SCC
3242	83	1910	TE DG SPR	8	SC
3243*	91	1910	TE DG US	6	SCC
3244*	245	1910	RR 'A'	6	SCC
3245*	259	1910	TR 5T	4	DCC
3246	–	–	Became 3310	–	–
3247	83	1910	TE DG SPR	8	SC
3248	82	1910	TE DG US	8	SC
3249*	78	1910	TE DG SPR	7	SC
3250	259	1910	TR 5T	4	DCC
3251	242	1910	RR 'B'	6	SCC
3252	222	1910	TE DG SPR	6	DCC
3253	259	1911	TR 5T	4	DCC
3254	78	1910	TE DG SPR	7	SC
3255*	83	1910	TE DG SPR	8	SC
3256	82	1910	TE DG US	8	SC
3257*	220	1911	TE DG SPR	7	DCC
3258	247	1910	RR 'C' 17 ton	7	SCC
3259*	82	1910	TE DG US	8	SC
3260	82	1910	TE DG US	8	SC
3261	242	1910	RR 'B'	6	SCC
3262*	91	1910	TE DG US	6	SCC
3263	101	1910	TE DG SPR	7	SCC
3264	259	1910	TR 5T	4	DCC
3265	249	1911	RR/TE	6	SCC
3266	259	1910	TR 5T	4	DCC
3267	–	–	Became 3309	–	–
3268	245	1911	RR 'B' 4-sft	6	SCC
3269	259	1911	TR 5T	4	DCC
3270	245	1911	RR 'A'	6	SCC
3271	74	1911	TE DG US	6	SC
3272	197	1911	SRL DG SPR	8	DCC
3273	197	1911	SRL DG SPR	8	DCC
3274	174	1911	RL DG SPR	7	DCC
3275	245	1911	RR 'B' 4-sft	6	SCC
3276	265	1911	W (DC) 5T	–	DCC
3277	197	1911	SRL DG SPR	8	DCC
3278	215	1911	SRL DG SPR	5	DCC
3279	197	1911	SRL(CSC) DG SPR	8	DCC
3280	99	1911	TE DG US	7	SCC
3281	217	1911	SRL DG SPR	6	DCC
3282	245	1911	RR 'B' 4-sft	6	SCC
3283	171	1911	RL DG SPR	5	DCC
3284	197	1911	SRL DG SPR	8	DCC
3285*	188	1911	SRL DG SPR	8	DCC
3286	91	1911	TE DG US	6	SCC
3287	259	1911	TR 5T	4	DCC
3288*	217	1911	SRL DG SPR	7	DCC
3289	265	1911	W (DC) 5T	–	DCC
3290	265	1911	W (DC) 5T	–	DCC
3291	197	1911	SRL(CSC) DG SPR	8	DCC
3292	250	1911	RR/NW 'A'	5	SC
3293	250	1911	RR/NW 'A'	5	SC
3294	259	1911	TR 5T	4	DCC
3295*	172	1911	RL(S) DG SPR	6	DCC
3296*	91	1911	TE DG US	6	SCC
3297*	223	1911	TE DG SPR	6	DCC
3298	242	1911	RR 'B' 12 ton	6	SCC
3299	98	1911	TE DG SPR	6	SCC
3300	242	1911	RR 'B' 14 ton	6	SCC
3301	249	1911	RR 8 ton	5	SC
3302	197	1911	SRL DG SPR	8	DCC
3303	265	1911	W (DC) 5T	–	DCC
3304	91	1911	TE DG US	6	SCC
3305*	242	1911	RR 'B' 12 ton	6	SCC
3306	172	1911	RL DG SPR	6	DCC
3307*	101	1911	TE DG SPR	7	SCC
3308	259	1911	TR 5T	4	DCC
3309	82	1911	TE DG US	8	SC
3310	77	1911	TE DG US	7	SC
3311	215	1911	SRL DG SPR	5	DCC
3312	245	1911	RR 'A' 12½ ton	6	SCC
3313*	253	1911	RR 'A' 10 ton	5	DCC
3314	250	1911	RR 'A' 10 ton	5	SC
3315	259	1911	TR 5T	4	DCC
3316	82	1911	TE DG US	8	SC
3317	91	1911	TE DG US	6	SCC
3318	259	1911	TR 5T	4	DCC
3319	267	1911	W (DC) 5T	–	DCC
3320	242	1911	RR 'B' 13 ton	6	SCC
3321	91	1911	TE DG US	6	SCC
3322	222	1911	TE DG US	6	DCC
3323	98	1911	TE DG SPR	6	SCC
3324	77	1911	TE DG US	7	SC
3325	223	1911	TE DG SPR	6	DCC
3326	77	1911	TE DG US	7	SC
3327	98	1911	TE DG SPR	6	SCC
3328	83	1911	TE DG SPR	8	SC
3329	82	1911	TE DG US	8	SC
3330	247	1911	RR 'C' 16 ton	7	SCC
3331	91	1911	TE DG US	6	SCC
3332	77	1911	TE DG US	7	SC
3333	256	1911	TR 5T	4	SC
3334*	197	1911	SRL DG SPR	8	DCC
3335	222	1911	TE DG SPR	6	DCC
3336	259	1911	TR 5T	4	DCC
3337	242	1911	RR 'B' 12 ton	6	SCC
3338	247	1911	RR/NW 'C'	7	SCC
3339	247	1911	RR 'C'	7	SCC
3340	247	1911	RR 'C'	7	SCC
3341	259	1911	STR 5T	4	DCC
3342	91	1911	TE DG SPR	6	SCC
3343*	172	1911	RL(S) DG SPR	6	DCC
3344	71	1911	TE 'Irish' DG US	5	SC
3345	71	1911	TE 'Irish' DG US	5	SC
3346	250	1911	RR/NW 'A'	5	SC
3347	245	1911	RR 'A' 12 ton	6	SCC
3348*	221	1911	TE DG SPR	8	DCC
3349	259	1911	TR 5T	4	DCC
3350	172	1912	RL DG SPR	6	DCC
3351	255	1911	RR/TE	5	DCC
3352	165	1911	RL(S) DG SPR	8	DCC
3353	–	–	Became 3397	–	–
3354	259	1911	TR 5T	4	DCC
3355*	259	1912	TR 5T	4	DCC
3356*	242	1912	RR 'B' 12 ton	6	SCC
3357	245	1912	RR 'A'	6	SCC
3358	267	1912	W (DC) 5T	–	DCC
3359	254	1912	RR 6 ton	4	DCC
3360	267	1912	W (DC) 5T	–	DCC
3361	259	1912	TR 5T	4	DCC
3362	267	1912	W (DC) 5T	–	DCC
3363	259	1912	TR 5T	4	DCC
3364	253	1912	RR 'A' 10 ton	5	DCC
3365	215	1912	SRL DG SPR	5	DCC
3366	242	1912	RR 'B' 14 ton	6	SCC

Engine No.	Page Ref.	Date Built	Type	NHP	Cyl
3367	91	1912	TE DG US	6	SCC
3368*	223	1912	TE DG SPR	6	DCC
3369	259	1912	TR(S) 5T	4	DCC
3370	267	1912	W (DC) 5T	–	DCC
3371	197	1912	SRL(CSC) DG SPR	8	DCC
3372	197	1912	SRL DG SPR	8	DCC
3373	267	1912	W (DC) 5T	–	DCC
3374	259	1912	TR 5T	4	DCC
3375	259	1912	TR 5T	4	DCC
3376	245	1912	RR ‘A’	6	SCC
3377	259	1912	TR 5T	4	DCC
3378	–	–	Became 3463	–	–
3379	259	1912	TR 5T	4	DCC
3380	171	1912	RL DG SPR	5	DCC
3381*	255	1912	RR/TE	5	DCC
3382	91	1912	TE DG US	6	SCC
3383	245	1912	RR ‘A’	6	SCC
3384	267	1912	W (DC) 5T	–	DCC
3385*	96	1912	TE DG US	6	SCC
3386	267	1912	W (DC) 5T	–	DCC
3387	259	1912	TR 5T	4	DCC
3388*	242	1912	RR ‘B’ 12 ton	6	SCC
3389	259	1912	TR 5T	4	DCC
3390	172	1912	RL DG SPR	6	DCC
3391*	77	1912	TE DG US	7	SC
3392	172	1912	RL DG SPR	6	DCC
3393	174	1912	RL(S) DG SPR	7	DCC
3394	267	1912	W (SC) 5T	–	DCC
3395*	172	1912	RL DG SPR	6	DCC
3396	91	1912	TE DG US	6	SCC
3397*	259	1912	TR 5T	4	DCC
3398*	255	1912	RR/TE	5	DCC
3399*	101	1912	TE DG SPR	7	SCC
3400	253	1912	RR ‘A’	5	DCC
3401	267	1912	W (DC) 5T	–	DCC
3402	98	1912	TE DG SPR	6	SCC
3403	91	1912	TE DG US	6	SCC
3404	197	1912	SRL DG SPR	8	DCC
3405	77	1912	TE DG US	7	SC
3406	220	1912	TE DG SPR	7	DCC
3407	82	1912	TE DG US	8	SC
3408	242	1912	RR ‘B’ 12 ton	6	SCC
3409	255	1912	RR/TE	6	DCC
3410	82	1912	TE DG US	8	SC
3411*	245	1912	RR ‘A’ 10 ton	6	SCC
3412	267	1912	W (DC) 5T	–	DCC
3413*	217	1912	SRL DG SPR	6	DCC
3414	245	1912	RR/NW	6	SCC
3415	259	1912	TR 5T	4	DCC
3416	222	1912	TE DG US	6	DCC
3417	259	1912	TR 5T	4	DCC
3418	171	1912	RL DG SPR	5	DCC
3419	163	1912	RL SD SPR	10	DCC
3420*	101	1912	TE DG SPR	7	SCC
3421	223	1912	TE DG SPR	6	DCC
3422*	77	1912	TE DG US	7	SC
3423*	174	1912	RL(S) DG SPR	7	DCC
3424	267	1912	W (SC) 5T	–	DCC
3425	259	1912	TR 5T	4	DCC
3426	242	1912	RR ‘B’ 12 ton	6	SCC
3427	77	1912	TE DG US	7	SC
3428	259	1912	TR 5T	4	DCC
3429	–	–	Became 3468	–	–
3430	78	1912	TE DG SPR	7	SC
3431	250	1912	RR/NW ‘A’	5	SC
3432	101	1912	TE DG SPR	7	SCC
3433*	259	1912	TR 5T	4	DCC
3434	172	1913	RL DG SPR	6	DCC
3435	259	1912	TR 5T	4	DCC
3436	267	1913	W (DC) 5T	–	DCC
3437	267	1912	W (SC) 5T	–	DCC
3438	74	1912	TE DG US	6	SC
3439	267	1913	W (SC) 5T	–	DCC
3440	242	1913	RR ‘B’ 12 ton	6	SCC
3441	197	1913	SRL DG SPR	8	DCC
3442*	259	1913	TR 5T	4	DCC
3443*	188	1913	SRL DG SPR	8	DCC
3444*	197	1913	SRL DG SPR	8	DCC
3445	220	1913	TE DG SPR	7	DCC
3446	269	1913	W (DC) 5T	–	DCC
3447	197	1912	SRL DG SPR	8	DCC
3448	253	1913	RR ‘A’	5	DCC
3449	259	1913	TR 5T	4	DCC
3450	197	1913	SRL DG SPR	8	DCC
3451	245	1913	RR ‘A’	6	SCC
3452	267	1913	W (SC) 5T	–	DCC
3453*	259	1913	STR 5T	4	DCC
3454	267	1913	W (SC) 5T	–	DCC
3455*	172	1913	RL DG SPR	6	DCC
3456*	249	1913	RR 8 ton	5	SC
3457	259	1913	TR 5T	4	DCC
3458*	259	1913	TR 5T	4	DCC
3459	245	1913	RR ‘A’ 10 ton	6	SCC
3460	91	1913	TE DG US	6	SCC
3461	74	1913	TE DG US	6	SC
3462	250	1913	RR/NW ‘A’	5	SC
3463	222	1913	TE DG SPR	6	DCC
3464	259	1913	TR 5T	4	DCC
3465	259	1913	TR 5T	4	DCC
3466	217	1913	SRL DG SPR	6	DCC
3467	82	1913	TE DG US	8	SC
3468	245	1913	RR ‘A’	6	SCC
3469	268	1913	W (DC) 5T	–	DCC
3470	197	1913	SRL DG SPR	8	DCC
3471*	217	1913	SRL DG SPR	6	DCC
3472	268	1913	W (DC) 5T	–	DCC
3473	171	1913	RL DG SPR	5	DCC
3474*	104	1913	TE DG SPR	8	SCC
3475	259	1913	TR 5T	4	DCC
3476	245	1913	RR ‘A’	6	SCC
3477	230	1913	TE (D/T PE) DG US	8	SCC
3478	268	1913	W (DC) 5T	–	DCC
3479	91	1913	TE DG US	6	SCC
3480	171	1913	RL DG SPR	5	DCC
3481	259	1913	TR 5T	4	DCC
3482	250	1913	RR ‘A’	5	SC
3483*	197	1913	SRL	8	DCC
3484*	250	1913	RR ‘A’	5	SC
3485	267	1913	W (SC) 5T	–	DCC
3486	259	1913	TR 5T	4	DCC
3487	114	1913	PE Universal	20	SCC
3488	114	1913	PE Universal	20	SCC
3489*	172	1913	RL DG SPR	6	DCC
3490	268	1913	W (DC) 5T	–	DCC
3491	77	1913	TE DG US	7	SC
3492	230	1913	TE (D/T PE) DG US	8	DCC
3493	223	1913	TE DG SPR	6	DCC
3494	268	1913	W (DC) 5T	–	DCC
3495	259	1913	TR 5T	4	DCC
3496	268	1913	W (DC) 5T	–	DCC
3497*	259	1913	TR 5T	4	DCC
3498	99	1913	TE DG US	7	SCC
3499	268	1913	W (DC) 5T	–	DCC
3500	98	1913	TE DG SPR	6	SCC
3501	251	1913	RR/NW	6	SC
3502	268	1913	W (DC) 5T	–	DCC
3503	77	1913	TE DG US	7	SC
3504	259	1913	TR 5T	4	DCC
3505	220	1913	TE DG SPR	7	DCC
3506	253	1913	RR/NW 8 ton	4	DCC
3507	268	1913	W (DC) 5T	–	DCC
3508	259	1913	TR (CRL) 5T	4	DCC
3509*	215	1913	SRL DG SPR	5	DCC
3510	256	1913	TR 5T	4	SC
3511	82	1913	TE DG US	8	SC
3512	217	1913	SRL DG SPR	7	DCC
3513	268	1913	W (DC) 5T	–	DCC
3514	220	1913	TE DG SPR	7	DCC
3515	259	1913	TR (S) 5T	4	DCC
3516	91	1913	TE DG SPR	6	SCC
3517	268	1913	W (DC) 5T	–	DCC
3518	268	1913	W (DC) 5T	–	DCC
3519	221	1913	TE DG SPR	8	DCC
3520	74	1913	TE DG US	6	SC
3521	268	1913	W (DC) 5T	–	DCC
3522*	104	1913	TE DG SPR	8	SCC
3523	222	1913	TE DG SPR	6	DCC
3524	259	1913	TR 5T	4	DCC
3525	268	1913	W (DC) 5T	–	DCC
3526*	217	1913	SRL DG SPR	7	DCC
3527	268	1913	W (DC) 5T	–	DCC
3528	82	1913	TE DG US	8	SC
3529*	221	1913	TE DG SPR	8	DCC
3530	172	1913	CRL DG SPR	6	DCC
3531	259	1913	TR 5T	4	DCC
3532	268	1913	W (DC) 5T	–	DCC
3533	268	1913	W (DC) 5T	–	DCC
3534	259	1913	TR 5T	4	DCC
3535*	253	1913	RR ‘A’	5	DCC
3536	75	1913	TE DG SPR	6	SC
3537	268	1913	W (DC) 5T	–	DCC
3538	268	1914	W (DC) 5T	–	DCC
3539	268	1914	W (DC) 5T	–	DCC
3540	259	1914	TR 5T	4	DCC
3541	91	1914	TE DG US	6	SCC
3542*	172	1914	RL (S)	6	DCC
3543	259	1914	TR 5T	4	DCC
3544	220	1914	TE DG SPR	7	DCC
3545*	259	1914	TR 5T	4	DCC
3546	268	1914	W (DC) 5T	–	DCC
3547	197	1914	SRL (SC) DG SPR	8	DCC
3548	259	1914	TR 5T	4	DCC
3549	259	1913	TR 5T	4	DCC
3550	259	1914	TR 5T	4	DCC
3551	259	1914	STR 5T	4	DCC
3552	268	1914	W (DC) 5T	–	DCC
3553	268	1914	W (DC) 5T	–	DCC
3554*	259	1914	TR 5T	4	DCC
3555*	215	1914	SRL DG SPR	5	DCC
3556	245	1914	RR ‘A’	6	SCC
3557	259	1914	TR 5T	4	DCC
3558	82	1914	TE DG US	8	SC
3559	230	1914	TE (D/T PE) DG US	10	DCC
3560	259	1914	TR 5T	4	DCC
3561	197	1914	SRL DG SPR	8	DCC
3562	259	1914	TR 5T	4	DCC
3563	232	1914	TE (D/T PE) DG US	6	DCC
3564	230	1914	TE (D/T PE) DG US	8	DCC
3565	71	1914	TE ‘Irish’ DG US	5	SC
3566	71	1914	TE ‘Irish’ DG US	5	SC
3567	230	1915	TE (D/T PE) DG US	8	DCC
3568	221	1914	TE DG SPR	8	DCC
3569	232	1914	TE (D/T PE) DG US	6	DCC
3570	232	1915	TE (D/T PE) DG US	6	DCC
3571	245	1914	RR ‘A’	6	SCC
3572	253	1914	RR 8 ton	4	DCC
3573	230	1914	TE ‘Irish’ DG US	5	DCC
3574	259	1914	TR 5T	4	DCC
3575	259	1914	TR 5T	4	DCC
3576	259	1914	TR 5T	4	DCC
3577	232	1914	TE (D/T PE) DG SPR	6	DCC
3578	91	1914	TE DG SPR	6	SCC
3579	197	1914	SRL DG SPR	8	DCC
3580	114	1914	PE Universal	20	SCC
3581	114	1914	PE Universal	20	SCC
3582	249	1914	RR/NW 8 ton	5	SC
3583	268	1914	W (DC) 5T	–	DCC
3584	253	1914	RR ‘A’ 10 ton	5	DCC
3585	172	1914	RL DG SPR	6	DCC
3586*	101	1914	TE DG SPR	7	SCC
3587	98	1914	TE DG SPR	6	SCC
3588	259	1914	TR 5T	4	DCC
3589	259	1914	TR 5T	4	DCC
3590	197	1914	SRL DG SPR	8	DCC
3591	245	1914	RR ‘A’	6	SCC
3592	268	1914	W (DC) 5T	–	DCC
3593*	172	1914	RL(S) DG SPR	6	DCC
3594	259	1914	TR 5T	4	DCC
3595	259	1914	TR 5T	4	DCC
3596	259	1914	TR 5T	4	DCC
3597	83	1914	TE DG SPR	8	SC
3598	82	1914	TE DG US	8	SC
3599	197	1914	SRL (CSC) DG SPR	8	DCC
3600	242	1914	RR ‘B’ 10 ton	6	SCC
3601	259	1914	TR 5T	4	DCC
3602	245	1926	RR ‘A’	6	SCC
3603	259	1914	TR 5T	4	DCC
3604	172	1914	RL DG SPR	6	DCC
3605	171	1914	RL DG SPR	5	DCC
3606	259	1914	TR 5T	4	DCC
3607*	77	1914	TE DG US	7	SC
3608	253	1914	RR ‘A’	5	DCC
3609	277	1915	TE DG SPR	6	SCC
3610*	197	1914	SRL DG SPR	8	DCC
3611	99	1914	TE DG US	7	SCC
3612	222	1914	SRL DG SPR	6	DCC
3613	259	1914	TR 5T	4	DCC
3614	171	1914	RL DG SPR	5	DCC
3615	259	1914	TR 5T	4	DCC
3616	269	1914	W (DC) 5T	–	DCC
3617	259	1914	TR 5T	4	DCC
3618*	259	1914	TR 5T	4	DCC
3619	174	1914	RL(S) DG SPR	7	DCC
3620	259	1914	TR 5T	4	DCC
3621	171	1914	RL DG SPR	5	DCC
3622*	259	1914	TR 5T	4	DCC
3623	269	1914	W (DC) 5T	–	DCC
3624	259	1914	TR 5T	4	DCC

Engine No.	Page Ref.	Date Built	Type	NHP	Cyl
3625	104	1914	TE DG SPR	8	SCC
3626*	259	1914	TR 5T	4	DCC
3627	269	1914	W (DC) 5T	–	DCC
3628	269	1914	W (DC) 5T	–	DCC
3629	99	1914	TE DG US	7	SCC
3630	259	1914	TR 5T	4	DCC
3631*	259	1915	TR 5T	4	DCC
3632	172	1914	SRL DG SPR	6	DCC
3633*	174	1914	SRL DG SPR	7	DCC
3634	269	1914	W (DC) 5T	–	DCC
3635	269	1914	W (DC) 5T	–	DCC
3636*	220	1915	TE DG SPR	7	DCC
3637	259	1915	TR 5T	4	DCC
3638	259	1915	TR 5T	4	DCC
3639	259	1915	TR 5T	4	DCC
3640	221	1915	TE DG SPR	8	DCC
3641	215	1915	SRL DG SPR	5	DCC
3642	165	1915	RL SD SPR	8	DCC
3643	259	1915	TR 5T	4	DCC
3644	269	1915	W (DC) 5T	–	DCC
3645	256	1915	TR 5T	4	SC
3646	256	1915	TR 5T	4	SC
3647	256	1915	TR 5T	4	SC
3648	165	1915	RL DG SPR	8	DCC
3649	259	1915	TR 5T	4	DCC
3650	259	1915	TR 5T	4	DCC
3651*	279	1915	RL(S) DG SPR	7	DCC
3652	269	1915	W (DC) 5T	–	DCC
3653	259	1915	TR 5T	4	DCC
3654	269	1915	W (DC) 5T	–	DCC
3655*	222	1915	TE DG SPR	6	DCC
3656	259	1915	TR 5T	4	DCC
3657*	277	1915	TE DG SPR	6	SCC
3658	259	1915	TR 5T	4	DCC
3659	197	1915	SRL (CSC) DG SPR	8	SCC
3660	217	1915	SRL DG SPR	6	DCC
3661	269	1915	W (DC) 5T	–	DCC
3662	259	1915	TR 5T	4	DCC
3663	259	1915	TR 5T	4	DCC
3664	269	1915	W (DC) 5T	–	DCC
3665*	277	1915	TE DG SPR	6	SCC
3666	269	1915	W (DC) 5T	–	DCC
3667	250	1915	RR 'A'	5	SC
3668	83	1915	TE DG SPR	8	SC
3669*	215	1915	SRL DG SPR	5	DCC
3670	279	1915	RL DG SPR	6	DCC
3671	269	1915	W (DC) 5T	–	DCC
3672	259	1915	TR 5T	4	DCC
3673	259	1915	TR 5T	4	DCC
3674	269	1915	W (DC) 5T	–	DCC
3675	217	1915	SRL DG SPR	6	DCC
3676*	277	1915	TE DG SPR	6	SCC
3677	259	1915	TR 5T	4	DCC
3678	259	1915	TR 5T	4	DCC
3679	221	1915	TE DG SPR	8	DCC
3680	269	1915	W (DC) 5T	–	DCC
3681	259	1915	TR 5T	4	DCC
3682	279	1915	RL(S) DG SPR	7	DCC
3683	269	1915	W (DC) 5T	–	DCC
3684	269	1915	W (DC) 5T	–	DCC
3685	259	1915	TR 5T	4	DCC
3686*	220	1915	TE DG SPR	7	DCC
3687	220	1915	TE DG US	7	DCC
3688	249	1915	RR 8 ton	5	SC
3689*	259	1915	TR 5T	4	DCC
3690	83	1915	TE DG SPR	8	SC
3691	269	1915	W (DC) 5T	–	DCC
3692	275	1915	TE DG SPR	7	SC
3693	259	1915	TR 5T	4	DCC
3694	165	1915	RL(S) DG SPR	8	DCC
3695*	278	1915	TE DG US	8	SCC
3696	223	1915	TE 'Irish' DG SPR	5	DCC
3697	269	1915	W (DC) 5T	–	DCC
3698	269	1915	W (DC) 5T	–	DCC
3699	245	1915	RR 'A'	6	SCC
3700	259	1915	TR 5T	4	DCC
3701	269	1915	W (DC) 5T	–	DCC
3702	101	1915	TE DG SPR	7	SCC
3703*	279	1915	RL(S) DG SPR	6	DCC
3704	220	1916	TE DG SPR	7	DCC
3705	259	1915	TR 5T	4	DCC
3706	269	1916	W (DC) 5T	–	DCC
3707	259	1915	TR 5T	4	DCC
3708	278	1916	RL DG SPR	5	DCC
3709	259	1915	TR 5T	4	DCC
3710	269	1916	W (DC) 5T	–	DCC
3711*	279	1916	RL(S) DG SPR	6	DCC
3712	269	1916	W (DC) 5T	–	DCC
3713	146	1916	RL DG SPR	8	SC
3714	217	1916	SRL DG SPR	7	DCC
3715	197	1916	SRL DG SPR	8	DCC
3716	269	1916	W (DC) 5T	–	DCC
3717	269	1916	W (DC) 5T	–	DCC
3718*	259	1916	TR 5T	4	DCC
3719	259	1916	TR 5T	4	DCC
3720	279	1916	RL DG SPR	6	DCC
3721	275	1916	TE DG SPR	7	SC
3722	259	1916	TR 5T	4	DCC
3723	279	1916	RL DG SPR	6	DCC
3724	197	1916	SRL (CSC) DG SPR	8	SCC
3725	259	1916	STR 5T	4	DCC
3726	276	1916	TE DG US	6	SCC
3727	269	1916	W (DC) 5T	–	DCC
3728*	275	1916	TE DG US	7	SC
3729	259	1916	TR 5T	4	DCC
3730	75	1916	TE DG SPR	6	SC
3731	269	1916	W (DC) 5T	–	DCC
3732	269	1916	W (DC) 5T	–	DCC
3733	242	1916	RR 'B' 12 ton	6	SCC
3734	269	1916	W (DC) 5T	–	DCC
3735	277	1916	TE DG SPR	7	SCC
3736	275	1916	TE DG US	7	SC
3737*	104	1916	TE DG SPR	8	SCC
3738	259	1917	TR 5T	4	DCC
3739*	222	1916	TE DG US	6	DCC
3740	276	1916	TE DG US	8	SC
3741	259	1916	TR 5T	4	DCC
3742	259	1916	TR 5T	4	DCC
3743	269	1917	W (DC) 5T	–	DCC
3744	279	1916	RL DG SPR	6	DCC
3745	259	1917	TR 5T	4	DCC
3746*	222	1917	TE DG SPR	6	DCC
3747	220	1917	TE DG SPR	7	DCC
3748	250	1917	RR 'A'	5	SC
3749	259	1917	TR 5T	4	DCC
3750	276	1917	TE DG SPR	8	SC
3751	279	1917	RL DG SPR	6	DCC
3752	259	1917	TR 5T	4	DCC
3753	259	1917	TR 5T	4	DCC
3754	259	1917	TR 5T	4	DCC
3755*	277	1917	TE DG SPR	6	SCC
3756	270	1917	W (SC) 5T	–	DCC
3757	259	1917	TR 5T	4	DCC
3758	223	1917	TE DG SPR	6	DCC
3759	254	1917	TR 5T	4	DCC
3760	269	1917	W (DC) 5T	–	DCC
3761	278	1917	TE DG US	8	SCC
3762	259	1917	TR 5T	4	DCC
3763*	276	1917	TE DG US	6	SCC
3764	269	1917	W (DC) 5T	–	DCC
3765	275	1917	TE DG US	7	SC
3766	275	1917	TE DG US	6	SC
3767*	275	1917	TE DG US	7	SC
3768	223	1917	TE DG SPR	6	DCC
3769	269	1917	W (DC) 5T	–	DCC
3770	275	1917	TE DG US	7	SC
3771*	276	1917	TE DG US	6	SCC
3772*	222	1917	TE DG US	6	DCC
3773	270	1917	W (DC) 5T	–	DCC
3774*	276	1917	TE DG US	6	SCC
3775	275	1917	TE DG US	7	SC
3776	259	1917	TR 5T	4	DCC
3777*	278	1917	RL DG SPR	5	DCC
3778	275	1918	TE DG US	7	SC
3779	220	1918	TE DG SPR	7	DCC
3780	276	1918	TE DG US	6	SCC
3781	250	1918	RR 'A'	5	SC
3782	222	1918	TE DG SPR	6	DCC
3783	259	1918	TR 5T	4	DCC
3784	223	1918	TE DG SPR	6	DCC
3785	259	1918	TR 5T	4	DCC
3786*	259	1918	TR 5T	4	DCC
3787	197	1918	SRL DG SPR	8	DCC
3788	277	1918	TE DG SPR	7	SCC
3789*	220	1918	TE DG SPR	7	DCC
3790*,	223	1918	TE DG SPR	6	DCC
3791	259	1918	TR 5T	4	DCC
3792	276	1918	TE DG US	6	SCC
3793	270	1918	W (SC) 5T	–	DCC
3794*	222	1919	TE DG SPR	6	DCC
3795	259	1919	TR 5T	4	DCC
3796	269	1919	W (DC) 5T	–	DCC
3797	276	1919	TE DG SPR	8	SC
3798*	222	1919	TE DG SPR	6	DCC
3799	279	1919	RL DG SPR	6	DCC
3800	270	1919	W (SC) 5T	–	DCC
3801	277	1919	TE DG SPR	7	SCC
3802	259	1919	TR 5T	4	DCC
3803	276	1919	TE DG SPR	8	SC
3804*	279	1919	RL(S) DG SPR	7	DCC
3805	276	1919	TE DG US	6	SCC
3806	146	1919	RL DG SPR	6	SC
3807*	259	1919	TR (CRL) 5T	4	DCC
3808*	259	1919	TR 5T	4	DCC
3809*	278	1919	RL DG SPR	5	DCC
3810	279	1919	RL(S) DG SPR	7	DCC
3811	220	1919	TE DG SPR	7	DCC
3812*	223	1919	TE DG SPR	6	DCC
3813	222	1919	TE DG SPR	6	DCC
3814	259	1919	TR 5T	4	DCC
3815*	259	1919	TR 5T	4	DCC
3816*	223	1919	TE DG SPR	6	DCC
3817	217	1919	SRL DG SPR	7	DCC
3818	277	1919	TE DG SPR	6	SCC
3819	242	1918	RR 12 ton	6	SCC
3820	259	1919	TR 5T	4	DCC
3821	278	1919	RL DG SPR	5	DCC
3822	217	1920	SRL DG SPR	6	DCC
3823	259	1919	TR 5T	4	DCC
3824*	278	1919	RL DG SPR	5	DCC
3825	220	1920	TE DG SPR	7	DCC
3826	259	1920	TR 5T	4	DCC
3827*	197	1920	SRL (SC) DG SPR	8	DCC
3828	224	1920	TE DG SPR	5	DCC
3829*	279	1920	CRL DG SPR	6	DCC
3830	217	1920	SRL DG SPR	6	DCC
3831	275	1920	TE DG US	6	SC
3832	278	1920	RL DG SPR	5	DCC
3833*	197	1920	SRL DG SPR	8	DCC
3834	223	1920	TE DG SPR	5/6	DCC
3835	223	1920	TE DG SPR	6	DCC
3836*	222	1920	TE (S) DG US	6	DCC
3837	215	1920	SRL DG SPR	5	DCC
3838	222	1920	TE DG US	6	DCC
3839	259	1920	TR 5T	4	DCC
3840	197	1920	SRL (SC) DG SPR	8	DCC
3841	277	1920	TE DG US	7	SCC
3842	275	1920	TE DG SPR	7	SC
3843	269	1920	SW (DC) 5T	–	DCC
3844	270	1920	W (SC) 5T	–	DCC
3845	278	1920	CRL (S) DG SPR	5	DCC
3846	259	1920	TR 5T	4	DCC
3847*	279	1920	RL(S) DG SPR	6	DCC
3848	259	1920	TR 5T	4	DCC
3849*	278	1921	RL DG SPR	5	DCC
3850*	259	1920	TR 5T	4	DCC
3851*	259	1920	TR 5T	4	DCC
3852	259	1920	TR 5T	4	DCC
3853	275	1920	TE DG SPR	7	SC
3854	277	1920	TE DG SPR	6	SCC
3855	275	1920	TE DG SPR	7	SC
3856	278	1920	RL DG SPR	5	DCC
3857	259	1923	TR 5T	4	DCC
3858	278	1920	RL DG SPR	5	DCC
3859	255	1920	RR/TE	5	DCC
3860	277	1920	TE DG SPR	7	SCC
3861	259	1920	TR 5T	4	DCC
3862*	259	1921	TR 5T	4	DCC
3863	270	1920	W (SC) 5T	–	DCC
3864	255	1925	RR/TE	4	DCC
3865*	197	1920	SRL (SC) DG SPR	8	DCC
3866	197	1920	SRL (SC) DG SPR	8	DCC
3867	269	1920	W (DC) 5T	–	DCC
3868*	259	1920	STR 5T	4	DCC
3869	279	1920	RL(S) DG SPR	6	DCC
3870	276	1921	TE DG SPR	8	SC
3871*	217	1921	SRL DG SPR	7	DCC
3872	197	1921	SRL (SC) DG SPR	8	DCC
3873	277	1921	TE DG US	6	SCC
3874	217	1921	SRL DG SPR	6	DCC
3875	221	1921	TE DG SPR	8	DCC
3876	–	–	Became 4071	–	–
3877	269	1923	W (DC) 5T	–	DCC
3878*	217	1921	SRL DG SPR	6	DCC
3879	197	1921	SRL (SC) DG SPR	8	DCC
3880	242	1921	RR 'B' 12 ton	6	SCC
3881	269	1922	W (DC) 5T	–	DCC
3882*	276	1921	TE DG SPR	8	SC
3883	270	1921	SW (SC) 5T	–	DCC
3884*	197	1921	SRL (SC) DG SPR	8	DCC
3885	197	1921	SRL DG SPR	8	DCC

Engine No.	Page Ref.	Date Built	Type	NHP	Cyl
3886*	197	1921	SRL (SC) DG SPR	8	DCC
3887*	197	1922	SRL (SC) DG SPR	8	DCC
3888*	197	1921	SRL (SC) DG SPR	8	DCC
3889	217	1921	SRL DG SPR	6	DCC
3890*	217	1922	SRL DG SPR	7	DCC
3891	–	–	Never Made	–	–
3892	279	1921	RL DG SPR	6	DCC
3893	–	–	Became 4050	–	–
3894*	223	1921	TE DG SPR	5/6	DCC
3895*	222	1921	TE DG SPR	6	DCC
3896*	197	1921	SRL (SC) DG SPR	8	DCC
3897	279	1921	RL (S) DG SPR	7	DCC
3898	215	1921	SRL DG SPR	5	DCC
3899	–	–	Never Made	–	–
3900	–	–	Never Made	–	–
3901	–	–	Never Made	–	–
3902*	224	1921	TE DG SPR	5	DCC
3903*	224	1921	TE DG SPR	5	DCC
3904	–	–	Never Made	–	–
3905	–	–	Never Made	–	–
3906*	215	1921	SRL DG SPR	5	DCC
3907	277	1921	TE DG SPR	6	SCC
3908	224	1922	TE DG SPR	5	DCC
3909*	197	1922	SRL (SC) DG SPR	8	DCC
3910*	217	1921	SRL DG SPR	7	DCC
3911	–	–	Never Made	–	–
3912*	197	1921	SRL (SC) DG SPR	8	DCC
3913	224	1923	TE DG US	5	DCC
3914	275	1921	TE DG SPR	7	SC
3915	–	–	Never Made	–	–
3916	222	1921	TE DG SPR	6	DCC
3917*	224	1921	TE DG SPR	5	DCC
3918*	277	1923	TE DG SPR	6	SCC
3919*	277	1922	TE DG SPR	6	SCC
3920	277	1921	TE DG SPR	6	SCC
3921	222	1921	TE DG SPR	6	DCC
3922	275	1921	TE DG US	7	SC
3923*	220	1922	TE DG SPR	7	DCC
3924*	275	1922	TE DG SPR	7	SC
3925	222	1922	TE DG SPR	6	DCC
3926	215	1921	SRL DG SPR	5	DCC
3927	215	1921	SRL DG SPR	5	DCC
3928	226	1921	TE DG US	7	DCC
3929*	251	1921	RR 'B'	6	SC
3930	278	1928	RL DG SPR	5	DCC
3931*	250	1921	RR 'A' 10 ton	5	SC
3932	197	1922	SRL DG SPR	8	DCC
3933*	217	1922	SRL DG SPR	7	DCC
3934	253	1922	RR 'A' 10 ton	5	DCC
3935*	226	1922	TE DG US	7	DCC
3936	197	1922	SRL (SC) DG SPR	8	DCC
3937*	278	1922	RL DG SPR	6	SCC
3938*	197	1922	SRL (SC) DG SPR	8	DCC
3939	276	1922	TE DG US	8	SC
3940	220	1922	TE DG SPR	7	DCC
3941*	278	1923	RL DG SPR	5	DCC
3942*	250	1923	RR 'A' 10 ton	5	SC
3943	253	1923	RR 'A' 10 ton	5	DCC
3944	275	1924	TE DG US	6/7	SC
3945	217	1922	SRL DG SPR	7	DCC
3946*	249	1922	RR 8 ton	5	SC
3947	253	1923	RR 'A' 10 ton	5	DCC
3948	197	1923	SRL (SC) DG SPR	8	DCC
3949*	197	1923	SRL DG SPR	8	DCC
3950*	278	1924	RL(S) DG SPR	5	DCC
3951*	–	–	Became 4028	–	–
3952	217	1923	SRL DG SPR	7	DCC
3953	274	1924	W (SC) 6 ton	–	DCC
3954	270	1923	W (SC) 5T	–	DCC
3955	250	1923	RR 'A' 10 ton	5	SC
3956*	249	1923	RR 8 ton	5	SC
3957	253	1924	RR 'A' 10 ton	5	DCC
3958	–	–	Became 4021	–	–
3959	253	1923	RR 'A' 10 ton	5	DCC
3960	–	–	Became 4034	–	–
3961	253	1924	RR 10 ton	5	DCC
3962*	249	1923	RR 8 ton	5	SC
3963	273	1923	W (DC) 5T	–	DCC
3964	253	1923	RR 'A'	5	DCC
3965	222	1923	TE DG SPR	6	DCC
3966	253	1923	RR 'A' 10 ton	6	DCC
3967	188	1923	RL(S) DG SPR	8	DCC
3968	209	1924	SRL (SC) DG SPR	8	DCC
3969	209	1924	SRL (SC) DG SPR	8	DCC
3970	250	1924	RR 'A' 10 ton	5	SC
3971	224	1924	TE DG US	5	DCC
3972	253	1924	RR 8 ton	4	DCC
3973*	249	1924	RR 8 ton	5	SC
3974	221	1924	TE DG SPR	8	DCC
3975*	221	1924	TE DG SPR	8	DCC
3976	253	1924	RR 8 ton	4	DCC
3977	275	1924	TE DG SPR	7	SC
3978	217	1924	SRL DG SPR	7	DCC
3979*	279	1924	RL(S) DG SPR	6	DCC
3980	209	1924	RL(S) DG SPR	8	DCC
3981	273	1924	W (DC) 5T	–	DCC
3982	–	–	Became 4011	–	–
3983	222	1924	TE DG SPR	6	DCC
3984*	275	1924	TE DG US	7	SC
3985*	249	1925	RR 8 ton	5	SC
3986*	250	1924	RR 'A' 10 ton	5	SC
3987*	250	1924	RR 'A' 10 ton	5	SC
3988	–	–	Became 4022	–	–
3989	226	1924	TE DG SPR	6/7	DCC
3990	250	1924	RR 10 ton	5	SC
3991*	250	1924	RR 'A' 10 ton	5	SC
3992	277	1924	TE DG SPR	7	SCC
3993*	253	1924	RR 'A' 10 ton	5	DCC
3994*	253	1924	RR 8 ton	4	DCC
3995	209	1924	SRL SD SPR	8	DCC
3996*	278	1924	RL DG SPR	5	DCC
3997	226	1924	TE DG US	6/7	DCC
3998	226	1924	TE DG US	6/7	DCC
3999*	250	1924	RR 'A' 10 ton	5	SC
4000*	209	1925	SRL (SC) DG SPR	8	DCC
4001	274	1925	W (SC) 6 ton	–	DCC
4002	245	1925	RR 'A' 10 ton	6	SCC
4003	274	1925	W (SC) 6 ton	–	DCC
4004*	253	1925	RR 8 ton	4	DCC
4005*	250	1925	RR 'A' 10 ton	5	SC
4006	270	1925	W (SC) 5T	–	DCC
4007	–	–	Became 4031	–	–
4008*	270	1925	W (SC) 5T	–	DCC
4009	–	–	Became 4046	–	–
4010*	278	1925	RL DG SPR	5	DCC
4011	279	1925	TE (3982) DG SPR	4	DCC
4012*	250	1925	RR 10 ton	5	SC
4013	250	1925	RR 'A' 10 ton	5	SC
4014*	224	1928	TE DG SPR	5	DCC
4015	264	1925	TR 7¼ ton	5	DCC
4016	–	–	Became 4041	–	–
4017	253	1925	RR 8 ton	4	DCC
4018*	253	1925	RR 8 ton	4	DCC
4019*	224	1925	TE DG SPR	5	DCC
4020	224	1925	TE DG SPR	5	DCC
4021	197	1925	SRL (SC) DG SPR	8	DCC
4022	253	1925	RR 8 ton	4	DCC
4023	–	–	Never Made	–	–
4024	253	1925	RR 8 ton	4	DCC
4025*	253	1925	RR 8 ton	4	DCC
4026	278	1925	RL DG SPR	5	DCC
4027	274	1925	W (SC) 6 ton	–	DCC
4028*	264	1925	TR 7¼ ton	5	DCC
4029	274	1926	W (SC) 6 ton	–	DCC
4030*	209	1925	SRL (SC) DG SPR	8	DCC
4031	226	1925	TE DG US	6	DCC
4032*	275	1925	TE DG SPR	7	SC
4033	277	1925	TE DG SPR	6	SCC
4034	270	1925	W (SC) 5T	–	DCC
4035	274	1926	W (SC) 6 ton	–	DCC
4036	274	1927	W (SC) 6 ton	–	DCC
4037*	224	1926	TE DG US	5	DCC
4038	209	1926	RL(S) DG SPR	8	DCC
4039	197	1926	CRL SD SPR	8	DCC
4040*	250	1926	RR 10 ton	5	SC
4041*	250	1926	RR 10 ton	5	SC
4042	209	1926	RL(S) DG SPR	8	DCC
4043	245	1926	RR 'A' 10 ton	6	SCC
4044*	253	1926	RR 10 ton	4	DCC
4045*	224	1926	TE DG US	5	DCC
4046*	249	1926	RR 8 ton	5	SC
4047	250	1926	RR 10 ton	5	SC
4048*	275	1926	TE DG US	7	SC
4049*	226	1926	TE DG SPR	6/7	DCC
4050	277	1926	Formerly 3983	–	–
4051*	275	1926	TE DG US	7	SC
4052	253	1926	RR 8 ton	4	DCC
4053*	226	1926	TE DG US	7	DCC
4054	274	1927	W (SC) 6 ton	–	DCC
4055*	224	1927	TE DG SPR	5	DCC
4056	253	1927	RR 8 ton	4	DCC
4057	264	1926	TR 7¼ ton	5	DCC
4058*	249	1926	RR 8 ton	5	SC
4059	253	1927	RR 8 ton	4	DCC
4060*	250	1927	RR 'A' 10 ton	5	SC
4061*	253	1927	RR 8 ton	4	DCC
4062*	253	1927	RR 8 ton	4	DCC
4063*	276	1927	TE DG SPR	8	SC
4064	274	1927	W (SC) 6 ton	–	DCC
4065	249	1927	RR/NW 8 ton	5	SC
4066*	278	1927	RL DG SPR	5	DCC
4067*	253	1927	RR 8 ton	4	DCC
4068	274	1928	W (SC) 6 ton	–	DCC
4069*	250	1929	RR 'A' 10 ton	5	SC
4070*	250	1927	RR 'A' 10 ton	5	SC
4071*	259	1927	TR 5T	4	DCC
4072*	259	1927	TR 5T	4	DCC
4073*	253	1929	RR 8 ton	4	DCC
4074*	278	1927	CRL DG SPR	5	DCC
4075	–	–	Never Made	–	–
4076	–	–	Never Made	–	–
4077	253	1927	RR 10 ton	5	DCC
4078	274	1927	W (SC) 6 ton	–	DCC
4079	–	–	Never Made	–	–
4080	224	1929	TE DG SPR	5	DCC
4081*	275	1928	TE DG US	7	SC
4082	274	1928	W (SC) 6 ton	–	DCC
4083*	249	1928	RR 8 ton	5	SC
4084*	259	1927	TR 5T	4	DCC
4085	–	–	Never Made	–	–
4086	274	1928	W (SC) 6 ton	–	DCC
4087	277	1928	TE DG US	6	SCC
4088*	275	1930	TE DG US	7	SC
4089	–	–	Never Made	–	–
4090	228	1929	TE DG SPR	8	DCC
4091	209	1930	RL(S) DG SPR	8	DCC
4092	197	1930	SRL DG SPR	8	DCC
4093*	278	1931	RL DG SPR	5	DCC
4094*	276	1932	TE DG US	8	SC

General Index

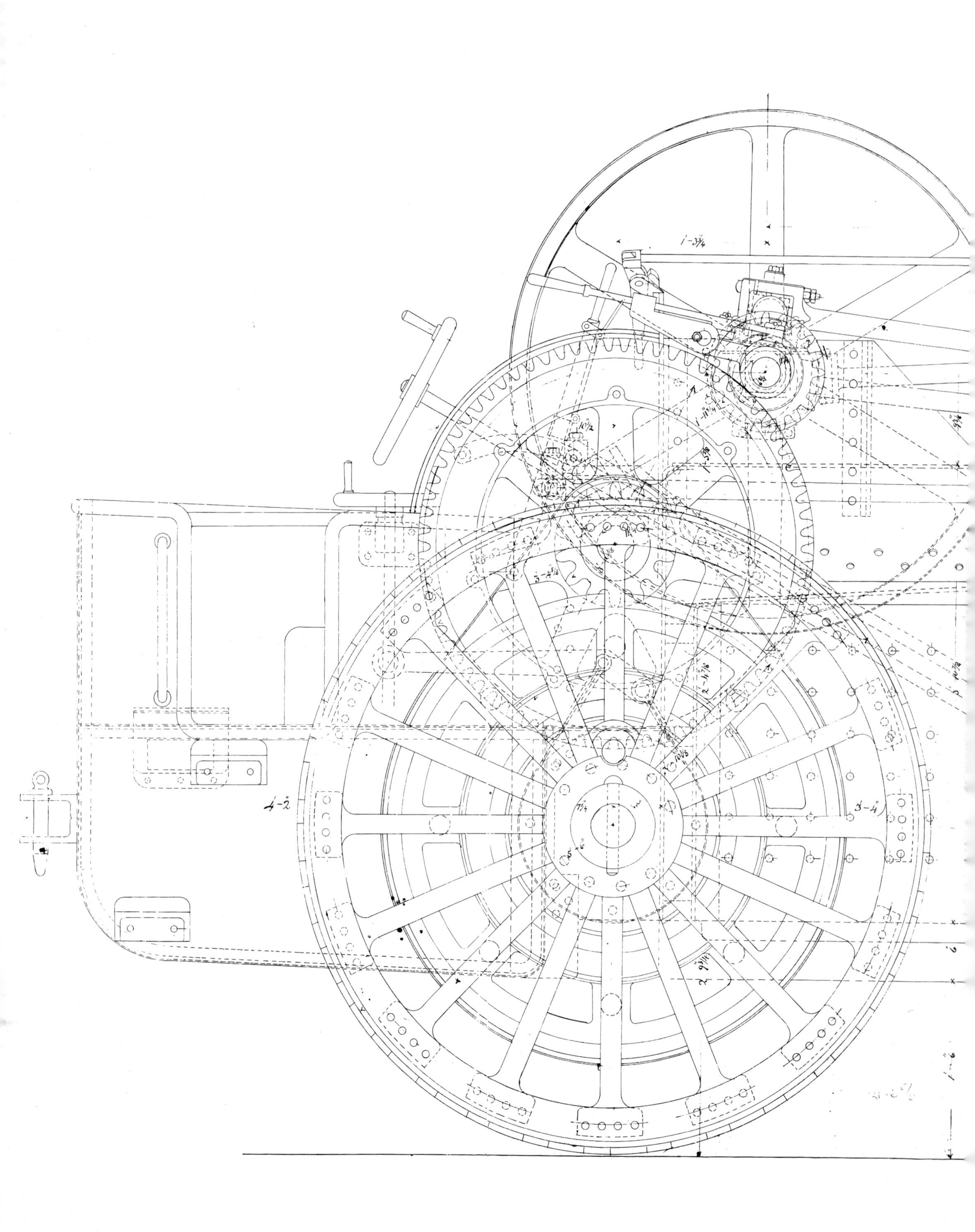